# DARK WIZARD

BONDS OF MAGIC
BOOK ONE

BY
JEFFE KENNEDY

**Lord Gabriel Phel** wants one thing: to rebuild the shattered fortunes of his people and restore his ruined house to its former station in the Convocation's highest tiers of elegant society. Fortunately, through a wild chance of birth, he was born with powerful wizard magic, the first in his family in generations. If he can obtain a familiar to amplify his magic, a highborn daughter he can marry, to be mother to his children, he'll be that much closer to saving his family. With her by his side, he can ascend to such a position of power in the Convocation that he can destroy it forever.

**Lady Veronica Elal**, captive in her tower, has only one way out. To her bitter disappointment, she will never be a wizard. Instead, through a twist of fate, and despite her expensive Convocation Academy education, Nic is doomed to be a familiar like her mother. Forced to participate in the Betrothal Trials, she receives a wizard suitor for one night each month. Whichever man impregnates her will bond her to them forever. With no choice but to serve the one who wins her, Nic has one hope for control over her life: a wizard she can manipulate.

Gabriel Phel seems like the perfect choice for Nic's gambit—he's desperate and untutored in wizardry—but within moments of meeting him, she feels the bonds of magic tying them together. Afraid of losing her will to the compelling wizard who touches her heart like no other, Nic does the unthinkable: she runs. Pregnant and alone, Nic eludes monstrous hunters, searching for a safe haven. But when Gabriel catches up to her, their adventure has only begun.

# DEDICATION

*To Darynda and Grace.*

*You know why.*

# Acknowledgments

Many thanks to the New Mexico Beta Readers group, organized by the eminently capable Emily Mah Tippetts. I am grateful to Emily and the rest of the group—Reese Hogan, Darynda Jones, J. Barton Mitchell, and Jim Sorenson—for multiple reads, in some cases.

Serious love and endless gratitude to Grace Draven and Darynda Jones, who read early versions of these pages. Their love for this story made me persevere through setbacks that might've had me giving up on the book. I cannot express enough how much their sincere support meant in getting this book and world out there.

Also many thanks to longtime crit partner Marcella Burnard, who I trusted to give the final verdict, and gave it in the best way possible. Even if she did call me a terrible human being for giving her writer envy. Best compliment there is!

To Jennifer Udden, your edit letter was insightful, thoughtful, and served as a beacon of light in a dark time. You have an amazing editorial eye. Best of luck to you in your new enterprise! Can't wait until we can share prosecco again.

Many thanks to all the readers who encouraged me when I talked about this story concept, especially Dark Storm, who I think cheered for it every single time.

Bubbly and sunny days to Megan and Charlie—my stalwart Pandemic Pod—for campfire drinks and listening to me ramble about this tale and my travails. #Beerchurch forever.

Thanks and love to Carien Ubink for All The Assisting.

As ever, love and immense gratitude to David, who is there every day, and who makes everything possible.

Thank you for reading!

Credits
Developmental Editing: Jennifer Udden (reedsy.com/jennifer-udden)
Proofreading: Pikko's House (www.pikkoshouse.com)
Cover: Ravven (www.ravven.com)

# ~ I ~

GABRIEL PHEL CRESTED the last ridge of the notorious Knifeblade Mountains that guarded Elal lands on nearly three sides, and faced the final barrier. The path through the mountains had been narrow, crooked, with blind endings and unexpected pitfalls.

Not unlike his life, Gabriel thought with grimly sardonic humor.

He halted his gelding, Vale, several lengths short of the border, sensing the repulsion spell that prevented the uninvited from crossing. It was a highly refined enchantment—he'd expect nothing less of the powerful Elal wizards—one that barred only humans, but allowed animals and weather to cross freely. Gabriel dismounted so he and Vale could both rest a moment before the last leg of the journey, while the Elal border guardians confirmed his identity. Lord Elal was famously insular and fanatical about guarding what was his. And, as the most powerful wizard in the Convocation, Lord Elal had a great deal to call his.

Finding a spot with a good perspective of the serene and rolling valley below—level enough to stand on and just shy of the border spell palpable to his wizard senses—Gabriel took a stance and opened the placket of his leather pants to empty his bladder. He would honor his first visit to the hallowed soil of the Convocation's greatest High House appropriately.

With a grim smile, he aimed his stream across the border, marking his territory as he studied the land of his enemy.

House Elal stood at the center of the valley below, a towering edifice amid winter-quiet fields and clusters of farmhouses. Some of the smaller dwellings—those with families not wealthy enough to afford fire elementals for heating—had chimneys with smoke coiling fragrantly against the late afternoon light spreading to the horizon. An enormous river, so large that it remained unfrozen, ran through the valley, and House Elal sat in a crescent bend of it that also served neatly as a moat. The house—more accurately, a castle—sprawled in all directions, wings, courtyards, and towers added over multiple generations. At least three kinds of stone had gone into its building over the centuries, judging by the different colors easily picked out from this distance, probably more.

Between the moat, the high walls, and the edifice's sheer complexity—not to mention the guarded narrow passes through the Knifeblade Mountains—House Elal was virtually unassailable. Except via the weapon he currently held in his hand.

*Take that*, Gabriel thought, shaking his cock dry and tucking it away again. He did so carefully, as that member had important work to do that night. All he needed was some unlucky accident to render him unable to plant the seeds of desperate ambition.

Lowering, when a man's future depended on that kind of

performance. But then, nothing much made rational sense when it came to the Convocation's bizarre and arcane laws regarding their precious familiars and breeding the next generation of power-mad wizards. Gabriel didn't like it, but you can't win the game unless you play the game. If he wanted to restore House Phel and ensure comfort, security, and peace for his own people, like that enjoyed by the people below, then he needed to win.

Once, he would have said that there would never come a day when he'd go crawling to the Convocation for anything. But then, the idealistic certainties of youth had a way of collapsing before the exigencies of the present. To be a wizard powerful enough to challenge the likes of Lord Elal, he needed the magical amplification a familiar would give him. Who better than the most powerful available familiar in the Convocation? It was just a bit of extra satisfaction for him that she was Lord Elal's daughter.

The ancient volume on enchantments that Gabriel had found in a moldering library at what was left of House Phel had seemed to guarantee the moon-magic fertility spell would work—and that it would be undetectable. It wasn't cheating, exactly. The extensive Betrothal Trials rules booklet provided by the Convocation only forbade House Refoel interference with fertility, not other enchantments. Gabriel had read the cursed thing enough times to be sure.

*Still*, his annoying conscience whispered, *it seems unethical.* He banished the thought with a sharp shake of his head. Lady Veronica Elal was in the Betrothal Trials for the same reason he was. As a familiar, she needed to be paired with a wizard, just as he needed a familiar if he wanted to be more than a rogue wizard from a fallen house. She was a daughter of a High House, with a Convocation education and admirable magical potential scores. He was her fourth suitor, and he imagined she'd be glad to be done with being locked up.

He knew he'd hate it.

*But will she be glad to be saddled with a no-tier house like yours?* Apparently he hadn't banished his irritating conscience firmly enough. Such considerations had no place in his life. House Phel had an opportunity to rise from the ruins, to escape the cycle of poverty that had them forever scraping for the leftovers of the Convocation's wealthier lands.

Returning to his horse, he checked Vale's hooves, then the gelding's tack for fit and chafing. Another hour or so's ride wouldn't change much, but no sense losing his bid for a kingdom because his horse went lame short of the finish line. Satisfied all was well, he extracted his flask of water, tugged off his glove, and poured some into his palm for Vale, the chill biting bright on his wet hand.

How long would these border guardians make him wait? Probably just long enough to make his role as supplicant to the mighty House Elal very clear.

Upon the heels of that thought, a cloaked and hooded figure stepped out of a cloud of fog, closely followed by a bare-headed young man in House Elal livery.

"Lord Phel," the cloaked woman said, tipping back her hood to reveal a stern face made sharper by ruthlessly scraped-back dark hair—and the depthless black eyes of a wizard. She wore a gold pin on one shoulder, the House Elal crest of spirits intertwined in a braided circle. The young man remained a pace behind her, head bowed. "I am Tyrna, wizard to House Elal. Welcome to Elal."

He offered her a nod of greeting. "Thank you." *I think.* Remaining wary, Gabriel kept one hand near the hilt of his sword. Not that mere metal could defend him from a House Elal wizard, but the blade might offer him time to summon a defensive enchantment.

She smiled mirthlessly. "You need not be concerned, Lord Phel. You are expected and may proceed onto our lands. Do not, however, stray from the main road. It will lead you straight to House Phel. You should have no reason to diverge from that path."

"No reason, indeed," he agreed curtly. At least there was some comfort in discovering Elal hospitality was as forbidding as he'd been warned.

"Good luck in your efforts tonight," Tyrna offered with a smirk, looking him up and down and making it clear she thought no amount of luck could help him win the prize. "We're all so interested in the future of House *Fell.*"

Amazing how people managed to make the alternate meaning clear, even while smiling politely. It hadn't taken him long at Convocation to clue into the insult.

Not dignifying her little joke with a reply, Gabriel waited. Perhaps she hoped he wasn't enough of a wizard that he couldn't detect the barrier. Another fine joke for her to get him to walk face-first into the invisible wall, thinking she'd already opened a crossing. If that was her game, she'd be disappointed. A moment later, with a hint of an annoyed scowl, the wizard yanked off her glove and held out her hand in an impatient gesture. The young man behind her stepped forward, placing his bare hand in hers.

Gabriel watched with close interest. He'd never seen a wizard work with their familiar before. There wasn't much to see, however. No burst of transferred magic, at least to his unpracticed eye. The young man never moved while the wizard made a complicated gesture with her free hand, and an opening formed across the road, like a curtain drawing back. Taking Vale's reins, Gabriel walked the gelding through the opening, then turned back to the wizard with a nod.

"Come, Feny," the wizard said, turning on her heel—tugging her familiar along by the hand—and stepping into a cloud of fog that vanished again, leaving no sign of them. A nifty parlor trick. A waste of magic, though, just to look impressive.

Though, in Gabriel's limited experience, the Convocation wizards seemed excessively interested in anything that made them look good.

"Come, Vale," Gabriel said aloud in snooty tones to mimic the Elal wizard as he mounted again. Swiveling back his ears, Vale snorted in apparent appreciation of the humor. On this side of the border, the road opened up to a welcoming width—in stark contrast to the difficult trail through the Knifeblades, more suited to mountain goats than horses—and Vale kicked into a sprightly pace. Unsurprisingly, the prickle of unseen eyes still followed them.

Among the numerous skills in their magical arsenal, the wizards of House Elal commanded air elementals and other spirits mostly invisible to the human eye. There were tricks to making them visible. Gabriel could condense some fog or mist to reveal their movements. But, as much as he disliked being spied on, he wouldn't. He'd do nothing to jeopardize this gambit.

Once the well-maintained road—kept dry and clear of snow and ice by more fire elementals bonded during its construction—finished winding down from the foothills, it ran arrow-straight to the gates of House Elal. Now that they were on a level with its base, the castle loomed with majestic splendor, more fortress than home from this angle.

Gabriel began to encounter other travelers, too. Farmers, merchants, and craftspeople—all bundled in wool and furs against the chilly weather—passed by, some with smaller handcarts, others with wagons propelled by air elementals. The people looked well-fed, well-clothed, and reasonably happy, though they gazed at Gabriel with suspicion, eyeing the house crest on his shoulder in puzzlement. A prosperous people, but not so complacent that they didn't notice an armed stranger in their midst—and a foreign wizard at that.

Gabriel nodded in greeting, otherwise ignoring their scrutiny. He'd like to say he was inured to the stares, but one didn't come to wizardry as he had—relatively late in life and with cataclysmic suddenness—without being keenly aware of how people reacted to the sight of him now.

Needing to distract himself, he pulled out the miniature of Lady Veronica Elal and studied it, for the one-millionth time, probably, since he'd received it in the Convocation packet announcing her Betrothal Trials. Her image captivated him, though she was no great beauty, despite the painter no doubt flattering her as much as possible. She had the high Elal forehead and strongly arched nose. Her brows, black as a raven's wing and flattened with a hint of impatience, framed lushly lashed eyes the artist had no doubt intended to look soft and appealing. The green of them had been perhaps difficult to capture, for they looked far too hard—almost unnatural—with nothing inviting about them. Lady Veronica's lips had been fashioned into a pretty bow shape, shaded a deep red. Not prim, however, her lips were lush—and also seemed to be holding back a slicing remark. Her pointed chin tilted with the arrogance he'd expect of House Elal, but the picture overall evoked something else. She struck him as both sad and angry. Frustrated, perhaps, almost to the point of despair.

That, more than anything else, appealed to him about her. He understood frustrated ambition, and the despair that followed close behind. The other available familiars had been presented as handsome and pretty and sweetly serene—obediently invisible like Tyrna's familiar, Feny—and without any spark that interested him. Nothing that made him want to spend his life bonded to them.

Maybe he imagined what he wanted to see in Lady Veronica. After all, how much could one read into a portrait intended as an advertisement of goods? The painting served primarily to confirm the familiar being offered. As the Convocation packet made clear by highlighting Lady Veronica's magical potential scores, her value as a familiar and for the children she could breed were the grand prizes. The miniature had been clearly labeled as assurance that the chosen wizards would indeed be bedding the woman who accompanied the scorecard. Certified and guaranteed by the Convocation.

Yes, all so very cold-blooded, but Gabriel had been assured that the Betrothal Trials were voluntary, so Lady Veronica must be hoping to find a good wizard partner and husband.

The sense that he and Lady Veronica might at least find some common ground had been the final spur that decided him to try for her. Yes, her magical potential scores were desirable, too much so, because that meant he was reaching high. That she was of House Elal, with an expensive Convocation Academy education, also meant she could help him navigate that legal, professional, and social hierarchy.

When he succeeded in impregnating her—which he would, thanks to the spell he'd found—and they married... Well, it wouldn't be a love match like his own parents had. Perhaps, though, he and Lady Veronica had enough in common that they could find a way to being friends.

Regardless, some wizard would have Lady Veronica for their familiar. And none of them could possibly need her more than Gabriel did. It might as well be him, especially since the future of House Phel depended on it.

Pocketing the miniature, he set his sights on House Elal and firmed his resolve.

He would be the one.

## ~ 2 ~

SKIRTS SWIRLING ABOUT her ankles, Lady Veronica Elal paced restlessly to the heavy velvet curtains that covered the barred windows of her round tower room, and slipped behind them. Shivering in the chill trapped there, she hooked her fingers into the slats of the shutters anyway, ignoring the cold bite of the metal. It was a ridiculous habit she'd developed over the last months of seclusion, as if she could make the spaces between the rigid slats wider, so she could glimpse just a bit more of the outside world.

The gray sky had dimmed to early evening. It would soon be full dark, and Lord Phel would invade her small territory. She'd watched him cross the bridge across the moat a while ago, but she hadn't been able to make out much from the tower's height except that both his hair and his horse's coat looked totally white—and that could've been the dusting of snow.

Now they must both wait for sunset, as decreed by Convocation law, for the night's trial to begin. The rose-scented unguent felt slick on her vulva, ready to ease Lord Phel's assault of her womb. She'd learned that lesson in preparation from her first wizard suitor, Lord Sammael.

As her mother had advised, Nic had been prepared with wine, food, and entertaining topics of conversation. *Your eventual marriage and working relationship with your wizard master will be much more pleasant if you can start out on congenial footing,* Maman had said. *If you want to have influence over your wizard master, then you will find sweetness gets you much further than sarcastic words and dour moods.*

The Convocation ran on elegant manners, so Nic had expected the night with Sammael to be civil and courtly. She wasn't so silly as to hope for romance, even though she and the other students at Convocation Academy had swooned over the tale of the dashing wizard Sylus and his beautiful familiar Lyndella. When Lyndella had been forced by her greedy family into marrying Sylus, she'd been reluctant, even afraid. But she and Sylus had fallen in love, the magical Fascination between wizard and familiar forming a bond that none of their enemies could break, despite the pair's many epic adventures and trials.

The Convocation teachers had been far more practical on the matter, explaining in detail that the Fascination some familiars claimed to feel for their wizard masters had never been adequately proven, despite intensive experimentation. The Convocation paired wizards and familiars according to their magical potential scores, ensuring their compatibility, and the Betrothal Trials guaranteed their combined fertility. The ritual bonding sealed the familiar to their wizard, not love.

Now that Nic had endured the attentions of several suitors, she was grateful that she didn't feel even a glimmer of that mythical Fascination for the wizards who applied for her. Sammael had barely bothered with a hello. He'd simply bent her over the arm of the big chair by the fire, tossed up her skirts, and entered her. They'd never even reached the bed, and the various oils and cremes arrayed there to help them along.

Nic hadn't told Maman the unpleasant details of that encounter. Her mother had enough to worry about without fretting over some girlish tears and a bit of chafing. Still, it had *hurt*. And, worse, it had been humiliating, leaving Nic feeling soiled in a way that wouldn't be cleansed, no matter how much she coaxed the fire elementals to boil the wash water ever hotter.

She'd hated that she'd shed tears over Sammael's treatment of her. It didn't do for a daughter of the House of Elal to be weepy. With the shedding of those tears, though, she released the hurt and shame—and resolved to learn from the experience. She couldn't change her fate. Much as Nic had been certain she'd manifest as a wizard, that she'd follow in her father's footsteps to become head of House Elal someday, she was doomed to be a familiar. And a familiar didn't have many choices in life. So she'd wield those few choices to the best of her ability.

If Sammael's seed had taken, Nic would've had to marry him and become his familiar. Those were the Betrothal Trials rules, and she'd agreed to them—because the Trials at least gave her the power of summary dismissal. As long as she accepted at least twelve of the Convocation's list of compatible wizards—enough for a year of trials—then she could eliminate the rest at will.

At least until the year was up. If she didn't quicken by then, she'd have to face some of the more sordid possibilities. But that was a worry for the future. The current list was as good as she and Maman could get it.

With Maman's canny insight as Lady Elal, Nic had carefully reviewed the list of potential suitors and removed any wizard she wouldn't be able to handle, and then further culled the list of suitors to include only those from houses where Nic could rise to power. According to Maman, a clever familiar could subtly manipulate her wizard master to her liking. Also, though Nic might be only a familiar, she was forever and always the eldest child of the most powerful house in the Convocation. Lord Sammael was his house's heir apparent, so Nic would've been on track to be Lady Sammael.

Odious though the man might be, she would've found a way to control Sammael—and perhaps help tilt his descent to the grave with a bit more of a downward slant. An early widowhood was about the only path to freedom for a bonded familiar. If, that was, Nic could avoid being acquired by her husband's heir, but she'd navigate those waters when she reached them. Once she was married and on track to be lady of a house, preferably a High House, she could begin to consolidate power of her own. It was her best choice of a crop of terrible ones.

Sammael had been… not cruel, exactly. But he also hadn't been kind or gentle, nor had he seemed much interested in the person end of her body. He'd also been her first time with a man—not that she'd been unprepared. Maman had gone through eight months of Betrothal Trials until Nic's papa impregnated her and she came to House Elal. She'd given Nic the tools and ointments to stretch her woman's passage enough so her first time wouldn't be painful—not physically, anyway—and the oils to ensure that Sammael's entry would be sufficiently eased.

No amount of preparation, however, could have eased the casually arrogant way he seemed to not hear anything Nic said, before he suggested—ordered, really, in that imperious way of a wizard addressing a familiar—that she not speak at all. *I know you're an innocent*, he'd said, *but no one cares what a familiar has to* say. *If I want intelligent conversation, I'll talk to another wizard.*

So much for Maman's advice to engage her suitors in conversation.

Thus, Nic had been relieved when the Convocation proctor and her oracle head pronounced her not with child after Sammael. Though Nic hadn't much liked suitors two and three, Lords Tadkiel and Ratsiel, either, she'd still been a bit disappointed their seed hadn't taken. Either wizard would've been relatively easy to manipulate. Also, she didn't want to endure the Betrothal Trials month after month. If she didn't quicken after a year of this, things got considerably more dire. Which was saying something.

Some of the familiars she'd schooled with had gone for over a year before quickening. The guys had an easier time of it, as they didn't need to be sequestered for their Trials. The female familiars, however, had to stay locked in their tower rooms under guard, to ensure any child conceived belonged to the wizard who'd paid for the opportunity to acquire a familiar and brood mare to powerful children in one swoop. Or to the male designated as stud by a female wizard.

Infamously, Lady Sarai Byssan had gone over three years without conceiving before she'd exhausted the wizards of the High Houses *and* the tier-two houses. House Byssan had offered her for bonding to the lady wizards, but none wanted a familiar who couldn't be bred. She'd then faced the choice of trying suitors from lower-tier houses—or, worse, unlanded wizards—or dedicating herself to the Convocation.

Sarai had chosen a life of service to the Convocation and whoever had the wherewithal to hire her. Most of the familiars at Convocation Academy had agreed they'd rather continue with the Trials rather than serve as a Convocation familiar, but Sarai hadn't been able to face the Trials any longer. A sentiment Nic understood much better now.

But, face them she must. She couldn't back out of the Betrothal Trials now, much as she didn't look forward to bedding Lord Phel.

All right, in the privacy of her own head, she could admit that she was dreading it. And look at her—hiding behind the curtains like they might save her from the night ahead. Even without the metal shutters to discourage any attempts at an ill-conceived escape, the fall from her tower would kill her.

Nic was far too stubborn, too determined to make the best of her bad fate, to succumb now. She'd survived discovering she'd never be a wizard. She'd even held her head high through the subsequent, possibly even more painful blows when her younger sister and brother, Alise and Nander, manifested as wizards. One of them would succeed Papa as head of House Elal, while Nic would become the property of another house. The cold metal bit into her fingers, she gripped the slats so hard.

Making herself leave her limited view behind, she paced past the little table holding the wine and delicacies between the companionably placed chairs before the cheerful fire, and eyed the small vial of House Aratron potion she could add to her own wine. Many of the familiars used it, male or female, so it was said. Arrogance and casual cruelty came naturally to wizards, lord and lady alike. The potion wasn't an aphrodisiac—contrary to the exaggerated tales circulated at school—but it did make being willing a bit easier.

Tempting, with the dread whittling at her insides.

Still, her pride might be a failing, as her mother so often warned, but Nic wouldn't resort to an Aratron apothecary's mind-clouding to see this through. She'd agreed to the Betrothal Trials, so she'd face the wizard clear-headed and with a brave heart. She'd gone through this three times before and—unless Phel managed to plant his seed—she would again. The trick would be extracting her own brand of triumph from it.

Lord Phel was desperate, she reminded herself—she and Maman had gone through everything the Elal spirit spies could dig up on the wizard who'd emerged from the unlikely swamps of Meresin—and a desperate man could be led in the direction a clever woman wanted him to go. House Phel had once been a High House, long since removed from the Convocation roster when they stopped producing progeny with any measurable magical potential. A disaster for any house, let alone a High House. But their catastrophe could be her opportunity, especially since, two generations later, they'd unexpectedly produced a wizard with astonishingly high MP scores.

Perhaps he'd be her ticket to, if not actual freedom, then the ability to control her own destiny. Nic had the fire and drive to be lady of her own house. Due to an accident of birth, she couldn't do that as a wizard, so she'd find another way. She was an Elal, first and foremost, and that meant something.

There, that was better. She was stronger than a hapless wizard from a fallen house.

A knock at the door had her whirling as if a snake had rattled a warning. Her heart skipped a beat. Her gut clenched.

So much for her newfound bravery.

She snatched up the potion vial and slipped it into a pocket of her skirts. Just in case. She could always drink it straight, bitter though it might be. If she needed it, she wouldn't mind a bit of foul flavor. Composing herself, Nic folded her hands and lifted her chin. A picture of elegance and poise even Maman would praise.

"Enter," she called, keenly aware that it was more than her chambers she invited entry into.

The lock clicked, and the door swung open. Nic steeled herself for the first glimpse of the man she'd soon be taking between her thighs—likely within moments, if he was anything like Sammael. Maybe he'd be the last. *Come on, lucky number four.*

Lord Phel stepped in, draped in a dark-green cloak, deeply cowled hood drawn around his face. A shine of power radiated from him, cool and pale as moonlight on still water, and palpably shimmering with danger. Tall and broad-shouldered, he ducked slightly and turned a bit sideways to pass through the doorway of the ancient tower, which was admittedly on the small side. Still, no one else had had trouble with it.

He turned and closed the door, cocking his head at the click as the guard locked it from the outside.

She refused to acknowledge the sinking sensation of being trapped. That was cowardice sneaking in. He was as trapped as she was, since they'd be sealed in together until the guard let them out. The Convocation proctor wouldn't allow him to spend less than the entire night, and the Betrothal Trial rules wouldn't allow him to harm her. Not physically, anyway. Not much. She was letting her imagination run away with her.

He stayed there for a long moment, back turned to her, shoulders making a tense line in the cloak. If he weren't a wizard with staggeringly high MP scores, Nic would've guessed him to be nervous. Lord Phel turned, tipping back his cowl, and Nic stared.

His hair was entirely white, silver as moonlight, save for a black streak that ran from the right side of his forehead, weaving with the long strands that fell to his shoulders. It should've made him look ancient, but his dusky skin was smooth as a young man's. His wizard-black eyes, opaque and depthless, glittered in his sharp cheekboned face. Though his strong jaw was set in a determined line, his lips were well-formed, surprisingly soft-looking.

Nic couldn't seem to look away. She'd never felt so… drawn to a wizard. Sure, familiars were attracted to wizard power, that was their nature, but this felt far more potent. Like a kind of… Fascination.

*No!* With a burst of panic, Nic tried to shake herself from her rapt stare—and found herself unable to wrench her gaze from his. It couldn't be Fascination. That would be a bad, bad sign.

Lord Phel still stood by the door, returning the examination, until he quirked a brow in sardonic question. Thankfully, that small movement broke the spell holding her rapt. Chagrined, shaken, and determined not to be further rattled by a mild attraction to an admittedly handsome man—that was surely all it was, as Fascination was a myth, wasn't it?—she lifted a hand to gesture to the empty chairs. It shook slightly, so she buried it in a fold of her skirts. *Get ahold of yourself, Lady Elal*, she instructed herself firmly.

"Welcome, Lord Phel," she said. There. She sounded perfectly composed. "There's a hook there, for your cloak. Will you sit? There is wine, and a fire to warm you after your journey." *Please sit and don't go at me right away.*

She held her breath as his opaque gaze fell to the elegant wine decanter, the pair of crystal glasses, the tray of rich delicacies—and her heart fell as his lip curled. Nic braced for the command. *Turn around and bend over. Lie down and spread your legs.* She pressed her thighs together to assure herself that plenty of unguent remained to grease his way. She didn't know why tradition demanded the pretense of courtship when every suitor ate *after* he'd planted his seed—leaving nothing for her to eat—before falling asleep to snore until dawn when they could be released.

She'd learned to eat a hearty meal at midday and have a snack at midafternoon, to stave off hunger until morning.

*Morning.* In the morning he'd be gone, and she could be left alone for a few blessed weeks. Something to cling to.

He lifted his hands, the draping sleeves falling back to reveal long fingers and pale moon nails. He slipped the pin from the brooch fastening his cloak, the polished metal flashing as he stowed it in a pocket, before hanging the cloak on the hook. Then he strode purposefully toward her. Leaner than she'd first thought him, lanky and long-legged, he moved like a cat, graceful and predatory—and she found herself shrinking back, despite all her prideful resolve.

But he surprised her by shifting his penetrating gaze from her to the chairs. Bypassing the closer one, he sat—leaving her usual chair for her. Had he noticed the faint indications of use that revealed the one to be her favorite chair? It seemed unlikely. Raising that expressive brow at her, he pointed at the other chair. "Won't *you* sit, Lady Veronica?"

All right, then. She'd gotten her wish, so she'd be happy. She shouldn't feel *more* nervous.

She edged between him and the fire, easing into her chair—which didn't feel nearly as comfortable as usual—and perched on the edge. Arranging her skirts, she regretted the color. The forest-green velvet gown was new from House Ophiel, sent along with one of their dressmaker wizards to tailor it, along with a whole new wardrobe for her. Papa had been generous in providing her with new gowns during her trials, an unvoiced message of encouragement that meant so much. She'd disappointed him by not becoming the wizard they'd hoped she'd be, so she was grateful that he supported her quest in the trials to do her best as a familiar.

The forest-green gown had instantly become her favorite for its sensually full skirts and lovely embroidery of silver leaves. At that moment, though, she could wish that she wasn't wearing a color so akin to Phel's cloak.

He studied her while she fidgeted, gaze whispering over her skin and leaving a trace of steam behind. Where his cloak had been made of rich cloth, his clothing veered toward the simple side. Of course, he'd traveled days to get to Elal on horseback, which she'd have known by the earthy smell if she hadn't observed for herself. He either refused to barter for a magically propelled conveyance, or he couldn't afford it. He also smelled of snow and fresh winter air, and she found she didn't mind the combination. Better by far than the perfumes her carriage-borne other suitors had sported. She caught herself inhaling his scent again, savoring. *Stop it.*

"Shall I pour?" he prompted, arrogance tempered with that hint of uncertainty.

*Eesh.* What was wrong with her? She was hardly impressing him with what a wonderful hostess of House Phel she'd make. Of course, rumor had it that the actual house was in ruins. Still, she'd been raised better. Wizard or familiar, she was a lady of a High House. "Apologies," she murmured in her most gracious tone, plucking up the decanter and pouring a healthy portion for him.

He quirked that brow, black as his eyes, as that one streak in his hair. "Aren't you indulging also?"

The vial burned in her pocket, and she poured herself a small allowance of wine, in case she needed to drink the potion. He gave her small portion a quizzical look, lifted that long-fingered hand and slid his glass to sit beside hers, as if to compare the vastly different levels. He raised those sardonic black eyes to hers, then tipped his glass to add to hers until they were even. "In this, at least," he said, "let us begin on equal footing."

Plucking up his glass, he lifted it, waiting pointedly for her to do the same. "To a fruitful night," he suggested, watching her keenly.

She echoed him in a quiet murmur—trying not to think about what would happen between them, her nerves whispering a warning despite his courteous manners—and he clinked his glass against hers, his eyes never leaving her face. Slowly he brought the glass to his lips, then held it there, waiting again for her to mirror the action. The silence—and unexpected tension—stretched out, a hum in it like quiet magic. Finally, Nic took a sip, one he mimicked exactly in length and swallow.

"Oh, for goodness sake," she burst out, plunking her glass down ungracefully, all politeness dropped, nerves forgotten at the implied insult to House Elal. "It's not poisoned."

"I never imagined it was," he replied evenly, also setting his glass down, but not mimicking her abrupt speed. "It is delicious, however. From Elal vineyards?"

"Naturally. Our coastal vineyards are the best in the Convocation, each vine tended by its own earth elemental. This vintage is set aside for the family." She picked up her glass and spun it slowly, observing the rich red. It was her favorite, and she'd miss it greatly when she left.

"I'd be able to tell if it were poisoned," Lord Phel remarked conversationally. "Water magic extends to wine. That has to be on my MP scorecard, which you've no doubt studied."

He had her there. "Then why the charade?" she demanded.

He shrugged a little and sat back in his chair. "I wanted to see what you would do."

Flushed and flustered, she picked up her glass and took a hearty swallow. "There. Satisfied?"

Cocking his head, he continued to study her, as if she were already his to extract power from. "Are you always this high strung, or is it the circumstances?"

*As if the circumstances aren't enough?* "Maybe it's you," she snapped, regretting it instantly. He looked so intrigued.

Leaning forward again, he set his forearms on his knees, lacing his fingers together. "Surely you're not frightened of me."

She managed a nicely derisive laugh. "I am not."

He considered her, nostrils flaring as if he smelled a lie. Perhaps he could, though Nic didn't think his skills should extend to that. She wasn't afraid. Wary, yes. Her nerves singingly alert at the strength of his magic, filling the room like bright moonlight. Wishing the whole thing over and done with already. But she refused to be afraid. "Shouldn't we get to business?" she inquired, gesturing at the bed nestled in the curve of one wall.

"Business," he echoed, looking as if he tasted something unpleasant. "Is that what this is to you?"

"What else would you call it?"

"If we make a child between us tonight, we'll be married," he said slowly, feeling his way through the words. "We'll be tied together as family, as the leaders of House Phel, and as wizard and familiar. Those aren't matters of business."

If Nic hadn't already known that Lord Phel hadn't grown up in the Convocation, had never trained at Convocation Academy, that bit of naivete would've given him away. "It's nothing *but* business," she said. "The business of perpetuating the Convocation and assuring our families that our bloodlines will continue. Everything else you list is about politics, power, and you becoming the most powerful wizard you can be—also business. That's why this cold-blooded arrangement. There's no reason to put ourselves through the Trials otherwise."

"Isn't there?" He seemed to be turning over her explanation, gaze still weighing her. *This entire conversation is a test.* Nic's estimation of his intelligence—and strategy—rose considerably. None of the other three suitors had bothered to assess her this way. If she failed his test, would he walk away without planting his seed? Surely not, as he'd forfeit his gambit—a steep price indeed. She doubted the nascent House Phel's meager coffers could afford the loss.

"His scores are all in water and moon magic," Maman had said. "True to House Phel's historic strengths, but it's unfortunate that they don't have more useful affinities. What can one make with moon and water magic, so pale and yielding? Even before their MP scores declined, the house could never compete with others, and they never did amass much of a fortune."

But Lord Phel's magic didn't feel pale and yielding at all. With prickling unease, Nic became very aware of the danger this wizard presented. He would not do for her plans. He saw entirely too much, was far too canny. She'd never be able to manipulate this man. She should try to fail his test and escape with her future intact—if he'd let her. Taking a fortifying swallow of wine, she considered how to outwit him.

"Shall we eat?" Lord Phel asked into the silence that had gone on far too long for politeness. At her puzzled frown, he gestured at the tray of food. "I assume that's why this is here."

"Yes," she hastened to reply, kicking herself. *You need to sharpen up, girl, or this wizard will eat you alive. Perhaps literally.* "Allow me to fix you a plate."

She took up one of the dainty ceramic plates—so fine you could see light through them—delicately painted in gold leaf with the House Elal crest. As she began selecting from the tray, she became aware that he was again copying her, taking up a plate and adding the same exact tidbits she'd placed on the one she held. With some exasperation, she paused, waiting for him to glance up. "It seems you'd prefer to prepare your own plate?"

"No, indeed," he answered, smoothly polite, but his eyebrow twitched as if longing to arch in that sardonic style. "I'm simply returning the favor by preparing *you* a plate. Equal footing," he reminded her when she couldn't muster a response.

Nic set her teeth. Whatever game he was playing, she was losing. With determined focus, she picked all of her favorite foods, watching him follow suit across the table. When she'd loaded it sufficiently, she handed it to him, receiving the plate he'd fixed in turn.

They looked identical. Staring at it in consternation, she shook her head. She wasn't even hungry, having planned on not eating. "This is ridiculous," she muttered.

"How so?" he inquired silkily, holding his plate and not eating either. Of course he wasn't eating, since she hadn't touched hers yet.

"Aren't you hungry after your long journey?" she inquired in the same tone. She knew full well he hadn't stopped in the half day since Elal's guardian spirits had him riding through the Knifeblades.

"Famished," he conceded, glancing at the plate. "This looks as delicious as the wine."

"Maman will be pleased to hear it. She goes to some pains to impress my suitors."

Lord Phel raised his brows, a half smile ghosting over his full lips. "A spontaneously offered personal detail," he said lightly. "Not about you, but I feel this is progress."

He still held his plate, and Nic was tempted to dash it out of his hands. "Eat," she ground out, past politeness, "if you're so hungry."

"When you do," he replied. Not angrily, but making it clear he wouldn't be moved.

She set her plate down. "Then you'll go all night because I'm not hungry."

"No?" He set his plate down also. Of course. "Do you not typically eat an evening meal?"

She'd had about enough of this *congenial conversation*. "Are we going to bed or do you plan to interview me all night?" It just figured that he'd pushed her into hurrying *him* along. It turned out that drawn-out apprehension was more fraught than the over-and-done-with approach.

He sat back in his chair, steepling his fingers. Watching her. "We have a lot of time to do both," he noted. "Sunset to sunrise lasts a good fourteen hours in the dead of winter like this. We have wine, a cheerful fire, a cozy room out of the winds. Good food," he added pointedly.

"Please eat," she said on a sigh. "I promise it's not poisoned. I'm just not hungry."

"I know it's not poisoned," he reminded her, making no motion to take up his plate. "Why aren't you hungry—is it nerves about what's to come?"

Her knotted stomach agreed, but she kept the telltale reaction from her expression and scoffed. "Hardly. You're not my first suitor."

"No," he agreed slowly. "Number four in the lottery for a daughter of House Elal, I believe."

Nic felt the bitter twist of her lips before she valiantly pressed them into a pretty smile. "What a delightful way of phrasing it. Thank you."

He didn't take the bait, considering her solemnly. "Euphemisms may try to gild an ugly truth, but too often fail."

"If this tradition is so distasteful, why are you here?" she shot back.

His turn to grimace. "Desperation." Because he was watching her face, he nodded to himself at whatever he saw there. "I was warned, you know, that House Elal has the best spies—spirits and elementals, I'm sure, are excellent for that—and that you'd know everything about me. I figured it would be foolish to pretend otherwise."

He leaned forward, an abrupt and urgent movement,

propped his elbows on his knees, and rested his chin on steepled fingers. "I am a house of one wizard, Lady Veronica, and many dependents. I need you to give House Phel a future. Will you marry me, be my lady wife, familiar, and mother of my children?"

# ~ 3 ~

HER STUNNED EXPRESSION might've been comical if it hadn't been so uncomplimentary. Oh, she swiftly replaced the initial appalled disgust with serene, even regal contempt—but he'd shocked Lady Veronica Elal all right. At least, Gabriel congratulated himself, he'd managed to elicit an honest reaction out of her rather than the prickly façade she'd presented so far.

"Your proposal is entirely out of order," she finally said, tipping up that pointed chin in a haughty gesture he'd already grown perversely fond of.

"It seems," he pointed out, very reasonably, he thought, "that if we plan to have sex and attempt to make a child—and later marry if we succeed—then you should agree to all of that first."

"I'm here, aren't I?" She twirled a finger at the round tower room. "Believe me, I wouldn't be spending a year locked up in here if I hadn't agreed to the Trials."

"You didn't agree to me," he replied, wondering at himself for pushing his luck. She clearly didn't like him, so he was only asking for trouble. "To marrying *me*, in particular."

Firming her lush lips—they truly were the deep red as in

the miniature, like the blood poppies in Meresin—she shook her head. The sharp gesture made her glossy black curls bounce where they dangled from the pile on her head. He wasn't sure what he'd expected when he walked into her tower room, but he hadn't thought she'd be dressed as if for a formal event, dazzling in her elegant deep-green gown and sparkling with jewels.

Or that she'd fascinate him so. It had to be her native power as a potent familiar. He'd known—mostly from terribly dry tomes that described the wizard–familiar relationship in painfully erudite and obscure terms—that gaining a familiar would amplify his abilities.

He hadn't known that being near her would be more warming than the magically heated castle, or the fire crackling in her hearth.

"In point of fact, I did agree to you in particular," she replied crisply.

"On paper," he countered.

She shrugged that off. "What are we, besides our dossiers? I could've summarily dismissed you and didn't." Some bitterness crept into her tone, and he welcomed it as far more honest than her polished manners.

"We are human beings, too," he argued. "More than our MP scores. People, with thoughts and feelings."

She actually laughed, though without humor. "We are not. Wizards and familiars don't have courtships. Thoughts and feelings are irrelevant in our world. The Convocation chose you for me, Lord Phel, and—as I had no reason to refuse the selection—I'll abide by that choice."

"Gabriel," he said.

She paused, black lashes lowering, then lifting again for her gaze to pierce him. "Excuse me?"

"My name is Gabriel. If you're considering marrying me, it seems you should call me by my given name. What should I call you?"

"Lady Veronica Elal," she said with crisp enunciation.

"Is that what your friends call you?" He tried for charming, falling far short in the face of her scorn.

"I think you are not a fool," she said, clearly implying the reverse, fixing him with those clear green eyes he seemed unable to look away from. "The rules of the Betrothal Trials clearly state that you must successfully impregnate me before we can marry."

"I know the rules," he replied mildly. He'd read them first with incredulity, then with growing anger, and finally memorized them with dull resignation. He wouldn't get anywhere defying the Convocation's rules. No, he'd play by their draconian laws. Until the time was ripe to kill the beast from the inside.

"Since you know these rules so well," Lady Veronica said, parsing her words with false patience, "then you know that if you successfully plant your seed in me, I will marry you. Further discussion is moot. I'll also remind you that you have one night to accomplish the deed, so perhaps—since you're clearly not going to eat—we should get to it?"

He forced himself to sit back, to appear relaxed. With a woman like her, he had to move carefully. He'd come to House Elal determined to win this prize. But it wouldn't be enough to simply win her hand. He wanted her on his side. Not unlike attempting to tame a wild cat from the western marshes. Fortunately, he didn't mind a few scratches.

"As I mentioned earlier, all night is a long time," he said mildly. "Though I'm flattered by your confidence, I doubt I'll manage more than five or six attempts."

She looked so briefly startled that he wondered if her other suitors had managed much more. There were all sorts of spells for *that* kind of thing, which could be purchased from itinerant minor wizards, legitimate and otherwise. He'd gone for potency over performance. A good call, as she looked so fine-boned, so soft-skinned, he worried about hurting her. His gaze strayed to the table beside the bed, arrayed with all sorts of oils and unguents. Some of them numbing cremes, he'd read in the instructions packet. Charming.

"Five or six," she murmured, fluttering her lashes. "So many as that."

He couldn't tell if that was sarcasm, an attempt to flatter him—or some of those nerves he kept sensing from her. "I'm happy to limit the number as you prefer," he offered, knowing as soon as he said it that he'd misstepped, the way she cleared her expression and flicked that away.

"It's entirely up to you, wizard," she replied. "I'm at your disposal for the night."

"You don't have to, if—"

"I do." She'd cut him off so sharply he was tempted to check if his tongue was bleeding. Her green eyes sparkled with gold fire. "Enough of this dithering. I'm not backing out. Are you?"

"No." He restrained a sigh. *Eyes on the prize.*

"Five or six *attempts*, then," she declared, as if they'd been negotiating. "Have you figured any sleep into your schedule?" She was all sweetness with that question, the hard light in her eyes belying her tone.

"This is an important night," he answered, holding her gaze. Her eyes were truly blue, a light grayish blue, flecked with gold like a cat's, so they appeared green from a distance. "I don't plan to sleep tonight at all."

She laughed. "With five or six attempts, even spaced a couple of hours apart, with no napping between, that leaves a lot of unoccupied time. I do have plenty of books. I suppose we could read while we wait for your cock to recover for another go."

He set his teeth against her taunting. "I thought we could talk."

"*Congenial conversation?*" she inquired, coloring the phrase with a peculiar hint of mockery.

"A worthy goal," he replied drily. "We could get to know each other, in case."

She picked up her wineglass, found it empty, and frowned at his still-half-full one. "Now who isn't playing the game correctly?"

"I wasn't aware we *were* playing a game." He allowed himself a smile at her consternation. It hadn't been intended as a game. He'd simply been trying at first to match her energy, to get a feel for her. It was an outgrowth of his magic, to observe and reflect. Well, and he'd wanted to simply revel in the generous, sparkling power radiating from her, as comforting as the cheerful fire she didn't really need. Then he'd realized how his mirroring her had rattled her enough to drop some of her smooth defenses and prickly deflections, to reveal something of her true self—and he'd been unable to resist needling her for more.

He'd clearly annoyed her, but she drew in a careful breath and mastered herself. Excellent self-discipline. No surprise, given her high marks from schooling on the subject. She wasn't as calm as she wished to appear, however, still sitting on the edge of her chair, not in the well-worn curve where she clearly nestled her bottom normally. She sat here often, he imagined, curled up like a kitten in that big chair by the fire, reading one of her many books.

"You said you're hungry," she said in that perfectly polite, highborn tone. "Please don't wait for me. I really couldn't eat anything more. Not because of nerves, but because I ate a large luncheon and a substantial snack before you arrived."

An actual confidence there, he tasted the truth of it—and she wasn't looking at him in proud defiance, instead gazing rather mournfully at her empty wineglass. Picking up the priceless crystal decanter, he held it poised over her glass. "Will you have more wine, then?"

After a bare hesitation, she nodded, her fingers passing over a lump in her pocket, so briefly he nearly missed it. Brushing his magic over it, he sensed liquid and tasted the contents of a small vial. A soporific. Not one she'd taken, however. No, one she was keeping it in case she needed it.

He hadn't been told she might drug herself to get through this night. She hadn't yet done it, so perhaps it depended on how things went. Given her skittishness so far—and the way she kept pushing him to get it over with, as if she'd be relieved to have a nasty duty behind her—he suspected things hadn't gone well with her previous suitors. From the few Convocation wizards he'd met so far, that didn't surprise him. She was sipping her wine, watching him warily, still more inclined to scratch than purr.

"Why would you eat," he asked casually, "if you know you'll be having a meal?" He picked up his plate and began eating the very excellent food. Far better than his impoverished community had ever managed.

She narrowed her eyes, then let out a sigh of resignation, cradling the glass in her hands. "My previous suitors were disinclined to share."

Ah. He began to understand now. That had been the key to the puzzle. "And disinclined to *congenial conversation*, too, I suppose?"

She frowned, the expression speaking far more than any words she'd given him. "One barely spoke to me at all, except to give instructions," she confided. Then, seeming surprised at herself, she glared accusingly at her wine and set it down. "It's of no matter."

"It is," he insisted. "I asked."

"Sizing up the competition?" she asked archly.

"Not at all. They're not competition anymore, right? The rules say we get the one night only, with no opportunity to try again. Unless I misread?"

"You have it correct," she replied. "And thank the Convocation for including that one."

"That bad?" he asked, watching her intently, his senses on her emotional pulse.

That pulse roiled, hurt and shame in it, though nothing showed on her face as she glanced away at the fire. "I think it's really not appropriate to gossip about," she replied airily. Then cast him a sharp green glance. "After all, you wouldn't want me to detail your sexual techniques with the next fellows to try their luck."

"You're assuming I won't succeed, then," he said softly.

She rolled her eyes. "With your seed planted in that chair and not in my womb? I feel like this is a safe assumption."

"I have all night to get it there," he reminded her.

"So you keep saying. Remember that even a long winter's night doesn't last forever. I don't understand the reason for your delay."

"I thought it would only be civilized to get to know each other a bit, before..." He waved vaguely at the bed.

She snorted indelicately. "There is nothing civilized about this situation. It's a fancy veneer plastered over a barbaric ritual."

"Then why are you engaging in it?"

Throwing up her hands, she flung herself from her chair in a burst of graceful motion. "What do you care, Lord Phel?"

"Gabriel," he insisted, but she only stared back, lips firmly closed, and he bit back a sigh. "If we end up married, I'd like to know what you want from the institution, from me." He filled his plate again, since the first serving had barely made a dent in the hole gnawing at his belly—and since he no longer felt guilty eating when she wasn't.

She turned her back to the fire, gazing at him as if she suspected he was crazy. A fair suspicion, given the various madnesses that had plagued House Phel before it was removed from the Convocation roster. "You have it backwards, you know. Marriage is nothing so intimate as the wizard–familiar bonding."

How intriguing. "I didn't know. Then what would you want from being my familiar?"

"Nobody asks a familiar what they want," she replied with considerable exasperation—and that bitter edge again.

"I'm asking."

"All right, then. I want out," she snapped. Her eyes roved the tower room, as if seeing beyond it, then settled on him. "I may be only a familiar, but I want my own life, my own house, to shape my own destiny."

"Only a familiar?" he repeated with some surprise. "I've seen your MP scores, and you have more magic than almost anyone in the Convocation."

"Yes, but I can't use it myself, can I? I need a wizard for that." She gestured at him needlessly.

"You could ally with a wizard without going through this."

"No, Lord Phel. That is not an option." She huffed out a dry laugh, shaking her head so those long, glossy ringlets swung. "So, if I have to be bonded, which I do, I want a first-tier house, and wizard," she added, giving him an unreadable look.

"House Phel isn't first tier," he told her, unnecessarily, he felt sure.

She shrugged that off as a minor detail. "It was before. All indications are you intend to make it that way again. Or you wouldn't have gambled so much of your meager fortune on me." Her eyes sparkled with canny intelligence.

"Ah. Your research is, of course, excellent." It still surprised him, even given House Elal's reputation for spying, as he'd thought he was the only one to know exactly how meager House Phel's fortune was, especially after paying the Convocation's extortionate prices.

She gave him a wry smile. "That was something of a guess, actually. I'm not a fool either."

Tipping his head, he acknowledged her point. "Regardless, I'm sure you know I won't be able to house you like this." He echoed her twirling finger gesture, expanding it to indicate all the rich lands of Elal and its many magical conveniences. "Not now. Maybe not ever."

"I know," she replied. "That's not important to me."

"What is?"

An answer moved behind her eyes, there and gone. He could maybe pull it out of her mind—though her training might be good enough to stop him, from what he understood—but that seemed like a bad way to start a partnership.

"I have ambitions," she acknowledged cagily. "And they're none of your business, especially not yet. Besides which, the Convocation matched us, so they must think you have *some* merit." She made it sound like she seriously doubted their judgment, and he had to suppress a smile.

"Who else did they choose for you?"

"That's not your business either," she shot back, "as you should know."

If House Phel were a fully operational house, he'd have spies of his own to ferret out that information. The Betrothal Trial suitors were confidential, but members of other Convocation houses could hardly come and go in secret, especially given Elal's tightly guarded borders. But he didn't have those resources, so that was a dead end. Not unless she confided in him. "If we are joined as husband and wife—and wizard and familiar," he added when she frowned, "we won't have secrets between us," he pointed out.

She stared at him in patent astonishment, then burst out laughing, the keen edge of disdain slicing him. "Dear me—you *are* naïve. You might be wise to simply engage in congenial conversation with me all night and keep your seed. I suspect I'm not at all what you're looking for."

He suspected she was right. When he'd signed up for the Betrothal Trial information packets, he'd imagined gaining a partner and helpmeet, a familiar to amplify his magic and a companion to cuddle at night. Someone to ease the loneliness of his new and bizarre existence. Lady Veronica Elal was far from cuddly. *You picked her for her fire, too*, he reminded himself, the miniature a weight in his pocket.

"Unfortunately I can't afford to do that," he replied, setting aside his empty plate. "You guessed very well: I've gambled my entire fortune on this chance."

Her lips parted, only breath hissing out. "I take it back. You *are* a fool."

He grinned at her. "I prefer 'confident risk-taker.'"

"You seem more like a lazy procrastinator to me," she taunted. "All talk and no action."

"Are you truly so averse to spending some time getting to know each other?"

"There's no point. Either we'll never have cause to see each other again or we'll have a lifetime to learn each other with excruciating thoroughness."

So much bitterness there. So many questions he wanted to ask her. Was she always this difficult, or was it the circumstances? "Perhaps *I* want to learn what sort of person you are before I'm tied to you for life," he bit out.

She smiled, not nicely. "Afraid to put the viper to your breast?"

Indeed he was. And yet, he'd spoken the truth when he'd said he'd gambled it all on her. It would take him years to accumulate enough to bid for a familiar again, and still he'd never be able to afford one of her power. No, he must take his chance with Lady Veronica. And he might as well proceed. The book had indicated the potency spell would work better with her receptive, but the longer they talked, the more he seemed to be repelling her rather than winning her trust.

"All right," he said, brushing his trousers for any stray crumbs, then patted his knee. "Come here."

"The bed is over there," she said, pointing, as if he'd perhaps failed to notice it.

"I saw." He patted his knee again. "I'd like you to come here."

She firmed her lips, wary and taken off balance. "I don't see why."

"Don't the rules say you're supposed to accommodate my requests?" Actually, the rules said she must follow his commands for the night, but he hadn't cared for that phrasing and wouldn't repeat it. *One barely spoke to me at all, except to give instructions.* At least he could try not to be that wizard, whoever it was. Possibly just as well she wouldn't say, since Gabriel would want to punch the asshole. "This seems like a good way to ease in," he explained. "Please."

"Fine," she spat out, then stalked over and plopped herself ungracefully—and somewhat painfully—on his thigh. She perched there stiffly, arms crossed, glaring at him. "I'm not terribly experienced, but I do know that—no matter what tales the silly youngsters tell—your seed will not penetrate layers of clothing."

A smile stretched his lips, the bubbling amusement a welcome sensation. She was prickly as a thorn bush—her wit as sharp as one—but he'd never be bored with her. That fire and ambition of hers could make all the difference in his plans.

If he could coax her into working with him instead of knifing him in his sleep.

"I thought we'd start with a kiss." He made his voice gentle, reaching up to touch her cheek, thinking to urge her closer. She flinched as his hand neared, so he touched one of the trembling ringlets instead. Like spun silk. She watched him warily, rigid with tension. "Are you afraid?" he asked.

"Hardly." She lifted her chin boldly, but he felt it in her, the damp frisson of dread, the still, cold fog of fear.

"Did the others hurt you?" He followed the spiral of her ringlet to where it dangled against the wing of her collarbone, moving his touch to her skin. She held still, but twitched under the touch. Waiting until she relaxed under it, he traced the delicate line of her bone under the skin.

"What do you care?" she challenged, but without much punch behind it.

He raised his eyes to hers. Blue and gold, faceted like jewels. "I don't want to hurt you, or do anything you don't welcome."

"That's not in the rules," she sounded breathier now, and she'd softened under the caress, no longer perched on his knee like a bird about to take flight. "It's not required. I advise you to maximize your investment and commence with your five or six attempts."

"In good time," he mused. Sliding his fingers along the swanlike column of her neck, he savored the silken texture of her skin. He coaxed her to lean in, cupping the back of her neck. "A kiss?"

Her gaze dropped to his mouth. Lifted again. "So do it."

"I thought maybe you would kiss me." He caressed the sensitive nape of her neck, enjoying her shiver of awareness.

"That's not how this usually goes," she replied, a touch acerbic, a bit more intrigued.

"All the more reason." Whatever those louts had done to her, he was determined to do otherwise—as much as possible. As long as he surprised her, he could be reasonably sure he wasn't treading the same brutal path. Even having met Convocation wizards and liking exactly none of them, he'd have thought they'd have at least treated a treasure like Veronica gently.

Apparently he'd been wrong about that, too, among so many things.

"I don't know how," she confessed, studying his mouth again. "I never have."

And yet she'd been bedded by three men already. Later, after they were married, he'd extract those three names from her, and those cretins would be the first to crumble in House Phel's rise.

"Lips to lips," he whispered, daring to put his other hand on her hip, moving beneath her slight weight so she settled more cozily against him. He brushed his thumb over the nape of her neck, soothing, arousing, savoring. "Like this, but with lips."

She laid a hand on his shoulder, giving herself leverage, and leaned in. She smelled of hothouse roses and warmed red wine. He closed his eyes, reining in the urge to drink her up in great greedy swallows. The whisper of her lips against his registered as a breath, a bare hint of a kiss.

She withdrew marginally and held herself still, waiting. He didn't move. *Come here, little butterfly, and sip of me.*

Lured in by the honeyed call, she returned, bending her stiffened arm a bit more to allowing a less fleeting press of her lips to his. Letting her control the kiss, he gently responded, moving to mirror her touch, reflecting her burning heat, much as he had before. Just enough to meet her halfway.

She tested, tasted, the bright curiosity in her opening up, spilling through the cracks in her tough, disciplined mental walls. Seeming to be unaware of it, she leaned into him, the soft rounds of her breasts tantalizing as they swept against his chest. Taking the chance—wasn't he with all of this?—he slid the hand at her hip up her slender back, the silken velvet nap hot from the fire and from the woman within.

When he parted his lips, inviting her in, she made a small sound of surprise, but didn't draw back. Yes, she hesitated… but then opened her mouth, now mirroring him, and sank in with heat and a rush of heady passion.

Their combined desire billowed and swirled, their energies meshing and sparking, her fire heating him to boiling. He groaned, pressing her to lie fully against him, holding her close. This. This was all he'd hoped for. And with only a kiss. When she was his and they started truly combining magic, the results would be even more spectacular.

But, as she kept pointing out, first things first. The rules stipulated they needed to make a child, so make a child they would.

With a thrill of triumph, he surged to his feet and carried her to the bed. She felt good in his arms—a perfect fit in every way—supple and sparkling with delicious power that warmed even the cold, damp hollows of his heart. With her hands looped around his neck, she gazed at him with wide green eyes gone fulgent.

Oh yes. Together they would conquer the world.

# ~ 4 ~

NIC WAS LOST. Boneless, boundaryless, she tumbled into the deep lake of Lord Phel's deliciously cool magic and powerful presence. Distantly, and ruefully, a part of her acknowledged that those epic stories of Fascination might have a grain of truth. Besides the immortal tale of Sylus and Lyndella, there were other ballads and novels of such magical pairings, always culminating in tragedy. They plucked the heartstrings nicely on cold winter nights, or long sweetly warm summer ones, and she'd shed tears over more than one such story, reveling in the heartbreaking tales of love lost.

When she'd been too young to know better. And that did not mean she wanted to live through one.

She'd been so certain, especially after the awful other suitors, that those stories had been entirely fictional, products of wishful thinking, or perhaps deliberate propaganda to sugarcoat what was, at its heart, an exploitative relationship. How do you persuade a familiar to be happy living their life as magical food for someone else? Persuade them that it will be emotionally and sexually fulfilling, and that what looks like indentured servitude is actually an epic love affair!

Focusing on Lord Phel's depthless black eyes—she refused

to think of him as Gabriel, as that implied a friendship that could never exist—Nic gave herself a mental slap. This was how magic worked. Wizards were ruthless sorts; no one attended the Convocation Academy without observing that universal truth. To be fair, wizards had to learn to be hard. The same traits that enabled them to learn the complex spells and rituals, and to survive the viciously competitive academy, were the same that made them into cold-hearted monsters.

Kindness got you killed in the Convocation.

Lord Phel was obviously manipulating her. All's fair, she supposed, as that was what wizards did. He'd simply used different tactics than the others. Instead of attempting to establish immediate mastery, he'd capitalized on her Fascinated attraction to him, softening her up with kissing and *congenial conversation*. Her other suitors had been the fools, not taking the time to coax her into opening like a parched flower drinking in the cooling rain. How little time it had taken him to do it, too.

One thing she knew: This man was more dangerous than she could have guessed. And she'd made herself vulnerable to him, totally unable to help herself. She'd tried to hold him at arm's length, keep their relationship to cold business… and utterly failed.

Lord Phel set her on her feet beside the bed, making her realize how fully she'd surrendered to his embrace. She hadn't offered the slightest protest when he'd picked her up and carried her. His black eyes glittered with passionate intensity, nearly burning her, his magic palpable as his rough fingers stroked her shoulders where the gown bared them. Hands accustomed to manual labor, and wielding physical weapons, too, not soft like most of the gentleman wizards of the Convocation. The dossier on him said he'd grown up poor, no better than the other farmers of Meresin who sometimes took up arms to defend their lands against scavengers. Until his developing wizardry had taken him from that.

Or, more accurately, she knew now that she'd met him: until he'd grasped that opportunity to lift himself and his relations out of the hole they'd fallen into.

She should have put all of that together right away. Lord Phel was certainly desperate, but he wasn't a victim of that desperation. No, he'd tempered that into a drive to win at all costs. This man would never be manipulated the way she needed. She could only hope that his seed—like the others—would fail to find purchase.

How to steel herself against him, though? Where she'd been able to endure the assaults of the others, those banal encounters seemed easy in retrospect compared to the enormity of walling out how this man affected her. Developing feelings for him would doom her. If she did have to become Lord Phel's familiar, succumbing to this Fascination for him would be a disaster.

Hopefully she'd never have to face that day.

He smiled slightly, watching her face, and she hoped he couldn't read her fears more than he already had. He'd seen through to her building dread, somehow divining how profoundly she'd hated those other couplings, something even Maman hadn't realized. She hadn't wanted her mother to know, but she didn't want *him* to know either. How had he figured her out so easily? She hadn't sensed him using mind magic on her, but he'd used the insight as expertly as any bladesman, wedging the sharp edge into a tiny crack and slipping through her defenses. She had to put a stop to that. *He wants to use you, so use him instead.*

Tracing the skin where her dress clung to her upper arms, he canted his head in question. "Can we take this off?"

A near-hysterical laugh bubbled up, but she squelched it. *You are allowed to do anything to me you wish*, she thought, but didn't say. Asking for what he could have commanded was simply another ruse to lull her into this yielding complacency. Nodding, she turned her back, sweeping aside the long ringlets that trailed from her elaborately coiled hair and showing him the long seam of her gown.

A pause made her look over her shoulder.

"I don't know how this fastens," he admitted with a frown. "No laces?"

"It's a House Ophiel gown," she replied. When his frown didn't clear, she added, "Magic. Just run your finger down the seam and will it to part. Anyone can do it—even commoners with no magic at all."

"*If* they can afford a House Ophiel gown," he muttered, and she had to concede the point.

The cloth parted, and he drew in an audible breath—in admiration for the slick mechanism, she thought, until he traced the line of her spine from the nape of her neck, which he'd so stirringly caressed before, all the way to the cleft of her buttocks. She shivered, suppressing a moan of pleasure.

"You are incredibly beautiful," he breathed.

Finally, something to snap her out of her trance. "You needn't ply me with pretty lies," she hissed, stepping away from him and tugging her arms out of the tight sleeves. "At least do me the courtesy of being honest."

He regarded her curiously, a hint of anger in his tightening jaw. "I am many things, but a liar is not one of them."

Angry in turn—a far more useful emotion than that drugging desire and humiliating temptation to snuggle up to him like a kitten in need of petting—she stripped off the gown and let it fall in a puddle. There, better to be fully undressed than play along with this game of seduction. Standing before him naked except for her heeled slippers—she was loathe to give up any height compared to his—she punched her fists to her hips, lifted her chin, and dared him to comment.

"You want to know me?" she challenged, dragging his gaze up from her nakedness. "Then know that I am a realist. I know my value rests in the power I offer, both magical and political, so don't insult me with empty compliments."

His anger seemed to decline with the rise of hers because he grinned at her, dark eyes lowering to wander over her. "You're flawless," he murmured, almost to himself. "A pearl beyond price. Would you take your hair down for me?"

With nothing to push against, Nic found herself flailing. "It will be a mess," she warned, plopping herself down on the side of the bed and kicking off her shoes. With practiced efficiency, she pulled the various jeweled straight pins that held the unruly mass of curls in place, tossing them on the bedside table to scatter among the cremes and oils, then shook out her hair. Fingers combing it, she wrestled it to temporary obedience to hang down her back. Glancing up at Lord Phel, who seemed mesmerized, she lifted a questioning brow. "Satisfied? Perhaps you'd like to examine my teeth also."

He didn't take the bait, instead seating himself beside her, the firm pallet bending under his greater weight. Lifting a hand, he hovered it near her hair. "May I?"

She rolled her eyes, seeing through his ploy. By getting her to agree to one thing after another, he'd soon have her agreeing to everything. *Oh, Master, yes, please, Master!* She set her teeth against the image of that particular future. "You don't have to keep asking," she bit out. "You bought the right to do whatever you want to me, so long as you don't damage the goods."

Studying her, he didn't move his hand. "Even more reason to ask, then." When she snorted, he shook his head minutely. "You and I didn't make these rules—and we have to play by them, for now—but there's room here to be human to each other. I'd like to touch your hair, if that's all right."

"If you're going to solicit permission for each bit of me you touch tonight, you'll never get to one attempt, much less six," she replied. When he still didn't move, she blew out an exasperated breath. He'd just wait her out, as he had with the wine and the food and… everything. Eventually she'd wise up. "Fine. Yes. Touch my hair."

He smiled, a hint of smug triumph in it that grated. "Would you turn to face me?"

Huffing, she did, turning so she sat on one folded knee. He did the same, lifting his other hand, too, and threading them both into the wildly curling mass. "Your hair is extraordinary," he breathed. "I've never seen the like."

"Really? It's bog-standard Hanneil hair. My mother's house. We practically have an entire family almanac dedicated to techniques and recipes for managing the stuff."

Smiling still, absently, he tugged his fingers gently through her hair. "It's phenomenal. I fancy it's curling itself around my fingers."

Traitorous stuff probably was, as drawn to him as the rest of her. His magic pulled at her, the opposite charge of wizardry a magnet to her familiar nature. Or that water magic calling to the fire in her. That had to be what was making her want to nestle into his thirst-slaking silvery calm. "I'd cut it all off if I could," she informed him, just to be spiteful. If he'd stop being so gentle, pretending to be so admiring and kind, maybe she could resist this pull.

He paused, searching her face. "Why can't you?"

She swallowed back her surprise. He really didn't know? Then she wouldn't be the one to tell him. If—perish the thought—she ended up bonded to him, he'd find out soon enough. She doubted she could deploy the knowledge to her advantage, but it didn't hurt to try. "My parents would have a fit," she cheerfully replied. Not really a lie at all. The best kind of deception, especially with a wizard who could likely detect untruths.

Hmming deep in his throat, he wound the curls around his hands. "When we're married, you can do as you like, of course—but I hope you won't cut it."

She barely restrained a snort. How could he know so little about Convocation marriages, and about the wizard–familiar relationship? Came of being an outcast from a fallen house, she supposed. She'd grown up so steeped in Convocation customs that she couldn't really separate what she'd learned at home from what she'd learned at school. But then, Lord Phel was self-taught as well as burdened with an ignorant upbringing.

She could almost feel sorry for him. No matter what Lord Phel said, she doubted he'd abandon his aspirations if he failed with her. He'd find someone to be his familiar and lady wife. A long, difficult road lay ahead of him, and he was just the type to dash himself brainless against the closed fortress of Convocation society. She had no doubt he'd destroy himself rather than give up. Regardless of how this night turned out, Nic would probably have to watch his annihilation someday.

The thought gave her a curious pang of dismay.

Lord Phel tugged her closer and, in her misplaced compassion, she yielded. And when he lowered his mouth to hers, waiting for her to close the breathless margin, she kissed him, hard and full of determined passion. His lips, deliciously soft with a tingling border of prickles from where his morning shave had begun to grow in, the inside of his mouth unbearably intimate. He tasted of cool water on a hot day and silver bright wizardry, a delicious and heady flavor. Taking over the kiss, he gently but inexorably tugged her hair to tilt her head back, devouring her mouth—as he'd no doubt devour her, in every way.

Well, she wouldn't allow it. Lord Phel would have her that night, but she had to cling to the hope that he wouldn't have her permanently. She couldn't control the outcome of the trials, but she could control her own mind and heart. She'd cursed well better.

Lord Phel was easing her onto her back, and she went pliantly enough. Finally he'd discharge his duty, and she could put this night behind her. Despite his boasting, he'd be unlikely to rouse himself five or six times. Knowing her other suitors, and given the gossip from other female familiars—along with the lamentations of male familiars facing unreasonable performance demands—men just couldn't do that. Also, considering the fact that Lord Phel had ridden a long journey, he'd certainly fall asleep after.

At that point, without his disturbing presence focused on her, she could regain some peace of mind. Sure, he might wake before dawn and have at her once more—Sammael and Tadkiel had—but that would be it. He'd be gone, and she'd be able to think clearly again. She just had to get through this.

"Are you all right?" Lord Phel murmured, brushing her hair back from her face and easing onto one elbow.

"Yes, I'm fine," she replied, biting back the urge to tell him to stop asking her that.

"You're more than fine," he purred, nuzzling her throat and sliding a rough hand over the curve of her waist and hip. "You're spectacular. A feast for the senses. Perfectly formed, fire made flesh, delightful in every way." He murmured the praise like a litany of prayer, feathering kisses over her skin with each phrase.

She squirmed, the fire that always breathed through her blood billowing into brighter flame. When his hand lifted to cup her breast, she found herself pressing into his touch, craving more. "You're still wearing too many clothes," she managed to say, though not as caustically as she'd planned.

"I know, but I don't want to pause to deal with them just now." When his lips closed over her nipple, she cried out in surprise at the shock of pleasure. He lifted his head, smiled in satisfaction, then delicately licked—watching her reaction. Though she tried to hold still, to give him nothing, she shuddered. The unguent between her legs seemed to spread to her thighs, slicking so much more, and the scent of heated roses filled the intimate bed space.

"You smell like a garden in summer," he said, moving to her other breast, kissing and licking that nipple while gently fondling the first one, now taut and tingling.

"It's the creme," she said, trying to bring them back to the reality of this trial, though she sounded far more breathless than she'd wanted. "To ease your entry," she added.

He raised his head and glanced at the bedside table. "You applied it before I arrived, then."

Not a question. "Naturally. A woman learns not to expect a man to think of such things."

He winced, stroking a soothing hand down her hip and thigh. "I apologize on behalf of my ilk."

Momentarily taken aback by the unexpected apology, Nic only nodded. "It doesn't matter."

"But it does. You don't have to lie to me. You asked for honesty, yes? Then give me the same." He brushed her lips with a kiss, sweet, almost… affectionate?

She fought back a sudden burst of emotion. Who was she kidding? She wasn't holding herself aloof at all, but tumbling headlong down a pitched slope, where a swamp no doubt lay at the bottom, ready to drag her under into mindless and delighted servitude. "Regardless," she told him coolly, as if she weren't lying naked and nearly panting in his arms, "there's plenty more if needed."

"I'd be remiss if I didn't use more pleasurable methods to ease my eventual 'entry,' as you so charmingly call it." His mouth tilted in a half smile at her puzzlement. "Allow me to tend you, Lady Veronica."

Kissing his way down her fluttering belly, he eased her thighs apart and settled between them. Apparently he did mean what she'd guessed. "Is this all right?" he asked.

"It's not necessary."

"I beg to differ." He turned his head and kissed the inside of her thigh, a soft caress.

"It won't plant your seed in me," she clarified. And it might just be too much for her. Already he had her in the metaphorical palm of his hand. She trembled, wanting this—afraid to take it.

He smiled, slow and dangerous, turning to trail kisses down her other quivering thigh and shattering her senses as he did. "The wandering path might not be the quickest route, but it provides many delights along the way." He looked up her body, wizard's eyes black as a starless night, the firelight silvering his pale hair, the single black lock like a bolt of night. "May I?"

With a groan of defeat, she let her head fall back, giving in to him and her own craving. "Fine. Just do it already."

He chuckled, clearly amused by her, and nuzzled her mound. "Glossy curls, even here," he noted. "And you are as lovely here as everywhere. Fragrant, and so warm. My rose." He placed a lingering kiss on her pearl of pleasure, and her back bowed at the lightning spearing her.

"Gabriel!" she gasped—but only had a moment of chagrin to regret the lapse, because he began exploring her with his tongue. Digging her nails into the coverlet, which they hadn't bothered to pull down, she realized, Nic stared at the high wooden canopy of her bed. So many times she'd lain here since the House Refoel wizard unlocked her fertility under the Convocation proctor's eagle eye, plotting her future, determining how to take firm grasp of her own destiny and never be a wizard's witless puppet.

Now, as Gabriel wreaked his wicked destruction on her senses, her carefully constructed strategy flew apart. She had no thoughts to cling to, instead writhing and mewling. She gave up on clinging to the unrewarding coverlet and drove her fingers into that extraordinary silver hair, like metal made silk, winding it around her hands, she urged him closer, sighing, then screaming as he found the exact rhythm to shatter her.

And shatter her again.

At last, thoroughly wilted as any hothouse rose plucked and left too long, she let her hands fall limply to her sides, gasping for breath, trying to remember what she'd been so determined to resist. Gabriel kissed his way up her body, pausing to savor the sensitive skin along her hip bone, to trace his tongue in the divot of her belly button, to place reverent kisses on her breasts. "My rose," he sighed. "You are more than I could have imagined. If I could, I'd woo you like this until you trusted me enough to take me inside you out of true desire."

She cracked her eyes open, studying him, seeing that he meant it. "You're a strange man, Lord Phel." That was right: keep a formal distance and remind him of it.

"Am I?" He considered that, tracing his fingertip lightly along the line of her jaw. "I suppose that could be true. Not surprising all in all."

Bemused that he'd admitted to it—and wondering what thought had sobered him—she gave him a long look. "You've won this right. Plant your seed and take your chance. You don't need me to trust you."

"No." He swept the caress over her lower lip, looking wistful. "But I can wish for it."

"Take your clothes off," she urged him, feeling oddly gentle. He'd pleasured her when he hadn't needed to, been kind to her. Maybe it hadn't all been manipulation. She could return the favor of—how had he put it?—being human to him.

Never mind that wizards and familiars had nothing of humanity about them. He'd learn that lesson eventually, no doubt in the hardest of ways.

With a sigh, he levered himself up, toeing off his boots and beginning to strip away his layers of dark riding clothes. She turned on her side, leaning up on one elbow to observe with interest. None of the other three had done more than open the placket of their trousers. Gabriel watched her watching with an odd smile, parting the ties of his shirt to reveal a broad-shouldered chest silvered with snowy hair that served to highlight the rippling definition of his muscles. The muscles of a laborer and the eyes of a wizard.

The silver arrowed down as if engraved that way, a glittering trail that disappeared beneath the black leather pants that clung to his narrow hips. He undid the fastenings, and hesitated with his thumbs in the waist. "I am not so comfortable in my skin as you are," he observed wryly, bending to shuck his pants.

"You've clearly had lovers," she noted, rather touched by his shyness. Or was it another gambit to soften her? "Surely you've been naked in front of women before."

"Yes." He joined her on the bed before she got a good look at the rest of him. "But I'm chagrined to note that your good opinion seems to matter."

*Oh, Gabriel.* Nic closed her eyes in pain at his honesty. Had no one warned him not to give her kind those sorts of emotional advantages? Wizards were taught to rule their familiars for good reasons. "Shh. No more talking."

She turned, pulling him atop her, shivering at the skin-to-skin contact. His long legs twined with hers, and he propped himself on his elbows, looking down at her. Brushed a wayward curl from her cheek. "Are you sure?" he asked.

Nic managed not to roll her eyes. Opening her legs, she lifted her hips. "I've always been sure." At least since she received that first stomach-dropping scorecard, annihilating her ambitions to be the reigning wizard of House Elal and relegating her to life as a familiar. She wasn't lying, and the truth of her statement reassured him. The method might be unpleasant, but the trials would get Nic where she wanted, where she *needed* to be. No matter the outcome, she'd make sure of that.

He kissed her lingeringly, then slid a hand between them to position himself. Their breath blended in a long sigh as he slid into her, the shivering delight unlike anything she'd felt before. Arching against him, Nic clung to his shoulders, savoring the glide of his skin against hers, the sweet fullness of him filling her. His magic, dark and rippling deep, spiraled into her, and she drank it in, then offered her own fire back. The joining felt like it calmed something in her, the puzzle piece fitting into place to at last reveal the full image.

"Gabriel," she sighed, and he pressed his lips into the hollow of her neck, shuddering. He moved in her, finding a pace that pleased them both, gradually accelerating, sending them spiraling higher. Their magic intertwined, bright and dark, new shoots of spring vines curling around each other, blending and mingling to make something new and larger, more wonderful.

Nic had never felt so laid open, so completely revealed—and so completed. His body moved under her hands like the sea, rolling and wild, his magic uncoiling and filling her every pore, slaking a thirst she hadn't known she suffered from.

When she again reached a peak, her body bunching, clenched tight—and then exploding into showers of release, he threw himself after her, catching her in midflight and diving with her, his hoarse cries of pleasure a dark harmony beneath hers as he emptied himself into her. At last planting the seed she could only pray wouldn't take.

# ~ 5 ~

"PREGNANT?" NIC STARED at the Convocation proctor, and the always unsettling oracle head staring at her from the shadows of its protective tabernacle. "I *cannot* be pregnant."

"The familiar is with child," the mummified head hissed through brittle lips. "Successful implantation confirmed."

The gilded scrollwork embedded in the ancient wood of the tabernacle glittered merrily in the stark winter light coming through the lattice of the metal shutters. The pretty decorations only highlighted the horror of the bodiless head entombed inside, the oracle's gleaming eyes open and staring into her. "I *can't* be pregnant," Nic repeated, voice cracking on the strident rise. Not with Gabriel Phel's child.

The proctor gave her a wry look as she shut the hinged doors on the oracle, the lapis-inlaid eyelids on it lowering as she did. "I know you understand the mechanism of such things, Lady Veronica. You *can* be pregnant, and you are. It's the point of the Betrothal Trials, after all. Look on the bright side. You're done after only four tries. Many a young lady would envy you the speedy quickening."

"But that means it's Lord Phel's," Nic said, her hopes and

plans dropping straight through her stomach to fall somewhere at the bottom of her cursed tower. This was a disaster.

"I'm relieved that you understand that much cause and effect." The proctor—a mid-level wizard from House Tadkiel who served the Convocation—shook her head for the foolishness of familiars. "I'll write up the report and have a Ratsiel courier communicate it to Lord Phel immediately."

"Wait." Nic grasped the proctor's wrist. "Please don't do it yet."

The woman hesitated. She was accustomed to obeying High House members, but Nic was only a familiar. "It's my duty, Lady Veronica. Even you must understand that the rules require it." She tugged on her wrist, and Nic released her. "I'm sure it's upsetting," the proctor said more kindly, "to have your fate linked with a houseless wizard like Phel. He's little better than a rogue, but the sooner you accept the truth, the sooner you'll be able to reconcile yourself to it."

"I know," Nic said. "I know." She needed to *think*—and she couldn't do it naked. And she couldn't think about being naked without thinking of Gabriel—*Lord Phel*, she firmly reminded herself—and that long, magical, intimate and completely unnerving night. It had been two weeks since he'd kissed her goodbye in the dimness before sunrise. The fire had burnt to crimson-edged coals, the fire elementals long since coaxed to quench their light, neither of them stirring themselves from the cozy bed where they'd finally snuggled under the covers.

And where he'd had her six more times. "Number seven for luck," he'd whispered, kissing her belly over her womb before pulling her to ride him astride. She'd gazed down at his strong face in the silvery morning pre-dawn light creeping past the curtains, his hair like snow across the pillow—except for that wicked black streak as dark as his eyes. Those wizard's eyes had been half-lidded in pleasure as she rode him, his hands gentle on her breasts, and he'd murmured sweet promises of the future.

A future she couldn't possibly reconcile herself to, not unless she could somehow embrace losing all of her free will. Nic yanked on her simple gown. "I know you have to send the report," she repeated, willing herself to think. A Ratsiel courier would relay the communication within hours, and Lord Phel would come for her without delay—she knew enough about him to be sure of that. She'd have to marry him. He'd bond her as his familiar, and she'd have no choice but to give him whatever he required of her. Judging by the deep attachment to him she'd formed over the course of that one night, she'd succumb to his powerful persuasion over and over until she had nothing left of herself.

Nic had been certain that the oracle head would declare her free and clear of pregnancy, not allowing herself to consider any other possibility. Mind over matter. *An Elal commands the world; the world doesn't command an Elal.* Papa had said that so many times that she'd believed it. She'd been determined that Lord Phel's seed—no matter how many times provided—would prove no more potent than the previous three suitors. Of course, she'd been certain she'd be a wizard like Papa, and look what happened to that ambition.

She had terrible luck, that's what it came down to. Her younger siblings, sweet Alise and none-too-bright Nander would be wizards—Nander's magic a rare variant strong in their mother's House Hanneil blood, too—while Nic was stuck being a familiar. And now she'd gotten stuck with the overpowering Lord Phel, too. None of the other three suitors had succeeded, so why had he? Because the maddening wizard *would* be just that obstinate to defy the odds.

The proctor had been carefully packing away the oracle tabernacle while Nic attempted to think. "It can be a shock to face the reality of it," the proctor said, not without sympathy as she shouldered her bag. "Though you familiars know going into this what can happen—what *will* happen with time and luck—it can be upsetting when the successful candidate is not who you'd choose. Just remember: There are good reasons that the Convocation selects the candidates they do. Your instincts are unreliable, just as the unbonded magic of a familiar is an unstable force. Trust that your wizard will know what's best for you, submit to your wizard's will, and you will be content."

Nic sucked her lips between her teeth and bit down on the unwise retort wanting to spew forth.

The proctor noted her rebellious expression. "I'll remain in House Elal to monitor your status," she said, moving into a more formal recitation of guidelines she'd no doubt told hundreds of female familiars in a similar position. "So don't be thinking up any crazy plans to rid yourself of the child. It won't do you any good, regardless. Your compatible fertility has been confirmed, so even if you miscarry, you'll still be bonded to Lord Phel whenever he chooses to claim you." She softened. "It's in your best interests, Lady Veronica, to do your utmost to maintain the pregnancy. They always treat the pregnant ones better. It gives you a reprieve of sorts, from the more invasive incantations. Do you understand?"

Because the woman looked so earnest, Nic nodded. Convocation Academy had been thorough in teaching wizard–familiar dynamics, and she harbored no illusions there of just how invasive the advanced incantations could be. That prospect didn't frighten her nearly as much as imagining how she'd lose herself to Lord Phel, with his sweet words and devastating presence.

The proctor nodded with her. "A pregnancy gives you time to get to know each other, and for you to establish yourself as lady of the house." She frowned then. "Such as it is, in this case. At any rate, I'll send in Lady Elal. Your maman will be a comfort to you."

With a bow, she left the room—and left the door unlocked, for the first time in over four months.

Nic couldn't even savor that happy freedom. She went to window and stared through the rigid slats of the shutters, winding her fingers into the cage of chill metal. It had begun to snow, thick flakes falling in a graceful dance that blurred the features of the landscape beyond the curve of the river. Dare she hope the building blizzard would delay Lord Phel's arrival? She could hope some, she decided. But no more dreaming of the impossible. Since Lord Phel seemed to use horses instead of magically fueled conveyances, it would be at least a three-day ride from Meresin. Imagining that Lord Phel would be counting the days until her testing and would thus be ready to ride out immediately—and considering his determined nature—better figure on two and half days before he arrived to take possession of his prize.

That gave her two days to think of something.

But what?

She was smart, well-educated, from a powerful family. There had to be a way for her to escape this. A radical thought—but it was also her only hope if she hoped to retain possession of her own mind and will. She couldn't resist Gabriel's effect on her, she had to confront that daunting truth. So the only option she had was… figure out a way to never see him again.

"Nic," Maman cried as she swept into the room, her face a painful mask of tentative happiness. She opened her arms, and Nic buried herself in them, inhaling the scent of carnations and lilies that was her mother's favorite perfume. "So it's Lord Phel."

"Apparently so," Nic said, letting her fear and real distress thread her voice as she normally wouldn't. Now was not the time to protect Maman from worry. She needed her mother as an ally.

Maman brushed Nic's disordered curls away from her face, giving her a long look. "Is it so terrible?" she asked softly. "He's a rogue wizard, yes, but not landless. He's powerful enough to rebuild House Phel. And you'll have no competition in his household. It could be worse."

"I don't want this, Maman. I don't want *him*."

"Oh, Nic." Maman took her by the shoulders in exasperation. "The time to decide that was before the trial night. You had an opportunity to summarily dismiss him—I suspect the

Convocation expected you would, given his status—but you can't back out now. You know that. The rules are explicitly designed to prevent exactly this kind—"

"Maman," Nic interrupted and kept going, speaking fast. "I didn't tell you this before, because I didn't want you to worry—and I hoped, no, I was so determined that it wouldn't come to this—but..." She faltered. It was too much. Tears forced their way into her eyes.

"Oh, my darling." Maman embraced her again. "Was he cruel to you?"

"No," Nic whispered. "Much worse."

A perfunctory knock on the door heralded Nic's maid Tasha, who entered with a tray holding a decanter of Elal Summer Red—though it was barely midday—and a plate of Nic's favorite chocolate meringue cookies. "I thought the occasion called for a celebration," she said, smiling. Then she took one look at Nic's face and sobered. "Or comfort."

"Thank you, Tasha," Maman said, taking the tray and nodding at Nic to seat herself by the fire. "So the news is spreading through the household already?"

"I'm afraid so." Tasha grimaced at that. "The proctor is telling everyone she encounters. She's implying that Lady Veronica may not be perfectly happy with her lot."

Stupid, Nic reflected, to have been so transparent. If she'd pretended to be happy, the proctor wouldn't have been so on guard. Too late now.

Maman nodded in resignation. "Please turn away any visitors. Tell everyone I'm... celebrating, in private with my daughter."

Tasha bowed, sent Nic an encouraging smile, and left again. Maman sat and poured them wine, took a cookie for herself, and settled back, watching Nic with a shrewd expression. "Tell me."

"I felt it," Nic said, and bit into the cookie to relieve the bitter taste of the words. The melting sweet slid into her senses with all the reassuring comfort of childhood. A sip of the wine swirled the swelling berry flavor of grapes bursting under the midsummer sun to blend with the chocolate. The taste of home. *Savor it while you can.* "I think it's... Maman, I was Fascinated by him."

"Oh, Nic," her mother said in an appalled hush. "Are you sure?"

"How can I be sure?" Nic demanded, feeling perilously close to tears. "No one at school ever explained exactly what it feels like. Most of my teachers said it's myth, that it's the bonding that secures familiars to the wizards that claim them, not some..." She waved the cookie wildly, unable to find words to explain it.

"A feeling that you'd give him anything he asked of you, and love doing it, even at your own expense?" Maman filled in gently.

Nic stared at her, so many pieces falling into place. How Maman never defied Papa in any way, always melting to his will instantly, with a happy smile. "You've felt it, too."

Maman nodded. Sighed. "With your papa. Even before the bonding. I so hoped you wouldn't inherit this propensity from me. I should've warned you it was real, but... I hoped it wouldn't happen to you."

Both of them hoping for things that would never be. Nic resolved then and there never to trust hope again. It was a convenient lie, a happy trap that held you in place until the jaws closed on you. "I don't want this," she repeated. "This isn't at all how we planned things. How can I manipulate him if I'm Fascinated?"

"You can't." Maman pressed her lips together in regret, the lines around her mouth deepening. "If only..." She didn't finish. *If only Nic had been born a wizard.* "There's nothing we can do now. It won't be all bad, you know. There are tricks I can teach you to—"

"There is something I can do," Nic interrupted. She didn't want to hear Maman's tricks for appeasing her husband and master. Nic had seen enough of their interactions to guess.

Maman eyed her warily. "What are you thinking, Veronica? You know your impatient nature gets you into trouble."

Nic shook that off. This wasn't being impatient. "I have to get away, to not be here when Lord Phel arrives to claim me."

Maman stared at her, aghast, then drank down her goblet of wine in one swallow. "You don't know what you're saying."

"I do know," Nic insisted. "I can run away. There are stories of familiars who escaped the Convocation." Lyndella had tried to escape Sylus. Of course, Sylus had found her almost immediately—and saved her from a roving band of rogue wizards who'd been intent on raping her before draining her of her magic.

"Stories," Maman scoffed. "Romantic tales and nothing more."

"There could be a grain of truth in them."

"More likely there's a hefty dollop of wishful thinking. The Convocation has ways of chasing familiars down—secrets that only wizards speak of—and they wouldn't be happy to lose a familiar of your status and potential. The consequences would be severe."

"More severe than me becoming a mindless slave?" Nic retorted.

Maman's face crumpled into a rictus of shame and grief, and Nic instantly regretted her hasty words. "I'm sorry, Maman. I didn't mean that you are—"

"Don't be sorry," Maman bit out. "I know what I am and the cage I live in better than anyone."

Nic took Maman's hand. "But I *am* sorry. I know how unhappy you are." Maman's melancholy had always been a part of Nic's life, like a sorrowful, dark music in the background. That was part of why Nic normally tried not to distress Maman with her own worries.

"Most days I'm not unhappy," Maman said crisply, withdrawing her hand as she spoke the lie. "But I don't wish my life on you. It grieves me to think of you, my fierce and talented daughter, being relegated to…" She trailed off with a grimace.

"That's why I have to escape," Nic replied firmly. "There has to be a way."

"Even if there is, escape is only the first step. You can't live without a wizard to bleed off your magic. Not and be sane."

"I know, but I don't *have* to be bonded for that. If I can make it to a place beyond the reach of the Convocation, then I can figure out the rest, put my education into practice. We did it at school for practice, and for-hire familiars work that way with the Convocation. I can find a low-level rogue wizard without the wit or knowledge to bond me who can bleed off my magic. I just need to be gone before Lord Phel arrives. That's the urgent part."

"You make it sound easy, and it's not," Maman warned.

"But you are Lady Elal. Can't you do *anything* to help me?"

Maman chewed her lip, then nodded. "I can, but—only so far. Much of the burden will be on you, on your ingenuity."

Nic breathed an internal sigh of relief. This could happen. She would never have to see him again. She could be free. "You always said I could do anything I set my mind to." *Except be a wizard. Except escape this Fascination for Lord Phel.* "I can do this," she said firmly, drowning out the doubts in her mind.

"If anyone can do this, it's you," Maman agreed, though she didn't sound happy. "I figure we have three days, two and a half on the inside, before Lord Phel arrives to claim you. Maybe more, with the storm, but we can't count on that."

"Exactly what I calculated," Nic replied, beyond relieved that Maman would help. "But where can I go—and how?"

"That will take some planning. We'll have to time it carefully, because they watch for familiars to bolt immediately following the news of a successful match. We'll have to devote ourselves to planning your wedding. Be consumed by that and nothing else. You will be allowed out of the tower now—that's something—and you will be joyful, telling everyone how pleased you are."

"Will they believe me joyful about a match with Lord Phel, though?" Nic pondered the possibilities. Given the proctor's disdainful assessment, she rather doubted it.

"Well, you can be justifiably proud of conceiving on your fourth suitor," Maman allowed. "Not many are so fertile and receptive, and they will envy you that at least. As for the rest…" She eyed Nic speculatively. "You are in love with him."

"In love?" she echoed. She wasn't. She couldn't be. The wizard had affected Nic, but that was the Fascination at work, surely. That was what made her thoughts dwell on him and on the way he'd touched her, the depthless sense of his magic and how it crept under her skin with such dizzying effect.

"Infatuated, then," Maman revised crisply, waving a hand at the impossibility of it. "No one expects love. That can't happen in a single night, but everyone cherishes the romance of the Fascination stories. You'll have to pretend that you are infatuated—and not horrified—even to Tasha. She saw you overcome with emotion is all. I think I've taught you well enough to carry off a suitable performance. Yes?"

"Yes?" Infatuated with Gabriel. Possessed by an overpowering Fascination. Dreaming of him at night, daydreaming of the silver silk of his hair and his scent like…

"Nic—pay attention. I know this is all going very fast, but time is not on our side. Can you pretend to everyone, including your father, that you are dizzyingly attracted to Lord Phel?"

"I can." That would be easy enough. The trick would be remembering how very dangerous for her that attraction was.

"And you must seem to be delighted by your pregnancy and impending marriage," Maman coached. "You will be a familiar who believes utterly that her wizard master will rebuild his house, returning it to its former glory."

"I can pretend to all that." Nic wasn't at all sure about the future of House Phel—though if anyone could pull off the impossible, Lord Phel could. "Though won't I seem stupid not to observe how unlikely that is?"

Maman shook her head. "Not if you convince everyone you're besotted. Wizards can have that effect, Fascination at work or not."

"All right, then what?"

"I will make arrangements." Maman twisted her hands around her wineglass, brows lowered in intense thought. "I'll call on favors owed me. It will be tricky. I must ensure that your papa knows nothing."

"Papa… He can't know?"

"No, Nic. *Think.* If he knows of our plans, he'll stop you."

"But… I won't be able to tell him goodbye." Papa would take this as a personal betrayal. He'd never forgive her.

Setting down her wineglass, Maman took Nic's hand in both of hers. "Oh, daughter of mine. I know this is a hard awakening, but you have to look with open eyes. Your papa loves you, yes, but as his baby girl. His first child. He's loved to pet and spoil you, and even when you were tiny, you preferred him. I never minded because your relationship has always been a beautiful one. But you are a woman grown now, a valuable asset to House Elal and the Convocation."

"I could return here eventually," Nic argued, "and serve as a familiar to the house."

"That was never really an option, and now it never can be. You are pregnant with a wizard's child, which makes you Lord Phel's familiar already under Convocation law. That will change you in your father's eyes. He's a Convocation loyalist." Maman leveled a stern look on her. "The lord of a tier-one High House, the most powerful in the Convocation. I know you two have always enjoyed a special bond—but your papa has never gone against Convocation law in his life."

"Maybe he hasn't had good reason to," Nic protested, knowing that she might as well be arguing against the snowfall.

"This won't be reason enough. I don't wish to be cruel to you, but you must make this decision with a clear head. No fanciful tales. This is reality."

Nic searched Maman's face, seeking a hint of exaggeration, but there was none. In her heart, Nic knew it, too. That was the final, unspoken reason she hadn't asked to be excused from the Betrothal Trials. When she'd made jokes about it, mentioned some classmates who'd opted out in favor of the few other, admittedly unhappy choices, Papa had cut her off immediately. He'd been so proud of her talents, her innate power—and he'd been perhaps more disappointed than anyone when Nic didn't test as a wizard.

He'd changed toward her even then, no longer discussing Convocation politics and house business with her, instead praising her many virtues in terms of the credit she'd bring to House Elal. The wizard she'd someday marry and what a jewel she'd be for him. Maman spoke only the truth.

Papa loved and treasured her—and he'd hand her over to Lord Phel without a backward glance. "Lord Phel deserves a chance to rebuild his house, same as any other man," Papa had said when he told her he'd approved Lord Phel's application and appreciated that she hadn't summarily dismissed him. "More than most of these soft, indulged scions who can barely charm a fire elemental to burning brighter. He's got balls even trying for you, kitten. I'm not going to deny him that opportunity, no matter the naysayers. I'm glad you're not either."

No, Papa would never forgive her reneging on Lord Phel, or for breaking Convocation law. The glum thought had Nic nearly reconsidering. But Maman was also right that Papa wouldn't give a thought to what Nic's life would be as Lord Phel's familiar. After all, he didn't hesitate to use Maman until she was fainting. Hadn't Nic seen that all too many times? Papa loved Maman, too, treasured her, even. Unstinting in his praise and petting of Maman, he still chided her if she failed him in any way.

She rarely failed, and now Nic fully understood why.

Maman was watching Nic, wisely staying silent, as if she knew the path of her daughter's thoughts. Probably she did. "All right," Nic finally said. "I'll make sure Papa never guesses." When her mother visibly relaxed, Nic reminded herself of the great risk Maman would be taking on her behalf. "When they discover I'm gone, you must also make sure to be shocked and surprised. He can't suspect that you were part of this."

"I know how to manage my wizard," Maman replied tartly. "That's no business of yours to think about." She relented then, squeezing Nic's hand. "I will be careful." She smiled sadly. "I'm going to hate losing you, but I'll make sure your tracks are well covered so they can't follow you. After that, it will be up to you to ensure you're never found."

*What? Never?* "Am I... never coming back?" Here she'd been wistful about not getting to drink Elal Summer Red as often. Clearly she had yet to think through just how much she would be giving up to make this escape, how much she'd be giving up. *Everything.* "How far am I to go?"

Her mother's hands tightened, giving hers a brisk shake. "Far enough that the Convocation laws can't reach you. Otherwise, you can be brought back, and it won't be pretty."

"Are the rumors about the Tadkiel hunters true?" Nic asked in a hush.

"Some of those stories are true, but the hunters will be only part of your worries. Lord Phel will be beyond angry. Remember that he's desperate—and you'll be stealing his child and his hope for the future of House Phel."

*His child.* "This is my child," Nic replied stubbornly.

"Not according to the Convocation."

That was true.

"If you decide on escape," Maman continued, taking in Nic's subdued frown, "and you don't have to—you can still change your mind. But if you do, you're committed. For life. You must make certain that neither Lord Phel nor the Convocation ever finds you."

She would never see her family and friends again. She would be alone, raising a child. Pregnant and giving birth, all on her own. "How will I do this all alone?" she asked plaintively, feeling suddenly much younger than her years.

"I'll make sure you're well funded," Maman promised. "Compared to the rest of it, that part is easy."

Money wasn't what Nic had been thinking of—which,

perhaps, was a sign that her priorities were misplaced. With House Elal's wealth, Nic had never wanted for anything. She had but to ask for something and it was hers. Often it was hers before she formed the desire. Lord Phel had made note of that, his observation sardonic, even self-deprecating. *I won't be able to house you like this. Not now. Maybe not ever.* She imagined a silvery caress and the scent of water, wondering if she even had two and a half days.

"I think we'd better plan to have me gone before two days have passed," she said in a burst, the urgency gripping her.

Maman took note with narrowed eyes. "You have that much connection to him?"

Nic stilled, feeling the blood drain from her face. "Is that possible?"

"It's not usual, but yes—possible. Especially given the Fascination."

"Maybe so, then. I just have… a very strong feeling."

"Then we take note of that. We need to have you gone two nights hence. But try not to think about him too much, as that feeds the connection. Don't give him anything to track you with."

*Don't think about him.* Right. Don't think about the silver sea monster taking up all the space in the room, either.

"Nic?" Maman had a warning in her voice.

"I understand."

"When you're on the run, too, you pay attention to that feeling. Promise me. It will warn you if he's managed to track you, if he's closing in."

How was she to both not think about him but also pay

attention to that sense of his nearness? This began to seem impossible. "But you'll make sure he can't track me, yes?" she asked, panic fluttering in her breast. The image of those wizard-black eyes gone hard and ruthless drifted through her mind. Lord Phel would be even less forgiving than her father. *All the more reason not to let him catch you.*

"I'll use every trick I know, call in every favor I can," Maman promised, then let go of her hands. "But remember: he's a wizard. You know the reasons their kind rules ours. You'll have to be smart, courageous, determined, and cool-headed. No letting emotions—of any kind!—cloud your thinking."

"I won't. I mean, I will do my utmost."

Maman softened, stood, and patted Nic's cheek. "I know you will. If anyone can pull this off, you can, my brilliant daughter."

"Maman!" Nic rose, too, clutching her mother's sleeve. "Come with me. You could help me when the baby comes. You can get away from all of this, too."

Maman's eyes filled with unshed tears. Never once had Nic seen her mother actually weep. "It's too late for me," she said softly. "These wizards, they get their hooks in you. Once, I thought I'd do as you are doing. In fact, I crafted an excellent escape plan." Her expression hardened and turned proud. "It's a good plan. Clever, solid. And not a waste, it turns out, as you're going to use it. I couldn't put it together so fast otherwise."

"You… thought to escape… Papa?" Nic's mind stuttered at putting that together, far more than it should have. Too many shocks in the bare space of an hour.

Maman's mouth twisted, her expression ugly for a flash. "Who else? When he arrived to bed me, I prayed his seed wouldn't take. I knew within moments of meeting him how it would be with him. That my life, my self, my mind—my very will—would never be wholly my own again."

"You never said."

"No, a mother doesn't share such things with her child, not about her beloved papa." Maman looked around the chamber, her gaze focused on distant memories. "You understand now, though, how they overwhelm you. Your papa isn't a bad man. But he is a wizard of the Convocation. The predator desires the prey—he can't have any mercy in his heart for it."

Nic had known Maman wasn't a happy person, that the melancholy made her subject to spells of ill health. Now a terrible guilt crept over her that she hadn't fully realized the reasons. Her throat dry, she asked, "If you knew how it would be, and you had a plan for escape, why didn't you go?"

Maman focused on her again, mouth turning down unhappily. "It was too late. I already loved him. I couldn't do it, couldn't tear myself away, even to save myself."

"Then you *do* love him!"

Maman blinked at her. "Of course I do. That's entirely the problem. I wouldn't give him so much of myself if I didn't love him with all my being. If I'd been smart, I would've run anyway. Then it was too late. Too late then, far too late now."

*Oh.* Nic turned that over in her mind, examined the traitorous desire in her heart to see Gabriel again. *Lord Phel*, she corrected herself firmly. Was it all Fascination? It would be easier to sort out if she hadn't liked him. If only he hadn't been kind to her, seeming to care about whether she ate and making certain she experienced pleasure in his arms. Of course, she knew it had all been a seduction. That was the entire purpose, wasn't it?

She should never have kissed him. That had been her worst mistake, one that led to all the others, a cascade of catastrophe. Much as she burned to escape, a traitorous part of her longed to see him, just once more—and grieved at how hurt and betrayed he'd be.

Maman was watching her with shrewd eyes. "Is it too late for you, too?" she asked softly.

"No," Nic replied immediately, making it be true. She was an Elal, and she could control this, if only this. If she had to chew off her own paw to escape this trap, she would. She would be stronger and smarter than Phel. She'd elude him, and eventually he'd grow weary of the chase and find another familiar. "But I'll miss you..." And all of her family, her home, and friends. Everything.

Maman shook her head in doubt. "This will be the hardest thing you've ever done, but you must determine to eschew all tender feelings—for me, for your papa, your brother and sister, for all your friends I know you've missed and hoped to see again, for your life here. But you must especially banish any sentiment for Lord Phel."

Nic nodded. Never see any of them again. Gabriel would be so thrilled about winning his gamble—and blazingly angry when he learned of her defection.

"Unless you *want* to marry him?" Maman asked. "It's the

easier path by far. You'll be congratulated, celebrated. The bonding will reconcile your mind to being his. You might enjoy that life. Many familiars do. It is our nature to be bonded to a wizard. You may find that you feel... incomplete without that."

So the stories said. Lyndella had pined for Sylus when they were separated, only made whole when he claimed her.

"I'm mostly worried about being lonely," Nic confessed.

Maman smiled with affection, laying a hand on Nic's cheek. "But you won't be alone. You'll have your child. I can tell you with perfect honesty that you, Alise, and Nander—you are my joy. I wanted that for you, and now you'll have it. It might be enough for you. You could marry Lord Phel, find satisfaction in being his familiar and mother of his children."

Tempting. Far too tempting. "But I won't have freedom. Lord Phel is young, and a wizard of his power will be long lived. Barring extraordinary events, I would never be a widow. I'd never think for myself again."

"I wish I could tell you otherwise." Maman stared at the fire in wistful contemplation, then she straightened and gave Nic an encouraging smile. "You have time, though, to make your final decision. We'll proceed as if the wedding will happen. You will throw yourself into convincing everyone that you're deliriously happy. I'll handle the escape plan. If you choose not to use it, then there's no harm, no foul. You need think of nothing else but your wedding plans."

And making the most difficult decision of her young life.

# ~ 6 ~

"OH, PAPA," NIC breathed. "It's gorgeous! You shouldn't have."

Papa cleared his throat, looking misty eyed. Like Lord Phel, he had the black eyes all wizards acquired through magic working, but sprays of laugh lines softened his. With the bushy brows and duskier skin framing them, too, the black of his eyes blended more, not standing out in stark contrast as with Lord Phel's silver shades. With a mental shake, she banished the thought of him. *Don't picture him. Don't wonder how close he is. Don't imagine him riding through the blizzard, flushed with triumph, eager to claim you and—*

"Of course I should have," Papa said, thankfully breaking into her thoughts. "My first daughter, getting married. And after only four trials." He put his hands on her shoulders. "I'm so proud of you, kitten."

Nic beamed back at him, wishing in the back of her mind that he'd be proud of her for more than her easy fertility—and moved at the same time. Papa was never lavish with praise, so she soaked up the moment. Especially knowing what he'd say, what he'd think of her, when he found her gone.

*Don't think about that either.* One of the tricks to a good performance was staying in character, and Nic's role was to be the chirpy, happy princess. Besides, while her papa generally allowed his children privacy, not spying on them with his pet spirits, he wouldn't hesitate if he suspected rebellion on the level she contemplated. "Thank you, Papa," she said, then impulsively: "I love you."

"I love you, kitten." He kissed her on the forehead, then turned her to face Maman. "What do you think, precious? Isn't our daughter perfect?"

"She is, Papa," Maman agreed with Papa, as she always did, and always with sweet smiles and sparkling eyes. No one would guess that she was anything but utterly delighted with her place in life. It had never occurred to Nic before to question that her mother also called him "Papa," as if she were one of his children. Now, especially understanding the will-sapping power of Fascination, it made her deeply uneasy to hear that, and she had to pretend to fuss with her skirts to hide the dimming of her smile. "The gown is perfect for a winter wedding."

Nic twirled in a semblance of glee, spinning away her qualms, not needing to pretend to delight in the beautiful gown. Of Ophiel make, and sewn of precious imported silk, it shaded from pure white to ice blue, depending on how the light and shadows hit it. Embroidered with white and blue thread, the flowers that were Nic's namesake twined thickly over the fitted bodice and spilled over the full skirts, lavishly sparkled with tiny crystals. "You had to have had it made already."

Papa smiled smugly. "I knew you'd prove your trials quickly. I arranged with House Ophiel for the gown the same day you signed the Betrothal Trials contracts. They'll be able to apply for High House status with the fortune I've paid them," he added with a wink. "My surprise for you. A small part of the dowry I'm settling on you."

The dowry. Nic had been shocked when Papa sat her down the evening before and showed her the extent of it. Somehow she hadn't figured that Lord Phel would have counted her dowry into his gamble. He'd recover his application price twice over.

"It's a pity," Maman added, "that we must have such a small house wedding. A gown like that deserves to be seen in a grand ceremony with all the Convocation in attendance. I wish that Nander and Alise weren't away at Convocation Academy, and that Nic's friends could attend and celebrate with her."

Papa dismissed that with a snort. "Might as well wish for midwinter to be midsummer, silly bird. Lord Phel should arrive in two days, and we'll have the wedding the day after."

Nic avoided looking at Maman. "I do hope the heavy snows won't delay him." A misplaced stab of concern for Lord Phel's well-being—an emotion she needed to thoroughly root out—infused her words with truth.

"Eh, don't worry about Phel," her father said. "It would take more than a bit of weather to delay him from claiming this prize. I'm not at all surprised he's the one. He's a determined, virile sort." He gazed at Nic, unseeing, seeming to reflect on some absorbing thoughts of his own.

"I do worry about the future of House Phel, however," Maman put in, probably to distract Papa from Nic, who felt even more green at how casually Papa spoke of her impregnation and being a prize for another wizard. Maman was right in this also: Already her Papa had begun to change how he treated Nic. "What if Lord Phel can't restore his house status with the Convocation?"

Papa shrugged that off, sitting behind his big desk and moving some documents around, pausing to read one. "Every wizard faces challenges, precious," he said absently. "Phel will prove himself to the Convocation or he won't. If he succeeds in restoring House Phel, we'll have gained a permanent ally. Phel won't forget what he owes me."

"But if he fails, our Nic will suffer with him."

Papa raised his head from the document, staring at Maman as if he'd never seen her before, then transferring the uncomfortable gaze on Nic. Was he considering her possible dire fate? "That's a familiar's role in life, to support their wizard, in success and in failure. Our Nic has already tied her fate to Phel. The wedding is simply a formality of a sacred bond already forged between them. Else she wouldn't have conceived. That's the natural order of things. You understand that, don't you, kitten?"

"Yes, Papa," she replied demurely, folding her hands so she wouldn't fiddle with the priceless silk. This would be the only time she'd wear this gown, if all went according to plan. She shouldn't feel bad about that, especially with all else she'd be giving up, but it seemed a crime that such a painstakingly crafted work of art would lie unused.

"I hope you wouldn't have abandoned me, precious, had I proved less successful," Papa said, pinning Maman with a questioning look, a hint of anger in it. He held out an imperious hand. "You promised to love me and support me in all things, no matter how fate treated us."

"Oh, Papa," Maman said, immediately rising and going to him. "Never imagine such a thing!" She gave him her hand, and he gripped it firmly. "Have I ever denied you any part of myself?"

"No." He smiled at her, black wizard eyes unblinking on her face, his magic intensifying so that some of his bound spirits manifested to Nic's eye, straining at their leashes, eager to obey his will. "You've never denied me, not even to spare yourself. And I'm grateful. So why the doubts about our Nic?"

"Not doubts, no," she hastened to assure him. "I'm just emotional."

"Is that all?" He didn't stand or change his grip, but something changed between them. Maman seemed to wilt, slowly sinking to her knees, continuing to crumple until her forehead touched the expensive rug, until the only part of her not on the floor was her hand in his. A spirit flitted over and through Maman, and Papa frowned. "You are in a turmoil, precious."

"I know," Maman said, her voice muffled. "It's so hard to let her go, not to worry about her."

"Look at me, precious," he commanded, and Maman raised her head. Tears wet her ravaged face, making Nic deeply uncomfortable at witnessing something she should not. Despite the weeping, Maman smiled at him, radiant in her love and trust.

"Let her go we must," he said, very seriously, but not unkindly. "You've raised an elegant, well-mannered young woman who will make Lord Phel a fine wife. With the magic she inherited from me, she'll make him a powerful familiar."

"So true," Maman said. "Lord Phel could not have done better."

Neither of them seemed to remember that Nic was in the room. She held herself very still, riveted—and yet wishing she could flee unnoticed. Though Papa reprimanded Maman sometimes in front of them, and occasionally borrowed her power for spontaneous workings, intimate interactions like this occurred in his arcanium, where no one else was allowed. Suddenly it occurred to Nic that this little scene was no accident, that Papa wanted her to observe. And learn from it. Learn what, though—obedience to her wizard master?

"Our daughter is getting married, precious," Papa said, voice thick with emotion. "The years have gone by so fast."

"Faster all the time," she murmured.

"We've given her everything," he said reflectively, still holding Maman's hand and stroking his thumb over the back of it. "If Nic meets with a bit of privation and struggle, well, that builds character. It will be incentive for you, kitten," he said, turning his head to pin Nic with glittering black eyes. No, he definitely hadn't forgotten her presence. "You must strengthen your own power and abilities, to aid Lord Phel in his climb. Remember that now you will grow and succeed through him. That is a familiar's nature, role in the world, and greatest source of joy."

"Yes, Papa," Nic said, sticking with safe acquiescence.

"All right." He dropped Maman's hand and waved them both off. "I've bored the two of you long enough with the philosophy of wizards, familiars, and life. You ladies have a wedding to plan, so go have fun doing that."

Maman climbed to her feet, grasping the edge of the desk to do so. Papa, already absorbed again in his documents, didn't seem to notice her struggle. Maman smoothed her gown and came toward Nic, not meeting her eyes.

"And, precious?" Papa said casually, Maman instantly freezing in her tracks. "I have a complicated incantation to work today. I'll need you in the arcanium for the entire afternoon, possibly into evening. Make sure you're rested."

"Yes, Papa," Maman said, and hurried Nic out of the room.

"IT REALLY IS a pity you'll never wear this," Maman said brightly, helping Nic out of the incredible gown herself.

"Did you know he was going to do this?" *Did you know he was going to do* that? Nic wasn't having much luck with eschewing all emotion. In fact, she felt more emotional than ever. That scene in Papa's study had shaken her, fueling her panicky need to escape. At the same time, a stupid part of her *wanted* to wear that dress, to have her papa place her hand in Lord Phel's, to see Gabriel's dazzlingly wicked smile again, for him to tell her how beautiful she looked and—just once more—savor that feeling of his magic as it... *Stop it*, she ordered herself.

"Papa told me he'd take care of obtaining the gown, and I

had our seamstresses give him your measurements. Other than that, no, I didn't know." Maman was chattering on about the details, perhaps indicating she was as shaken by the conversation—and demonstration—in Papa's study as Nic had been. Maman carefully hung up the gown, enclosing it again in the protective slipcase, triggering the built-in magical fastenings that would seal it.

Nic—not quite ready to pull on ordinary clothes again—shrugged into her dressing robe and gazed about the room, thinking about what she should take with her. Her girlhood rooms had already been converted into a guest suite months before, all of her childhood toys and mementos put into storage. Once a familiar entered the Betrothal Trials, they didn't go back to innocent childhood. They moved on, through one path or another, but never backward. Even those who managed to stay with their houses moved into new quarters to reflect their changed status. An unbonded familiar could still be useful to the household wizards, within limitations.

Conversely, the tower room had been redecorated expressly for her, with the fabrics, colors, and furniture Nic had chosen. At first she'd been thrilled by the new, sophisticated rooms. Now she missed her old dolls and beloved, if ragged, plush animals. It hadn't occurred to her before this to keep any of them—it had been years since she paid the childish things any attention, anyway, especially being away at Convocation Academy for months at a time. Her private room there had been furnished by Papa's generosity exactly as she'd pleased, too, her every whim granted. And she'd been determined to be as adult as possible.

Nothing in this room held any sentimental value for her—and it occurred to her that perhaps that was a deliberate step, also, when a familiar entered the Trials, preparing them for the break from their family, sending them without ties to serve the wizard who had acquired them.

To shake her mood, she wandered to the window. The heavy curtains had been pulled back to let in the thin winter light, and the metal shutters had been removed, leaving the glass windows clear. Now that Nic was happily set to wed, apparently no one worried about foolish attempts to fling herself from the tower heights. She'd been at least that convincing, though the proctor visited her frequently, asking probing questions. Glad as she was to have an unobstructed view again, she missed the cold bite of the slats against her fingers. The prisoner grown accustomed to the cage.

The snow fell as thickly as ever—possibly more so—enshrouding the hills, flowing white as Gabriel's hair, except for the dark line of the river, black as the single streak, cold and deep as his magic. Two more nights before he arrived, according to the multitudes of Elal elemental spies and sentry spirits. That meant Nic would be out there in that snow soon. Could she evade those spies and survive on her own, raise a child in some distant land that had barely heard of magic?

The idea seemed more dauntingly impossible than ever.

"Have you changed your mind?" Maman asked softly. She came to Nic's side, gazing out also.

"Should I?" Nic asked bluntly. She laid her fingers on the chilled glass, the dewy warmth of her fingers making smudges like clouds. "What Papa said… He'll think me soft and spoiled, that I'm too selfish to assist Lord Phel with rebuilding his house."

"It would be true," Maman agreed, "if that was your reason. Is it?"

"No, but Papa will think so." Nic wasn't sure she could bear for him to think so poorly of her.

"Your papa said what he did because it would never occur to him to think how you'll feel if Lord Phel makes you his familiar. You saw what you saw today." Maman took a breath. "I wouldn't have chosen for you to see that, but you did, and we won't pretend it's not so."

Nic glanced at Maman, worrying her lip as she studied her mother's face, still pale and drawn. "Is it awful?"

Maman dipped her chin. "Sometimes. Other times it's fine, even… fun." Her mouth twisted. "But with your papa… There is no halfway with him. He *will* have everything—from me, from his house, from his children, from all the world. You know how he is." She managed a rueful smile for Nic, then turned her gaze out to the snow-covered landscape and sighed. "Sometimes I think he'll drain me dry in his quest to have everything—and that knowledge can be awful."

"Maman…"

"Now," Maman said briskly, "if we'd managed to snare you a wizard you could control, it would all be different. But the Fascination changes everything."

"True. I don't care about the struggle," Nic said. At least, she thought she didn't. She might change her mind once she was in the world without support. "I think I'm not that shallow. I do care that I might live with the regret that I didn't seize my chance at freedom when I could." *I'm afraid I'll be like you in twenty years*, she didn't say aloud, *emptied of everything and unable to keep anything for myself. Living in fear that the man I love will accidentally kill me because he loves power more.*

"All is ready for you to leave tonight," Maman said, still not looking at her.

*So soon.* But, of course, it had to be.

Maman finally turned to look at her, gaze wistful now. "I'll miss you… so much."

"I don't know what I'll do without you," Nic confessed.

"You'll be fine." Maman's eyes shone with pride. "You're strong, clever, braver than I ever was. If anyone can do this, you can. Unless you've changed your mind? Last chance. After this, you mustn't waver."

Nic took a deep breath. She would not waver. Her future self would thank her, so her present self would do what was needed, no matter how torn she felt. "What do I need to do?"

Maman patted her cheek. "Exactly as I tell you."

NIC LEFT IN the early hours before dawn, in the freezing darkness. Maman didn't come herself, as she didn't dare risk Papa's guardians tracking her unusual movements in the night. Instead she sent Tasha with servant's clothes for Nic to dress in. Tasha helped her dress in the darkness, as they didn't dare coax the lantern elementals awake. That was the downside of leaving at this time of night. Every tiny elemental attached to daily conveniences as simple as the lanterns could attract the attention of any of the dozens of Elal wizards in the house.

Even conveniences bought or bartered from another house, like the Iblis door locks, sent up small flares of magic when activated. If the Convocation proctor or sentry wizards were paying attention—as the former might be and the latter certainly should be—then they'd notice unusual activity. And anything beyond the baseline level of ongoing vigilance from the fire elementals that heated the sprawling castle or the fiercer spirits that warded Elal from attack counted as unusual.

That meant servant's clothing for Nic, and not just for the disguise they provided. Servant's clothing didn't have magical fastenings like the gowns Nic had always worn. That made the rougher pants and layers of tunics ideal for a stealthy escape, but Nic was soon chagrined by her clumsy fumbling with something as simple as buttons. It reminded her of Gabriel's confusion in the face of magical fastenings, a thought she had to banish along with the remembered shiver of his finger tracing her spine.

"It will be easier in the light, when you can see," Tasha whispered as Nic cursed at the length of sash. Tasha took the sash, her fingers brushing Nic's to guide them. "Thread the purse and dagger sheath on first, like this, then tie it on."

Of course. What an idiot she was, not to have thought through such a simple, logical order. It didn't help that her heart was pounding, cold sweat running down her spine. Part of her expected Gabriel to burst through the door, roaring at her betrayal.

*Don't think about him.*

She tapped the copper bracelet she'd found in her jewelry box, a simple twining serpent with onyx eyes—nothing too valuable for a servant to own—and that had sharp metallic fangs. She pressed them painfully into the sensitive skin on the underside of her wrist, punishing herself for allowing the thought.

It was a self-discipline technique they'd learned at Convocation Academy, to train mental discipline and willpower. Maybe if she did it enough times, she'd train herself to keep *him* out of her head.

Tasha finished winding the thick sash around her waist, tying it off in a knot to one side. "When you undress, pay attention to the knot," she whispered, "so you can do it yourself."

"I wish I'd practiced this," Nic grumbled. Tasha didn't comment. With the proctor popping into Nic's rooms unexpectedly, that had been too great of a risk.

"You'll be fine. Follow me."

They slipped out the thankfully now unguarded chamber doors, then around a corner to take the back servants' stairs. At least there, small elementals burned constantly at every other step, lighting the way—if gloomily—for hapless servants summoned to tend their betters in the night. Or day, Nic supposed, as there were no windows that she could see to let in natural light. Probably the dim staircase was this dark all the time.

Tasha moved with the quiet grace of someone accustomed

to being unobtrusive until summoned. Nic tried to imitate her, but suspected she was hopeless at that, also. It was sinking in that she'd trained for one purpose only—and with this escape she'd be running headlong into a life where none of those skills would be useful. Tasha led them down past numerous doors to various levels, down below the ground floor, into the cellars, where a few elementals glowed here and there, but lay mostly in darkness. A cobweb brushed over Nic's face, and she stifled a scream, heart tripping even faster.

"I hate the spiders, too," Tasha said quietly, reaching back for Nic's hand. "I keep asking to have the anti-pest spells renewed, but Housekeeper says they're low priority."

Nic stifled a sigh of guilt over that. Probably anything that bothered only the servants was low priority, and House Ariel bargained fiercely for their services controlling animals. Clutching Tasha's hand, she followed closely in her wake, not even trying to see, trusting in Tasha's familiarity with the winding aisle between barrels of wine, crates of various supplies, and shelves full of who knew what. Finally they reached some steps that led up, a bitter draft billowing down. Tasha had braided Nic's hair tightly, but stubborn wisps escaped to blow around Nic's face. She shivered, that wind cutting right through her clothes, and she thought miserably of her fur-lined, sapphire-velvet cloak, so warm and the envy of all at school, even many of the wizard students.

"We have outer gear for you in the stables," Tasha murmured. "Just hold on."

She led Nic up through a slanting door set into the foundation and into one of the inner courts. Open to the winter sky—

not black but gray with overcast—the courtyard swirled with snowflakes sharp as knives. They didn't take the fast way across to the stables, even though the walkway that Nic had followed so many times was temptingly direct and clear, the beautiful tiles inlaid with elementals that burned them clear and dry. No, Tasha kept them to the shadows along the walls, where they struggled through the snow, powdery new over crunchy old, piled knee deep in places. At least Nic's high boots were good, but she chafed at the cold and the struggle.

She was so not cut out for this kind of thing. *You could go back*, a voice whispered in her mind. *Back to your magically warmed bed and pretty clothes, where you don't have to make any decisions for yourself. You don't have to be miserable. You can marry Gab—* She hastily stabbed the serpent bracelet's copper fangs into her wrist, gasping at the sharp sting. A slick of warmth against her fingers indicated she'd drawn blood, but at least she'd woken herself out of that dragging self-pity. And the fantasy of a life she couldn't afford to want.

She would not take the easy way out and doom herself. *I will not.*

Finally they made it into the stables, the quiet warmth as sweet as the scent of hay and horses. Tasha quickly wrapped Nic in a heavy cloak—not her fancy one, of course, but a peasant's thick wool, roughly spun by nonmagical hands—and drew the deep cowl around her face. She handed Nic mittens, assisting when her numb fingers failed to grasp them. They were thick and clumsy, with no articulation for Nic's fingers, and she sighed for her matching fur muff. She'd have to pull the mittens off to do anything.

Tasha wound a long scarf around Nic's hood, knotting it loosely and securing the folds of the cowl to hide her face. "I wish you could come with me," Nic said, hoping she'd say yes.

Tasha smiled sympathetically. "They'd find you through me." Holding up her hand, she let her sleeve slide back to display the Elal crest of intertwined spirits tattooed on her forearm, tiny elementals bound to the ink. "Remember?"

Oh, right. The mark gave their people the protection of House Elal—and safe passage back to their lands through the guardian barrier, should they have difficulty returning home—but that marking also identified them. Even the most minor Elal wizard could read information from the elementals, and anyone with eyes could see the crest. "Will you be all right?" it occurred to Nic to ask. "After helping me?"

"Lady Elal will make sure of it," Tasha whispered. "But thank you for your kind thoughts. This way."

Nic followed, lumbering like an overstuffed mattress on feet, and somehow still not warm. In the carriage barn, a sled waited, piled high with crates stamped with the House Elal crest. A shipment of conveniences powered by bound elementals, one of House Elal's main exports, which would be sold at market to anyone with coin enough to pay to make their lives a little easier. A dark tunnel gaped in the middle, just big enough for a body lying down. Bending her knees to see better, she examined the narrow space with resignation.

"The sled is scheduled to leave soon," Tasha explained, "so it should seem like business as usual. Try to sleep. When you wake in a few hours, you'll be met and transferred to something else."

Nodding—and figuring this was only the beginning of the uncomfortable life she'd be embracing—Nic crawled into the tight space. Tasha helped to stuff the cloak around her, and Nic reflected that she'd become yet another carefully crafted export of House Elal.

Tasha whispered a goodbye and best wishes, then lifted and latched the sled's gate, closing out even the meager light of the barn. With the crates stacked around her, and the thickness of the cloak taking up the available space, Nic could barely move. She might as well be packed in a crate herself.

As the wagon lurched into motion, she let her eyes close. Nothing to do but sleep, and trust that, wherever Maman had sent her, she'd open her eyes again to a brighter future.

# ~ 7 ~

"WHERE. IS. SHE?" Gabriel parsed the words slowly, attempting to keep the demand to a low growl instead of a roar.

Lord Elal had the grace to look apologetic—though he also didn't move from his thronelike chair behind the big desk. Lady Elal stood just behind him, her hand on his shoulder, chin tilted at the exact regal angle her daughter assumed at her most obstinate. Her mother had the same glossy black hair that Veronica had said she inherited from that side of the family, but Lady Elal's eyes were a misty blue. Hard to say where the green had come from. Maybe from her father, but Lord Elal's eyes were of course totally black now from working magic.

"Won't you sit, Lord Phel?" Lord Elal suggested smoothly, and not for the first time. "The brandy is excellent, and I'm sure you could use the warmth after your long journey through this weather."

A long, bitterly cold journey only to find his bride had disappeared. "With all due respect," he gritted out, "I want answers."

"And you shall have them," Lord Elal replied, losing some of his politeness, "but I insist that you sit and cease looming so threateningly." A static of unpleasant needlelike sensations burst over the back of Gabriel's neck—not painful, but a sharp reminder that Lord Elal could use unseen spirits against him. Gabriel might be able to combat them, but he was on enemy territory, and Lord Elal held the position of First in the Convocation for reasons beyond his wealth and inherited rank. A rank that far exceeded Gabriel's own, not incidentally. Even if he triumphed in a contest of wizardry—doubtful, especially with Elal's bonded familiar right there—he'd absolutely be sanctioned by the Convocation. Perhaps to the point of destroying any hope of restoring House Phel.

"Once you have calmed yourself," Lord Elal added, "we can rationally address your questions."

With ill grace, Gabriel plopped himself in the expensive leather chair, plucked the full brandy snifter from the desk where Lady Elal had set it, and downed it in one gulp. Pretending the fire of it didn't burn his throat enough to make his eyes water, Gabriel thunked the glass onto the desk again and stared down the other wizard.

Unperturbed, Lord Elal lifted a finger, and Lady Elal picked up the brandy decanter, leaning across the desk to refill Gabriel's glass—without ever removing her hand from her husband's shoulder. An indication of Lord Elal's willingness to wield powerful magic. Ever since Gabriel had been ushered into this study, Lady Elal had kept her hand on her husband's shoulder. They both clearly worried about Gabriel's reaction to the bitter news that Veronica had disappeared. Not that he'd expected her to meet him at the gates with excited smiles and a warm welcome, but...

All right, yes, he'd fantasized exactly that scenario, more the fool he. By the end of that long, luscious night together, he'd imagined that she'd softened toward him, that she might have grown to like him somewhat. He knew he hadn't imagined that she'd responded to his touch with real pleasure, even caressing him in return. He'd gone over that night an endless number of times in the last weeks, replaying it as fodder for fantasies to sustain him until he had her in his bed again.

And now she was gone.

Since raging would clearly get him nowhere with the coldly composed Lord Elal—clearly the apple hadn't fallen far from *that* tree—Gabriel picked up the refilled snifter and cradled it in his hands. Like everything at House Elal, both the glass itself and the brandy were exquisitely crafted. Had Veronica fled in the face of his poverty after all? Or, far worse, it suddenly occurred to him, had she been abducted? He drilled down the rising panic. House Elal was too powerful to cross. They'd be able to recover Veronica before anything terrible happened to her. *If they're so powerful, then how did they lose her to begin with?*

"So," he said, managing to take most of the bite out of his voice, "fled, abducted, or merely misplaced?"

Lord Elal sighed and steepled his fingers, elbows braced on the arms of his big chair. "We are not entirely certain. She was not here this morning when her maid went to wake her. We thought perhaps she'd gone to the library for more books, or perhaps on some other errand."

"Nic has been enjoying the freedom to leave her tower room," Lady Elal put in, making it sound like it was Gabriel's fault her daughter had been locked in there to begin with. "We were not concerned at first."

*Nic.* So the formidable Lady Veronica Elal had a nickname—one she hadn't offered to him, despite their other intimacies. Gabriel sighed to himself. He had been a fool to imagine she'd softened toward him.

"But you're concerned now?" he asked, leashing his impatience.

"We did not expect you until tomorrow," Lord Elal admitted, "so we do not yet have a comprehensive report. I have determined that Nic is not anywhere in House Elal. My sentry wizards noticed nothing unusual. No magical attack or other incursion took place. I had just begun examinations of the household staff when we received word that you'd arrived at the border." Lord Elal managed to sound put out by Gabriel's early arrival. No doubt there had been a flurry of panic at how to deal with an angry jilted wizard. The image rather soothed him. They *should* be worried.

"I made good time," Gabriel replied, not apologizing by tone or gesture. He'd been so stupidly thrilled that his gambit had paid off, so excited to see his fiancée again, to begin their life together. "Then you believe she fled," he said flatly.

Lord Elal's visage blackened, fury and disappointed betrayal leaking around the edges of the polite mask he'd been wearing. "She wouldn't *dare*," he hissed, fingers tightening on each other. Lady Elal blanched, swaying slightly, her eyes unfocused. "My daughter is obedient," Lord Elal declared, "to the Convocation and to me. She would never defy me or humiliate House Elal in this fashion."

"Nevertheless," a smooth feminine voice said behind Gabriel, nearly making him wrench his neck, he was so startled someone had snuck up behind him. "Lady Veronica seems to have effected her escape in the night." The Convocation proctor gave him a thin smile, clearly amused that she'd surprised him. He should have sensed when she entered the room, but no—which spoke to high-level cloaking, though he read her as a mid-level wizard. Her smile for Gabriel turned sympathetic, as if she understood his confusion. "She isn't the first familiar to attempt to break the rules—her breed is sadly inclined to fail to see how those rules are in place to protect them—and I daresay she won't be the last. I've sent a message to the Convocation. In the interim, I can make preliminary determinations."

"House Elal will handle the situation," Lord Elal told her, nearly shouting as his temper frayed.

The proctor approached the desk and set down an elaborately decorated wooden tabernacle, like a small cabinet, inlaid with metal foil and arcane runes. The ancient, incredibly potent magic that oozed off of it made Gabriel's skin crawl, and he fought the urge to scoot his chair farther away from it. What in the dark arts was in that thing?

"Never seen an oracle tabernacle before, Lord Phel?" the proctor inquired. She made a tsking sound. "But I forget, you don't have a formal education. Pity." Gabriel ignored her pointed remark—far from the first or the rudest insult he'd heard. "The Convocation will handle this, Lord Elal," she continued. "I would have been on the case earlier, had I been immediately notified, as I should have been according to protocol." She held up a hand as Lord Elal opened his mouth. "Regardless, I have been alerted and, I, as the Convocation proctor assigned to this case and as an *objective* observer, will lead the inquiry."

"Now, see here—" Lord Elal said, rising from his chair, a swirl of spirits taking shape in the air around him.

The proctor pointed a finger at him. "Stand down, Lord Elal," she commanded, "or you will receive even more severe sanctions than you already face. This is a Convocation inquiry, and *you* are a suspect."

"What?" Aghast, seeming staggered by that, Lord Elal sank into his chair. "You can't think that—"

"Can't I?" the proctor returned coolly, making it very clear she could—and did. "Lord Phel here is hardly the ideal son-in-law and ally, not for a High House like Elal. No insult intended, Lord Phel. I'm sure you understand."

Gabriel swallowed a reply along with a sip of brandy, keeping a wary eye on the tabernacle. *Oracle tabernacle*—where had he read about that?

"There are other incriminating indicators, Lord Elal," the proctor said, her fingers working an incantation pattern over the tabernacle's locked doors. They looked like the entrance to a castle, two of them, arched to meet in the middle, with detailed latches. "Lady Veronica, while an exceptionally well-trained familiar—as all of our Convocation Academy graduates are—is also a naïve and sheltered young woman. Living here, in the lap of luxury…" The proctor glanced around the lavishly appointed room with a thin-lipped expression of contempt, and possibly envy. "Lady Veronica is soft, sheltered, and blissfully unequipped to cope with the greater world. She could not possibly have executed an escape on her own."

"We don't know that she—" Lord Elal burst out.

"*I* know," the proctor interrupted in a repressive tone, "and so does the Oracle. Observe." She opened the doors of the cabinet, not with the dramatic flourish Gabriel expected, but with meticulous care. Fascinated despite his intuitive horror, he sat up to look. It seemed to be a sculpture of a human head, the skin made from leather, though from an unlovely, rough-cured variety. The lips were thin and colorless, no hair on the smooth scalp, eyebrows made of delicately etched gold. Its eyelids had been inlaid with lapis outlined in gold leaf, and—had it moved? Surely not.

He leaned closer.

It opened its eyes—and he threw himself back in the chair.

It was alive. Or alive-ish. The open eyes had the glisten of living mucus membranes. They held no real intelligence, even as they seemed to look through him, but the sense of an impossibly old, intensely magical presence filled the room. Gabriel forced himself to stop clutching the arms of his chair like a frightened child and wrenched his eyes from the Oracle's horrible gaze to the proctor's grimly amused one.

"The first few encounters with one can be unsettling," she commented. "Though you shouldn't need to inure yourself, Lord Phel, as I have. The oracles are precious commodities provided by House Hanneil"—she nodded to Lady Elal, who didn't seem to notice—"exclusively for the Convocation judicial council. In this case, we represent your interests and will ensure you recover your valuable property."

*My valuable property.* Gabriel wanted to object that Veronica was a person, not a lost jewel or stolen horse. And yet, the proctor would be his ally in finding her. The fuming Lord Elal and barely cognizant Lady Elal weren't on his side. No one was on the side of House Phel except himself and a handful of barely magical relations. He'd bankrupted his House on a foolish gamble. Setting down the still mostly full brandy glass and rubbing his forehead, he asked, "And if Lady Veronica cannot be recovered?"

"The judicial council will have to rule once all of the facts are in hand," the proctor replied evenly. "Regardless of any other extenuating circumstances, however, the child in question belongs to House Phel. Highest priority will be placed on ensuring the babe is brought to term healthy and in safety. The Convocation values our children. Have no concerns in that regard, Lord Phel."

Gabriel hadn't thought that far to have those concerns, but he didn't like the way the proctor spoke of Veronica as some kind of incubator for their child, who was clearly also property in the Convocation's eyes. Would they lock her up again until the babe was born? Sure sounded like it.

"First, however," the proctor said more brightly, patting the roof of the Oracle tabernacle, the head inside staring blankly, "we need to locate Lady Veronica, then we'll determine the circumstances of her… unexplained absence, shall we say, and make a plan to proceed from there. Is that acceptable to you, Lord Phel?"

Gabriel nodded. Unsavory as the Oracle was, he needed answers—and he would recover Veronica himself. No matter the circumstances surrounding her absence, he didn't trust the Convocation to handle her gently, not the way this proctor spoke.

"Silence, please," the proctor requested, moving her hands in a complicated pattern. Gabriel recognized the evocation of a binding spell with compulsion elements.

The Oracle's desiccated lips parted. "What do you ask of me?" it hissed in an inhuman voice.

Gabriel found himself clutching the arms of his chair again, pushing himself back in it and away from the thickening magic of compulsion.

The proctor held a piece of silk and lace under the thing's wasted nose, like giving scent to a bloodhound. "The Lady Veronica Elal—is she within this house?"

"I told you, I—" Lord Elal began.

"*Silence!*" the proctor cut him off. "Oracle?"

"She is not."

"Where is she?"

"It is dark where she is. I cannot see."

"Is she stationary or moving?"

"She is in motion, moving south and west."

"Has she been restrained or compelled in any way, magically or physically?"

"No."

Lord Phel made a sound, thumping the meat of his fist on the desk, expression a mask of cold fury.

"Is Nic all right?" Lady Elal burst out, startling Gabriel, who'd kind of forgotten the woman could speak. Her eyes were wide and full of emotion, the hair at her temples damp with sweat.

"Hush, precious," Lord Elal commanded, as if he hadn't been guilty of interrupting himself, putting his hand over hers on his shoulder. "Let the proctor work."

The proctor observed the exchange with interest also. "What is the condition of Lady Veronica's physical, mental, and emotional health?"

"She appears physically unharmed but is in a state of great agitation."

"Is she afraid?" Lady Elal asked tremulously, her lord's hand crushing hers. She seemed not to notice.

The proctor, looking from Lady Elal thoughtfully, repeated the question, and the Oracle said yes.

"There," Lady Elal said to Gabriel. "Nic is afraid. She's been taken against her will. My poor baby girl." Tears welled in her eyes, though they didn't fall.

"Precious," Lord Elal said in a hard voice. "You are overwrought. You should assume your alternate form. You'll feel better for it."

"No, Papa," she protested, sounding even more upset. "Please, no. I won't be able to speak, and—"

"Which is more restful for you and for us. *Now*, precious. Don't make me compel you."

"Papa, please, I promise, I'll—"

With a sharp sigh, Lord Elal flicked his fingers in another compulsion pattern, this one too fast for Gabriel to follow, and Lady Elal's voice changed to a long animal wail as she vanished. Lord Elal bent over, retrieving something from the floor. Lifting a large black cat with misty blue eyes, he deposited it on his lap, petting its silky fur. The cat mrowed unhappily but curled up obediently, only the tip of its tail flicking.

"I apologize for the interruption," Lord Elal told the proctor, ignoring Gabriel. He was sure his appalled reaction showed on his face. He'd known that powerful familiars had an alternate form, but witnessing the shift—and that the wizard had been able to compel it—left him feeling a bit ill. This was the life Veronica faced. Though he'd never compel her that way. Not that she could know that, but…

"So, my daughter was abducted," Lord Elal said. "I shall send wizards south and—"

"No," the proctor broke in. "That is not a foregone conclusion. A familiar who has escaped against the will of her family and wizard master would be afraid, also. I believe that is the mostly likely explanation at this point. Lady Veronica has hidden herself inside something and is attempting to evade her sacred responsibilities. The situation will be addressed accordingly. Have you any other questions for the Oracle, Lord Phel?"

Gabriel started, not expecting the question. He couldn't imagine what he'd ask that the Oracle could answer. *Does Veronica hate me? Why did she run rather than talk to me?* He shook his head, then paused. The proctor lifted an inquiring brow. "Can it, ah, the Oracle, can it know—is Lady Veronica alone?"

The proctor repeated the question. "There are no other people near her," it replied.

"Then how is she traveling?" Gabriel mused. Already he

plotted the course in his head. She couldn't have more than a few hours on him. "And when did she leave here?"

The proctor gave him a reproving look, using a gesture to break the enchantment. The Oracle head closed its eyes, and she shut the tabernacle doors, locking the device. "The Oracle can only determine what is, not what happened before. That it is dark around Lady Veronica implies that she's hidden inside something."

"One of our merchandise sleds, no doubt," Lord Elal put in wearily. "Hundreds go out every night, in all directions, delivering exports."

"But no one is driving it?" Gabriel asked, perplexed.

Lord Elal gave him an impatient look. "Are you a complete country bumpkin? It's guided and propelled by a trained air elemental."

That was enough to go on. Gabriel stood. "I'll be on my way, then."

Lord Elal stood also, holding the cat in his arms. She blinked at Gabriel, showing no sign of human intelligence, or any hint of Lady Elal's earlier upset. "You are, ah, welcome to stay here at House Elal, Lord Phel, while we wait for word. Nic cannot have made it far. Very likely we'll have her back by evening, and we can hold the wedding immediately."

A wedding Veronica had risked her life to avoid. He couldn't think about that. Not until he'd spoken with her. "No, thank you. I'm going after her myself."

"Lord Phel," the proctor said, "I recommend that you return home. The Convocation will locate and retrieve Lady Veronica. We are well equipped to recapture recalcitrant familiars."

"*Recapture?*" He pounced on the word. "That implies she was a prisoner to begin with."

"A figure of speech. Nevertheless, Lady Veronica will not return to House Elal. She will be recovered and taken into protective custody by trained Convocation personnel. Once she has been safely installed at the Convocation Center, we'll send—"

"House Elal is closer," Lord Elal asserted. "Have Nic brought here."

"Not an option. You have lapsed in your duty once, Lord Elal. You will not be trusted again." She turned to Gabriel. "Once Lady Veronica has been safely installed at the Convocation Center, we'll send word, and you may attend then to discuss next steps."

"Next steps?" he echoed, feeling several steps behind, indeed.

She gave him a mock sympathetic smile. "Even an experienced wizard may lose control of a recalcitrant familiar, even more so one who is, shall we say, largely uneducated in the more refined techniques used in Convocation circles. Regardless, even were you a highly trained wizard, the Convocation wouldn't release a feral familiar into your control. She poses a risk to our reputation, and it wouldn't be fair to you. Lady Veronica must be punished, disciplined, and retrained. If you still wish to bond her—which I don't recommend—then you will need to be assisted by our Convocation trainers to ensure that she is properly subdued."

His head spun. *Punished. Disciplined. Retrained. Subdued.* "If

I still wish to bond her," he said, grasping one piece of it. *Don't think about those bastards hurting her.* "What options do I have?"

"Now, now," Lord Elal said. "Let's not be hasty to—"

"You may, of course, eventually apply for a different familiar." The proctor smiled at Gabriel, ignoring the sputtering Lord Elal. "In fact, my superiors will no doubt recommend that course of action. It may take some time for an appropriate familiar to be available, but you will likely be much better off with a more docile choice."

"And what would happen to Lady Veronica in that case?"

The proctor shrugged, as if it hardly mattered. "You shouldn't concern yourself, Lord Phel. We have many tools at our disposal for breaking a willful familiar, after which she will be useful to the Convocation. We'll be well compensated for our expenses incurred in this unfortunate incident."

"I shall petition for my daughter to be returned to House Elal," Lord Elal declared. "If Phel chooses to repudiate her."

"We shall see," the proctor replied, lifting the tabernacle, her tone making it very clear she doubted he'd be successful. "The Convocation is unlikely to be forgiving in this matter, Lord Elal, no matter your influence. There will be an inquiry as to whether your daughter was spoiled at home—or perhaps given radical ideas."

"I won't repudiate her," Gabriel said, jumping in as Lord Elal sputtered. "I want Lady Veronica."

"I suggest you wait for the trainers' assessment, Lord Phel. Though your loyalty is admirable, being saddled with a toxic familiar is worse than having none at all. Go home," she added, not unkindly, "and allow the Convocation to handle this. We are very good at our jobs."

Gabriel shook his head, pulled his gloves out of his clock pocket, and yanked them on. "I'm going after her myself." *South and west. How hard can it be?*

The proctor narrowed her eyes. "I must caution you, Lord Phel, that you cannot interfere with the Convocation hunters. Their primary task is to capture, subdue, and transport Lady Veronica. They will not be gentle with you should you come between them and Lady Veronica."

"She already belongs to me, by Convocation law," he argued, the chill of the proctor's impersonal assessment settling in his gut. He wouldn't think about how they'd subdue and transport her. He didn't need to because he'd get to her first.

"The hunters are not lawyers, Lord Phel. They are simple creatures and single-minded in their purpose. Go home. Wait to be summoned by the Convocation. Trust us to deal with her. That's my best advice."

Gabriel glanced at Lord Elal, his docile familiar drowsing on his lap with no more interest in the conversation than any cat would have. Spirits shimmered and twined behind him, and his eyes glittered with resolve. Lady Veronica's father had no intention of waiting for these hunters to reach his daughter first either, Gabriel was sure of it. The proctor noted it also.

"Need I caution you, Lord Elal, that you must not interfere either?" she inquired silkily. "Any actions on your part will be regarded as prejudicial to your case. The judicial council will not be tolerant."

Lord Elal nodded jerkily. "As you say, Proctor," he said in little more than a snarl, clearly not agreeing.

"Lord Elal. Proctor." Gabriel bowed stiffly to them both and strode out of the room. He could use their enmity to his advantage. In order to marshal his forces, Lord Elal would have to evade the proctor's notice or wait for her to depart. With any luck, these hunters she mentioned would have much farther to travel, if they were at the Convocation Center. Gabriel should be well ahead of both.

He'd get to Veronica first. And then...

Well, then they'd see, wouldn't they?

## ~ 8 ~

NIC WOKE WITH a start, disoriented by the total darkness, hemmed in on all sides. *Trapped.* She was trapped and unable to move. Frantically, she squirmed against the cage that held her, barely able to move. A scream bubbled up in her.

*Wait, no.* Not a cage. Crates. On the export sled. The hiss of the runners over snow penetrated her hidey-hole, the smooth glide of the sled as it hurtled to parts unknown barely felt. How long had she slept? Where in Elal was she? If she was even still on Elal lands.

Her body, at first heavily numb from lying in the same position for so long, began to tingle painfully with returning circulation. Unable to do much to alleviate the discomfort, Nic groaned. As if in sympathy, her stomach rumbled. She was thirsty as well as hungry, *and* she needed to pee rather desperately. Though she understood Maman's abundance of caution in keeping Nic ignorant of the specifics of her plan—mainly because they didn't dare discuss them—the staggering extent of her vulnerability hit her hard.

How much longer would she be stuck in this sled? Tasha had been vague. If Nic got desperate enough, she supposed she could just pee in her clothes—after a point, she wouldn't have a choice there—but what if something had gone wrong? She'd die of thirst in here. The sled might travel for days before reaching its destination. Or it might get stuck in a snowdrift. Papa had fumed about those kinds of incidents often enough, enraged that he had to send actual, expensive workers to dig the sleds out.

*Keep calm*, she told herself. *Maman would've planned for that. She'd know you'd need to get out before days passed, or she'd have given you water, at least.* Still, Nic wriggled down until her booted feet pressed against the closed gate of the sled. Or the crate between her feet and the gate. Had Tasha put a crate there? Nic fervently wished she'd paid better attention. What if Tasha had been supposed to give her water and forgot? No, Tasha never forgot things like that.

*Calm down*, she ordered her hammering heart. Panicking would get her nowhere.

Bending her knees for as much power as she could muster, Nic readied to kick down hard against the gate, then thought better of it. If the gate opened, that could alert any observers that she was inside. Or she'd discover that she couldn't open it, and then she'd really start to panic.

Thick and too warm, the air became difficult to breathe. Nic's heart accelerated even more. What if she never got out of this hole? She'd die in here, buried in a coffin of these crates, and no one would ever know what had become of her. Maman might even think her off living free in wherever the sled was going, but no. Instead she'd molder in this unmarked grave of export crates and—

The sled slowed. Did it? Yes, the pitch of its gliding runners had definitely decreased. *See?* she scolded herself. *All that panicking for nothing. You need to get smarter.*

Her imagination, however, already going at high speed, simply switched tracks to a new worry—and she began to fret about why the sled was slowing, was that planned, who would open it, where would she be and what would happen next... At least Nic managed to roll her eyes at herself. Slowing her breathing, using the meditative techniques she'd learned at Convocation Academy, she did her best to lie and wait. Not like she could do anything else. Lie and wait *calmly*.

The sled came to a full stop, muffled voices calling outside. Not in alarm, though. Workers, maybe. The sled lurched, then moved slowly in fits and starts, the shouts fading. Then it came to a full stop. Nothing happened for a while, and Nic began to consider kicking her way out again. Then the sound came of the latches on the gate releasing.

*See? You could never have kicked it open anyway.*

The gate fell open, a gust of cold, fresh air flooding in. Nic inhaled it gratefully.

"Do ye need help getting' out of there, gel?" a man asked, sounding unsurprised to finding her packed in with the crates, so that was a good sign. She hoped.

Nic wiggled, trying to do it on her own, to scootch herself down—with little result except heated puffing and painful knocks to her elbows. "Yes, please," she replied, trying not to sound as pitiful as she felt.

Hands grasped her ankles and pulled, none too gently, and Nic fervently wished she'd been clever enough to position herself for this extraction. As it was, she felt much like the cork in a bottle of wine must—and she emerged from the wagon with a similar *blerp*, falling to the ground in an ignominious heap. She groaned, hurting everywhere she wasn't numb.

"Better get up," the man advised. "Laziness draws attention 'round here."

Figuring the advice was well meant, if not terribly helpful, Nic rolled onto her hands and knees, grateful when the man grasped her arm to pull her to her feet, steadying her as she got her bearings. She was inside a large building stacked with crates and barrels, the snow-packed floor providing a highway for the sleds moving in a steady stream down a nearby aisle. Workers moved in and among the crates, loading and unloading sleds much like her own, which was currently parked in a shadowy back corner, away from the bustle of activity. This had to be a distribution center—but of Elal's or a larger joint distribution center, like the ones Elal shared with other houses? "Where am I?"

"Elal," he replied curtly, releasing her arm and adjusting the crates in her sled so the cavity she'd occupied was no longer evident. He gave no sign of knowing who she was, or any interest in finding out. "I gotta put this sled back into circulation. If these get too far outta order on the manifest, the sled-pixies get confused, bork things up, and then there's *questions*." He made questions sound like the worst thing possible, which—especially in her case—they probably were.

"What should I do?" she asked tentatively as the man hopped onto the bench at the front of the sled.

"Return to the main aisle for unloading," he instructed the air elemental bound to the sled. He jumped down again as the sled lurched into motion, caught Nic by the elbow, and ushered her out of the way. "Best stay clear, gel," he advised. "Them pixies ain't none too bright. Soon as run over ye as blink."

The sled, repositioned, glided back to the main aisle and turned, nearly colliding with an oncoming sled. The man sighed and jogged off, calling to someone else to slow their sled and, not incidentally, abandoning Nic.

"The next time I stage an escape," she muttered to herself, "I'm going to know what the steps are." At any rate, *her* next step was urgent: She needed to find a relief room. With so many people working in this vast building, surely there had to be one. Unfortunately, the towers of crates made seeing any distance impossible. Nic worked her way along an aisle too narrow for the fast-moving sleds, nicely shadowed.

"Not that way," a voice said behind her.

This would get old fast.

Nic whirled around to see a jaunty young woman, about her same age, with red hair in long braids on either side of her head. "You go that way," she confided, "and you'll be caught and bundled off to face Convocation judicial before you can say House Tadkiel."

"I'm looking for a relief room," Nic replied, pressing her legs together.

The girl cocked her head. "A what then?"

"I need to pee," Nic clarified, and the redhead's face cleared.

"Ah. You want the pit, then. This way. I'm Dary."

"I'm Nic."

"That your real name?"

"A nickname. My real name is—"

"I wouldn't," Dary interrupted. "Probably you shouldn't even use your nickname. Too easy to ask around about you. Me, I'm not going to spill, cuz I'm getting paid well, and I've got just enough wizard talent that I'm immune to compulsion. Can't *do* much, but it's handy for this business. Here's the pit."

Nic looked at the trench cut into the frozen ground with some dismay. An angled platform on stilts kept the snow off, at least, but in summer, this had to reek to high heaven.

"Squat," Dary instructed, bundling up her cloak and dropping her pants. Hanging her naked bottom over the open trench, she peed a steaming stream to mingle with the rest. No earth elementals to vanish the waste here.

And Nic had thought she'd miss the wine at home. Determined to buck up, Nic pocketed her mittens and followed suit, bundling her long cloak and tunic out of the way and undoing her trousers. She still bungled it, getting pee running down her thighs as much as in the trench. Well, if she smelled bad, no one would mistake her for a High House familiar.

"Ain't ye never peed in a trench before?" Dary asked with a dubious frown. "Basin for washing up is there."

"Thank you," Nic replied, rather than answering. She dipped her hands in the water, freezing and cloudy with dirt, so she didn't feel much cleaner.

"Soap," Dary said, poking the yellow cake swinging from a rope. She washed her own hands, drying them on her cloak. "Ready?" she asked once Nic had done the same, striding off at a fast clip without waiting for an answer.

"Is there water?" she asked.

"Out and in, eh?" Dary winked as she dug a flask out of a pocket and handed it to Nic. "You can keep that. This is for you, too." She rummaged in another pocket and produced a packet. "That will have to last you a few days, so go easy on it."

Nic, chugging the water, belatedly slowed her pace and replaced the cap on the flask, stowing it and the packet in pockets of her own cloak. "Where are we going?"

Dary pointed without pausing. A long pier protruded across thick ice, ending in a dark pool of open water where several unremarkable barges were tied up. The boat version of the export sleds. Workers and wheeled wagons trundled up and down the planking of the pier, continuing the busy process of loading and unloading. "I'm going on the river?"

"The sea," Dary corrected. "This is the estuary. Best way to shake the Elal ghosties, doncha know, traveling over salt water—confuses the border spirits so they can't sense your tattoo, as long as you're not out in the open."

Did Papa know about that weakness in Elal's defenses? Nic at least found the wisdom to keep it to herself that she had no tattoo. The lack would mark her as High House.

"Best pull your cowl more around your face, just in case there's anyone around who might know you," Dary said, trotting down wooden steps that led to the pier. She strolled along jauntily, occasionally greeting people, and Nic did her best to look both inconspicuous and like she belonged.

"Who's this, then?" an older man demanded, stepping in front of them and halting their progress. "New girl?"

"Yeh." Dary gestured to Nic without interest. "This is Rency. I'm to show her how to instruct the barge control elementals."

The man scowled at her, then jabbed out a hand to squeeze her arm through the thick cloak, grunting in disgust. "I guess barge control is all she's good for. I need muscle. Can't they send me workers with muscle?"

Dary shrugged. "Mining pays better, if ye got the muscle for it."

"If you don't count having to pay House Refoel to clean out your lungs every couple of moons." The man wagged a finger at them both. "You gels aren't too young to start thinking of these things. Cheaper to maintain your health than fix what's already gone to shit."

Dary spread out her hands. "We're here, aren't we?"

"Yeah, yeah." The man waved them on. "Hey, Rency," he called after them, and Dary elbowed Nic hard when she didn't turn. Right.

"Yeh?" she asked, imitating Dary's accent.

"You know your numbers?" he asked.

Dary grunted a soft sound of negation.

"Nope," Nic replied.

"Figures," he grunted and went on his way.

"Good answer," Dary muttered. "But you got to get sharper, eh? Use a new name every place you stop, and remember to answer to it. You got no education and you're none too bright. You just do what you're told."

"Do you… do this kind of thing often?" Nic asked.

Dary raised brows as red as her hair, wrinkling her freckled nose. "You really want an answer to that?"

No, Nic figured she was better off not knowing. Though it was clear Dary was part of a system that handled helping people escape. But who—other familiars? Or maybe people besides familiars hoping to evade their circumstances. The image of Tasha holding up her arm and showing her House Elal tattoo that would allow her to be tracked anywhere came to mind.

"Is there any chance they'll send the hunters after ye?" Dary asked abruptly.

"Hunters?" Nic debated what the discreet answer would be. "Probably."

Dary grunted. "Well, keep yer senses sharp."

"Have you ever seen a hunter?"

"Nope. Most of my clients don't rate. Ye seem like maybe you would—ye got that fancy air—so if anything looks, sounds, or smells weird..." She trailed off without offering any more advice than that.

Nic followed Dary across a gangplank, slowing as they trailed a ponderous cart to the back of the barge. Abruptly, Dary turned and squeezed between huge crates, stacked two high. Edging into an even narrower crack, she crouched and felt along the planking, then pried up a board. A dark and dank hole lay beneath. "Yer carriage, milady." She grinned at her joke.

Nic stared at the hole, aghast. "Will I be able to get out on my own?"

Dary pondered. "Shouldn't need to. Less'n things go wrong."

"And if they go wrong?" Nic asked drily.

Dary looked at the hole, then back to Nic. "Then I guess ye'll be powerful motivated to get out, eh? Now in ye go. Make it snappy, someone's coming."

With no real alternatives, Nic sat on the edge of the hole, dangling her feet over the edge and peering in. The feeble winter afternoon light didn't show much, but she could see it wasn't that deep. Just a bit more than she was tall. Jumping down, her boots squelched unpleasantly. She had just enough time to take in the square space—and the short bench perched on one side—before Dary replaced the plank, plunging the hole into darkness.

With hands out in front of her—at least she could stand more or less upright in this hidey-hole—she made her way to the bench and sat. She considered drawing up her feet, but then she'd get her one dry spot wet. If she took off her boots, she might be barefoot if she suddenly had to run.

Finally, she settled for lying on her back on the hard bench, dangling her booted feet off the end. Staring up at the darkness, feeling cold and more than a little miserable, Nic fingered the copper snake bracelet, grazing her skin with its scraping fangs. What was happening at home? Surely her absence had been discovered—but did Gabriel know yet, and what was his reaction?

Pressing down hard, she gasped at the bite of fangs. *Don't think about him.*

Or about the hunters, whatever *they* were.

RIDING FAST THROUGH the swirling blizzard, Gabriel used his water magic to guide the icy snowflakes away from his face and Vale's. He also did his best to clear the accumulated ice and snow from the road before the horse's hooves struck it, though that wasn't easy at speed. Vale, bred for his endurance as well as speed, galloped gamely on. It helped that Elal's excellent grooms had given him a good rest while Gabriel was in House Elal. Of course, he'd thought at the time that they'd be staying at least overnight, if not a few nights. Gabriel had imagined Veronica wanting to celebrate their wedding with her family, perhaps waiting for friends to arrive to stand up with her, to say her goodbyes slowly before she accompanied him to Meresin.

Not once had it crossed his mind that he'd be back on the road in an hour, chasing after his fleeing betrothed.

For a while it had helped that the main Elal road south was kept meticulously clear of snow and ice by bound fire elementals, but with every league put between them and House Elal, more icy patches began to appear, particularly where the bitter wind blew snow over the road. In some places, so much snow swirled across the road that Gabriel couldn't make it out, and it seemed Vale flew through clouds. Viciously cold clouds that could send them sprawling with broken bones in a ditch.

Occasionally, the swirling blizzard cleared enough for Gabriel to glimpse the Elal export sleds shooting past a distance away, off the main road. They went several times faster than Vale, and because they moved over the snow, they weren't slowed by weather conditions. If Veronica traveled by one of those, she'd be gaining on him, rather than the reverse.

He could only take heart that the other pursuers would be even farther behind. Lord Elal's spirits wouldn't be hampered by transportation considerations, but Gabriel had no idea if he could send them beyond his line of sight. Most wizards were limited by the extent of their physical senses. Of course, House Elal must employ many wizards. If Gabriel had the luxury of that kind of staffing, he'd have them distributed throughout his lands, ready to be mobilized to handle problems. But it was easy to armchair strategize such things, and he had no real idea of how an actual Convocation house conducted business. Still, even if Lord Elal had wizards in place to call on, it would take time to enlist them to the purpose of chasing Elal's daughter—if he wasn't too proud to make her escape known, which was possible.

The Convocation hunters were another matter. By the sound of it, they might not be human at all, and thus not confined to physical travel.

No sense worrying about what could go wrong, as far too many things could.

His thoughts drummed in circles with Vale's galloping. Why had Veronica run? Why did Veronica hate him? Why hadn't she confided in him? Why had she risked so much rather than facing him and telling him her mind? Now that he'd glimpsed more of what familiars might endure at their wizard masters' hands—Lady Elal forced into silent cat form, submissive Feny at the border—he understood why she'd been bitterly caustic about her fate. Surely, though, she couldn't think he'd treat her so badly? If she did think so, why had she gone along with—no, urged him—the bedding?

There were no answers to be had, not until he had her in his grasp. After that, they would have a long, involved conversation, and she *would* answer his questions. He was determined to reach Veronica first, and he would. He'd overcome greater odds than this just to get this far. He had her scent, the feel of her inherent magic, the connection they'd forged that long night together. That gave him an advantage, no matter how slight.

As daylight dimmed, the cold grew more bitter, and Gabriel faced that he'd have to stop for the night. Even the great-hearted Vale couldn't keep going like this. And though Gabriel was far from great-hearted himself, he didn't have it in him to drive his steed into the ground. So when he saw the lights of a town, he slowed Vale and looked for an inn.

Having to deal with the inn, the askance stares at his appearance, the averted gazes when they took in his wizard-black eyes, the shocked ones at his white hair—all of it broke him out of his circular thoughts. He tipped the stable girl well to walk Vale cool, rub the gelding down thoroughly, and give him an extra portion of feed. And he tipped the boy in the pub well to bring himself an extra portion of feed, also. Gabriel sat by himself in a shadowy corner, using a simple moon spell to reflect curiosity away from himself.

He was more tired than he'd realized, feeling sleepier by the moment as warm food settled into his stomach. He wasn't used to winter's bite. And he'd pushed hard to reach House Elal, thinking he'd have days of rest after the wedding. Sopping up the last of the rich mushroom gravy with the excellent fresh bread, Gabriel settled back to savor the rest of his wine—an excellent, robust Elal red, though not as good as Veronica's special reserve—and watch the room.

Thus, he was in the perfect position to see the hunters arrive.

He knew them for inhuman even before they fully entered the busy tavern. The air seemed to bend before their passage, adjusting to the presence of that which should not exist in this world. There were six of them, slinking into the room like an amalgam of a jackal and a weasel in vaguely human shape, arching like hounds to sniff the surfaces they passed. Nobody else seemed aware of them, so Gabriel made sure to look past the hunters also, focusing on the minstrel blithely singing a song nearby, exhorting the crowd for coins.

He needn't have bothered, for one of the hunters lifted its snout in the air as if scenting something interesting and fastened one eye on Gabriel. It slunk in his direction, pausing to steal a handful of coin from the oblivious minstrel's tip basket. It tossed one on the table before Gabriel, an insolent sneer on its distorted face.

"Wissard," it hissed, revealing inhumanly sharp teeth—several rows of them.

"Hunter," Gabriel returned. He readied himself, though his water and moon magic seemed unequal to dealing with a creature like this. The books in the House Phel library, at least the legible ones, were short on spells for martial application.

Under the table, he loosened his sword in its scabbard, a far more reliable defense.

"You know what I am. Good. I ssseek a familiar, on behalf of the Convocation. Have you ssscented one?" It pushed the coin toward him with a sharp, curving claw.

"This place reeks of sweat and ale," Gabriel replied. "I'm sure any good familiar would turn tail and hide in their room."

The hunter sniffed the air all the while Gabriel spoke, barely listening. "You have no familiar."

"Unfortunately, no. I am but a minor wizard." Gabriel drew more moon reflections around himself, just in case any of his power leaked through. On the advantage side of being a moon-based water wizard, it was a quiet magic, and often overlooked.

The hunter fixed one ochre eye on him—the length of its snout making looking forward with both eyes at once impossible—and made an unpleasant choking sound. Laughter? "Why are you here, wissard?"

Gabriel gestured at his cleaned plate. "Best mushroom gravy in all of Elal."

The hunter eyed him for another excruciatingly long few moments. Without another word, it slunk out again, its cohorts streaming to join it, pouring out the door again like smoke. Gabriel blew out a breath, quaffed his wine, and went to his room for the night—dropping the coin, plus a few more, back in the minstrel's basket.

In his room, gazing at the unpacked bags he'd tossed on the chair before heading down to eat, Gabriel considered fetching Vale and riding through the night. But the bitter cold hadn't lessened, and both Vale and he would do far better for a good night's rest.

"You knew those hunters were out there," he muttered to himself and going to the window and staring out at the unrelenting blizzard. "Laying eyes on them changes nothing." Though it did change things: he was more afraid for Veronica than ever.

He had to accept that he was no longer ahead of the others who sought Veronica—if he ever had been—so he needed to be smarter than the hunters. Returning to his thoughts before the hunter arrived, Gabriel considered how to find Veronica. The moon would be gazing down on them both, if not obscured by clouds. Its light still filtered through, however, so he should be able to follow that silvery thread up to the moon high above, then down to her. If he conjured her scent, like roses and red wine, the feel of her fiery nature, the heat of her a perfect complement to his cooler, watery one, then... Yes.

A stirring out there. Veronica. Holding on to that thread, he layered it with silver moonlight, moving automatically to shutter the window and trip the magical lock that would seal the door. Stripping off his clothes, he hung them on the heating rack that already held his drying cloak, then climbed naked under the covers. Closing his eyes and dropping into much-needed sleep, he commanded his wizard senses to travel the thread to Veronica.

And hold on to her.

# ~ 9 ~

BY THE TIME the barge docked, Nic was certain she'd never be dry again—nor could she recall what it felt like not to rock constantly. She had no idea if she'd been in that hole for hours, days, or weeks. Well, not weeks, or she'd be dead since she'd emptied the little water flask Dary had given her a long time ago. And she'd felt the buzz when they'd crossed the Elal border early on. All she knew now was the barge had been stopped for a while—on water that didn't move much, thankfully—while the shouts of workers and the scrape of cargo filtered faintly down to her.

When it had been silent for a while, she'd begun to seriously contemplate trying to get out on her own. As for powerful motivation, being out of water counted. She'd gotten desperate enough to taste the bilge that seeped into her cubby—quickly spitting out the brine. At least that had been an easy decision to make, as she'd been dubious about diseases she might contract from the stuff. She had to be especially careful, she supposed, with the pregnancy. Though she felt nothing yet—the Refoel wizard at House Elal had told her she might not for a couple of months—Nic was also cognizant that she knew next to nothing about caring for her unborn child.

If she sickened, she'd have to appeal to a House Refoel wizard for healing. While House Elal had a barter agreement with House Refoel—to the point of exchanging in-house wizards between them—Nic doubted House Refoel would be inclined to honor it with a runaway familiar. She'd have to identify herself to them, and that would get her captured. That left paying them outright like any commoner, and the coin Maman had promised had yet to appear.

Not that it would matter if she died in this dank hole.

"Not dying in this dank hole," she muttered to herself, climbing to stand on the bench. As soon as her eyes had grown accustomed to the darkness, she'd dragged the bench to be directly beneath the opening she'd come through. Or as near to that as she could figure. Crouching on the bench—which at least gave her good leverage—she pushed on the overhead plank, hoping to feel some give.

Nothing. Nothing. Nothing.

She pushed harder, putting some effort into it while still being quiet. It might take pounding to budge the thing, but that would be loud. If anyone unfriendly was nearby, they'd hear. Maybe those hunters Dary mentioned. After resting a moment to master the wave of dizziness from lack of adequate food—she'd eaten all of the dried fruit and meat Dary had given her long ago—she pushed with all the might she could summon.

And it gave! The trap flew open, leaving her blinking in astonishment like a cornered mole rat at the swarthy face staring down at her—a young man with a knitted hat tugged down well over his ears. He rolled his eyes. "Oh, great. *Another* one. I don't suppose you have coin?"

"No, I—"

"Figures." He held down an arm. "Well, come up anyway."

Nic grasped his arm with both hands. He smelled rather unpleasantly of fish and sweat, and his rough wool jacket was damp, but she clung to her rescuer regardless as he hauled her onto the now empty deck of the barge. Staggering to her feet, she took in her new surroundings—the night-dark shipyard, the flat coastal plain disappearing into fog in one direction, the still harbor in the other. Chilly, but not as bitter cold as Elal, and no snow in sight. "Where am I?"

The man snorted in disgust. "They just stow away in barges like trusting lambs, not knowing where they're going," he said to no one, gesturing in exasperation. "Say, you don't have a tattoo, do you?"

Nic pulled off her soggy mittens, extended her arms through the slits in the cloak, and let her sleeves fall back in demonstration. He grunted. "That's at least something."

"And I am where?"

He gave her a sour look. "Port Anatol. Wartson."

"Wartson," she repeated, less in question than trying to kick her sluggish brain into recalling the place.

"Not in the Convocation," he explained, "so you wouldn't have heard of it. Your houses like to sell to us just fine, though, so"—he threw his arms wide, striding away—"welcome to beautiful, historic Wartson. We hope you'll enjoy your stay, however long that might be."

"Do you have some water I could drink?" she asked, trotting to keep up.

"Let me guess, you forgot to bring food and water with you. There's some up at the inn ahead. They might have work for you, too. That's what we usually do with you sorts. Do you have any skills?"

Nic had plenty of skills, yes—but none that sounded immediately useful for working at an inn. "I'm a fast learner," she said. "I can do whatever is most needed."

He snorted at that but didn't comment. Probably everyone said the same thing, whoever all these other stowaways were. Did they all get put on the barge by Dary and the warehouse guy—or were there others? And who was supposed to have met her? Maman had gotten her this far, and she'd never deliberately strand Nic without funds. Maman had been confident that money would be the least of her issues, but…

"How many people like me have you freed from the barge hidey-holes?" she asked.

He made that snorting sound that seemed to be his favored mode of communication. "Seems to be once every few days lately. It's gotten so I check the new arrivals every night, just in case. The dead ones make a mighty stink, and the houses get pissed at us if their inbound cargo smells of rot, so…" He shrugged and slid her a wry grin. "Your lucky night, huh?"

Maybe later she'd feel lucky. As it was, Nic was hard-pressed to banish the image of herself dead, rotting, and stinking up House Elal imports from Wartson. "If you do it so often, I'd think you'd bring water with you," she muttered.

"You've got fire, then. That'll help. You'll need it, if you want to stay free."

"Do many of the people you rescue make it?" she asked. "Stay free," she clarified when he slid her a dubious look.

"I don't make it my business to know. Better for all that way." They'd cleared the shipyard and entered a town with tall buildings—mostly dark—bordering a narrow winding street. "Most don't stick around anyway, not if they're smart. We get some pursuers asking after them, now and again. Sometimes I recognize a few coming back the other way, all chained up and collared. You know how the houses do."

"No, I don't," she replied stiffly. Some wizards collared their familiars, sure, parading them around on leashes in human or alternate form, but that was considered gauche and over the top in polite society. Everyone in the Convocation knew that a familiar's true bonds were invisible—and more unbreakable than any chain.

"Regular ray of sunshine, aren't you?" He pointed at the sprawling building ahead, generously lit with both standard lanterns and elemental ones. "There's the inn. We did have a pair—star-crossed lovers or some such—come through a few weeks ago. They headed on pretty quick, but I'd lay odds on them making it. Smarter than most," he added, sliding a look at her, "except the sacrificing-it-all-for-love part."

"You don't believe in sacrificing for love?"

He snorted. "No way. Why, do you?"

"Love is just a nice word for an invisible collar and chains," she replied.

"Now that's the smartest thing you've said."

GABRIEL STUDIED THE vague expression of the young redhead scuffing the toe of her boot in the dirty snow. Veronica wasn't here. He'd know it if she were, but that silvery thread pulsed on her faintly far away. Still, she *had* been here.

"Nope," the redhead drawled, "I ain't seen no fancy lady. We're a working transfer station. Cargo only. No passengers. Sorry, milord." She turned to go, giving him a wave.

"Not so fast," he ordered, and she halted, turning back reluctantly. "Your boss says he saw you two days ago with an unidentified young woman who has since disappeared." Two days it had taken him to triangulate on this shipyard, which crawled with Lord Elal's people. At least he hadn't seen the hunters again, but if Lord Elal had recovered his daughter—likely, given that the warehouse was jammed with Elal exports and personnel—would he have sent word to Gabriel?

No. No, he would not.

The redhead—Dary, she'd said—screwed up her face in thought. "A lot of workers come through here, so I don't know that I remember... Ye know how it is, milord, they try it out and find it not to their liking. Mining pays better." She took in Gabriel's gear, Vale following behind him. "Or mebbe ye don't," she added with a sneer.

He didn't care to do this, but he didn't have time to waste. Dary had met Veronica. The magical tinge of roses and red wine hung faintly in the air around her. Gabriel invoked a spell of slow compulsion, water eroding stone.

Dary smiled thinly. "Did I mention I'm immune to compulsion? Bit o' wizard blood in me from way back. Besides, I can't tell ye what I don't know. Good luck to ye, though." She waved more cheerfully and ambled off, whistling idly.

Gabriel swore to himself, staring out to the estuary, where the current kept flowing through the icy borders by water elementals leading from the busy pier downstream to sea. Veronica had to have gone that way, unless this was a red herring. He didn't think so, however. That meant he'd have to find a boat. But to where? Dary's boss had said they had dozens to a hundred barges leaving every day, to any of seventy-three ports. Yes, Gabriel could still track Veronica, as he had been—but the technique required triangulating, something he could only do with his own ship. Taking a merchant vessel with a set destination would only waste his time, bouncing from place to place, eliminating ports one by one.

He didn't have that time to waste. He also didn't have coin to buy a decent ship.

Maybe he should let Veronica go. If she wanted rid of him this badly, to go so far as to travel over the sea, then maybe the honorable thing would be to let her go. And his child with her. He could apply for another familiar, and eventually rebuild House Phel's fortune again.

The thought of bedding another familiar left him more than cold, but better that than marrying a woman who'd hate him with every breath she drew. Weary to his bones and beyond disappointed to have it all end here, he turned to mount Vale.

And spotted the hunters.

They slunk like dirty fog through the shipyard, coiling down the steps to the pier—and to Dary, who sent up a bloodcurdling shriek. Ordering Vale to stay put, Gabriel ran to help the young woman, writhing in the grip of a hunter while another spoke to her. Her human fellows stood around in gaping confusion, unable to see what plagued her.

Gabriel skidded to a halt when the lead hunter slithered in front of him. "Ssso, wissard," it hissed. "We meet again. Strange coinssidensse."

"Get out of my way," Gabriel ordered. He wasn't sure what would kill this thing, but he put one hand on his sword and readied his magic.

"You will sstay here," the hunter said mildly. And Gabriel found he couldn't take a step.

Channeling power to a spell like a tidal wave to wash his path clear, he growled at the thing. "Let me go."

"No need for violensse," it said, canting its head to study him with its one unsettlingly slitted yellow eye.

"That looks plenty violent to me." Gabriel jerked his head at the now sobbing Dary.

"A girl of no conssequensse, and ssubsstantial guilt. We can disscover what you could not: the locashion of your errant familiar, yess, Lord Phel?"

Denying it was useless, as the hunter had clearly discovered his identity. Annoying, but not surprising. What other wizard would be tracking the same quarry? "Leave that girl in peace or I will kill you all."

"Will you?" The hunter snickered, droplets of spittle leaking through its sharp teeth. "It might be entertaining to ssee you try, but it iss of no matter." Dary went silent and collapsed in a heap on the pier, people clustering about her as the hunters oozed away, except for one that remained, claws around Dary's throat, choking her as she writhed feebly. "We have the informashion we need." He glanced at the dying Dary. "And you won't."

"Where is she?" he ground out, giving up on being circumspect in the face of needing to know.

The hunter gave him a canny smile. "Wouldn't you like to know? Go back to your sswampss, Lord Phel, and leave thiss work to uss. We are very good at it."

It slithered off to join its companions, the pack moving in a wave down to the barges. He could follow them, possibly buy passage on the same barge. But it would be smarter to get the information himself, then somehow contrive to arrive ahead of them. His water magic would come in handy there. Besides, he couldn't stand by and let that girl die, not if he could save her.

Abruptly, Gabriel could move, nearly lurching as whatever had held him back released. He ran down the steps to the pier, where poor Dary lay swallowed in a crowd. "Let me through," he commanded, and the workers gave way obediently.

"She had some kind of fit, milord," a woman told him. "Screamin' and carryin' on."

Another woman had Dary's head in her lap, dabbing at blood that leaked from the corners of the girl's mouth, bright against her pale freckled skin. "I don't know what's wrong with her," the seated woman told him anxiously, oblivious to the hunter a hand's breadth from her face, choking her friend.

"Let me," he said. He drew his silver dagger, one he'd bathed monthly in the light of the full moon, embedding it with enchantments to unravel the magical spells of other wizards. The hunter glanced at him, grinning in confident amusement—which turned to gaping shock when Gabriel drove the blade into its ochre eye.

The unnatural beast shivered, losing form as the enchantment that made it unraveled. It fell apart into a heap of quivering, mismatched flesh, smoke and ash wafting away. The woman holding Dary screamed at the sudden—to her—appearance of the mélange of hair, bones, and bloody tissue, and she scrambled away from it.

Gabriel crouched to take one of Dary's hands between his. "All of you, go about your business," he ordered the crowd, who quickly dispersed, muttering about evil magic. Whispering a restorative spell, he sent full-moon energy into Dary. He had no healing magic, but perhaps it would at least strengthen her.

The girl's chest pumped with a sudden, ragged breath, and she choked out a gasp. Flinging herself to her side, Dary coughed up blood, heaving with the effort. Gabriel retained her hand, letting the moon magic restore her physiological balance.

At last, Dary squinted up at Gabriel. "Did ye send those things to punish me?"

"No," he told Dary. "Those things are after my friend, also. If they reach her first, they'll kill her." They'd break Veronica's spirit, without doubt, so Gabriel didn't think that was overstating things. "Where did she go?"

"I don't know who you mean," Dary replied stubbornly.

"Veronica."

"Never met anyone by that name."

Gabriel set his teeth and tried the nickname she hadn't trusted him with. "Nic."

Dary let out a sigh, looking pained. "I kind of liked her." She fixed him with a stare. "You're her *friend*, huh?"

"I'm trying to be," he answered, hedging.

"Do you promise you have her best interests at heart?"

"Better than the things that attacked you," he said, keeping it as honest as he could. Lady Veronica would disagree, or she wouldn't have run.

Dary searched his face. "Were those things hunters?"

He hesitated, surprised that she'd identified the creatures, but Dary kept her expectant gaze fixed on his. He nodded.

"I'd been warned about hunters, but never seen 'em. I didn't want to spill, but my immunity to compulsion didn't do a thing. It's like they just plucked the information out of my head." She grimaced in remembered pain.

"Please, Dary. I have to get to her before the hunters do."

"Tell Nic I'm sorry," Dary said wearily. "Port Anatol. Wartson."

WORKING AT THE inn wasn't so bad. Missus Ryma, who ran the place, was a fair and generous boss. She hadn't blinked when

Nic's rescuer—whose name she never did learn—dropped her off on the kitchen doorstep. Instead she sat Nic down, gave her water, then food, and even had one of the kitchen boys clean and dry Nic's filthy boots.

And she never once asked Nic who she was or where she'd come from.

They quickly established that Nic had no experience cooking or serving food, but that she was familiar with the magical conveniences the locals bought from the incoming barges. Missus Ryma put Nic to bed, fed her a hearty breakfast in the morning, then put Nic to work on repairs.

Most of the people at Port Anatol had some conveniences that they'd gleaned from the incoming trade, but few knew how to maintain their expensive prizes. The fire elementals that powered the lanterns, for example, disliked the pervasive damp of the harbor city. Nic was able to coax the little spirits out of their sulks by drying them out and showing the lantern owners how to offer the creatures little treats like a tasty bit of fast-burning wood shavings to keep them happy.

Soon all the inn's elemental lanterns were shining bright, and Nic had repaid Missus Ryma for the fresh clothes she'd given Nic, and to cover her room and board. With a growing stream of clients looking for repairs and advice, Nic had accumulated enough coin to buy passage on a coach going inland. The inland part was all that mattered to her. She had no criteria to pick a destination, other than to get as far away from the harbor—and anyone chasing after her—as possible.

Nothing had happened yet to justify her nerves, but she also couldn't shake the tense foreboding, the persistent feeling that *something* was breathing down her neck. It could be that she'd inherited some of the House Hanneil clairvoyance. Or it could be *him*, as she sometimes fancied she caught a glimmer of silver moonlight in the bright of day, or scented fresh water wafting over the pervasive brine.

She didn't know how far she'd have to run to escape that sensation, but she was sure Port Anatol wasn't far enough. Maman had warned her to listen to her instincts, so listen she would. Only two things kept her lingering. One was the conviction that Maman had intended for her to be met. If her contact had been delayed, then she wanted to allow some time for them to find her. And provide that comfortable living. The other was Missus Ryma.

"If you stay a few more days," Missus Ryma said, dropping off Nic's lunch at the work table she'd set up in a corner of the common room, "you could make enough coin to have at least a small stake, when you get wherever you're going." She nodded at the line of people waiting with various broken or malfunctioning magical conveniences. "Folks inland don't have much in the way of these toys. How will you earn coin then?"

"I don't know." Nic focused on coaxing the water elemental in the purifying pitcher out of its sulk. They were less temperamental than the fire elementals, but also harder to please. The healer, Inytta, who owned the pitcher, looked on anxiously, eager to have her source of reliably clean water again. So far as Nic had been able to tell, House Refoel hadn't sent any wizards to Wartson, so the local healers relied on traditional remedies. The purified water had the additional benefit of cleansing infection when used to wash wounds—

making it a prized commodity.

"I'll figure something out, I guess. There," she said to Inytta, who took the pitcher reverently. "It's happier now, but don't store the pitcher too near the fire or any mage lanterns. The water elementals hate the fire ones. And take it to visit some of its kin from time to time, any natural freshwater source will do."

Inytta thanked her profusely, tipping her generously on top of the agreed-upon price. That met the price of passage, plus extra. Everything else went to her stake now. The next person in line stepped up, and Missus Ryma pointed at him. "You, wait. You, eat," she said, transferring the order to Nic. "You could stay here," she continued, once Nic took a bite of the excellent seafood pie. "I'll give you free room and board for maintaining my magic tools. And you can be in charge of purchasing new ones that come in. I bet you can tell the good ones from the cheap knockoffs some try to sell us."

It was tempting. The inn was comfortable, and Nic had begun to make some friends in town. People valued her contribution and had no preconceived ideas about her. Lady Veronica Elal didn't exist to them, which Nic found surprisingly restful. She could raise her child here, and Inytta could be her midwife. Of course, she'd greatly prefer to have a House Refoel wizard who specialized in childbirth assist, but failing that—as anywhere not in the Convocation would also lack the same—she'd take what she could. These women managed to birth healthy babes, after all.

She ate several bites of her pie, finding herself surprisingly hungry, and used eating to stall giving an answer. Finally she shook her head. "I wish I could," she told Missus Ryma sincerely, "but I just can't stay."

Missus Ryma took the empty dish, nodding in resignation. "I understand, but I had to try." She started to go, then turned back. "I know you're quality, child. No mistaking that. Someone was to meet you here, yes?"

Nic gazed at her, taken aback. Aside from assessing Nic's useful skills, Missus Ryma hadn't asked her any personal questions.

The innkeeper nodded to herself. "Some are on their own, you know. They pay the price of passage and cast themselves like leaves on the water. You don't strike me as that type. Whoever was to meet you must've gotten delayed. Why not give them a few more days to get here?"

Because a few more days would give any pursuers time to get to Port Anatole, too. "I better not," Nic said, as much for herself as Missus Ryma. She might have lingered too long already.

"All right," the woman huffed. "I tried."

IN THE MORNING, Nic boarded the coach heading inland—departing well before the day's barges would arrive from upcoast, a distinct relief. Every day when the shipyard horns blew, announcing a new arrival, she'd tense, casting out her senses for anything unusual.

Who was she kidding? She was checking for the scent of snow and silver moondust. *Him.* Resolutely, under the cover of the packet of food Missus Ryma had pressed on her—far more generous than what Dary had provided—Nic stung her wrist with the snake's copper fangs. *Don't think about him. Now more than ever.*

The coach was drawn by a team of horses, and thus far they were slower than the elemental-powered sleighs and carriages she'd been used to. But she was in motion, moving away from the harbor city and inland to parts unknown. Where Maman's agents wouldn't be able to find her to install her in the promised comfortable life, but also where no one else could locate her.

She watched out the window as the flat coastal plain grew gradually drier, the air warmer away from the sea. This much farther south, spring was already touching the landscape, with birds calling out their morning greetings, and pale green fuzzed the bare limbs of the low trees shaped like parasols.

The other passengers dozed—none of them people she'd met before, which suited her fine. She'd been slow to learn, but gradually she was getting more circumspect, not giving a name if not called to, or making up a new one on the spot if the person persisted. The trick there was remembering which name she'd given them. Not only had she left Lady Veronica Elal behind, she seemed to be forgetting other aspects of who she'd been. A disconcerting kind of loneliness to that.

Never mind. Once she found a place she liked, she'd settle in and establish a final and lasting identity. She had plenty of time before the child was born to think up a history for them.

The father would be dead, for sure, to forestall any curious searching. Lost at sea, perhaps. That had a grim ring of truth to it.

It wasn't until midday, after Nic had eaten her sandwich and dozed in the growing warmth of the inland sun, that she felt the silver tingle of warning.

Gasping—and then choking a little on her own spit—she sat bolt upright, startling the other passengers who'd also been dozing. Had she dreamed it, that sense of Gabriel's silvery magic, that cool caress of his gaze? She pressed the copper snake's fangs viciously into her wrist to banish that sense of him.

It didn't vanish. Instead, it grew stronger.

Panic lighting her nerves, she stuck her head out the coach window, looking back the way they'd come. Where the road crested a distant hillside, a lone rider galloped on a gray horse, dark cloak streaming in the wind of their passage as he lay low over his steed's stretched-out neck. *Gabriel.* Nic didn't have to wonder if that cloak was a deep forest green to know it was him.

How had he found her? *That doesn't matter*, she instructed herself. *Think.*

He'd be able to catch her if she went on foot, but she was trapped in this coach—and he was gaining on them. If she had any chance at all of eluding him, it would be on her own. Then she lost sight of him as he dipped into the valley. She yelled for the coach to stop, standing to pound on the roof of the coach. "Let me out!" She flung open the door, hanging on—fortunately not difficult at their moderate pace.

The driver slowed the horses, casting a look over her shoulder. "Rest stop isn't for another hour, ma'am."

"I don't care, I need to get off."

Giving her a dubious frown, the driver reined the team to a stop. Nic jumped off immediately. "I can't wait long," the driver said. "Are you ill? I have a schedule to keep."

"Don't wait," she called back as she waded into the tall grasses. "I changed my mind," she added on sudden inspiration. "I'm going back." When Gabriel caught up with them, that might not throw him off her trail long, but every bit helped.

"But, ma'am, your bag!"

"Keep it!" It was mostly clothes Missus Ryma had given her. And her winter weather garb, which she didn't need. She had her store of coin, food, and water in her pockets—she was getting smarter—and that was all that mattered.

She made it to the nearby tree line, breathing a bit easier to be out of sight—and that the coach finally moved on. The parasol-shaped trees didn't provide a lot of cover, but the thick ferns growing beneath them did, if she crouched. They also made for poor footing and slowed her progress with their dense tangles. Nic focused on going forward at an angle from the road. *Just keep moving, and he won't know which way you went.*

How long before he caught up to the coach? He'd been moving fast, so it wouldn't take him long. Maybe she should hide? *No, keep moving.* If she had any chance it would be getting far away from him. In case he could sense her thoughts, she concentrated on the ferns. *Ferns. Grass. Trees. That's all I am.*

She scuttled through the ferns for longer than she'd expected. Long enough that she began to wish she'd paced herself, her breath growing ragged and loud in her own ears. *Just the wind. Wind in the ferns.*

A presence slunk across her senses. Something dark and feral. Unsavory.

Not Gabriel. But what?

*Any chance they'll send the hunters after ye? Keep yer senses sharp. Anything looks, sounds, or smells weird...* Dary's advice echoed in her mind. Had that mounted figure been the hunters and not Gabriel after all? The presence smeared itself across her mind, sending a bolt of atavistic terror through her.

She broke into a flat-out run. And howls blazed into the sky behind her.

## ~ 10 ~

NIC RAN LIKE she'd never run in her life, as if death chased her with slavering jaws.

Very likely, it did. If only she'd stayed in the coach... Except even that might not have saved her. What would? Her thoughts flew in frantic circles, a sharp stitch in her side stealing what little breath she had left. The parasol trees were too spindly to climb—and then she'd just be stuck anyway, treed like a cat with hounds baying for her blood beneath.

A sob of despair tore out of her—and a dark shape flew through the ferns off to her right. The size of a large dog, the boneless leaping of a weasel. Another, off to her left. They were flanking her.

When a third stood up directly in her path, she had no breath to even scream.

Like an idiot, she simply collapsed, her limbs giving way in watery terror. Sobbing for breath, she stared at the thing. A beast from nightmares, the hunter had to be a creation of House Ariel, made for Tadkiel's cruel justice. It smiled with long jaws, rows of teeth sharp as a weasel's, canting its head to study her with one eye dark as old urine. "Lady Veronica Elal?"

"No," she replied. "I'm Marah, of Port Anatole."

Two more presences slunk up beside her, and another behind. "Pleasse, Lady Veronica Elal," the leader said. "Let'ss not make thiss more difficult than needed." It produced a flask. "Sssome water for you."

Nic eyed it, then gave the hunter a hard stare. "No."

It shook its head, almost seeming sad. "Foolisshness, familiar. We are tassked to bring you home ssafely. In good condishion."

"I'm not going anywhere with you," she spat.

"But you are," it replied. "You have no choisse. We musst bring you home—willingly or not. Sssave yoursself ssorrow and come with uss. We will not harm you."

The conversation had at least given Nic time to catch her breath, the angry stitch in her side easing. Holding out her hands in a facsimile of surrender, she got to her feet. "What if I don't want to go back?"

It shook its head, the same sad gesture. Small repertoire of humanlike mannerisms, perhaps. "You have no choisse. We musst bring you home—willingly or not."

Maybe a small repertoire of phrases, too. Nic turned in a circle, surveying her captors. Five of them. She obviously couldn't outrun them. Maybe if she pretended to go willingly, she could escape them at some point. Giving the leader a rueful smile, she pretended to sag in resignation. "You'll take me home if I cooperate?"

"Yess, Lady Veronica Elal, we will."

"All right, then. It's a long walk back to Port Anatole." Nic turned to head back toward the road. The hunters behind and to the sides of her tightened their circle, blocking her way. Her heart, still racing, climbed up to cramp at the base of her throat, the gut-watering fear making her shake.

"Wait, Lady Veronica Elal. We musst ssecure you."

"What?" She spun back around to the leader. Not that it was any less frightening than the others, but somehow the fact that it spoke to her made it seem... capable of reasoning with. "No. I'm going willingly."

"And we'll enssure that remainss to be true." Just as it had produced the flask of water, it produced a collar—the heavy metal locking kind—with a long chain dangling from it.

"No," she repeated, her voice a horrified whisper. All those dreadful stories of familiars wearing collars swam up to mock her. "You can't. I won't."

"The work of a moment," it promised. "It won't hurt."

It advanced on her, and Nic broke. In a panic, she tried to run, the hunters all tackling her, pinning her to the ground as she shrieked and fought. To no avail. The hunters held her spread-eagled on the ground, one on each limb, and the leader held her head still by dint of a hairy knee on her forehead. A dollop of drool fell from its fangs as it bent over her, slipping the collar behind her neck, the lock sealing with an audible snick and a burst of magic.

Revolted, devastated, utterly defeated, Nic lay there limply, no fight left in her. How ignominiously her bid for freedom had ended. How worthless she was. To come all this way just to be dragged home—and to face far worse consequences than she would have if she'd just married Lord Phel and capitulated to her fate. The moment she'd gotten those test results, confirming that she'd never be a wizard, she should've known what that meant: that she would never rule her own life. If she'd given up then, she could've spared herself so much misery.

The hunters stood around her, the leader wrapping the long chain around his clawed hand. He tugged it. "Up you go, Lady Veronica. Unless you prefer to be dragged."

Nic forced herself to her feet, her body feeling as weighted as wet sand. She was more exhausted than she'd realized, the aftermath of flight and terror leaving her weak and shaking. Hopefully she hadn't harmed the tiny life inside her. "Drink," the hunter leader said, thrusting the flask at her.

Eyeing it dubiously, Nic shook her head. "I have my own."

"No." It flicked clawed fingers, and the hunters swarmed her, a stifling and invasive search of her person she was unable to stop. It ended with her hands tied behind her back and all of her pocketed supplies—including her hard-earned coin—in the possession of the loathsome creatures. "Drink," the leader said again, yanking her head back by her hair and pouring the water down her throat, forcing her to swallow or choke.

She sputtered when it finally released her, shaking her head to rid her face of the spilled water, then spat the little in her mouth at the leader. "When I am in power, you will suffer," she vowed.

It grinned at her. "Lucky for me, that day will never come, Lady Veronica Elal. You are nothing but a familiar. Bessidess, you and I sserve the ssame massterss—and they are not kind to thosse who attempt to esscape their reach. I have the better of you, now and always. Come. Walk." It yanked her chain, forcing her to stumble forward, and they began the long trek back to the sea.

GABRIEL LEFT THE baffled coach driver behind. Securing Veronica's bag to Vale's saddle, he turned the horse back the way they'd come. How could he have missed her? He could only blame being overwhelmed by the enormity of her nearness, after following the thin thread of connection over that long distance of waves and days. Landing in Port Anatole had been like plunging into a vat of rose-scented red wine. Veronica was everywhere.

He set his jaw in frustration, trying not to give in to the fear. His barge had docked ahead of the ones the hunters had taken. He'd been sure of that much because he'd used all the water magic in him to make even that janky conveyance nearly fly through the waves. After that, it hadn't taken long to triangulate on the inn where she'd stayed for several days. If he'd only landed one day sooner. Or even a few hours...

Still, he'd been confident of catching up to her coach quickly. Overconfident, apparently. She'd sensed him coming—which, had he been thinking at all, he would have realized, that she would be able to sense the silver threads of attention he'd fastened to her—and she'd fled. Running from him yet again. By herself, with nothing, not even her bag, into a trackless grassland of ferns and slight trees that the locals had sorrowfully suggested couldn't be survived for long without plenty of supplies.

He considered taking a diagonal through the forest to intercept her, but thought better of it and walked Vale back to where she'd left the coach and the road. Vale needed to go at an easier pace for a while, and Gabriel could follow her physical trail better that way. Less chance of missing her by some ill luck. The grasslands weren't unlike parts of Meresin, and he'd grown up hunting there. She was on foot, so he'd catch up to her eventually.

And then, once he got his hands on her…

He didn't know.

"We'll just cross that chasm when we pitch headfirst into it, eh, buddy?" he muttered to Vale, who swiveled his ears in solidarity. That's what Gabriel told himself anyway.

He found the trail of bent and broken grasses fairly easily. If he'd been paying attention, instead of riding like a demon after the coach, Gabriel would've noticed the rather obvious trail angling away from the road. He had to admire Veronica's determination, though what she'd planned to do to survive out here, he had no idea. Probably she'd simply panicked when she sensed his pursuit and ran. More afraid of him than of perishing out here alone.

And wasn't that galling?

"I'll talk to her," he said as he mounted up to follow the trail, the horse keeping one ear swiveled back to listen. "I'll give her a ride back to town. We'll have a nice dinner, good wine, and we'll have a conversation like normal—" He broke off at the exact moment that Vale's ears shot forward.

Hunters. Their distinctive twisted magic oozed across his

wizard senses. They were coming his way from up ahead. He cursed viciously under his breath. They'd been on one of the slower-moving barges. How had they outpaced him?

Dismounting, he led Vale into a thicket of trees, gave the steed the signal to be silent, and drew moonlight around them. He made this shield thicker, enough to force the sunlight away so they couldn't be seen—and that they hopefully couldn't see through this time. He nearly violated his own command of silence, though, when the hunters came into view—dragging Veronica along by a chain attached to a metal collar around her neck, her hands bound behind her back. Barely swallowing his outrage, he forced himself to wait and watch. All this time, he'd looked forward to laying eyes on her again, to drinking in the sight of her bright beauty and shimmering magic. It killed him to see her brought so low, sagging in dejection as she shuffled along, defeated and clearly exhausted.

Then she lifted her head—and turned her head to look straight at him. The fiery fury in her sharp green gaze did his heart good, though he silently begged her not to reveal his presence. The hunters thankfully hadn't detected him—he didn't know how *she* had—but he'd rather not take on the pack of them without some preparation. After giving him a good, long glare, making it very clear she blamed him for her situation, she turned her gaze forward again, dismissing him with regal indifference.

Absurdly enough, he found himself smiling. They hadn't crushed her spirit yet—and at least he was in time to rescue her. Five-to-one odds weren't the best. He supposed he could figure it as five to two, if he counted Vale. Maybe five to three if Veronica would help him—though from the look she'd drilled in his direction, she'd just as soon knife him.

He'd have to take advantage of the element of surprise, and the circumstances wouldn't get better than this. No witnesses and a nice, clear road nearby to gallop down to escape any hunters he didn't manage to kill.

Better to kill them all, though.

Wishing he had spells to muffle sound, he stewed over how he might construct that kind of enchantment, which gave him something to do while he waited for the slow-moving group to wade through the ferns and tall grasses far enough that they wouldn't hear him emerge from his hiding place.

Once the trudging group had passed out of easy earshot, Gabriel gave Vale the signal to release, and the horse snorted in relief, stamping his displeasure. "Don't worry, boy," he muttered, leading the horse out of the tangle, "you'll get to burn off that energy in a moment."

Mounting, he held Vale to a stealthy walk, keeping to the softest grasses, until he had eyes on the group again. Looping the reins onto the hook of the saddle, he drew his silver blade in his right hand and the sword in his left, silently thanking the arms master who'd made his adolescence a misery and enabled him to fight with either hand. He was better with the sword in his dominant hand, but he strongly suspected he'd need the enchantment-banishing properties of the silver dagger, so dexterity with that took priority.

Gripping with his knees, he whispered to Vale to charge.

The sudden velocity nearly snapped his neck back, and he forced himself down against the wind of their passage, laying as low as he could. The hunters scattered, hearing him, and Gabriel dropped the reflection spell as a needless waste of energy. In such close quarters, the hunters could likely smell him. They spun to face him, two falling into a four-legged lope, barreling straight for him. The leader threw Veronica to the ground, and the remaining two took defensive poses before them.

Without breaking speed, Vale galloped straight for the snarling hunters racing toward them. Gabriel signaled him to take the right-hand target, using their momentum to sweep the sword like a scythe at the left, cleaving the creature nearly in half with the force of it. Vale struck out with sharp hooves, crushing the skull of his target.

With a leap to clear the body of his kill, Vale sped on, bearing down on the two hunters protecting their leader and captive. These had drawn weapons—spike-edged wheels they could grasp with clawed hands. They'd had time to gauge Vale's speed and were ready.

One dropped into an impossible bend, spinning to slice the sharp wheel at Vale's hamstrings. Acting without thought, Gabriel brought the sword over to that side, needing the reach, and sliced off the thing's arm. Vale added a cow-kick to knock the hunter away, but the hunter on the other side leapt onto Gabriel's unguarded left side like a mountain cat.

He let out a howl as the hunter's claws—all four sets—dug into his shoulder, side, and thigh. Vale echoed with a scream of his own as the hunter's hindleg lost purchase and dug into the horse's shoulder instead. The hunter's long, snapping jaws grazed Gabriel's cheek as he jerked his shoulder up, hunching to protect his vulnerable neck. The hunter coiled to try again—and Gabriel twisted in the saddle, bringing his left biceps up into the jaws and shoving his right hand beneath, driving the dagger straight into the beast's heart.

As Dary's tormentor had back on the dock, it dissolved, falling away in shreds of flesh and stinking smoke—nearly taking the silver dagger with it in the dragging plummet. Vale was already wheeling, rearing onto his hind legs and striking out at the intact hunter on the other side. Not even stunned by Gabriel's desperation strike with the sword, the hunter lunged upright, spinning the sharp wheels and going after the horse's vulnerable hind legs.

Worse, the first two hunters caught up then, confirming that a physical blow, no matter how deadly, only slowed them down. The one seemed oblivious to its smashed skull, and the other dragged its gory halves with determined malice. Only the enchanted dagger seemed to dispatch them permanently—and Gabriel couldn't use it from Vale's back.

Kicking free of the stirrups, he vaulted to the ground and square onto the back of the hunter trying to hamstring Vale. With its back turned, it made for a decent target, missing its lethal swing to sweep a shallow slice across Vale's haunch as the horse spun to deflect—then collapsing when Gabriel buried the silver dagger in its back.

Yanking the blade free, Gabriel turned to face the other two just as the crushed skull hunter tackled him. It buried its teeth in Gabriel's shoulder—fortunately missing his throat by the width of two fingers. Unfortunately, it had pinned Gabriel's dagger hand between them, and he couldn't turn the blade. He had the sword still in his left hand, so he brought it in to drive the hilt hard against the hunter's snout, wrenching it off his shoulder. Rolling with the momentum, he followed it around, dragging the dagger hand free and shoving it up into the underside of the thing's jaw.

Behind him, Vale shrieked in equine agony, and Gabriel lurched up, bracing against the dizziness as his head spun. Hopefully just from pain and magic work—not blood loss. The ragged mess of the cleaved hunter had a grip on Vale's hind fetlock. Not a strong one with its mismatched jaws, but Vale was hopping and cow-kicking in such a frenzy that Gabriel couldn't get near to help him.

Instead Gabriel spun to spot the lead hunter, standing calmly on all fours—on top of Veronica's prone body—with its jaws clamped over her throat above the metal collar. She strained away from it, chin stretched high as possible, an expression of revulsion contorting her face. Rolling her eyes toward Gabriel, she fixed him with an angry and defiant glare.

The lead hunter stretched its lips in a grin, exposing its sharp teeth, just in case Gabriel wasn't bright enough to understand its victim's peril. "Drop your weaponss, wissard," it snarled, its words no more distorted than usual for all that it had its teeth clamped to Veronica's throat. "Or your familiar diesss."

Behind him, Vale was stomping and snorting—hopefully trampling his attacker. Subtly, Gabriel changed his grip on the silver dagger. It wasn't exactly the right heft for throwing—and if he missed, he'd be reduced to scrabbling through the tangle of grasses to find it again—but all he had to do was hit it somewhere. It didn't need to be a killing strike, just enough for the enchantment to work.

"I mean it, wissard," the hunter hissed, tightening its jaws so that Veronica choked, a pitiful whimper escaping her as she strained for breath. Her gaze had softened, pleading with him. Gabriel dropped the sword.

And threw the dagger.

It hit the hunter's flank with a sideways *thunk*, dropping away again, but the thing sent up an unholy screech as if burned with fire. Releasing its hold on Veronica's throat, it convulsed, spine arching in agony. Gabriel hurled himself forward, skidding flat out onto his belly as he reached for the fallen knife. The hunter lunged, snarling, and he punched it in the muzzle with his left fist. His right hand closed on the dagger, and he buried it in the hunter's shoulder, shouting in triumphant relief when it exploded into chunks of goo—unfortunately all over Veronica, who gagged, yanking her face away.

Much as he wanted to help her immediately, Veronica was no longer in danger—except maybe of being thoroughly sick—and Vale might be. Seizing the dagger, Gabriel staggered to his feet to find Vale indeed trampling the hunter to a pulp. It took him a moment to calm the horse enough to back him off his enemy, but Gabriel managed, then plunged the dagger into the steaming, broken body. Just in case.

He knelt there a moment, drained beyond belief, then crawled back to Veronica. Rolling her away from the bulk of the hunter's remains, he used the blade to cut the rope binding her hands, then helped her sit up.

"Are you hurt?" he asked.

She spat something unsavory from her lips. "No. Though it was a near thing—you almost got me killed."

"It had orders to bring you back intact," he said, setting the precious silver blade beside him and feeling around the metal collar for the catch. "I knew it wouldn't hurt you. Lift your chin."

"Don't bother. It's magically locked. You won't get it off without a wizard from House Iblis."

Sure enough, the catch on the collar had sealed itself, feeling completely inert. With study—maybe with careful application of the dagger—he might be able to get it off of her, but now wasn't the time or place. He ran his fingers over the indentations on her formerly flawless skin from the hunter's teeth. "You'll have bruises."

She jerked away from his touch. "I'm hurt less than you are, if disgustingly filthy."

"I have stuff to clean up with," he told her. "Wait here."

"Really? I thought I'd go for a stroll. Such a pretty afternoon."

He supposed that if she was able to be sarcastic, that was a good sign. Not that he'd really expected her to fall weeping on him with professions of gratitude, but a thank-you wouldn't go amiss. He dug out water, a bar of soap, and a towel from Vale's saddlebags, unhooked her satchel, and brought it all to her. "Here," he said. "So you can clean up and change clothes. I won't look."

"You've already seen me naked," Lady Veronica called to his back. "And you own me regardless, so I don't see how it matters."

Without replying, he trudged back to Vale, who—now that the battle frenzy was fading—stood in wide-legged exhaustion, head hanging low with blood-flecked spittle falling from his muzzle. Gabriel only hoped it was from biting his foes and not a result of injury or overworking his great-hearted lungs. Stripping off the horse's tack and leaving it in a pile for later, he coaxed Vale into a gentle walk in the shade of the trees, talking to him gently all the while. When the horse breathed more normally, Gabriel led him back to the pile of tack and searched the saddlebags for another towel. The wounds were all shallow, the bleeding slowing. Conjuring water, he sluiced them clean and left them to close naturally. The bleeding would help rid the horse of any nasties.

He'd just begun rubbing down the sweat-soaked hide, when Lady Veronica—surprisingly clean, given the meager supplies, and wearing fresh clothes—took up the task on the other side. Doing it well, too.

"You know horses?" he asked.

She curled a lip. "I'm not an idiot. I might be helpless at taking care of myself in a fight, but I do know *some* things."

"I didn't mean to imply you're an idiot." Though he supposed he had made an assumption about her life as a lady of luxury. *Lady Veronica is soft, sheltered, and blissfully unequipped to cope with the greater world.* The proctor's words had clearly gotten into his head.

"You're dead on your feet, Lord Phel," she said, not unkindly. "Why don't you avail yourself of that soap and water and clean your wounds before they fester from whatever rotten meat was used to make those hunters. I'll take care of Vale here." With an affection she'd never shown Gabriel, she stroked Vale's neck. "That's right, brave boy. Let Nic take care of you."

The individual aches and throbbing wounds were building to a chorus of agony, making it difficult to think, so Gabriel took his towel and went to assess his wounds and wash up. The throat bite felt bad enough, but the burning pain down his left shoulder and back indicated much worse wounds. Struggling with his shirt, he tried to move it enough to get a good look.

"Do you have a spare shirt?"

He looked over his shoulder at Veronica, who held the enchanted silver dagger. He blinked at it in sudden dull alarm. Careless to have left it on the ground, but he hadn't wanted to sheathe it again with it so filthy. Then he forgot about it... Stupid. Veronica gestured at him with it, and he braced himself. Did she want free of him enough to attack him with it? And if she did, would he have the heart to stop her?

"Lord Phel," she said, almost gently. It occurred to him that he might not be thinking clearly, and she was conscious of that. "Your shirt is soaked with blood and gore. Better to cut it off if you have a spare one. It's so ripped up it's not worth saving."

"I do," he said, "but don't use that blade." Gingerly, he took the silver dagger from her, sheathed it despite the gore, and fished out another for her to use.

She took the replacement blade and began slicing his sleeves from the tops of his shoulders down, discarding strips as she worked. "Enchanted, is it?"

He grunted an affirmative, wishing he'd thought to sit down. The pain was making him dizzy.

"Where did you acquire an enchanted blade that would kill House Ariel creations?"

"I did it myself," he managed to say, his voice strained as she peeled the cloth away from his back, "with water and moon magic."

"You can't do that."

"But I did," he replied, aware he sounded defensive. He hadn't attended Convocation Academy. That ship had sailed without him, and it wasn't as if he'd go now and sit in class with adolescents. Sometimes not knowing what was supposedly impossible became an asset. "I read about the process in a book. As you can tell, it works just fine."

"That's not the point." She sounded exasperated. "You made an enchanted blade—and you're just using it, where anyone can see?"

"Yes—why?"

"Because only House El-Adrel can make enchanted artifacts. Their house has the exclusive license, and it's against Convocation law for anyone else to do it. Didn't anyone explain that to you?"

Huh. Guess he hadn't known that. "Not that I recall."

She made a sound of disgust, for his ignorance or for the wounds she'd revealed. Maybe both. "This is bad," she said, her voice clinical. "It's going to hurt like madness when I clean those wounds, and I'm going to have to put in some stitches to hold you until you can get to a healer. You'd better sit before you pass out."

"All right." Sitting sounded really good. He just needed to bend his knees and...

The world went black as he passed out.

## ~ II ~

GABRIEL WENT OVER like a felled tree, and Nic felt only a small stab of guilt as she nimbly stepped out of the way. It would have been a kindness to try to break his fall, but he would've crushed her. Besides, the grasses were soft enough, and she wasn't feeling all that kind at the moment.

Yes, he'd saved her from the hunters—hooray—but being captured by him was barely a step better. Gabriel might treat her more gently than the hunters had, but captive was captive after all. And it was her own stupid fault.

She shouldn't have lingered in Port Anatol. She should have taken advantage of Missus Ryma's good nature, accepted the night of rest and breakfast, and left again as fast as possible without worrying about paying her back. She hadn't needed to pay a coach; she could've walked. She'd been stupid and complacent—yes, and sentimental, as Maman had warned her against—and now she'd paid the price.

Nic knelt to adjust Gabriel's big body, the chain attached to the cursed collar falling in the way. She ended up winding it around her neck, like an annoyingly heavy and unlovely necklace, before returning to the task of making him more comfortable. She rolled him more firmly onto his stomach and turned his face to the side so he could breathe, picking his loose silver hair out of the throat wound. He had more beard stubble than the night they met. Days' worth. He must've been chasing after her without a pause for personal grooming. Probably he hadn't shaved since Elal, and she doubted he possessed a grooming imp. Despite his unkempt appearance—or maybe because of it—he looked younger in his sleep, almost boyish without those hard edges and penetrating black eyes.

She should take advantage of this opportunity to run. His horse was injured, but not too badly. She could take Vale and some or all of Gabriel's supplies—and simply leave him behind. With those deep gouges in his back and side, he would be in no shape to catch up with her, not without a horse. If he even managed to recover enough to travel at all. He wouldn't die… probably. If she was being smart—and ruthlessly without sentiment—she'd do it.

*Take Vale and go. Never look back.*

But she didn't have it in her. She couldn't leave Gabriel here suffering wounds he'd acquired liberating her from those skin-crawling hunters—even if he'd only done it to recover his valuable property.

With an exasperated sigh for herself, Nic went to get the soap, water, and towels. "This is why you'll never be free," she muttered to herself. "You're doomed to be a pet for the rest of your life because you don't have the spine to look out for yourself." *Because you're Fascinated by him*, a cautionary voice in her head whispered. *You don't* want *to walk away.*

Vale, happily grazing in the shade, lifted his head at her words, swiveling his ears to listen. "That's right, Vale," she said, giving him a pat, "you and me, fellow livestock in the service of Lord Phel." The horse snorted in obvious agreement, and she trudged back into afternoon sun.

Gabriel could've passed out in that comfortable shade, but no, he had to drop his big lump of an unconscious body in the middle of the grasses. Nic set to cleaning the sluggishly bleeding wounds where the hunter had clawed him, working briskly to finish before he woke up. She wouldn't wish that suffering on him, even if he was her greatest enemy. She'd have other problems, however, if he didn't wake before dark. No way could she move his bulk to the shelter of the trees, much less onto Vale's back.

If he didn't wake, they'd be sitting out here in the middle of nothing when night fell, which would get pretty cold, she figured, hot as the sun felt now. It was already declining, a hint of chill creeping under the slanting rays. Nothing to be done for it. She'd cope once she had him cleaned up.

At least she'd grown proficient with using soap and water. She still missed the dewy-clean feeling that water elementals gave, but soap worked, too. At first using their water stores sparingly, she quickly discovered that Gabriel's flask magically replenished itself, ever full. One advantage of keeping company with a water wizard, she supposed. It was skirting the lines of being a magical artifact, but at least this one fell within House Phel's traditional license, regardless of what Gabriel had negotiated for his house. If he *had* negotiated their license. She had a sinking feeling he hadn't known to do that either—and the Convocation was obviously not bothering overmuch to assist him in reestablishing House Phel.

Not surprising, as the existing Convocation houses had no doubt helped themselves to House Phel's provenance after its fall. They wouldn't be eager to give up any of it. As she'd guessed—possibly with a glimmer of Hanneil foresight—Lord Phel had no idea what he was up against.

She refused to feel sympathy for him. Bad enough that she wanted to linger over the texture of his skin, his silvery-cool magic lulling her even with him unconscious. She pressed the bracelet's copper fangs into her wrist, the sting a potent reminder. As if wearing a collar wasn't enough of one.

She rummaged through her satchel—clearly Gabriel been so confident of catching her that he'd gotten it from the coach driver—for the mending kit Missus Ryma had given her. Along with all the basic supplies for taking care of herself, Missus Ryma had also gifted Nic with a mage lantern, mostly because it was an easy way to house and transport a fire elemental, and the maternal woman didn't want Nic out in the world without at least that one convenience.

If it came to that, Nic could coax it into making a campfire for them.

With the wounds on Gabriel's back and side as clean as she could get them, she set herself to putting in some basic stitches. Sewing was obviously not one of her best skills. Magical fastenings were *so* much easier to use, and Nic had been privileged enough to have her clothes made and mended for her. Still, she'd learned the arts of embroidery and crochet. They were excellent for building dexterity, concentration, and attention to detail—all useful for a familiar—and kept her hands busy on long winter evenings while she chatted with her friends or they listened to music or to someone reading aloud. Usually the books they chose were of torrid love affairs between wizards and familiars—not something she wanted to think about just then.

Suffice to say, she could produce neat stitches and knots that held, though it turned out that piercing a man's skin with a needle wasn't at all the same as sliding it through fine Ophiel linen. After a few failed attempts, where the thread simply tore through the ragged edges of skin, she realized she'd have to stitch together the deeper tissues first, then draw the skin over the top with longer lengths of thread.

By the time she'd finished, the sun had declined considerably, and Gabriel showed no signs of waking. Just as well, as she needed to deal with the throat wound still. But she also didn't want to leave her makeshift stitches exposed, so she fetched the rest of his saddlebags and went through them for anything she could strip to make bandages.

She certainly wasn't tearing up her own clothes. Maybe she was being self-defeating and stupidly sentimental by not escaping while she could, but she wasn't sacrificing her few remaining possessions for him either. No doubt in her future, she'd want to give him everything, but at least she retained enough control of her own mind that she wasn't feeling it yet. He might've captured her, and he'd be able to take what he wanted from her, but she wouldn't give him anything willingly. She'd fight for every morsel of her autonomy.

*Of course, you're also staying here and helping him instead of helping yourself.*

Ignoring the voice in her head and pulling things out of the bags, she made a pile for ones that might be useful for sleeping in the meadow, and another for things to put away again. She found a blanket but set that aside as definitely more useful as it was than destroyed for bandages. Next, the plush softness of velvet met her questing fingers. She drew out the carefully folded set of clothes, noting the careful weave and exquisite silver embroidery. A stylized full moon hung over still water, so beautifully worked that the moon's reflection showed distinctly. The crest of House Phel—same as on the brooch he wore on his cloak. These must be Gabriel's wedding clothes, packed carefully and with anticipation of celebration.

It hurt her heart to see them, which made no sense. Gabriel Phel didn't need or deserve her sympathy. If she wanted to be as ruthless as she should be, she'd tear the velvet into strips for bandages. Instead, she packed them away again, telling herself it was out of respect for whoever had labored over that exquisite needlework, and determinedly not thinking of the beautiful wedding dress she'd abandoned. Venting her frustration on the shirt, she tore it into wide strips, sweating by the time she wrapped his wounds tightly, feeling her exhaustion from rolling his muscled bulk from side to side.

"Why couldn't you be wiry?" she muttered at him. "Or elegantly slim. No, you have to be the draft horse version of a wizard." With a last effort, she rolled him onto his back and examined the throat wound. Fortunately, that injury wasn't nearly as bad, and she was able to clean it fairly quickly, deciding against more stitches and bandaging it lightly instead.

Standing and stretching her aching back, she became aware of her own bruises from the hunters' ungentle treatment. The metal collar chafed the skin of her neck, weighing heavily against her collarbones, and her throat felt tight from the bruising. Resting a hand on her flat belly, she searched for any sign that the quiet life inside her had been disturbed. As usual, she detected nothing—neither good nor bad. But she felt fine, so she'd have to trust that all was well.

Resigning herself to a night in the meadow, she retrieved Vale and checked him over while she still had light. His wounds were surprisingly clean—Gabriel must've washed them, but flies had collected on the soft scabs, and he twitched, lashing his black tail and stomping in misery. She cleaned them out with more soap and water, just in case, decided the horse wouldn't stand still for stitches, and instead got out an unguent she'd spotted in Gabriel's bags. It smelled fine and didn't sting on her own scratches. Vale sighed and relaxed as she spread the unguent over his wounds, so she congratulated herself on that choice.

"Clearly I should be a familiar to House Refoel, or Ariel," she informed Vale, who bobbed his head in agreement.

She left Vale to keep an eye on Gabriel and scouted under the trees for fallen wood and tinder. Fortunately the grasses, though tall as later in the season, were spring green and full of moisture. Much as she'd have preferred to dig a fire ring, she had no shovel, and she had to acknowledge she was at the end of her stamina. Instead, she gathered stones to make a ring next to the still-unconscious Gabriel, then piled tinder in the middle and coaxed the fire elemental out of its lantern home.

Luck was with her, in that she managed to entice its curiosity. It danced brightly over the tinder and happily set it ablaze.

She kept the water flasks beside her—including her own flask, picked out of the disgusting piles of goo that had been the hunters—in case the elemental got ideas about setting the whole meadow on fire. They could get ambitious and ornery that way, but this one seemed content to obey her. It had been trained by an Elal wizard after all, which made it much tamer and more inclined to cooperate with her than a wild elemental.

The sun set, and the night grew colder indeed. Nic checked on Gabriel, who seemed to have passed from unconsciousness to sleep, so far as she could tell. She covered him with their one blanket and availed herself of some of Gabriel's food, as hers had gotten far too slimed to even contemplate. His supply was one of Missus Ryma's generous packets of food for travelers. He'd obviously tracked Nic to the inn. No surprise there, though exactly how he'd managed it was a puzzle.

She watched Gabriel sleep while she ate, feeling oddly lonelier than if she'd been alone. Finally she lay down against him—on the side closest to the fire, because she wasn't that much of a self-sacrificing fool—sliding under a fold of the blanket.

Exhausted, aching, and fighting the gray sink of depression, she watched the fire elemental dance over the wood, finally giving in to the drag of sleep. Maybe Gabriel would be dead in the morning. Then she could take Vale and keep going inland with a clear conscience.

She tried to convince herself that was a cheerful thought.

GABRIEL GROGGILY OPENED his eyes to an expanse of bluing sky—and Vale's dark-gray muzzle taking up most of the middle of it. Vale snorted, blowing grass-flecked spittle all over his face, waking him up quite thoroughly. "Good morning to you, too," he muttered, and pushed himself up on one elbow, groaning as his entire body protested—and bright pain blazed down his back and side. Deciding against sitting up, he lay back gingerly.

"Good idea. If you pull out your stitches, I'm not putting them back."

Rolling his head, he stared in considerable surprise at Lady Veronica Elal, holding the mug from his bags, sipping something that steamed in the chilly morning air. Her hair was pulled into a single thick braid down her back—though glossy dark strands escaped it to curl wildly around her strong face—and she gazed at him with that sharp green gaze, full lips in a flat line. The metal collar sat heavily on her neck, a chain looped around it like macabre jewelry.

In a sudden rush, the events of—the day before?—flooded his mind. "The hunters?"

She waved a hand at the grasses. "All piles of goo, thanks to your enchanted knife. You don't remember?"

"Just making sure." Braced for it this time, he rolled onto his uninjured side, the blanket that had been covering him falling away. The ground beside him was warm, the grass packed down like someone had lain there until just recently. He pushed into a sitting position, painful pulls against his skin confirming she wasn't kidding about the stitches. "You sewed up my wounds?"

"They're not pretty, but you didn't bleed to death. Alas."

He tried again. "Needlework is one of your many skills?"

"It might be a stretch to call it a skill, but yes—needlework is relaxing for me."

He grunted at that, eyeing the mug cupped in her hands. "Is that tea?"

"Port Anatole coffee," she corrected. "Fortuitously packed in the satchel you retrieved for me, so it didn't get slimed with dead hunter goo. Want some?"

"Please," he answered with considerable relief. He'd been prepared to argue about it. Rising, she came around to his side of the fire and handed him the mug.

"You only have the one cup, so..." She thrust it into his hands and went back to her previous spot—well away from him.

"I didn't think to buy two." He sipped the strong brew gratefully. Hot, robust, and sweet, it helped clear the last of the cobwebs from his head.

"One would think you would have," she commented, voice cool and expression narrow. When he raised a brow, she shrugged. "Since you were intent on recapturing me. I'd think you'd have come better prepared." She tugged on the collar. "The hunters did."

"I wasn't thinking that far ahead," he admitted.

"Not much of a plan, then." She held out her hands to the

cheerful blaze. "What, did you think you'd catch up to me and then charm me into going back with you?"

She said it so scathingly that he didn't want to confirm he'd been thinking exactly that. "Why did you run?"

He'd caught her by surprise with that blunt question, though she covered it swiftly. "I'd think that would be obvious," she said slowly, as if he might be brain addled. He might well be, considering how muzzy his head felt. When he simply waited her out, she shook her head in exasperation. "Because I don't want to be married to you. I don't want to be your familiar. I gave up *everything* to escape you, but could you let me go? No," she spat, her poise cracking. "No, you just *had* to come after me, and now you have me." She tugged on the collar in demonstration.

"I didn't put that collar on you."

"You might as well have," she hurled back at him.

"Veronica," he began. She picked up a cloth-wrapped package and hurled it at him. He caught it reflexively.

"You should eat," she said. "I already did."

Had she really, or was she playing her game again? She rolled her eyes, clearly reading the thought. "Eat or don't. I really don't care, but I'm sure you're hungry."

He was famished—and his body needed the sustenance to heal—so he began devouring a sandwich, contemplating her. Swallowing, he said, "I think you do care."

Her turn to raise a single eyebrow, though with cool disdain.

"Why are you still here?" he asked pointedly. When she sneered and opened her mouth, he jumped in. "You had the perfect opportunity to escape last night. You could have taken Vale and left me here to die. If you hate me so much, why did you clean my wounds, stitch them up, build a fire, and then sleep beside me all night?"

She glared at him, discomfited that he'd guessed correctly about the warm spot beside him. "It was cold, and you only brought *one* blanket."

"And the rest? Building this fire had to take work."

Dropping her gaze, she held a hand over the fire. An elemental like a lick of flame leaped out and danced on her palm. She pursed her full lips and blew—and it leapt back into the dancing fire. "I had it with me," she explained, "so easy enough."

"Cleaning my wounds and stitching me up couldn't have been easy," he persisted. "Thank you for that."

She shrugged, still watching the fire. Saying nothing more.

"So, why didn't you leave me—or at least rub dirt in my wounds?" He smiled at her, though she wasn't looking at him, trying for that shared humor they'd found before.

"How do you know I didn't?" she retorted. Flicking her gaze at him and away again, she sighed heavily, toying with a copper bracelet on her wrist, intricately designed so it looked almost like a living snake. "I don't hate you."

Well, that was something. "Is there someone else?" When her startled eyes met his, he clarified. "Someone you're in love with, who you want to marry instead of me."

She breathed a laugh, shaking her head in amazement. "You're really something, Lord Phel. That's an impressive level of hubris and arrogance that the only reason you can think up for me not to want you is that I want someone else more."

"Do you?" he asked, refusing to let her ruffle him.

"None of your business," she shot back.

"Why did you run?" he asked her again.

"To get away from you."

"Why?"

She set her teeth, jaw tight. "Maybe I find you revolting."

He considered that, chewing thoughtfully. "You didn't find me revolting when we were naked in bed together, when I was buried inside you and you were gasping my name in pleasure. In fact, I recall you—"

"Enough!" She fixed him with a baleful green glare. "If you're feeling sprightly enough to be all chatty, then you might as well mount up and ride back to Port Anatole. You need a real healer to treat those wounds before they fester."

"But I—"

"So does Vale," she interrupted, tipping her head at the horse grazing nearby. "I treated his wounds as best I could, but they need attention, too."

He leapt to his feet—correction: stood, and then nearly staggered—ignoring her snicker. Either she mocked his weakness or how easily she'd redirected his attention. He'd put coin on the latter. Veronica might want to act like she cared nothing for him, but her actions spoke louder than her sharp words. He made his way to Vale, checking him over. The wounds looked angry, but she'd found the healing salve he carried for the horse.

"Thank you again," he said, nodding to her. "I'm grateful."

She took out a lantern and began coaxing the fire elemental back into it. "He's a good horse. Brave and great-hearted. He deserves being cared for, and I was happy to do it." She pointedly said nothing about what Gabriel deserved, he noted.

"Well, thanks to you, he looks sound enough to carry us both to Port Anatole, if we take it slowly and rest often. We can make it by nightfall."

With the fire elemental back in its home, she closed the lantern door, shoulders sagging. "I don't suppose I could talk you into letting me go."

He went and crouched beside her. *Ouch.* No, crouching was too painful. He sat heavily and took the lantern from her, setting it aside so he could take her hands in his. She didn't refuse, but she didn't meet him halfway either. Her hands lay limp and cold as old lettuce, and she wouldn't meet his eye.

"Those hunters won't be the only ones the Convocation sends," he said gently. "They tracked you this far; others can do the same. The Convocation wants you retrieved at all costs. I don't think they'll ever stop trying." He hesitated, wondering how much to tell her. "Veronica, that proctor—she said some scary stuff about punishing you and how a recalcitrant familiar must be disciplined and retrained. That's what those hunters were taking you to."

She nodded stiffly, resignation in the lines of her body. Taking a breath, she raised her head, searching his face with green eyes gone thoughtful, even sad. "And what is *your* plan for me, Lord Phel?"

His entire "plan" had been to get to her first—a qualified success there—and talk to her, which wasn't getting him anywhere. "I'm taking you back to Meresin with me," he decided out loud, falling back on his original plan. She might hate him, but his reasons for applying for her hadn't changed. He'd known from the beginning that his marriage would be for ambition rather than for love, even if he'd sentimentally hoped for more. "I can protect you there," he added, knowing the words were inadequate.

She tugged her hands away and stood. "We've got a ways to go, so we might as well start."

"That easily?" he asked, eyeing her, not trusting her quick capitulation.

Tugging viciously on the collar, she rounded on him. "Where am I going to go like *this*?" she hissed. "How can I escape if you and those hunters can track me? Even if I somehow persuade you to let me go, *they* never will. You said it yourself. I've lost, and there's no way for me to win. I might as well start resigning myself to my fate."

Gabriel rubbed the back of his neck, wishing viciously that he felt just a little less like complete shit. When he'd imagined having this conversation, it had gone much better. Pushing creakily to his feet, he clucked to Vale to come over. His tack had been cleaned and oiled, yet another task Veronica had quietly handled. He slipped the bridle over the horse's head.

"Why did you put yourself up for the Betrothal Trials if you didn't want this?" he demanded, buckling the straps. Somehow, he'd ended up as the villain here when he'd entered into the deal thinking they at least had the same goals. The Convocation's arcane customs weren't his doing; he was just playing by the rules to restore House Phel. *There is nothing civilized about this situation. It's a fancy veneer plastered over a barbaric ritual.* "I asked you that night why you were engaging in the Trials if you thought they were so barbaric, and you said because you wanted to control your own destiny."

"Yeah," she drawled, "that didn't work out so well for me." She pointed to the collar, in case he'd forgotten.

Gabriel set his teeth and arranged the saddle pad on Vale's back, verifying that nothing would chafe the horse's wounds. The one positive of Vale being injured in full tack was that none of his injuries were under it. "Need I reiterate that I didn't put that obscene thing on you? I said I'd figure out how to get it off." He lifted the saddle and halted as agony lanced down his side, and nearly whimpering at the shock of pain.

"Oh, give me that," Veronica snarled, wresting the saddle from him easily and lifting it onto Vale's back. "I was serious that I'm not fixing your stitches if you rip them out. I had a moment of weakness, because I was stupid and sentimental and felt bad that you got wounded rescuing me from those *things*. If you pass out on me again, though, I might just leave you lying here and try my luck on my own. How much worse could it be?" she muttered to herself, tightening the girth.

"Worse," he ground out. "From what that Convocation proctor said, *much* worse."

"I only have your word for that, and what's *that* worth?" she retorted in the same tone, walking Vale a couple of steps until he blew out a breath.

Gabriel released a breath at the same time, unaccountably wounded by that accusation. "Lady Veronica Elal," he said through his teeth, "I have never once lied to you, nor have I given you any reason to think I had or would. I'd venture that you know what the Convocation will and will not do far better than I."

She winced as she finished the final securing of the girth. "You're right, Lord Phel. I apologize for that. I am… not in a good frame of mind."

"I can understand that." He eyed the stirrup, wondering if he'd be able to get himself in the saddle. She was right that he needed a healer. "I know you must have had a good reason to run, but I think we can help each other. We can work this out."

"What is there to work out?" she asked bluntly.

"Us," he replied simply.

"'Us' is a done deal. There's nothing to work out. I belong to you by Convocation law, and you've regained physical possession of your merchandise, so all is *worked out* in your favor."

He sighed. "Won't you talk to me about this?"

"You're not in shape for any kind of conversation," she replied, sounding more weary than mean as she stroked Vale's neck pensively. "Let's get you up on Vale and back to Port Anatole. We can talk when you're not bleeding out."

He glanced down at the bandages she'd wrapped him in, wincing at the bright-red blood soaking through the old. "Probably a good idea."

It took some doing, but he made it into the saddle—with a lot of help from her. When he offered her a hand, she shook her head. "I'll walk. Vale's hurt, too, and doesn't need more of a burden than you are."

He winced at that, feeling like a burden, indeed. And a villain. Not to mention a brute who rode while his lady—wearing a collar and leash—was forced to walk. "Maybe we can take turns," he ventured.

"I can walk, Lord Phel," she said curtly, "while you can barely keep upright. Just do your best to stay on. Spare me having to care for my enemy more than necessary."

He rather thought she'd muttered that last for herself and not for his ears. Still, he hated that it had come to this. He'd be married to a woman who regarded him as an enemy.

Somehow, that just figured. His entire life, staying true to theme.

# ~ 12 ~

THEY MADE IT to Port Anatole by sunset, though just barely. Gabriel had also managed not to fall out of the saddle, though that had also been a near thing. He'd insisted on dismounting several times, to rest Vale and to answer the call of nature—and managed both without Nic's help. She still had to help him back into the saddle. That was unfortunate, as she was required to lay hands on his muscular body to do it, which should not have been distracting in his current health and her dire predicament.

Yet, distracting it was. His cool, silvery depths drew her in like a moth to flame—knowing she'd be immolated and still unable to stop herself. Worse, he seemed unaware of his effect on her. All his "we can work this out" and "talk to me about your feelings," as if he didn't know he had only to look at her with those wizard-black eyes and she longed to kneel at his feet.

She'd had one window of opportunity to escape him, and now she never could. Even if he'd agreed to let her go, Nic suspected she would've found herself trailing after him like an abandoned puppy. After she'd taken such pride in her self-control, too.

It was all so lowering.

It had also begun to rain, a steady and sharply chilling spring rain that turned the dirt road to slop that she and Vale both skidded over. Soon she was covered in muck and miserably wet. To add insult to injury, her wet skin chafed fiercely under the metal collar, which grew ever colder and heavier.

She led Vale to Missus Ryma's inn—because where else could they go?—feeling very much like she was slinking back, tail tucked between her legs. Looking like a drenched and mud-spattered waif. Oh, and with a collar around her neck to demonstrate her physical humiliation in case anyone missed her metaphorical one.

Missus Ryma—apparently warned by the interested observers noting the approach of their odd party—met them at the steps to the inn. She took in Nic, her collar, the tired horse, and wounded warrior in one sweeping glance and took over in her practical way, for which Nic would be forever grateful.

Summoning the strapping lads who handled the heavy work of the inn, she had them lift the barely conscious Gabriel from the saddle and carry him to a room. Vale was handed over to the stable groom, who also served as animal healer. Nic, she tucked under her arm and hustled into the kitchen. Once she'd sent for Inytta for Gabriel, Missus Ryma sat down at the table where Nic nursed a mug of nurturing broth.

"How much of that blood is yours?" Missus Ryman asked, and Nic's heart turned over that *that* was her first question.

"None of it." She took a bracing sip of the broth, wishing it was wine. "Most of it is Lord Phel's. He is my husband," she added, figuring she might as well just come out with that, and keep it simple while she was at it.

"Ah. Then this calls for wine." Missus Ryma called out to one of her servers, who brought over a full carafe of a hearty red. Not Elal wine, but decent anyway. "Good thing I had the boys put him in my best room. Thought he looked like quality."

Nic winced. "I don't know how much coin he has on him." Or at all. At least Nic's carefully hoarded coin could serve to pay Inytta for the healing—and wasn't that perfect irony, that her escape fund should be spent on healing her captor?

Missus Ryma waved that away. "I'm sure he's good for it. Besides, I'm otherwise full tonight—had nothing else." She eyed the collar. "I can ask Inytta to keep the fellow asleep a few days. Long enough for you to escape."

Nic tugged on the collar, feeling much like an animal flailing at a trap, knowing it couldn't get free but irrationally exhausting herself trying anyway. "Lord Phel didn't do this," she explained, not sure why she was excusing him. Maybe because Gabriel was her enemy, but he wasn't evil. "He saved me from some... hunters"—she smiled mirthlessly to herself at the word choice—"who put this on me. It's magic, so I have to find the right person to take it off again."

"Hmm. Not easy, then, having so many after you." Missus Ryma patted her hand kindly. "I'd offer you your old room, but with this miserable weather, even that's taken. You could sleep in with my daughters, though."

Nic's eyes dampened at the kindness. What an exhausted mess she was. "Thank you, but I'll sleep in Lord Phel's room."

She had to face that she belonged to him and that this would be her life now. Besides, if he woke to find her missing, he'd likely rampage around the inn, waking everyone in his search for her. Her desire to stay in his room certainly wasn't because she was concerned about him, or that she hungered to be near him. This time, the copper snake's fangs barely made a dent in her overall pain.

"Take the wine with you, then. I'll have a hot bath sent up, and two full dinners as soon as they're ready. And have Inytta look you over, too. Can't hurt and might help."

"Thank you." Aware that she'd interrupted those dinner preparations, the other staff scrambling with the full house and to fill in for Missus Ryma's missing hands, Nic pushed to her feet and fished out her bag of coin.

"Keep your coin." Missus Ryma sniffed, indignant. "Your high-and-mighty husband wanted you so badly as to chase you down, then he can pay for your keep."

Nic smiled at the innkeeper's wink and picked up the carafe and her glass.

"You're sure now?" Missus Ryma said, standing also. "There's other ways of dealing with unwanted husbands, if you know what I mean."

Nic blinked at her, processing the broad hint. Did she mean she'd have him killed?

"The sea takes so many," Missus Ryma added with mock sorrow. "So many lost without a trace, all the time."

She tried to consider that option. If Nic had truly rid herself of sentimentality, she'd take that offer without another thought. But the hunters would still be after her. And, all in all,

Gabriel didn't deserve to die simply because he'd been lucky enough to plant a child in her. He'd been playing by the rules. It wasn't his fault that she'd trapped herself. She wanted to be free of him, but not enough to arrange his death. "I'm sure," she said. "We're working out our differences."

When she said the words, oddly enough, they didn't even sound like a lie.

GABRIEL WOKE, THIS time frowning at the slanted, polished wood ceiling of a cozy bedroom, the sound of rain sleeting against the roof. He lay in a comfortable bed, warm under a fluffy comforter, and he was blessedly free of pain. Turning his head on the down-filled pillow, he spotted Nic—no, Veronica, as she'd never given him permission to use her nickname—sitting on a low stool by a crackling fire. A full glass of wine sat on the floor beside her. She wore a gauzy nightgown that showed her lush figure in silhouette, and she had her hair down, combing the long fall of it dry.

She looked so lovely and relaxed, at peace, as she never was when dealing with him. With stark awareness, he realized that, from the first moment he'd laid eyes on her, she had treated him as the enemy. He'd known she was prickly and on guard, but he'd put that down to how the other bastards had abused her. Not that she'd hated and feared *him*, in particular.

He saw it, the moment she realized he was awake and

watching her. Her entire aspect shifted, going from calm, even languid woman enjoying a glass of wine and a warm fire on a wretched night, to wary prey facing the predator. Moving slowly—warily?—she turned her head to look at him, eyes lambent green as an owl's catching the lantern light. The hideous collar still hung around her neck, though it looked like she'd woven the chain around it more neatly.

"We're at the inn at Port Anatole," she informed him before he thought to ask. "The healer has seen to you, but she's not a wizard, so there's only so much she could do. You need to lie still and rest."

"Vale?" he asked, his voice rough with disuse.

She smiled a little, affection in it—for the horse, not him. "He's a real trooper. And in the stables, being cared for. You're paying extra for the best box stall, extra grain, and veterinary care. I hope you're not totally broke."

"He's worth it," Gabriel conceded, wondering exactly how much coin he had left. "I'm surprised to see *you* still here."

"And not in a hidey-hole in some barge trying to escape? No thank you." She shuddered delicately. "I don't care to repeat that experience, especially when I end up suffering for no gain."

So that was how she'd stowed away. It did sound harrowing. He wanted to apologize, but that seemed like the wrong sentiment.

"There's food, if you feel like eating," she said into the awkward silence.

"I would like that. Thank you." He shifted to sit up.

"Wait and let me help," she snapped, setting down the

comb and picking up her wine. She took a long drink, as if she needed the fortification, and set it on the nearby table. With her body silhouetted against the firelight, he could see every detail of her body through the sheer gown, even to the V at the juncture of her curving thighs. Gabriel quickly averted his gaze from the alluring sight, feeling like he was invading her privacy. Then she was at his bedside, slipping an arm under his shoulders to lift him enough that she could mound more pillows behind him. "Good?"

He nodded. Then—as soon as she turned her back—shifted to adjust them himself. She whirled, giving him a narrow green glare. "Inytta fixed you up, and her stitches are leagues better than mine, but you're still to be careful lest you pull them out. You popped at least half of mine on the ride here." She set a tray on his lap, the scent of Missus Ryma's excellent food making his mouth water.

"I don't want you to have to wait on me," he explained, though it came out sounding grumpy.

"Why not? That's what you bought and paid for."

He focused on chewing the succulent chicken in pastry and wine sauce, so as not to set his teeth in aggravation—or snap back a similar retort. Once he chewed and swallowed, he glanced at her, standing by the bed and holding her wineglass, watching him moodily. "Is there any of that to share?" He nodded at the wine.

She glanced at the glass she held, as if she'd forgotten about it. "Yes, but Inytta gave you some powerful herbs to dull the pain. I'm not sure they would mix well."

He raised a brow. "Do I need to do anything useful for the

remainder of the night, or am I under orders to stay in bed?"

"Good point." She went to the table where she'd gotten the food, poured a glass, topped hers off, and brought it back, giving him an arch look. "*I* certainly have no expectations of you, since you've already planted a child in my belly. Of course, if you do feel up to the task, you have the right to use my body any way you wish."

He sipped the wine, letting its warming qualities disperse her chilly accusations, and decided not to take her bait. He could assure her he had no intention of commanding her intimate affections, but demonstrating his restraint would go much further in winning her trust. If that were possible. "How are things with the pregnancy—are you feeling well that way?"

"I'm taking good care of your property. Inytta verified that all is well, so you need have no concern there."

Despite his best intentions, he set his teeth and carefully set down the wine. Giving her a long look, he waited for her to shift uncomfortably under the weight of his stare.

"Lady Veronica," he said softly, "you've made it abundantly clear that you are unwilling to discuss your reasons for running from our union." When she opened her mouth, he held up a hand to stop her. "Besides that you don't want to be married to me. I've offered to hear you out, but unless you are willing to explain why you apparently changed your mind about being my wife, familiar, and mother of my child, then would you kindly agree to leave off sniping at me about it? Either be honest with me and give me the full story—which is my first choice, by the way—or drop the subject."

She closed her mouth with a snap, glaring at him, then

sipped her wine. "Consider the subject dropped."

As much as he looked forward to a break from her ceaseless needling, he wished she'd chosen to talk to him. They would get there—and he'd start wearing her down now. Water eroded even the strongest rock eventually. Never mind that her stubborn will was granite.

"In return," she added, "can we not discuss my pregnancy?"

He regarded her thoughtfully, very much wanting to point out that not talking about it wouldn't make it disappear. Unless she'd miscarried and didn't want to say so. "It's a bargain." He patted the bed. "Why don't you sit? We can talk of other things."

"Congenial conversation?" she queried wryly. But was that a hint of a smile?

"I've heard it can be enjoyable," he replied lightly.

With a shrug, she went around to the other side of the bed and crawled onto it, balancing her wineglass deftly and surprising him by perching cross-legged in the middle of the bed. At least this way she was no longer so temptingly outlined by the firelight. That she had no intention of resuming amorous activities with him came as no surprise—not that he was up to it tonight anyway—but he still harbored regret. *This is what you get for playing the Convocation game*, he reminded himself. *You didn't go into this to please yourself, but out of duty to House Phel.*

Veronica regarded him with a carefully neutral expression, her lady-of-the-house demeanor—though she didn't pull it off quite so well with her unbound hair cascading over her white gown, drying into curls that seemed to stir with their own life. Only the hideous collar marred her beauty—that and the shadows under her eyes. She looked young, even waifish. Only the mature intelligence in her glinting green eyes showed otherwise. He ate his delicious chicken, considering what tack to take with her. Once again, she'd had a chance to run, to escape him during the hours he'd been unconscious. He barely recalled arriving at the inn, much less anything after. But she hadn't run. Instead, she was here, in the room with him, apparently for the night. At least she didn't hate him enough to avoid him entirely.

"The collar is chafing your skin," he said, noting the angry skin bleeding in places over her winged collarbones.

She grimaced, lifting it and running her fingers beneath. "I've always been sensitive to any metal but gold, and this is particularly poor quality. Apparently, the hunters aren't that well funded. Or they don't care."

Likely they didn't care. "Maybe we can wrap it in cloth until we get it off of you."

"Not a bad idea," she conceded. "I had a hot bath while you slept, and it helped to wash and oil my skin. Wrapping it would be good."

He studied the thing. "If nothing else, we can detach the leash."

"Please. Though it won't change anything about the—" She pressed her lips shut over the words.

The invisible chains that restrained her, he supposed she'd stopped herself from saying. At least she was honoring the agreement. "So, this Inytta," he said, trying for a neutral topic, "she is a healer, but not a wizard of House Refoel?"

"Right. There's not much magic in Wartson, besides imports like the lanterns and other simple conveniences. I met Inytta when I arrived in Port Anatole. I fixed her pitcher, which cleanses any fluid she puts inside. Handy tool for a healer. Otherwise, she's limited to nonmagical skills, but she does quite well, all things considered."

"The pitcher is enchanted?" He recalled Veronica telling him that he shouldn't have made his enchanted silver blade. Thinking of it, he groaned. He'd put it away covered in gore more than a day and night ago. It would be corroded.

Veronica followed his thought with uncanny insight. "Like your silver dagger? I cleaned it for you, by the way, along with the rest of your gear. And I tried it on this Iblis lock, with no luck. Maybe you can do better—I don't know what all you did to make it."

"Let's try now."

"Finish your meal first. You need sustenance, and I've had it on this long. Anyway, the pitcher is occupied by a water elemental, trained by an Elal wizard. It just needed a bit of upkeep. Elementals can get sulky, particularly the water ones."

Interesting. This conversation was probably the most she'd ever said to him. She might be a little tipsy, which could only aid him in breaking through her walls. "So you can manipulate elementals like the wizards in your family?" He still wasn't entirely clear on the difference between wizards and familiars, except that he'd thought that familiars couldn't actively wield magic.

She cocked her head in curiosity. "You're quite the puzzle,

Lord Phel—what you do and don't know."

"Easier to assume I don't know," he offered with grim amusement. He'd read every legible book in the House Phel library, but they focused on magic rather than Convocation laws, and were two hundred years out of date on top of that. He'd idealistically hoped winning a familiar and lady for House Phel would help remedy the holes in his knowledge.

"Hmm." Veronica clearly didn't think much of his ignorance, and he didn't blame her. "No, I can't manipulate elementals like I could if I were a wizard." A sigh escaped her, and he tasted the bitter grief in it. "An Elal wizard can summon spirits, tame and bind them to a task. The more powerful the wizard, the more powerful the spirits they can command. But anyone with Elal magic has an affinity for spirits. They... adore us, for want of a better term. That's just how the magic works—they're attracted to it in us, wizard or familiar. Elementals are pretty simple, so it's fairly easy for me to know what will please them, and so I can coax them to do what I want—especially if it's what they've already been tasked to do."

"That's why you're so good with Vale."

"Vale is a horse, not a spirit," she corrected with some asperity.

He knew that, but he didn't know how to frame his actual question. Veronica watched him with some amusement, swirling the wine in her nearly empty glass. "I'm getting more. You?"

"Sure." He handed her his empty glass—she hadn't given him much—and he couldn't help watching as she uncoiled to knee-walk off the bed. She wore nothing beneath the sleeping gown, and he caught a flash of slim thighs and dark nether hair when she unfolded her legs. The sight sent a bolt of longing through him, which he sternly doused in mental cold water. He wanted nothing more than to bury himself in her fire, to recover something of that intimacy they'd shared.

Or that he'd enjoyed and she'd endured. There. That thought sufficed to cool his desire.

"See, you're thinking that an animal spirit is like an elemental," she said as she walked around the bed, oblivious to his turbulent thoughts. "And you're not entirely wrong. Dealing with a spirit isn't entirely unlike working with an animal. Really, though, any talent I have that way comes from the Ariel side of the family. My father's mother was House Ariel."

Ah, this was something he'd wondered about. He accepted the glass she brought him, noting she'd given him a more generous portion this time. Did that mean she was less angry? She was certainly more forthcoming than ever.

"Done with the tray?" She eyed his clean plate. "Unless you want to eat the cutlery."

"I'm done. That was good, thank you."

"Thank Missus Ryma. I can order a second plate if you want?"

"No, that's plenty." Any more and he'd have a gut ache. Surreptitiously, he noted she stacked his plate on top of another. So she'd eaten, too. Good to know, since she seemed to get annoyed when he asked. "Bring me the dagger, and let's see to that leash at least," he said as she detoured to put another log on the fire.

She plucked up the blade and brought it to him, holding it out hilt first. Taking it, he recalled the moment he'd thought she might attack him—and how he'd been so dead on his feet she could've succeeded. She was unwinding the chain leash where she'd looped it around the collar, then rotated the whole thing and lifted her chin so he could see the lock.

Studying the mechanism, he continued the conversation. "This is something I don't understand about the Convocation. If the houses have been intermarrying all this time, why can the wizards of one family perform only one kind of magic?"

"Aha. The short answer is: That's not the case. Think about the Convocation scorecards. I know you saw mine. I assume you saw yours?"

He jerked his chin in agreement. He'd looked at it just long enough to verify his MP score was adequate to apply to restore House Phel, then tossed it in a drawer. As she seemed able to do, Veronica followed the thought, giving him a knowing smile, watching him down her long nose. "You barely glanced at it, didn't you?"

He shrugged, refusing to be embarrassed. The lock didn't seem to be responding, so he wedged the tip of the blade into the top link of the leash, whispering to the silver to release, which it did. The leash fell away, and he tossed it aside. She let out a sigh of relief, her breasts rising and falling with the breath, her nipples showing dark through the thin cloth. The scent of wine and roses thickened between them, and the urge to cup those breasts, stroke her nipples, to once again hear her moans of pleasure nearly overwhelmed him. Moans of faked pleasure, he reminded himself, clearing his throat and glancing up at her, to find her watching him warily again.

Moving with slow deliberation, so as not to alarm her further, he set the enchanted blade on the table beside the bed and picked up the wine. "I'm sorry, the lock isn't responding. We'll have to try something else tomorrow."

She considered him a moment, as if he'd surprised her. Then she stepped away, not quite fleeing, but close to it, and took up a strip of cloth he recognized as being his shirt in happier times. "I'm sure *you* memorized my scorecard," he suggested.

"Everybody does," she said, deftly winding the cloth around the collar. It wasn't that huge—about the width of three of his fingers—but looked large and far too heavy on her slender neck. "In the Convocation, it's like knowing someone's rank and house. The columns on the cards represent the major categories of magic, the rows are the subgroups that you showed strength in, the number your magic potential score in that category and subgroup. They only include the subgroups that we show any potential above a three in." She waggled her eyebrows. "I have a very long scorecard."

He recalled the many rows on her card but hadn't known what that meant, just that her overall score indicated high potential. His card had been quite short. Though she was being playful—definitely tipsy from the wine—he didn't respond in kind to the innuendo. "Then you have potential in many categories."

"Subgroups," she corrected. Finished with the cloth, she retrieved her wine and this time didn't bother to go around the bed, instead crawling over his legs back to her spot. "That's part of why I'm considered a high-potential familiar, along with the numerical scores. I could work well with a wizard from most any house. Familiars are paired by the Convocation with wizards that will be able to use their skills, and they then become part of that family, and house."

She went quiet, swirling her wine, and Gabriel spoke quickly to divert her from dwelling on that. "Do wizards not move to other houses?"

Blinking at him, she surfaced from her dark thoughts. "They do, but not often. Most wizards have MP scores in only one or two categories. Or their scores are overwhelmingly high in one category and unremarkable in others. Usually, a wizard's major talent is their family house's magic, and then they just stay there. You know, enter the family business, rise in the ranks, maybe take over as lord or lady of the house someday."

"But if a wizard has high scores in a different category than their family house, or scores high in multiple categories?"

"That's when it gets interesting. The houses licensed for that category of magic will offer to take those wizards on. Sometimes if a wizard has multiple potentials, it becomes a bidding war—and they get offered all kinds of incentives to join that house. Once a wizard contracts with a house, they're not allowed to use their subsidiary talents for anything but a nonprofit hobby—and even then, they don't flaunt the ability."

"Ah." He nodded and sipped his wine. Now that she'd relaxed around him, they were actually getting along. It was kind of lovely, sharing this cozy room with her, the rain now pouring outside, the fire crackling merrily, his belly pleasantly full and his head drifting with wine and pain herbs.

"That's why there's the appearance that, say, only House Refoel wizards can perform healing magic," she continued. "Many wizards in other houses have a smattering of healing magic, but they're not allowed to use it professionally. House Refoel holds the monopoly."

"That's why you were concerned that I created a magical artifact by enchanting the silver blade."

She toasted him with her glass. "It's particularly sticky when you cross a High House's license, as opposed to a lower-tier house. I'm certainly not going to tell House El-Adrel, but if any of their wizards come across your blade—or anything else like it that you may have made—then House Phel will owe them a penalty. I assume House Phel can't afford much in the way of penalties."

This was why he needed her. Or someone like her, but it was too late for him to take anyone else for his lady wife. "You assume correctly," he replied grimly, draining his wine and setting the glass on the table beside the big bed. He wondered what kind of penalty House Refoel would exact if they found out about the fertility magic he'd used to ensure success with Veronica—or worse, what her reaction would be. Bad enough that she felt trapped with him by chance. She'd likely see his manipulating the Trials as the worst kind of cheating, and possibly the ultimate betrayal. He rubbed the back of his neck. "Do these penalties always take monetary form?"

"Depends. The Convocation trade council makes the decisions, and those can get ridiculously complicated. It could be that you'd owe El-Adrel a slice of trade from whatever House Phel sells." She frowned. "*Are* you selling anything? We couldn't find out much there."

Because there wasn't much to find out. "I'm still working on that part."

The look she gave him was almost pitying. "What were they before?"

"What do you mean?"

She sighed for his obtuseness. "Before House Phel… fell." She kept a straight face, but a lilt in her voice told him she'd heard the jokes. "What was your major export?"

"I have no idea."

"Moon and water magic don't immediately inspire obvious ideas for marketable commodities," she pointed out.

"I'm aware," he answered in a dry tone.

She gave him a wry smile. "What did the records show?"

He hesitated. "I think you may have an exaggerated idea of the state of House Phel's records." And the house itself, perhaps.

She rolled her eyes. "The Convocation records," she clarified almost patiently. "In the archives? At Convocation Center. You should have been given access to them when you claimed status as Lord Phel." She studied his face with widening eyes. "They didn't tell you."

"No." Anger began a slow burn behind his eyes. "That would've been helpful."

"No doubt." She considered, finishing her own wine. "Do you want more?"

"I've had enough." He thought she had, too, but he had

zero intention of saying so.

"Good thing, as the carafe is empty, and I'm not inclined to order another. I'm exhausted." She crawled off the bed again, snagged his empty glass, and deposited it with hers, then set the entire tray outside the door.

With chagrin, he recalled that she'd walked all the way to Port Anatole, and that was after running from the hunters—and him—and spending a night outdoors. "Will you share the bed with me?" he asked tentatively.

She snorted with derision, fiddling with the copper snake bracelet. "You might be my enemy, but I'm not an idiot. The only reason I stayed was for the warm, dry bed on a miserable night." She put a screen across the fire. "There's always your ever-full water flask."

"What do you mean?" He had trouble following the mercurial leaps of her mind when he was sober, and he was feeling definitely light-headed—though perhaps as much from the dizzying thought of her in the bed with him as anything.

"Your water flask," she repeated, sending the lantern elementals to sleep. "That's a neat trick. A lot of people would pay good coin for one of those."

"Doesn't it count as an enchanted artifact?"

"Now you're catching on. No, you'd argue before the trade council that the bulk of the magic lies in the ever-replenishing water—squarely in House Phel's traditional aegis—and that the flask is simply the container. You can't exactly sell handfuls of water. Say, can you do wells?"

"I've never tried."

She came to him and began pulling away pillows, leaving

him with one that she helped him settle onto. He did his best to ignore her barely clad breasts brushing his bare skin. "That could be a lucrative service," she observed, and he had to drag his thoughts from her sensual beauty to the topic at hand. Not at hand—not his hands on her, but the topic of conversation.

"Speaking of which," she said, "why didn't you use wizardry on the hunters instead of going for the manual chopping-them-up method?"

Why hadn't he? "I didn't think of it. Water and moon magic isn't much good for combat either."

She flipped back the covers and slid under, bunching a pillow under her head with her arm crooked beneath as she lay on her side. Her black hair spilled over the white sheets and down-filled comforter, her skin gilded by the low firelight, eyes the shadowed green of an ancient forest. "You have to start thinking of these things, Lord Phel."

He knew it. "Why are you helping me now?" he asked softly, taking the chance. "If you see me as your enemy, why are you thinking of ideas for my house's future trade, giving me valuable information?"

Her eyes went opaque, face unreadable. "Regardless of my feelings, Phel is now my house too. I'm legally your familiar and wife, so I might as well start doing my job."

"You haven't contracted with House Phel," he pointed out.

"Familiars don't contract with houses," she replied flatly. "We become the property of a wizard, then go where they go. I belong to you, Lord Phel, whether either of us likes it, and I'd rather belong to a wealthy wizard than an impoverished one."

"You called me by my name before," he ventured. "It

seems odd for my wife to call me 'Lord Phel.' You could call me Gabriel."

"I don't think that's a good idea." She turned over to her other side, giving him her back.

A lock of her long hair had fallen near his hand on the comforter, and he touched it, coiling the silky curl around his finger, gently, so she wouldn't know. "Veronica?" he whispered. "I don't want to be your enemy."

She didn't reply, and he fell asleep with his fingers in her hair.

# ~ 13 ~

"YOU *BOUGHT* AN entire boat." Nic stared at the unprepossessing barge, then eyed Gabriel, who was coaxing Vale aboard. "You know, you don't act like a guy who spent his house's fortune purchasing a familiar he couldn't afford."

Gabriel gave her a dry look. "I considered the price of the barge well spent in recovering that investment. And would you stop saying I bought you? I paid the application fee to the Betrothal Trials, that's all."

"It's the same thing," she noted, hefting her satchel and carrying it aboard.

He caught her arm as she went past, his grip firm, exciting the longing for him she'd been fighting to suppress. "Lady Veronica," he said, spacing his words so he'd sound patient, though his frustration with her simmered beneath, "I thought we agreed you'd stop with these remarks."

He was right and she knew it. She was just so pissed at herself. The night before had been a mistake. Not only had she turned down what was likely her last opportunity to escape the man, she'd gotten tipsy—she blamed the exhaustion—and chatted merrily with her lord and master. She couldn't even remember everything they'd discussed, except that she'd been all kinds of forthcoming. *Congenial conversation*, she sneered to herself. Clearly another trap for the unwary.

But he hadn't made any move to have sex with her. There had been some moments when she'd been sure he'd been about to lay hands on her, and she'd teetered on the fine edge of terror and desire, poised to flee—or kneel in abject submission. Now that she was in his presence again, the Fascination grew by the moment. She shivered with need just being near him. When he looked at her that certain way, she wanted nothing more than to curl up in his lap. He'd called her beautiful once, and the caress of his wizard-black eyes actually made her feel that way. Her skin remembered his touch, craving it and prickling to attention at his nearness. She hungered to have him inside her. For him to whisper those sweet words in her ear.

Probably she should just stop fighting the pull and enjoy being possessed. Her familiar nature clearly craved it from him. When he'd held her leash in his hands, the rush of desire had nearly overwhelmed her. Then he'd tossed it away, making the choice not to touch her. She'd been almost disappointed. Even now, she wanted to lean into his grip on her arm, taste his mouth, and give herself over to those strong hands. Be his.

"Let me go," she said, and what had sounded like a cool command in her head came out as a breathy plea. In her mind, she begged him, not to release, but to take and—

But he complied immediately, holding up his hands to show he meant no harm. "Besides," he said, gaze lingering on her mouth, as if he'd been thinking about kissing her, "the dowry your father promised more than compensates for my application fee. If anything, you bought me."

That perspective was so absurd that the anger at least cleared her desire-fogged mind. She nearly retorted that Convocation law didn't see it that way, but he was right—unless she wanted to explain herself, she had to stop sniping at him. Too bad, as reminding both of them of her status kept her anger and resolve alive—a necessary reminder of why she couldn't give in to her Fascination with him. And Elal didn't give up without a fight. She'd about worn the fangs to a nub on the copper snake bracelet.

When she didn't reply, he took the satchel from her and put it inside the ramshackle cabin perched in the middle of the otherwise empty barge, then began divesting Vale of his tack. There was an overhang for Vale to keep him dry, and a manger that Gabriel filled with hay, a bucket of water attached. The rain had slackened, but it still drizzled enough to make the weather miserable. Nic explored the barge, which didn't take long, empty as it was, then checked out the little cabin. It was small but would keep them dry. There were benches to sit on, and a couple of cots for sleeping. Overall, the arrangement was not conducive to her resolve to avoid Gabriel as much as possible.

"There's no elemental pilot," she told Gabriel when he entered the cabin. He unclasped the House Phel brooch holding his cloak closed, pocketed it, then hung the water-beaded garment on a hook to dry beside her own poor garment. He took a moment to finger the threadbare cloth of her cloak.

"You need a warmer cloak," he said. "Meresin isn't as wintry as Elal, but the journey there will be cold."

"Yes, well, a girl fleeing for her life doesn't exactly get a choice of cloaks," she returned, then pointed a finger at him. "Don't give me that *look*. That wasn't sniping at you or my status as your familiar. Unless you want to forbid me from saying anything but *please, sir*, and *thank you, sir*, then you…" She trailed off, realizing that he could indeed command exactly that.

Gabriel strode over to her, jaw clenched. But, though he reached for her, he stopped short of seizing her again. Still, menace coiled around her in sharp silver swirls. Curse her, that sense of menace only aroused her need further.

"I would *never*," he said in a harshly quiet voice, the anger in it so intense that she'd almost prefer that he shouted. "I saw how your father silenced your mother. I remember what you said, about your suitor who barely spoke to you except to give instructions. I'm not that man. I've never *once* given you any reason to believe I'd treat you that way." He took a deep breath and a step back, his hands in fists by his side. "I don't know what I did to cause you to loathe me as you clearly do, that you think so little of me, but I've never told you to not to speak. In fact, I've practically begged you to talk to me."

Swamped by shame at his words, and helplessly drawn to his ferocity, Nic had to steel herself not to plead with him to forgive her. "I know," she managed to squeak out.

He looked past her, steadying himself, then focused on her again. "I only asked that you drop these slicing hints and insults because you seem to be using them instead of explaining why you jeopardized everything to escape me. Were you truly fleeing for your life?" His black gaze searched her face. "You can tell me. I want to know the truth. I want to help you."

She took a breath. Let it out again. What would he say if she told him? *You can't help me because you are the danger. I ran because I'm already Fascinated beyond redemption. I'm halfway in love with you, and when I fall completely, you'll own me in every way. I won't ever be able to tell you no or deny your least wish.* If she told him that, he'd know the power he held over her. The legalities were nothing compared to his emotional and sexual hold on her.

Perhaps that's why the Convocation continued to prefer the Betrothal Trials, it occurred to her. Yes, it proved fertility, but if the Fascination was sparked by the sexual pull, then it would subdue a willful familiar all the faster. Still, she was more than a sexual being. She had a mind and a will, and she would not willingly hand him the tools to reduce her to ultimate submission.

"I enjoy your wit," he finally said when she managed to say nothing, his smile wry, "even when it's aimed at me. I don't want you silenced. I find *congenial conversation* with you most stimulating."

Despite everything, she couldn't help wanting to return that smile. "Good thing, as we might be on this barge for the rest of our lives—they go that slow. And this one looks more rickety than most."

"The price was nicely low," he told her. "But maybe it can be fixed up for House Phel to use for that export trade you're dreaming up."

Nic surveyed the dilapidated cabin, happy enough to take the change of topic. "I would hope it was cheap, the shape it's in. I'm frankly surprised it's afloat. Besides which, my initial point remains pertinent: We're going nowhere without an elemental pilot. The one that brought you here must've been improperly bound because it's gone."

He grinned, the smile lighting his face, which otherwise tended toward solemn. "The barge was cheaper without it, and you don't need a puny elemental when you have a water wizard." He pointed out the porthole, and Nic registered with considerable surprise that the last of the Port Anatole harbor was streaming past. The barge was gliding, so smoothly she hadn't felt it, and about ten times faster than any other barge she'd seen.

"You're moving us?"

"I'm moving the water, and *it* is moving the barge along," he corrected, clearly enjoying himself.

"How long can you withstand the magic drain, though?"

"I did all right getting to Port Anatole. Going fast also means I don't have to sustain the magic as long."

"No wonder you caught me so fast," she muttered.

"It took me an extra half-day to purchase the barge or I would have gotten to you sooner." He lifted a hand, slowly, and when she didn't flinch, he stroked the bruised skin of her throat. "I wanted to get to you before the hunters did. I'm sorry that I failed you, that they hurt you."

She'd gone breathless, her mouth dry. His touch sent shivers through her, the fire leaping to flush her skin. "It's not your fault that I ran."

"Isn't it?" His expression darkened again. "I can sense that you're afraid of me."

She should've expected that. "Not because of anything you did," she offered tentatively.

"Then it's something about who I am," he suggested, black gaze searching her face. "Or would you have tried to escape whichever wizard succeeded?"

He was getting too close to the truth, so she stepped out of reach, and he let her go. She tried to tell herself she wasn't disappointed about that, staring out of the porthole blindly, the sea gray with misting rain, the horizon blurring seamlessly into the sky. "What did you mean, that you saw how Papa silenced Maman?"

Rustling behind her indicated he'd sat on a bench, weariness and pain in the grunt he let out. Nic had to remind herself he was still convalescing. Inytta had pronounced Gabriel miraculously recovered, enough so that Nic figured he had some healing magic in him. She'd already suspected as much, as her stitches wouldn't have held him as well as they did if his natural abilities hadn't stepped into the gap. The night before, Inytta had barely contained her incredulity at the sight of Nic's sewing job, advising Nic to leave stitches in flesh to the professionals in the future.

Gabriel, relieved to get out of bed, had been chomping at the bit to be gone from Wartson, though he thought the one pack of hunters had been all there was. Nic had found no excuse to delay. Dragging her feet wouldn't change her fate.

"When I came for you, at House Elal," he said, and his voice had a different edge to it. She turned, leaning her back against the rough planks, giving him her attention. He rubbed the back of his neck thoughtfully, a sign he was agitated, then sat forward, leaning forearms on his knees and lacing his fingers together. "Your lady mother was upset about your disappearance, understandably so, and Lord Elal told her to be quiet. When she didn't immediately obey, he… Well, he made it sound like a suggestion, that she 'take her alternate form.' She became agitated, saying she wanted to be able to speak." He flicked his gaze up at Nic in wry acknowledgment. "And she turned into a cat. I think he made her do it?"

The man really knew so little of their ways. It had to be deliberate sabotage by the Convocation, keeping him as ignorant as possible. They'd granted his application to restore House Phel, had adhered to the letter of the law about approving what he knew to ask for, but they truly didn't want him to succeed. More important, it became abundantly clear why Nic's contact in Port Anatole had never materialized. Had Maman been forced to remain as a cat all this time? Nic's stomach clenched at the thought. And all for naught.

"Did I upset you?" Gabriel frowned at her.

"No." She shook her head, then tried to shrug off the chill sickness. "I mean, I'm surprised they let you witness that little scene. It's usually more… private than that." Her poor maman. Nic went to sit on another bench, putting her back against the wall and drawing up her knees. "He did force her change. That's what wizards do. Familiars can't take our alternate forms on our own; a wizard must trigger the magic for us."

He considered that, seeming deeply unsettled, an odd expression on his face. "What is your alternate form?"

"I don't know, do I?" she replied evenly, trying to keep the sting out of it. "We'll find out when you trigger the change in me."

"Me?" More than unsettled—aghast, even horrified.

"You're my wizard now," she explained, feeling strangely gentle with him. "Once you bond me, you'll be able to trigger my alternate form. It is one of the positive incentives for a familiar to bond with a wizard."

"Then you... want to take an animal form?"

Nic wriggled to scratch her back against the planks. "For the most part, yes." She'd like to be able to fly, though there was no guarantee that her alternate form would have wings. It was a nice dream, much as Nic had grown wary of hoping for too much. Being trapped in a body without thumbs or words, or even much capacity for thought, though...

Gabriel watched her, looking like he wanted to say something, but he shook his head. Instead, he gestured at her wriggling. "Does your back itch?"

"Yes. The bath last night was nice, but I miss my oils. I'm a pampered daughter of a High House, if you'll recall."

"Let me scratch it for you." He turned to straddle the bench, patting the space in front of him.

She thought about refusing. She didn't want him to touch her again—and she wanted it too much. Something in the earnestness of his gaze and the sincerity of the offer also made her think he'd take it badly if she was that petty. Besides, her back did itch fiercely. She scooted over and sat in front of him, moving her long braid out of the way. He began with long, smooth scratching over her clothes, quickly zeroing in on the itchiest spots as she wriggled in pleasure.

"Would you be a cat, like your mother?" he asked, his voice a little gruff, though she wasn't sure what that indicated.

"Not necessarily. The animal forms are more individual than that. They don't follow family patterns."

"Can you change back to human form on your own?"

"No, sir," she replied cheerfully. "That's one of the ways a wizard controls their familiar. Our bonded wizards can keep us in alternate form for extended periods. It's a useful incentive to ensure good behavior." The explanation, learned by rote at Convocation Academy, came easily to her lips, so she was able to conceal how that aspect of wizard–familiar bonding horrified her.

"For how long?" he whispered, his voice holding the revulsion she hadn't expressed.

"Some wizards prefer to keep their familiars in their alternate form all the time unless they need them for magic work. That is one thing that saves us from being permanently kept as animals by those types—the wizard can't draw on our magic at all if we're in alternate form. They need us human for that."

"Why would you bond with a wizard at all if they can do that to you?" He was nearly growling now, his anger silver bright around them.

His scratching had slowed, so she turned to look over her shoulder at him. "Because we don't have many other viable options."

He regarded her gravely. "Except trying to escape."

"Which isn't an option after all," she replied in a quiet voice, "as we've discovered."

Lifting a hand slowly, he stroked her cheek, dark emotion in his eyes. She leaned into the caress, craving his touch and the silvery-cool soothing that suffused her. With him so close, his beautiful mouth was near enough that she need only cross a breath of distance to kiss him. He was watching her lips, too, the energy fulminating between them, molten with building heat.

"Veronica, I—" Gabriel broke off and leapt to his feet.

Crossing two strides to the door, he threw down the bar just as the latch moved. "Hunters," he snarled, drawing his sword. The door jerked and rattled against its hinges. Something thumped on the roof, jerking their gazes upward.

Nic ran to the porthole, belatedly aware of the hunters' feral and unsavory taint on her senses. "I see two, no—three more. And another crawling onto the deck." A snarling face popped up, fangs clashing against the glass, and she shrieked, jumping back and crashing against Gabriel, her heart pounding.

"Are you hurt?" His arm came around her, pulling her safe against him.

"No." She tried to catch her breath. "Just startled." How she *hated* those things.

The hunters pounded on the door. *Boom boom boom.*

"Stay here." Gabriel pressed the enchanted silver blade into her hand. "If any of those things make it into the cabin, stab it with this. Anywhere will do. You saw."

"You need it to destroy them." She tried to hand it back, but he stepped away.

*Boom boom boom.*

"I'll disable them, then we can use the blade to clean up." He bared his teeth in a savage grin. "The manual chopping method has its advantages."

Wood overhead splintered with a crash—and Nic squealed as a clawed hand punched through. Gabriel snarled and swung his sword, neatly chopping it off. The hunter howled, and outside, Vale screamed in equine agony.

"Stay inside. Let me out, then bar the door behind me," Gabriel ordered, poised at the door, sword at the ready. "Wait for my signal."

*Boom boom boom.*

"Now!"

Nic lifted the bar. Gabriel yanked the door open and charged out, skewering the hunter that had been pounding on it. She slammed the door and barred it with shaking hands, then whirled to face the splintered hole in the cabin roof. The hunter was still up there, biting at the wood, tearing at it with both hind paws and the remaining front one. Fragments of wood and bloody spittle rained down. It paused in its snarling efforts to thrust its snout through the shards of wood, pushing its way through. Nic swiped at it with the blade. Fruitlessly, as even the small cabin was taller than she could reach.

The hunter did jerk back, however, turning its head to eye her. "Lady Veronica Elal," it crooned, almost politely. "You will come quietly."

"I am Lady Veronica *Phel*, in the company of my wizard and husband, Lord Phel," she informed it loftily. "You will desist in your hunt."

"You are an outlaw and as ssuch cannot command uss," it

hissed. "We ansswer to the Convocation. Yield and come quietly."

Vale had stopped screaming, and Nic couldn't hear anything but the sound of waves slapping the hull and the cries of seabirds. The barge shimmied, turning in the waves and dipping enough that she had to steady herself against the wall. Gabriel's magic was no longer pushing them along, the barge bobbing at the mercy of the natural currents. Hopefully that meant he was preoccupied, not incapacitated. She had to get out there, but she didn't want this thing tackling her from the roof as soon as she emerged.

"All right," she said. "Come on in."

"You will come out."

"I don't think so." She ran a hand over her braid as if it were elegantly styled. "It's raining, and I don't want to mess up my hair."

"You will come out and come quietly," it insisted.

"Not too bright, are you? I have no intention of leaving this cabin."

"Then you will be dragged out." It yanked its head back and grabbed the ragged edge of the ceiling hole with long claws, tearing at it. Nic moved out of the way, clutching the enchanted dagger and preparing to strike. She could kill at least this one. Behind her, the glass in the porthole shattered, and she ducked, covering her head like a ninny. The hunter above tore away a board with a roar of triumph, and another shoved its snapping jaws through the porthole. Nic tightened her fist on the dagger—a strike anywhere would do—and plunged the blade into the soft black nose tipping the hunter's snout.

With a strangled howl, it jerked back—nearly pulling the blade from her hand—and then shattered into gobs of goop like the others had.

"Ha!" she shouted in excited victory. Not so helpless in a fight this time.

Her head snapped back, the grip on her braid painfully yanking her backward, nearly off her feet, and the stink of rotting meat made her gag. Claws raked her neck as they seized her collar. "What'ss thiss?" the hunter barked in her ear. "Where are the hunterss who collared you?"

"Dead," she snarled. With the dagger still in her fist, she punched down and back, catching the thing with a meaty *thunk*. It screamed in her ear, a howl of agony that drained into nothing as it faded away.

Two down. Were there five or six? Five had come after her, but it seemed like there had been six on the barge. Or she'd counted one twice.

Not giving herself time to think about it, she threw up the bar and ran out the door, skidding as her boots hit the slick of hunter goo from the one she'd killed at the porthole. "Ugh ugh ugh," she chanted, catching her balance on the bobbing deck and looking wildly around for Gabriel.

Nothing in sight but the pitching barge—surely it couldn't be good for them to be crosswise to the waves—the drizzling rain and the gray shoreline not far away. Struggling to stay upright, she clung to the cabin wall with her free hand, working her way stealthily to the attached overhang. Vale, white-eyed and frothing at the mouth, yanked on the rope halter that tethered him loosely to the manger. Blood ran down one flank, a crushed and twitching hunter under his hooves. At least the horse was intact and hadn't gone overboard.

"Good boy," she murmured, holding out her hand so he'd catch her familiar scent. He recognized her—or her Ariel magic—and snorted, calming. The hunter looked too mangled to be much trouble, but Nic wasn't inclined to take chances. Finding a decent-sized chunk, she plunged the dagger into it, observing its transformation to harmless goo with satisfaction. "Three," she declared.

Rising from her crouch, she stroked Vale's neck, leaning against him for a moment to steady them both. "Where's Gabriel, huh?"

Vale snorted an answer in horse, which she naturally didn't understand. Well, there were only two places Gabriel could be: the other side of the cabin or in the sea. She ducked under Vale's neck and flattened herself against the wall on the other side of Vale's manger, trying to move silently, and wondering what she'd do if Gabriel had been killed or drowned. She'd still belong to House Phel, but—so far as anyone knew—Gabriel had no heirs. Very likely the Convocation would deregister the house again and reassign her to another wizard—and she'd no longer have the right of summary dismissal. Her child would be taken away from her to become a ward of the Convocation. Not a pleasant prospect for either of them.

She'd reached the corner of the cabin, afraid to look. If Gabriel was dead or lost, she could maybe swim to shore. Casting a look in that direction, she mentally amended that idea. Instead of swimming, she could wait for the barge to break up on the rocks and hope to survive. Though, if Gabriel was dead or lost, she would be at the mercy of the hunters, who could overpower her.

Also, she didn't want him dead. Blame her stupid, sentimental heart for that.

Moving slowly, she peeked around the corner of the cabin—and clamped her lips on the gasp that wanted to escape. Gabriel stood like a statue, a furious giant compared to the two smaller hunters slinking around him as they swathed him in rope, tying him to a post used for anchoring crates. A third stood before him, black lips curled back from its fangs.

"Lord Phel, you have made a grave misstake interfering with uss. I told you back in Elal that there would be conssequenssess if you perssissted. You sshould have gone home."

"The familiar is mine," Gabriel ground out, struggling against more than the rope. Something held him in place, a magical compulsion of some sort. "You have no rights to Lady Veronica. She is mine by Convocation law."

"If sso, the Convocation will return your property to you. We will take cusstody of her now. My companionss will bring her out and we'll be gone. I ssuggesst you do not follow uss."

Gabriel's jaws clenched, his shoulder, chest, and arm muscles flexing, but he didn't budge. "Release me!" he roared.

The hunter's jaw dropped into a mockery of a grin. "I don't think sso, Lord Phel." It flicked its gaze to the quiet cabin, snapping its jaws closed. "Get the familiar," it told its minions. Both slunk toward the cabin.

A golden opportunity. With a scream of rage, Nic raced toward the hunter leader, dagger at the ready. Both hunter and wizard gaped at her in identical shock. Gabriel recovered faster. "Nic, no!" he yelled.

"Use your magic, you idiot!" she screamed. She flung herself at the hunter, hoping to get a lucky strike in. This one was smarter than most, deftly grappling her, its sinuous limbs stronger than they seemed. Magically enhanced, no doubt. She disregarded its intimidating teeth and claws, counting on the fact that the hunters had instructions to bring her back unharmed. She managed a shallow slice with the knife—and it screamed in pain—but the strike wasn't enough to dissolve it.

Worse, it now knew to disarm her. Its clawed fingers wrapped around her knife hand as it threw its shoulder into her breast, shockingly painful on the tender tissue, and stretched her arm out. Her shoulder and elbow ligaments shrieked at the overextension, and it felt like her wrist bones were fragmenting under the crushing grip.

The hunter sank sharp teeth into her forearm, and she dropped the blade.

A wave of water doused them both, and they went skidding across the tilting barge deck. "Nic, hold on!" Gabriel shouted.

Easier said than done. She scrabbled for purchase, digging her fingers into a lucky gap between planks—ignoring the bite of splinters. Blinking salt water out of her stinging eyes, she glimpsed the hunter not far away, all four sets of claws dug into the wooden deck, jaws open in a feral snarl, black tongue hanging between multiple rows of fangs. A wave of water rose behind it, curling unnaturally as it built—and then slammed down on the hunter, dragging it toward the edge.

It fought, its formidable claws raking furrows in the deck. Nic struggled to her hands and knees. Glimpsed the hunters galloping on all fours for Gabriel. "Behind you!" she screamed, crawling up toward him.

He tried to pivot, curse him for a fool, muscles straining against the ropes as he tried to lift the sword hanging limply by his side. "Use *magic*!" she yelled at him, lunging to wrap one hand around his booted ankle, holding on for dear life. "*Hot* water!" she added, and he focused his wizard-black eyes on the hunter nearly upon them.

A wave leapt from the sea, billowing with steam—and engulfed the hunter. It yelped, spasmed, and went still. Its fellow tried to dodge, but the boiling water, coiling like a living thing, curled and pounced. The hunter howled and thrashed, then went limp, leaving the nauseating scent of cooked meat in the air.

The lead hunter had regained its feet, stalking toward them, holding up its clawed hands in surrender. "Lord Phel," it crooned. "I wass perhapss hassty. Let uss—" The bubble of water narrowed to a lance and shot straight through the center of its chest. It swayed, astonished, the sea visible through the hole in its lean body. Then it collapsed in a heap.

"The dagger," Gabriel said. "Before they heal."

Nic let go of his ankle and looked around wildly, not seeing it anywhere. "I think it went overboard."

"Then they will, too. I can move again. Cut me loose."

"I can shove a body overboard. You concentrate on keeping us off those rocks." Nic pointed at the perilously looming crags.

Gabriel's head whipped around, and he cursed viciously. The barge shuddered as the sea grabbed it, as if giant hands had taken ahold of the vessel. Spray fountained around them at the sudden resistance. Nic staggered to the lead hunter, intent on getting him and whatever spell he'd used to immobilize Gabriel into the water. Already the tissue was knitting around the edges of the gaping hole in its chest. If it could heal from that, it likely couldn't drown—but it also wouldn't be in any shape to swim or chase after them anytime soon. With any luck, something would eat it while it was disabled.

With a grunt, she rolled the hunter over the edge and into the foaming sea. The barge lurched massively just then, and she nearly pitched in after it.

"Nic!" Gabriel shouted, hoarse and desperate. She flung herself backward and, deciding she was better off on all fours, crawled on hands and knees back to Gabriel. "Cut me loose already," he snarled at her.

"Keep your pants on," she snapped back, searching said pants for another knife. The man kept enough blades on his person. She cast a glance at the two boiled hunters, but they weren't showing signs of life. They actually looked more like hairy stew with chunks of bone, which was an image she needed to immediately erase from her mind. The stench of steamed meat and singed hair didn't help.

She sawed at the ropes around Gabriel's ankles first, letting him kick the coil free once she got one strand undone. Then she went to work on the rope binding his muscular thighs to the post. The wet leather molded to their long length, leaving little to the imagination. She mostly managed to ignore the enticing bulge near her face, until his cock visibly hardened. As the rope came free, she glanced up to find Gabriel watching her with an intent expression, lust in the set of his lips.

She pointed the dagger at him. "You'd better not be indulging in some sexual fantasy of me kneeling here at your feet."

His face cleared—going both guilty and studiously blank at once. "I'm not," he protested, much too strongly. "I'm concentrating on keeping the barge off the rocks."

"Likely story," she muttered, grabbing ahold of his belt to clamber to her feet, the barge pitching beneath her. The barge jolted, an ominous grinding sound shuddering through the boat. "Concentrate harder," she advised, sawing at the rope holding his arms to his sides.

"I'm nearly drained," he admitted, lurching as he came free of the post. He did look gray, his skin sunken against the bones of his face, a haunt of a death mask in his visage. No, she didn't want him to die.

And they were bound together, chained to each other by chance or destiny, it didn't matter which. His fate was hers.

"Use me." She held out her hand.

He stared at it like it was a snake. "What?"

"Use my magic." She flapped her hand at him. It hurt, and she looked down, realizing it was covered in blood from the hunter's bite. She shoved the aching appendage into her pocket and held out her uninjured hand instead. "That's what I'm good for." The *only* thing she was good for, she didn't say.

His lip curled in revulsion, black gaze snapping up to hers. "I won't use you that way."

"I don't want to drown. Think of it as saving me."

Hesitating, he gazed at her proffered hand. "What do I do?"

"What comes naturally, wizard," she replied. "Take my magic and make it yours."

# ~ 14 ~

HATING HIMSELF FOR it—though Nic had gauged him perfectly, prodding him with the lever of saving her life—Gabriel took her hand and drank of her wine-red, rose-suffused magic.

Her fire filled him with blazing heat, thawing his aching muscles, and stirring his thready magic into new life. Drawing her close, he folded his arms around her in a fierce embrace. She wrapped her arms around his waist in return, holding on tightly, cheek pressed against his chest. Her magic roared into him, along with the wave of overwhelming lust ignited by the press of her lush body against his. So many times over the last weeks he'd imagined her embracing him, just like this.

No, not just like this, because she was only touching him out of fear for her life. Yielding up her very essence to wield as his own. And he was very aware that he was taking it from her, his still sometimes unfamiliar wizard senses acting intuitively to seize and devour the magic he so desperately needed. *Take my magic and make it yours.* He grappled with the sheer potency of her magic, enormous and nearly beyond him. It was like riding a wild stallion—and trying to direct that galloping power while using all his strength just to hang on.

The sea wasn't easy to manipulate either. These weren't obedient currents easily coaxed into a purpose very like what they'd been doing anyway. So close to this bend of the coastline, the surf hurled itself against the rocky headland with the enormous weight of an ocean behind it. It resisted the suggestion to go in any other direction. Every time his magic tried to encompass the enormity of it, the vastness of the water slipped from his hold. The water magic immediately sieved through his splayed hands.

"It's too much," he ground out, exhaustion darkening the edges of his vision.

A small hand gripped his jaw, and he looked down to see Nic staring at him in fierce demand. With her black hair slicked back, skin misted with rain, her sharp cheekbones and high forehead stood out as if etched with vivid life against the gray mist. Her eyes, blazing green with flecks of gold fire, dominated her face. Droplets clung to her lush black lashes, brows drawn to a point as she glared at him, the tips winging high.

"Stop being so heavy handed," she ordered, and he cringed with guilt. He'd been trying to be gentle with her, to coax her along, but—she exhaled in exasperation. "The magic. Don't try to control the whole sea. Scale it down. Turn the water touching the barge. Don't fight the current, go sideways. Perpendicular to the current."

Feeling as if he could drown in those green eyes, he reached out with his magic, aware of her accompanying the thrust of it this time. Her magic intertwined with his, as it had that night, when they'd lost themselves in that sensual commingling. It aroused and fueled him, making him feel as powerful as never before. Drawing on her seemingly endless well of magic, it flowed into him like the thrumming from her body, and he followed her terse instructions, working the water that cupped the barge, moving them in a scraping transect across the current instead of against.

Wood and metal wailed, but he kept them moving. Nic, green gaze locked with his, lost some of her fierce expression. Gradually her face smoothed, lips unfurling from their tense press, the scent of roses and the heady feel of red wine swirling through his senses. As it had when they'd made love, their magic intertwined, filling the spaces in the other's. Sexual heat, already alight in his belly, billowed and unfurled, craving more and more of her.

Then they were loose, the barge floating free of the rocks.

"Stay with it," Nic murmured.

It almost felt as if she guided his mental hands, showing him where to be more precise, altering his grip on the current to move them at an angle from the coast. The barge moved ahead, stabilizing as it cut assertively through the waves, carried by a measured, precisely controlled current.

Nic's full mouth curved into an actual smile, her grip on his jaw relaxing. She caressed his cheek, dragging her nails over the smooth skin he'd finally shaved that morning. "Well done," she said, eyes glowing with… affection? No—probably relief and pride. Her gaze dropped to his mouth, her own lips parting invitingly.

Her fingers traced the line of his jaw, sliding behind his neck under his hair, caressing the sensitive nape so he shuddered in response. Gabriel could imagine the taste of her, the contrast of her hot mouth and cool, silken skin, and he wanted nothing more than to kiss her, to sink into her fire, stroke her curves and hear the gasps and moans of pleasure as she'd voiced so sweetly that night.

She melted against him, mirroring desire in her eyes. "Gabriel…" She almost whimpered his name, and in her eyes he also caught the glint of fear.

Fear, because that sweet yielding in her tower room hadn't been real. She'd been trapped with no options, and she'd given him what he expected of her. What he'd told her he wanted, as she'd been ruthlessly trained by that vile Convocation Academy to do. She'd faked her pleasure, since he'd been so determined for her to give him that, too. *Use me.*

And, oh, how he wanted to.

Which was the worst realization of all. But he refused to be that person. He'd reconciled himself to being a wizard because it meant restoring his house—and because the magic used him if he didn't use it—but he wouldn't turn this fiery woman into a tool and a pet.

It took everything in him, but he unwound her from his arms and, taking her firmly by the shoulders, set her away from him. Surprise flickered over her face—and she blushed as stark reality cooled the heady desire that had nearly swept them both away.

He cleared his throat and raked his wet hair back from his face. They were both soaked through. "Are you hurt besides the bite on your arm?" he asked, the words coming out stiffly formal.

She lifted the hand and stared at it, as if she'd forgotten. "I don't think so. Are you?"

He grimaced, feeling it now. "I may have torn out some stitches."

"Inytta would be displeased," she replied, a glimmer of dry humor in it.

"You go in and clean that bite, get dry. I'll take care of these." He gestured at the ungainly piles of meat, bone, and hair, the hunters he'd boiled alive—and that were beginning to twitch with life, impossible as it seemed. Though these creations were abhorrent, whatever enchantment gave them enduring life would be a useful one to know. "And I should check on Vale."

"He has a wound that needs tending," she agreed. "I can do that."

"No," he said, too harshly because she flinched. He needed some time away from her, but he hadn't meant to sound mean. "You go take care of yourself."

She gave him an opaque look. "I hear and obey, Lord Phel." She turned to go, the peasant clothes hanging wet and heavy on her elegant frame, and she still managed to look like a queen. An offended one.

His fingers twitched, and he nearly reached to catch her arm. To say… what? He had no idea what to say. She glided to the cabin without a backward glance. Then she popped back around the corner, catching him staring after her like a lovelorn and abandoned puppy.

"There are remains in here, also," she informed him, "since you volunteered for disposal duty."

"I'll get a shovel," he promised. There was one by the

manger, he recalled, meant for shoveling livestock manure. It ought to work fine for this purpose.

She inclined her chin in cool acknowledgment, then disappeared again. This time, she didn't return.

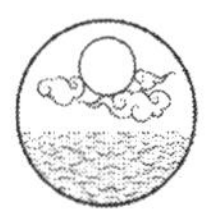

NIC KICKED AT the broken glass from the shattered porthole, using the side of her boot to scrape the shards into the corner as best as possible—wishing she had a little house spirit to do the job. Fortunately, a hinged door intended to cover the porthole let her close off the flow of cold air. She dragged one of the benches to straddle the pile of goo that had been the rooftop hunter, so she wouldn't accidentally step in the disgusting stuff. The space was small enough that it was a clear danger, and she'd had about enough of being slimed. All she needed was to humiliate herself even more.

"What is *wrong* with you?" she muttered to herself, though she knew the answer full well. She was completely Fascinated with Gabriel. She'd yielded up her magic to him—voluntarily—and now she could never go back. The copper snake around her wrist seemed to wink at her knowingly, and she pulled it off with a huff of disgust, tempted to hurl it against the wall. It wouldn't work to stop her Fascination now—if it ever could have. A lot to ask of a pretty bit of jewelry.

She stripped off her filthy and sodden clothes, even though

she didn't have much else to wear at this point. She'd learned from experience that the hunter goo didn't come out. Even Missus Ryma's excellent launderers hadn't been able to get her other clothes clean, and this had been her last decent set. Maybe she could piece some things together. Naked, she began sponge bathing herself with Gabriel's never-ending fresh water supply, sluicing the bite wound generously. While she was grateful to be able to use as much water as she needed to, it was seriously chilly. The luxurious hot bath of the night before felt like it had happened in another lifetime. There wouldn't be any cozy inn at the end of this miserable day.

Shivering, she regretted she hadn't gotten out the fire elemental before she undressed, but she'd felt so filthy and… yes, too humiliated to think straight. She'd just had to throw herself at the wizard, hadn't she? "Oh, Gabriel," she mimicked herself ruthlessly, making it extra breathy. How fast the mighty had fallen, eh? In the space of an hour, she'd gone from determined resolve to avoid the man as much as possible to practically humping his thigh and begging him to kiss her.

An offer he'd refused with a cold expression as he pried her off of him.

A knock came on the door. As if there weren't just the two of them on this huge barge. "Come in," she bit out.

Gabriel opened the door, entered with a shovel, and stood there looking as if she'd hit him with it. "Ah, um, I beg your pardon," he stammered, quickly averting his gaze from her nakedness.

She didn't bother to point out—again—that he'd seen it all before. Or that she clearly didn't care either way. Instead she pointed at the pile of soiled clothes. "You can scoop those overboard, too."

"I hear and obey, Lady Veronica Elal," he answered, echoing her own words in a bitingly faux-humble voice, tempting her to kick him.

"Phel," she corrected crisply. He might have rejected her just now, but he was stuck with her. "If you're going to mock me, at least acknowledge that I'm Lady Phel now, whether either of us likes it or not."

Gabriel didn't comment, simply finished scraping the goo and her former clothes together, then left again. Nic wrapped herself in the blanket, now that she was as clean as possible. She'd have to borrow a shirt from Gabriel, which meant she'd have to ask him for it—something that really went against the grain, especially right then. But she shouldn't put one on until her arm stopped bleeding anyway.

She eyed the stain on the floor, no doubt the source of the remaining stink in the air. Probably the goo taint wouldn't come out of wood any more than clothes. Why that small problem tipped her over the edge emotionally, she didn't know, but it all felt abruptly overwhelming. Exhaustion turned her limbs liquid, and she sat with an ungraceful thump. The furor of the fight was fading away. That, compounded by the drain from all the magic she'd given Gabriel, had left her empty. She'd practiced magic transference before, naturally, and she'd been top of her class at Convocation Academy, much praised by her teachers for her meticulous technique in offering up a channel for the wizards to pull from.

But, as with everything to do with Gabriel, she'd lost that

careful control. Some of it was his fault, as he clearly had zero practice with using transferred magic. But the rest was hers. In the impulse of the moment, she'd given him everything of herself, denying him nothing. Exactly as she'd feared, only worse—because he didn't even want her.

A bitter laugh escaped her, and Gabriel entered just then. "Something funny?" he asked.

She raised a brow. "No knock this time?"

He smiled without humor. "I figured it was pointless."

True. She couldn't tell him no, and he was realizing the truth of that. "How is Vale?"

His grim expression softened. "He'll be fine. I think they hurt him mostly to lure us out. But if you're done with the soap and water, I should clean his wound."

She handed him the soap and the flask. "You don't need this, you know," she pointed out, waggling the flask. When he frowned in puzzlement, she sighed. "You could condense water out of the rain. You can pull seawater to you and make it fresh. You're thinking like a commoner without magic instead of like a wizard."

He gazed back at her, thoughts opaque. "I spent a lot more of my life as a commoner without magic than I have as a wizard."

"Well, little pauper boy, you're a prince now, so you'd better figure out how to run your kingdom or it will run you."

Cocking his head, he gave her a wry nod of acknowledgment. "A fair point, princess." The door banged shut behind him as he left again, and Nic forced herself to her feet. The blanket wasn't nearly enough to warm her up with her shoulders and legs bare.

Pushing a couple of benches together in one corner, she made a kind of low table of them, laying out their combined supplies so she could sort them more efficiently. She should've done this when they arrived, instead of indulging in congenial conversation with Gabriel. Letting him scratch her back. Talking about her parents. *Confiding* in him.

Shaking her head at herself, she made a pile of Gabriel's clothes—except for that guilt-inducing wedding suit, which she packed away again—and a much smaller pile of her assorted spare pieces. No extra shirt of her own had magically appeared, so begging Gabriel to clothe her lay in her future. *Oh joy.*

In refolding a spare set of his pants, she felt something hard and square in the pocket. Withdrawing it, she didn't need brighter light to recognize the miniature from her Betrothal Trials packet. Countless reproductions had been made of the portrait, so it came as no surprise to see it. Why had Gabriel carried it with him, however? He knew what she looked like.

Tucking the miniature back and tying the blanket firmly around her, she coaxed the fire elemental out of its lantern. It danced on her palm happily enough. If she were a wizard, she could task it to heat the cabin. Letting it burn campfire logs was simple and within its normal habits. Heating a space without burning anything was more complex—and not something a fire elemental would enjoy naturally. All she could do was ask for more heat than light, and hope it wanted to please her. Returning the elemental to its home, she set the lantern on a bench in the center of the cabin. It wasn't bright, so maybe it would indulge her request.

Gabriel returned, gaze roving over her neat piles. "Looking for something?"

"I was hoping my clothes might've magically reproduced while I wasn't looking," she replied.

He picked up the copper snake bracelet from where she'd cast it aside, turning it in his long fingers, making her feel oddly exposed. "I thought you never took this off. You've been wearing it since I found you."

She plucked it from his hands and shoved it in her bag. "It doesn't work anymore. Careful of the lantern—I asked it to burn hot to warm this place up."

He held out his hands to it. "Feels like you succeeded. Are you cold?"

"Aren't you?"

"A little chilled," he admitted. "Help yourself to any of my clothes, though they'll be big on you."

Grateful he hadn't made her ask, she smiled. "I think I'll have to. Tell me which you care about the least and I'll adapt them."

He gave her an odd look. "No, you pick what works best for you. Any of it is fine by me."

She wanted to tell him it was too freaking late to pretend to kindness. Except it wasn't pretense—he *was* trying to be kind to her. She just didn't understand why he was running hot and cold like this. "Fine." She moved to sort through the stack of shirts.

"Let's see about your arm before you dress," he suggested, holding out a hand.

Looking him up and down, she shook her head. "Not until

you bathe. You'll just get hunter goo in my wounds again. We'd better check your stitches, too."

"Good point." He pulled the shirt over his head, halting momentarily with a hiss, then continuing on with determined movements. His muscles flexed and rippled, smooth skin gleaming golden from the low lantern light, his silver chest hair shining in contrast. She took the shirt from him—salvageable, as he'd managed to avoid being spattered in hunter remains as she had.

"Might as well take the rest off, too. Those pants need to dry." She gave him a look when he hesitated. "I've seen it all before, too," she reminded him, and gathered up her supplies while he sat to pry off his boots. "Come stand over this stain. Might as well use the spilled water to work some of the stink out. Mind the glass, though—there might be some shards still."

He came over, keeping his back to her. She handed him the flask and soap to clean his hands, and she began unwinding Inytta's expertly wrapped bandages—now stained with seeping fresh blood. He had a nice back, too, so being presented with it didn't help much to thwart her interest, if that was his intention. Broad shoulders, lovely muscles, his buttocks firm and taut, those strong thighs silvered with hair below.

"How did the hunter immobilize you?" she asked to take her mind off admiring his physique.

He grunted in frustration. "I was stupid. I don't know how it did it, but it did the same thing once before, back in Elal. I thought the hunters that caught you were that same group. Careless of me. I realize now that the ones in Wartson didn't know who I was. These did. And this hunter had some way of making me freeze."

"Probably some sort of canned spell it could deploy with a manual trigger. House Hanneil makes them, a bottled version of their mental magic tricks. Very proprietary. What I meant was, how did the hunter use it on you so easily, Wizard Phel?"

She set aside the bandages in a neat pile—the clean parts of those could be reused too—and began easing the blood-soaked pads away from his wounds. His muscles twitched, and he grunted in pain. "Sorry."

"Don't worry about it," he replied, sounding strained. "How was I supposed to stop it from using that spell on me?"

Nic wanted to thump him between his shoulder blades. "*Magic.*" She said the word slowly. "How is it that you're such a powerful wizard—remember, I've seen your scores—and you're such a clumsy idiot about using it?"

"Wow, thanks. Flatter me some more," he ground out.

She did thump him between the shoulder blades—on intact skin. It was like hitting a wall.

"Ow," he complained.

"I know that didn't hurt. Hand me the flask." He passed it under his arm, and she poured it over the wounds where the stitches had indeed split. Mostly they looked all right. She just wanted to be sure his injuries stayed clean—and she rather enjoyed the sight of the water sliding in ripples over the uninjured parts.

He flinched. "Warn a guy, would you? That stuff is cold."

"So warm it up. You boiled the water to cook the hunters, so warm this."

He grunted noncommittally, but the water warmed under

her hands. "There you go. Wasn't that easy? You're not a lost cause after all."

"Good to know. Now I can sleep tonight instead of fretting about being a shitty wizard." He sounded so disgusted that she allowed herself a smile.

Rubbing the soap between her wet hands, she gingerly washed the lacerations. "How old were you when the magic hit?" she asked quietly.

He let out a long breath, shifting his weight and propping his hands on his hips. The movement made his buttocks flex in a most interesting way, and she had to force herself to focus on cleaning his wounds. "Twenty-two," he said, sounding reluctant.

Nic nodded. That explained a great deal. "And until then, you figured yourself for a regular guy."

"Of course. Everyone else did, too. We were all regular people. You know this—nobody in Phel has had more than a glimmer of magic in generations. My great-grandmother was the last to have more than a bit useful for household tasks, and she didn't have a lot. Then, one day… *woosh!* I'm making it rain."

She suppressed a giggle at how appalled he sounded. "Is that how it happened?"

"More or less. We'd had a hot, dry spring, and seedlings that sprouted in the morning were crisped by sunset. We irrigated from dawn to dusk and couldn't keep them wet enough. I was so… frustrated. We stood to lose the whole crop, which would have a cascading effect on the entire growing season, and our stores were depressingly lean. I was staring out at those hills of brown seedlings, wishing for rain—and suddenly water gushed out of a clear blue sky."

Nic rinsed her hands, then the soap out of his wounds, picturing a gobsmacked Gabriel deluged by water pouring from nowhere, and swallowed a quiet snicker at the image. He heard it anyway. "Yeah, laugh, but I was horrified. Everyone ran screaming. I washed all the topsoil away before I figured out how to stop it."

"I can only imagine," she replied seriously, feeling empathy for that confused young man. "But after everyone got over the shock, your family must have been thrilled."

"Yes and no. They were upset for a long time. Much consternation and gnashing of teeth. A common man of twenty-two doesn't suddenly become a wizard, so they worried it was some kind of attack. Even if my family had any magic left, no one comes to it that late."

"That's not true. For many, especially males, it *can* be that late. If you'd been more a part of Convocation society, your magic potential would've been noted and measured early on—and you would've been educated in its use—but none of us know if we'll be a wizard or familiar until the final maturations happen in the brain. That can happen as late as our early twenties. The magic is there, but until the brain integrates the pathways that allow us to consciously control it, we can't use it. If we ever can."

He was quiet a moment. "I didn't feel any magic in myself."

"How would you have recognized it?" she argued. Probably the intact stitches would hold. Better to leave them as is than attempting any of her amateurish repairs. "You expected to be like everyone else, so you pretty much were. There were probably clues, but they'd be easily dismissed if you didn't know what to look for."

"True. I never saw anything unusual in myself, but I didn't have reason to. I was a relatively boring guy. I grew up learning to fight, take care of livestock, plow the fields, read books at night. I figured I'd have a life like my parents and grandparents. Marry a local girl, have some kids, later grandkids. I would've been happy with that life."

*Oh, hello, stab of jealousy.* "Was there a particular girl you had in mind?"

"A girl," he echoed in surprise. "Oh, that I wanted to marry? No. I mean, there were girls I kept company with, but I hadn't found the right one yet. Figured I had time." He snorted for his youthful ignorance. "Why?"

"You asked me," she countered.

"And you didn't answer," he replied immediately.

She breathed a laugh. "You still don't understand why that's such a foolish question to ask me."

"I *want* to understand," he replied quietly, much as she'd asked him how old he'd been when the magic hit.

"Are we trading stories?"

"Seems like a good place to start."

Fine, then. "I am a practical person, Lord Phel," she replied, taking up the towel to pat the wounds dry, the way Inytta had showed her. "I am also my papa's daughter. I had the opposite childhood of yours: Everyone expected me to have magic, and a lot of it. Papa, he..." Irritated with herself for faltering, she plowed on, forcing herself to be gentle as she applied Inytta's healing ointment. "Everyone believed I'd be Papa's heir. I had the magic potential, my scores so high that we all assumed I'd be a wizard, that I'd take over House Elal. Papa trained me for it, grooming me to take his place. I learned everything about the business, about managing our wizards, lands, and exports. Everything he could teach me shy of actually manipulating spirits and elementals. Those are wizard tricks that had to wait for my final maturation. When the scores finally verified I'd be a familiar, well..."

Eventually the searing grief of that day would fade. She hoped.

"How old were you?" Gabriel asked when she had to pause, for far too long.

Old enough to have begun to worry. Maybe part of her had known, even then. "Nineteen, nearly twenty."

"How did you find out?"

Gabriel started to turn around when she didn't immediately reply, and she clamped down on the tears wanting to rise up. "Don't move," she told him. "I'm putting on the bandages again." With a sigh, she made herself go on. "It wasn't so dramatic as yours. In fact, finding out you're a familiar is pretty much a nonevent."

"Tell me," he said softly.

"See, at Convocation Academy, they train us all together, so we learn the fundamentals of magic from both perspectives, wizard and familiar. You're only accepted to the school if the testing shows you have enough potential—and they test us regularly, because once we finish developing and manifest as either wizard or familiar, they move us immediately into specific classes for our way of working."

"That's why you know so much about wizardry."

"Yes, I was so sure that I'd be a wizard." She sighed for her youthful hubris, for all the dreams abruptly shattered. "I was the best at the school, top of my class. I know that sounds like I'm bragging, but—" She didn't know how to express what she wanted him to understand.

"No, it doesn't. You were confident. It had to be hard to lose that."

*Yes.* "So, when the scores confirmed I'd never be a wizard, I moved into the wing for familiars. It wasn't a disgrace, exactly, but..." It had been so lowering. Her wizard friends had dropped her, no longer interested in cultivating the acquaintance, especially given that they might have to master her someday. The other familiars welcomed her to their miserable company, but some had smugly enjoyed her downfall.

"Was your family upset?"

"It was a boarding school," she explained, realizing he might not know. "If Papa was angry, I never knew about it, because he stopped coming to see me."

Gabriel grunted in pain—she'd been winding the outer bandages too tight. Backing off, she loosened them and started again, more carefully.

"Didn't your mother come to see you?"

She laughed. "No. Familiars don't run around without their wizards. Maman came with Papa or not at all. I didn't see them again until after my graduation when I returned to House Elal to begin the Betrothal Trials. By then, my younger brother and sister had both tested as wizards, my sister, Alise, in Elal magic. Papa is teaching her to take over the house." She quashed the pang of bitter betrayal. It wasn't Alise's fault that she was all Nic could never be.

"Nic, I—"

"Why have you started calling me that?"

"Sorry. Your mother called you that, and it stuck in my head. I'll stop."

Nic looked at the back of his head, the silky fall of silver hair begging to be touched. It was nice to hear her nickname again. "You might as well use it," she said impulsively. "Much shorter."

"But do *you* like it?" He looked over his shoulder at her, not turning around.

"I do. Only the Convocation authorities call me Veronica. My family and friends all call me Nic. You should too."

His solemn visage lit up as if she'd given him a gift. "And you can call me Gabriel."

"Not Gabe?"

He gave a mock shudder. "Please, no. And no more 'Lord Phel.' Gabriel."

"We'll see." She rather enjoyed needling him with his title, but probably she should stop.

"Can I put on some pants now?"

Turning away so he wouldn't see her smile, she fetched his spare pair of leather pants. The leather shed the goo better than the woven fabrics. If they were going to have to fight hunters again, she should look into something like that. She shuddered as she settled on the nearby bench. It seemed certain more would be coming. A daunting thought.

He pulled on the pants, still facing away from her so he presented a most interesting view as he bent over. She made herself look away, squelching the pang of longing.

"How does all of that explain you being so practical that asking if you had someone you wanted to marry is a foolish question?" he wanted to know.

It was obvious to her, but… "Once I discovered I would be a familiar and not a wizard—and being well aware that my bloodline is too valuable to squander—I knew I'd be expected to breed. The Convocation prefers that female familiars in particular have their babies young, while they're still in the bloom of health. No matter what, I faced being paired with a wizard the Convocation selected for me. Even if they paired me with a female wizard, the Convocation would choose who impregnated me, to maximize the magical potential of my children. A practical woman doesn't nurse fantasies of romance given that reality."

Gabriel had fastened his pants and finally turned, regarding her with a somber expression. "Is that why you chose the Betrothal Trials, because it gave you at least some control of the outcome?"

"Exactly," she agreed, hoping he'd be satisfied with that answer.

He straddled the bench she sat on. "Arm, please."

She held it out, and he cradled it gently, studying the wounds, rough fingers stroking the sensitive skin of her wrist. Taking up a wet cloth, he began tenderly blotting the bite wounds she'd already cleaned, and she braced herself against the surprisingly bright pain. His black gaze flicked up to her face. "The punctures aren't too deep, but there will be a lot of bruising."

"The hunter was mostly crushing my arm so I'd drop the enchanted dagger. I'm sorry I lost it."

He shrugged slightly, dabbing his fingers in Inytta's ointment and smoothing it over her wounds. She wanted to moan, both at the bliss of the cooling relief from the throbbing pain, and at the shivers from his touch. He caressed the sensitive inside of her elbow, too, an absent stroking of his thumb where he held her arm, though she thought he might not be aware of it.

She was aware, however. Excruciatingly aware. Especially that she was naked under the blanket and he was still shirtless, his head bent over her arm as he tended it with exquisite care. He'd been like that in bed, too—meticulously patient, evoking pleasure from every fingertip of skin. If she leaned in, she could press her lips to his temple, inhale the moonsilver essence of him.

"We'll figure out something else," he said, and she had to jerk her thoughts from sex to focus on the conversation. "There have to be other ways to deal with those hunters. Magical ones, like you say. I might be a shitty wizard, but I can learn."

"I didn't mean it like that."

He looked up again, meeting her gaze. "I have my share of pride, but I can recognize my limitations. A green soldier with a sword can be more of a liability than having no one at all. That's probably a good comparison."

Nic couldn't bring herself to be so cruel as to agree.

He saw it in her face, though, and nodded. "So I'll learn."

"Convocation Academy?" she asked doubtfully.

"We are *not* going anywhere near your Convocation Center," he informed her decisively, all arrogant Lord Phel again. Then he grinned. "*You* will be the one to teach me."

# ~ 15 ~

"I HOPE YOU know where we are, because I sure don't," Nic said to him, impatiently shoving the wayward curls the brisk wind was whipping into her eyes so she could study the harbor town they approached. For a short, glorious time that morning, Gabriel had watched as she'd taken her hair out of the long braid. Grumbling about the lack of a brush, she'd run her fingers through the gleaming black waves, then braided it again.

Gabriel had nearly asked her to leave it loose, but they'd achieved a tentative peace he was reluctant to test. She'd been quiet since she'd told him the story of her past—and he'd been mulling what lay in the spaces between, the things she hadn't said. People could be cruel in their jealousy, and surely Lady Veronica Elal, with her highborn poise, keen intelligence, and the easy confidence of her immense magic, had been a target of envy. He could just imagine how the mean-spirited among her classmates had reacted to her abrupt reduction in status. Especially as the Convocation seemed entirely concerned with status, and also convinced that all of it belonged to wizards and none to familiars.

A bruising fall, indeed.

He also knew her well enough at this point to be sure she'd had some clever plan to control the outcome of the Betrothal Trials. Had she relied on a spell to prevent fertility as he'd used one to encourage it? But that made no sense unless persistent infertility would eventually release her into a situation with greater freedom. He doubted it, however. Whatever her plan had been, he'd clearly foiled it—and that's why she'd run.

He couldn't think about it right then, as limping the decrepit barge into the harbor took most of his concentration. He'd be grateful to get them onto land again, as his magic was wearing thin. He hadn't slept, wary of losing his grip on the magic they depended on to carry them against the current. On the way to Wartson, he'd drifted with the current more than he'd realized. The trip back had been much more difficult, though he hadn't let on to Nic. He didn't want to use her magic again. It felt too… parasitic.

"Hello to the pilot," Nic called through cupped hands. "Can you hear me?"

"Yes, I know where we are more or less," he replied.

She gave him the side-eye, eyes deeper green this morning, vivid against her black hair and lashes. She raised a winged brow at him. "Do I want to know how much less than more?"

"Probably not," he admitted.

"One would think a man buying a boat would also buy a map."

"I was following *you*," he replied. "I didn't need a map."

"Except to find Meresin again, once you captured me and hauled me back."

He decided not to touch that one. "I'll know Meresin when

I see it." He hoped. He gestured at the harbor city they approached, and the rocky hills rising behind it. "*That* is not Meresin."

"It's not Elal either, not with that granite," she observed, patting Vale absently. They were all waiting on the deck, bags packed and loaded onto the stalwart horse. Vale pricked his ears forward, sniffing the air of land. He'd be happy to leave the barge, too. "It could be Ophiel land."

"House Ophiel, of the exquisite gowns?"

"Aw, honey, you remembered."

"The first time I undressed you? Yes, every moment." He'd said it with fervor. Maybe a bit too much, as she blushed, glancing away. So far he'd managed to be neutral with her, but he couldn't regret that he'd affected her, if only momentarily.

"Anyway," she said, gazing at the approaching pier, "yes, House Ophiel is here, but they're a second-tier house, so it's not like being in the territory of a High House."

He'd known that. If nothing else, he understood the politics of borders—and border wars. "Ophiel is good news. We can ditch this albatross of a barge and ride to Meresin from here."

"So much for your grand plan to make this barge the flagship of the House Phel merchant fleet," she quipped.

"I'm pretty sure that plan sank along with most of the portside hull back on the Wartson coastline." Keeping the unstable barge afloat had been the major portion of the magic drain.

"Well, soon you'll have all that lovely House Elal money to spend," she noted cheerfully. "You can buy a magnificent fleet of barges with that."

Despite her acid comments regarding the hard and narrow cots on the barge, Nic had clearly slept well. He liked seeing her looking bright-eyed again, but the recovery of her spirits came with a resumption of her sharp wit. Had he said he liked that about her? He liked it better when she wasn't using it to slice at him. "I'll refuse the dowry, if that would help," he told her impulsively.

"Help what?"

He shook his head, too weary to explain. "Let's just dock this thing and go from there."

"To an inn?" she asked, hope in her voice. "I would love a hot bath."

"We are *not* stopping at an inn," he told her, not for the first time. "I can heat water for you when we camp tonight."

"Another sponge bath." She sighed, some of the sparkle leaving her eyes. "I would kill for hot food—a real meal."

He had to agree that several meals of cold sandwiches had made even Missus Ryma's excellent food lose its appeal. "Maybe a meal," he conceded, "but then we're riding for Meresin."

"Can we at least shop? I could buy some clothes," she added wistfully.

"You look lovely as you are," he told her, attempting a charming smile. The shirt dwarfed her, but she'd belted it over some woolen tights she'd brought from Elal. With their close fit and the heavier knee-high boots, her thighs looked like slender flower stems, and he had to set aside the persistent fantasy of running his hands up under the shirt to explore the blossoming flesh at their apex. She did need a warmer cloak, however, he reminded himself with a frown.

She noted his expression. "I have coin; you wouldn't have to pay for me."

"It's not that." He wasn't sure if she thought him truly a pauper or if she hated depending on him for anything. Probably both.

"I won't try to escape you," she added, pushing the curls out of her eyes. The wind whipped them back immediately.

"I know that," he replied with more impatience than he should have.

She glanced at him sharply, something vulnerable in her face before she swiftly covered it. "What do you know?"

Now he wondered what she was hiding. "Nic, if you wanted to escape me, you've had numerous opportunities. Most recently, you could've left me tied up on that barge while it foundered on the rocks."

"Not if I didn't want to drown or be hunter bait," she countered, tugging absently on the collar. She'd wrapped it in fresh strips of cloth, but they were looking worse for the wear. They needed to get that thing off of her. She was right that they should stay the night and resupply. He'd feel better if they could ride out for Meresin immediately, but it would be foolish to go without proper supplies and him exhausted, both physically and magically.

"Fine, we'll find an inn."

"Yay!" She clapped her hands together and kissed Vale's cheek, as if the horse had given her a gift—and the traitorous beast whuffled in affection, nibbling her temple in return. "Do you hear that, Vale? Our master will let us stay at a nice, warm inn. Isn't he kind?"

"Keep that up and you'll be sleeping in the cold tonight," he warned.

"Grumpy, though," she confided to the horse. "But this is what he gets when he acquires high-maintenance livestock."

Vale bobbed his head in apparent affirmation, and Gabriel stifled a sigh. "You're treading close to violating our agreement."

She fluttered her lashes at him, lips in a pretty bow of a smile, face a picture of innocence. "I was talking about Vale."

Sure she was. "I am not your master."

"In point of fact, you are," she replied, dropping the teasing façade. "You can't have it both ways, Lord Phel. Either I'm your familiar or I'm not. If I am, then you are my master. There's no such thing as a wizard–familiar partnership."

The barge scraped against the pier, hitting harder than he'd intended, and jolting Nic off balance. He caught her before she pitched over the edge, pulling her briefly against him. She softened, her fiery heat blazing into him, and she looked up through her lashes. "Thank you," she breathed, her lips parting invitingly. He nearly kissed her—he longed to, rather desperately—but he hated to think that she felt coerced. Pretending to want him, as she'd been so carefully taught, to submit to her wizard master.

"Why not?" he asked. The harbor workers shouted questions at him, throwing out ropes to tie up the barge. He held up a hand to hold them off a moment.

"Why not what?"

"Why aren't there wizard–familiar partnerships?"

She frowned, pushing at him, and he let her go, missing her warmth immediately. "The dynamic doesn't work that way."

"Are you sure?" He signaled the workers that they were disembarking. They'd be expected to pay a docking fee, but he was hoping the barge salvage would cover it.

"Which of us has the extensive education here and which of us is self-admittedly ignorant?" she shot back.

"Which of us has been extensively programmed to believe familiars have no rights and shouldn't expect to have any?" he replied evenly. She looked so stunned he had to smile. "How about you take Vale and pick out your inn? I'll negotiate getting rid of this barge and find you."

"You always do," she noted sardonically, but she'd brightened. "You trust me to go on my own?"

*Familiars don't run around without their wizards.* The way she'd said that so casually about her mother had stuck with him. He was putting together the puzzle of her, slowly but surely. If he could let her go entirely… Well, he couldn't afford to, for his sake or hers, so the best he could do was try to find a balance between them. A partnership. Why couldn't it work that way?

"Of course I trust you," he replied easily. "You're a grown woman."

"Plus you have some trick for tracking me," she added.

True. And if *he* could find her, so could another wizard. "When you pick the place, stay there, all right? I can pick up supplies for us."

She tensed, lifting her head. "I don't sense hunters here."

"Would you, though?"

"Maybe." She narrowed her eyes thoughtfully. "Maybe not, though. I think they have to be close before I do."

"Let's err on the safe side." He didn't want to mention to her that her father's people might also be searching for her. Would she elect to escape him after all, given the opportunity to run home? He couldn't take that chance. At least, that's what he told himself—while his conscience snickered, pointing out that he didn't *want* to let her go.

"All right," Nic agreed easily. "Come on, Vale. Let's put this floating disaster waiting to happen behind us." They both jumped the gap to the pier. Nic glanced back at him. "Do I have a budget?"

"I thought this was your treat," he replied, mimicking her lash-fluttering innocence gambit.

She snorted. "Nicely played. Fine, I'll see what I can afford."

"Nic," he called after her, so she'd turn again. "Pick out the best. I'm not that poor."

Flashing a wide smile, she bobbed a curtsy—quite the sight with her stocking-clad legs and boots under his shirt—and walked off with Vale, talking to the horse cheerfully about the merits of hot baths, lamenting that she didn't have a good book to read while she soaked in one.

Missing her vivid presence already, he turned to the approaching harbormaster, hoping it wouldn't cost him anything to rid himself of the barge.

NIC DID PICK out the best inn in town, after making a few inquiries of the locals for recommendations, and—since the price was actually quite reasonable—booked their best room. She also arranged hot lunch and supper for the both of them, plus a bottle of actual Elal wine and some brandy for the evening. This inn had every magical convenience imaginable, including indoor plumbing, so they could take as many hot baths as they pleased. No doubt Gabriel would be chomping at the bit to leave first thing in the morning again, but at least they had a good half day and all night to rest.

She would let him bathe first. Between the hot water, a good meal, and a few glasses of wine, maybe he'd relax enough to get some sleep. He'd clearly been awake all night audibly pacing the barge—and he'd drained his magic down to puffs of mist. The stubborn idiot wouldn't ask for her magical assistance, and she had no intention of throwing herself at him again. If he found using her magic so distasteful then fine, she'd keep it for herself. Never mind that she couldn't *do* anything with it.

Interestingly enough, she felt more than replenished after a night of sleep, as if giving her magic to Gabriel had increased her capacity to store it. Her teachers had mentioned that possibility, but she'd never experienced the effect. Certainly it hadn't been true of classwork transference. Those exercises had drawn down her magic, and it had taken time to replenish, unless she used some of the Aratron potions that accelerated recovery. She'd left all of those behind with her wedding trousseau at House Elal, however. Would Papa arrange to send all of that to her once they reached Meresin, or would he withhold her things out of anger?

No sense fretting about it. Gabriel would bring her clean clothes, and once he was asleep, she'd bathe, wash her hair—again, because she was sure she caught a whiff of hunter stink from it now and then—and finally feel something like herself again. Whoever that was now.

Sitting in the window seat of the lovely room, she studied the town through the glass, telling herself she watched for hunters, but really scanning for an Iblis locksmith shop. The innkeeper had said there were several in town. She might also be scoping out the dress shops. Her guess had been good, even though she'd never been to Ophiel before. That meant there should be plenty of shops with off-the-rack Ophiel-made clothing. Who knew what they'd have in the swamps of Meresin? She'd love to assemble a wardrobe, though Vale could only carry so much. Maybe she could talk Gabriel into buying a second horse.

The hair prickled on the back of her neck, a spark of Elal wizardry shocking her alert.

A presence had entered the room—though she hadn't heard the door open. Easing off the window seat, she slowly scanned the area, noting that the door indeed remained firmly closed. Still, someone was here. Her every instinct lit up with the certainty.

A spirit was here—a complex entity, by the feel. That

meant it had to be piloted by a high-level Elal wizard. But how had it found her, and so quickly? Nic had barely been back on land an hour. Papa must have sent every wizard and sentry spirit at his command to comb the Convocation lands for her.

She should have predicted he would.

At the moment, much depended on which wizard had found her. If only she had the ability to compel the spirit to manifest. Maybe, though, she could make it think she'd identified more than a vague sense of its presence. Typically spirits weren't all that bright, not even the complex ones. "Oh, hello," she said, turning her shoulder to the room and edging her hip onto the window seat. "What brings you here?"

Glancing casually out the window, she scanned the street, studying the people passing by this time, looking for the wizard. Guiding a spirit in a task as involved as searching for a particular person required a fair amount of magical attention, which attenuated over distance. Unless it was someone as powerful as Lord Elal himself, the wizard almost certainly had to be in line of sight.

The spirit condensed in response to her voice, wafting closer. Still not visible, though. Hovering near. Probably just keeping an eye on her while its wizard taskmaster sent a message that they'd found her. Unless there was a Ratsiel courier convenient—highly unlikely—Nic might have time to get away. Though not enough to dally and spend the night. Wistfully, she gave up the fantasy of being clean. She should've had that hot bath immediately, but too late now. She'd have to change their food order to cold sandwiches for the road—oh joy—and she needed to have Vale readied to go. At least the horse was somewhat rested from hanging out on the barge.

The spirit still hadn't made any moves, so it had to be keeping an eye on her. Hopefully Gabriel could deal with it and the wizard, neutralizing them before a message could be sent.

At the last moment before she turned away, she spotted the wizard on the corner across the street.

It was a faint flicker of Elal magic that caught her attention, unmistakable to anyone with their bloodline, even though the wizard was disguising himself—dampening his magic behind a shield and cloaking his distinctive bald head with a cowled hood. He couldn't hide from Nic, however, as she outmatched him in sensitivity to Elal magic, even if he was a high-level wizard. The prickle of fear caressing her skin turned into a cold sweat as she identified him.

A distant cousin from another branch of the family, Jan was one of House Elal's enforcers. And a ruthless one, too. Nic identified him, ironically enough, because she recognized Jan's familiar, Daniel—who was leaning against a wall nearby, a cheerful smile on his round face. Daniel the spaniel, Alise had dubbed him. It had been an apt moniker, made even more so by his alternate form as a nondescript hound dog. Nic had likely used it herself in the casual cruelty of youth. Hopefully never to his face.

She hadn't seen them in years—not since her better days, when everyone still believed she'd be a wizard and take over House Elal. Jan and Daniel were both older, more her parents' age, and she knew them mostly from family gatherings, as they were usually posted far afield. Like in Ophiel, apparently.

Either Jan had somehow tracked her—or experienced a stroke of blind luck.

The how didn't matter in the immediate moment. Jan's pet spirit had spotted and likely identified her. Nic needed to be gone before Jan decided he'd better detain her rather than waiting for instructions. Gabriel didn't have the skills to battle Jan, even if he'd been at full power. They should have been practicing having Gabriel draw on her magic. Too late.

The spirit whooshed out of the room—reporting back—and Jan looked up. Right at Nic. A triumphant smile cut his face in half. She had to get out of this room before Jan trapped her in it. Nic had managed to keep reasonably calm till then, but panic claimed her with full force, billowing into an inferno like a fire elemental in a field of dry grass.

She ran to the door—not pausing to grab even her cloak—yanked it open, and careened smack into a wall of Gabriel.

"Going somewhere?" He half-smiled, half-frowned, suspicion crossing his face.

"Let me go," she gasped, panicking, trying to push past his immovable bulk. "I have to run. Oh, *please*!"

He dropped his packages and caught her by the wrists. "Slow down. Hunters?"

"Worse," she nearly sobbed, tears springing to her eyes. "My father's wizard. An enforcer. He's coming and I'll never escape him."

"Where is he?" he asked tersely.

"Probably coming up the stairs right now. Let me go, Gabriel, please!"

He moved into the room, bringing her inevitably with him

and kicking the packages in with them. "It's too late if he's that close," he said, all cool reason to her fluttering panic as he closed and locked the door. "Deep breaths. We'll handle this. Are you sure he's here after you?"

"Yes." Nic took a breath as advised. "He sent a spirit looking for me."

Gabriel had found the brandy and poured her a finger. He pointed at a chair by the fire. "Sit. Drink. Be Lady Veronica who has nothing to hide."

"But—" *Knock-knock-knock.* She flinched at the sound, nearly spilling the brandy.

Gabriel put a hand on her shoulder. "Follow my lead," he said quietly. "You can do this. I've seen you."

*Knock-knock-knock.*

"Oh, Veronica," Jan crooned through the door. "I know you're in there." Three spirits oozed through the wood, then solidified. Jan had tasked them to take soldier form, complete with intimidatingly large, wickedly sharp curved swords.

"Those spirits," Nic hissed, hearing her own hysteria in it, "they can—"

"I know. Trust me."

Nic met his steady gaze, the silver-cool certainty of his magic calming. *Be Lady Veronica who has nothing to hide.* He was right: She knew how to do at least that. Taking a deep breath, she pulled her poise around her. Then nodded at Gabriel. He squeezed her shoulder and smiled, his approval nourishing in a way she didn't want to examine. He went to the door.

*Knock-knock-knock.*

"Veronica Elal! Let me in this instant or you will regret—"

Jan broke off as Gabriel yanked open the door.

"Can I help you?" he asked, icily polite.

Jan's face blanked momentarily, taking in Gabriel's big form, his wizard-black eyes, and Nic sitting by the fire, sipping her brandy with a calm smile. "I'm here to retrieve House Elal property," he declared with authority, sternly glaring at Nic. "You, whoever you are, will stand aside or pay the price."

"Is that so?" Gabriel inquired silkily, not budging. His magic coalesced in the room, silver bright, sharp as a crescent moon. Nic had forgotten two things about him. One, that his magic was of a dual nature. He'd depleted his water magic, but his moon magic remained potent. She had no idea how he could wield that in a fight. Still, Jan sensed the intensity of it, and he returned his attention to Gabriel, wary now. Daniel, just before and to the side of Jan—as he'd no doubt been tasked with the menial job of knocking—cringed, his cheerful face wrinkling with anxiety.

That was the second thing Nic had forgotten about Gabriel during these last few days of increasingly comfortable companionship. He'd been gentle with her, all kindness and care. Now he'd shed that personality as if it had never been. He'd gone cold and cruel, towering over even tall Jan, simmering with lethal magic.

Nic had to give Jan credit for having spine. The enforcer stared Gabriel down, seizing Daniel's arm so he winced even more, and summoned several more sword-bearing spirits to ring Nic. "That *is* so," he replied with confidence. He transferred his gaze to Nic. "Get up, Nicky. Come with me immediately. You've been a very naughty familiar."

Nic lifted her chin and raised a brow. "I'd reconsider how you speak to your betters, Jan. I outrank you."

Jan barked out a laugh and shook his head. "When was the last time a fine lady wore a collar?" he jeered, and Nic had to fight the flush of shame. "Familiars have no rank, kitten," he reminded her. "And you're a rogue familiar on top of that. You've brought shame on the house, and I'm taking you to face Lord Elal." The spirit soldiers flanking Nic caged her with their swords—which could cut like the sharpest steel. Jan wouldn't kill her, but he wouldn't mind making her suffer. A familiar didn't need fingers and toes to do her job. "I expect to be richly rewarded," Jan continued with a thin smile, "but I'd do it for free. I'm going to enjoy this so much."

Beside her, Daniel met Nic's gaze, his brown eyes soulful with some message she couldn't interpret.

Jan tried to shove past Gabriel, but he didn't budge. "Stand aside, wizard, or I shall make you suffer," Jan barked impatiently. "You have no idea who I am."

"I know you have no rights here," Gabriel replied with silvery menace. "I suggest you leave immediately."

Jan laughed, raking him with a scornful look. "I don't know who you are, but you have unlawfully taken possession of Lady Veronica Elal. You may have collared your prize, but you haven't bonded her yet. What's the problem, not enough power? Regardless, so you might get off with a milder sentence, but rest assured that I will report you to the Convocation." He bared his teeth. "Stealing a familiar is a major offense."

Gabriel braced his arms on the doorway, looming even

larger with malice—and Jan took a step back, catching himself quickly, but not before revealing he'd been intimidated. His face flushed with mortified fury.

"You have committed a grave error," Gabriel said softly. "This is Lady Veronica Phel, my wife by right of Convocation law and by her own free will."

Jan's mouth fell open. "*You* are Lord Phel?"

"Of course. And *you* are trying my patience."

Recovering his wits, Jan firmed his jaw. "Why haven't you bonded her, then?"

"I'm taking her to Meresin."

Jan frowned in disgust. "Traditionalists. You slay me—and that is *your* mistake. Little Nicky here isn't yours yet, perhaps not ever. The Convocation will decide if—"

"*I* will decide." Gabriel's voice cracked like lightning, making even Nic jump. "Run back to Elal, little wizard, before I decide to punish you for impertinence."

The spirit soldiers behind Gabriel moved, their swords flashing as they drove toward his back.

"Behind you!" Nic shrieked. A spirit sword pinned her sleeve to the chair, grazing her skin with a slice of agony. She dropped the brandy glass, and it shattered.

Gabriel gave no sign of hearing, but a shield of moonlight formed around him. The spirit warriors bounced off it like balls tossed by a child—and dissolved to nothing. Gabriel seized Jan by the throat with one hand, vising hard enough to stretch the wizard to his toes. With his other hand, Gabriel chopped down on Jan's grip on Daniel, separating them with the sharp blow. Daniel fell to his knees, cradling his head, and the spirits flanking Nic vanished.

She jumped to her feet, moving closer to Gabriel in case he needed her. He spared her a glance—noted the blood on her arm with a mercury-bright flash of purest fury—and tipped his head for her to stay back. When Gabriel returned his attention to Jan, the wizard let out a garbled wail. Gabriel put his face close to the other man's.

"Begone," he growled. "Run home to Lord Elal and tell him that his daughter is my problem now. If he menaces my wife in any way—or attempts to abduct her again—I will consider it an act of war."

With contempt, he dropped Jan, sending the slighter man staggering back, a look of shock on his face. "Daniel," he snapped. The familiar's head jerked up, a rictus of fear on his face. "To me."

Daniel crawled to Jan, leaning his head against the wizard's leg. "I'm sorry, master," he whimpered, tears in his eyes.

Jan wrapped his fingers in Daniel's hair, yanking his head back. "Bad dog!" he snarled. "Never abandon me like that again." He glared at Gabriel. "Declare your war if you are that much of a fool. Elal is not afraid of farmers from the swamps of Meresin."

"You should be," Gabriel replied. No threat or bluster. A bald promise. "You *will* be. Now go. If Nic or I sense you anywhere near, I will kill you."

Jan gaped in outrage, Daniel sobbing at the twisting grip in his hair. "You wouldn't dare—"

"Try me," Gabriel bit out. A swirl of moonlight sharpened to a slim spike hovering in the air before one of Jan's black eyes, and he froze. Gabriel smiled, not nicely. "Have a good journey."

And he slammed the door in Jan's face, locking it again.

## ~ 16 ~

GABRIEL TURNED BACK to find Nic staring at him, green eyes wide and expression unguarded. The altercation with Jan had rattled her deeply. He needed to see to her wound, but settling her shaken spirits came first.

"Nice inn," he said, removing his cloak and hanging it up. "Good choice. Comfortable room, too."

Nic's mouth moved, shaping silent words before she found her voice. "Gabriel, what was—"

He held up a hand to stop her, then pointed at the door. That Elal wizard might be lingering still, or his sentry spirits. He went to Nic, brushing a curl from her temple that had escaped the braid. "Are you all right?" he asked very softly.

She pressed her full lips together and nodded mutely, then leaned her face into his hand.

He bent to kiss her temple, brushing his lips over her ear. Then picked up her arm, pushing up the sleeve to examine the shallow slice in her lovely skin. It still oozed blood but didn't look deep enough to require stitches. "Can you sense whether they've gone?"

A line formed between Nic's elegantly winged brow as her eyes unfocused. "They're not so close, I think."

"Does he have anything watching us?"

"Don't *you* know?" Nic searched his face, noting his incomprehension. "Nothing is watching us, nor will there be. You ruptured Jan's grip on the spirits, and drained both him and Daniel down to nothing. He won't be able to summon anything for days."

"Excellent." That had worked even better than he'd hoped. He caressed the underside of her arm, her skin so soft, her magic as delicious as mulled wine. And made himself step away lest he want to touch—to take—more. The image of that poor familiar on his knees, weeping as the wizard cursed him, had left a sour taste in Gabriel's mouth. No wonder Nic was so wary of him. He didn't trust even himself with her. "I brought you some things," he told her, scooping up the packages he'd dropped.

"Things," Nic echoed, watching him as if he made no sense, automatically taking the cloth-wrapped package he handed her, but not looking at it.

"Clean clothes?" He looked her over. She still wore her fetching but arguably absurd outfit. "I expected to find you already bathed or still soaking in a hot tub."

"I… I thought I'd let you go first," she replied faintly. "I know you're exhausted—or I thought you were—so I figured a hot bath, food, and wine would let you rest, and then I could bathe after."

A curl of warmth moved through him. She couldn't hate him entirely, not when she considered his comfort like that. "It's a good plan," he agreed. "Let's do that."

"What? No. We can't, not with what happened. How did

you do that anyway?"

"Do what?" Since she wasn't opening the package, he took it back and set it with the others on a table. "How does the arm feel—are you hurt anywhere else?"

She passed a hand over the wound. "It stings, but that will fade, and it should heal clean. How did you use your magic that way—did you actually form those spikes out of moonlight?"

He shrugged. "I guess."

"He guesses." She recovered enough to glare at him. "You shouldn't have been able to do that."

"Is this another of those proprietary things?" Now that the confrontation was over, he wanted a drink. He picked up the bottle of wine, noting the Elal crest on the label. Excellent. If he couldn't drink up Nic, he could approximate her flavor, if not the heady buzz of her magic. "Don't tell me: House Better Than You holds the license for manufacturing silver spikes." The bottle seemed to be magically sealed. "How do you open this?"

With a huff of exasperation, Nic took the bottle from him. "We'd should leave it sealed. It'll travel better."

He gave her a knowing smile. "You say that as if we won't polish it off between the two of us. I'm surprised you didn't order two."

"Gabriel." She pointed the bottle at him. "You were right to begin with. We can't stay here. We have to leave, as soon as possible. I hope it's not too late to change our lunch order." She went for the button that would magically summon an inn worker.

"No."

She stopped, gave him a puzzled look. "No, you don't want our meals packed up?"

"No, we're not leaving." He examined the bottle. There must be a simple way to open it. Aha—there was the trigger, woven into the Elal crest. He pressed his thumb to the center of the circling spirits. A small bubble of magic burst under his skin, and the cork eased out of the neck.

"Clever," he commented, and poured them both glasses. He carried them to Nic, who stared at him like she thought he might be crazy, and handed one to her. He clinked his to hers and sipped. "Not the family reserve, but very good."

She didn't drink. "Gabriel. Jan doesn't need magic to hire a Ratsiel courier to send a message to Papa. He'll know where I am."

He nodded. "Yes. And that you're with me."

"You don't understand." She wrapped her hands around the glass as if to take comfort from it. "I escaped from my family, as well as from you. Papa didn't know anything about it. You have no idea how angry he'll be with me." She looked very young at that moment, fragile with the threat of her father's displeasure.

"I do have some idea," he replied, watching her closely. He hadn't really wanted to broach this with her yet, as she seemed to have a complicated relationship with her father, but he was also determined not to treat her like an ignorant accessory. Or an animal. *Bad dog!* Jan's snarling voice still echoed in his head. "When I met with your parents and the Convocation proctor, your father was—yes—very upset that you were gone."

At last, she sipped her wine. She looked too tense still, like she might shatter. "You mean that he was furious."

"Furious is a good descriptor. He vowed to send spirits after you, to bring you back to House Elal. The proctor forbade it, but I got the impression that..."

"That Papa wouldn't listen." She let out a huff of sound, too bitter to be a laugh. "No, of course he wouldn't. He'd want to reclaim me if possible."

"From what Jan said, it didn't sound to me like his intention is to protect you from the Convocation."

Nic cocked her head, considering. "Jan is a bully, so we can't judge from that. He'd say whatever he thinks would upset me the most. I truly don't know what Papa is thinking, except that I've betrayed him—shamed him—and he'll want to deal with me personally. That's one of his principles. *No one else cares about your interests as much as you do, so handle them yourself.*" She mimicked her father's voice quite well.

He nodded to himself. "I could see you were afraid of Jan, and the way he treated his familiar is abominable, so that's why I was happy to run him off, but..." He focused on her lovely face, wondering if he could really make himself give her up. He would have to because he could never make himself treat her like property. No matter how much he needed her, he wouldn't become like his enemies in order to destroy them. He'd find another way. "Nic, if you want me to take you home instead of to Meresin, I will."

She considered him for a long moment, then went to sit on the window seat, curling her stocking-clad legs under her. Watching him with wide green eyes over the rim, she drank down the glass of wine, then held it out in mute request. He crossed to her and refilled the glass generously. No matter what, they were staying the night. She was right—he was exhausted. Even more so now after the confrontation with the Elal wizard.

It was also his last opportunity to attempt to court her.

"Back to House Elal," Nic said reflectively, eyes downcast so her lashes fanned luxuriantly against her cheeks. He curled his fingers around the wineglass to keep from touching her. She glanced up just then, catching some expression on his face. "What about the baby?"

He edged a hip onto the window seat beside her. "You said you didn't want to talk about that."

She laughed softly. "Who *are* you? You pull steel out of thin air—"

"Silver," he corrected. When she frowned, he clarified. "Moonlight solidifies into silver. I don't know why, but it does."

"Well, of course it does," she replied, voice heavy with irony. "If you can do that, why didn't you use it against the hunters?"

"I hadn't thought of it yet," he admitted.

"When *did* you think of it?"

"Last night. I needed to stay awake to keep the barge moving, and I was thinking about what you said, how I needed to use my magic more. You're right, obviously, especially given what happened just now, as I doubt the innkeeper would've appreciated bloodshed from a more violent clash."

"Nor would House Elal," she murmured, "which is a real

problem despite your cavalier threats of war."

"Not threats and not cavalier, but solemn promises," he corrected, his resolve to make Elal pay stronger than ever. But Nic looked alarmed at the thought, so he dropped it. "Regardless, I spent the time walking around the barge and kept myself awake by testing what I could make out of moonlight that could be useful in a fight."

Clearly baffled, she stared at him. "You just... invented a whole new system of magic manifestation overnight?"

Cautiously, he nodded. "Isn't that what wizards do—make spells? I don't have a Convocation Academy education, but I've read plenty over the last few years. I learned how to channel magic into spells that the books described. Those were useful to learn on, but it seemed to me that wizards prefer to create their own spells."

She had an odd smile on her lips. "They have no idea just how dangerous you are."

Flattered by her assessment—because he knew, if he knew nothing else about her, that Nic never gave compliments idly, and particularly to him—he set the urge aside to ask her to go on. He needed to understand this more than he needed to bask in her admiration, even if it was only for his ingenuity. "You know I don't understand how Convocation wizards work. Why is what I did so odd?"

She gazed out the window pensively. The clouds had gathered to a heavier overcast, rain spitting against the glass windows. "My understanding is, of course, not complete," she said slowly. "As I explained before, I only learned the basics of wizardry, which were designed to be a foundation for the real teaching. Wizards guard their trade secrets closely, so I know mostly what I can guess from casual remarks. I can tell you this, however, that when Papa wanted to perform a complicated incantation, he isolated himself in his arcanium, and he required Maman's assistance. She would always be utterly drained after. It gave her terrible headaches. Sometimes she'd sleep for days."

An unhappy shadow crossed her face, and he risked touching her, putting a comforting hand on her stocking-clad knee. The cable-knit yarn was surprisingly silky, and the heat of her body beneath an alluring hint of how much softer her skin would feel beneath his hand. "I'm sorry," he said, awkward, not sure what else to say.

She met his gaze, the green deep and thoughtful. "What are you sorry for?"

So many things. So much he'd change between them if he could. Some of that would mean changing all the world, and how could one man accomplish that? Though… maybe two people could. "I think you worry about your mother. That doesn't sound like an easy life."

A quirk of a smile lightened her expression. "Maman would tell you that she enjoys the solace of wealth and position. And her children," she added, briefly resting a hand on her own belly, the first time he'd seen her physically acknowledge the life growing inside her.

He'd lived most of his life without wealth or position—and had barely scrabbled together either in recent years—but he rather doubted those were true compensations. Judging by Nic's pensive expression, she doubted, too.

"Anyway," she said, and sipped her wine, "my point is that you performed what the most powerful and experienced wizards would consider to be a complicated incantation—and, yes, most would love to create their own spells, but not all of them are able to—and you did it without the help of your familiar, not in an arcanium, but while pacing a barge on a rainy night, injured from a battle, and using half your magic to push said barge against the current."

"It wasn't half, exactly," he explained. "The water and moon magic overlap in some ways, but for the most part they're two different… wells to draw from. I could task the water magic to carry the barge and devote my attention to developing weapons with the moon magic."

She shook her head in disbelief. "See? Dangerous."

He didn't feel dangerous, but he *had* been determined to do a better job of protecting her. "Isn't an arcanium a fancy name for a workroom? I don't understand the significance."

"I suppose that's true of a lot of posers and pretenders to greater power than they have. You know, the bigger and more elaborate a wizard's arcanium, the more certain their ability is this big." She held up her thumb and forefinger in a pinch, amusement lighting her face. "Most wizards, though," she said more seriously, "keep their arcanium secret. They spend years refining the space to best concentrate and intensify their magic. Sometimes a house arcanium has been handed down over generations. House Elal's is that way, inherited by the next lord or lady. I've never been inside Papa's. Only he and Maman can enter."

"Interesting." If House Phel had an arcanium, he didn't

know where it was. Of course, most of the house still lay in ruins, with some parts literally under water. It could be anywhere, if it had even survived. "I've never used an arcanium."

"You need to start," she said, leveling a stern look on him. "And you need to start using your familiar. You should have wakened me last night to assist," she added.

He withdrew his hand, tucking it under his leg so he wouldn't inadvertently draw from her. Nic's magic was more addictive than wine, tempting him to take more and more. It was a sensation like no other, and he understood now, with brutal clarity, how these wizards came to rely on their familiars. "I don't want to use you that way."

Her eyes sharpened in a now-familiar exasperation. "You can't threaten war against the most powerful house in the Convocation in one moment and go all soft and sentimental about using the resources at your command the next."

He set his teeth, deliberately taking a sip of his own wine, knowing on one hand she was right and on the other annoyed at her scornful assessment. "I don't consider you to be either a resource or at my command."

"Then why did you set your sights on me?" she demanded. "You mortgaged House Phel's fortune on the gamble to acquire me for a reason. Why?"

"I needed a familiar and an heir if I wanted to restore the house. I needed a highborn wife who understands the ways of the Convocation. Everyone I went to for advice told me so."

"I'll bet they did. It's good advice. And they advised you to acquire the most powerful familiar that met those criteria that you could, didn't they?"

"What is your point, Nic?" he asked, feeling very much backed into a corner. Probably he should admit to how he'd hedged his bet to ensure it hadn't been much of a gamble at all.

"I think you know my point." She dropped her gaze significantly to her knee, though his hand was long gone. "You act like you shouldn't touch me and refuse your sexual rights even when I throw myself at you. You say you don't want to use me as your familiar, even offer to take me home. You chased me across half the known world, wouldn't bend when I asked you to let me go, but now you've made no move to bond me even though you know perfectly well how that jeopardizes your claim."

"Wait." He held up a hand. All of that was perfectly true, except for the last. "How does bonding affect our partnership?"

She actually rolled her eyes at him. "Really? Please don't tell me tha—" *Knock-knock-knock.* Nic froze mid-word, eyes going wide with fright.

Gabriel leapt off the window seat and retrieved his sword, just in case. "Is it?" he asked quietly.

Nic relaxed minutely, blowing out a breath and shaking her head. "No. I'm just on edge."

*Knock-knock-knock.* "Sir, madam—I have your lunch," a boy's voice called.

Nic closed her eyes briefly in pained acknowledgment. "Now I'm jumping out of my skin at *lunch*," she muttered.

Gabriel smiled at her caustic tone and went to the door, keeping his sword out anyway, just in case.

But it was only lunch, and the decidedly nonmagical boy

staggered under the weight of the tray as he carried it to the table. Gabriel took the opportunity to check the hallway. It was quiet, an inn empty of guests at midday. No sign of Jan or poor Daniel—nor any other magic he detected, beyond the many conveniences. Passing the boy a coin for his trouble as he exited, Gabriel closed and locked the door again.

Nic was already arranging the plates, humming happily at the prospect of hot food. No one would guess she'd been rigid with fear only moments before. She possessed an admirably resilient character. She'd retrieved his half-full wineglass, setting it on the table and topping it off, so he sat at that place.

"I hope you like your steak rare," she said, neatly slicing the substantial cut of meat and giving him the larger portion. "I do, and you weren't here for the ordering."

"That's fine," he said, though he preferred his meat thoroughly dead and not still bleeding. She added a generous portion of roasted vegetables, a hunk of fresh bread oozing with butter, and fragrant mashed potatoes. Glancing up at him, she raised a brow. "Gravy?"

"Yes, please."

She poured, paused, and looked at him expectantly. "More?"

"Leave some for yourself."

"There's plenty, and we can always send for extra. Places like this are generous with the stuff." She doused the potatoes with gravy and brought his plate around to set it before him.

"You don't have to wait on me," he said, bracing for her slicing reply.

But she paused. To his utter shock, she lifted a hand and

brushed his hair back, trailing her fingers down his cheek. "I know," she said quietly. "Maybe that's why I don't mind doing it."

She returned to her side of the table and prepared her own plate. Noting that he'd waited for her, she scooped up a bite of potatoes—hers as liberally doused with gravy as his—and popped it into her mouth. Making a sound of ecstasy, she wriggled in her chair, face suffused with almost erotic pleasure. "They make them with garlic and real cream here," she said when she'd swallowed, pointing her utensil at him. "Try it. It's best piping hot."

Deciding not to mention he'd been enjoying watching *her* eat, he took a bite—and had to agree. "This is amazing." He regarded his loaded plate, and the remaining food, with some dismay. "Did you say you ordered dinner, too?"

"Dinner will be lighter," she informed him, green eyes sparkling as she sipped her wine. "You needed a heavy meal to replenish your magic. Then hot bath, long nap, a light meal, and a full night of sleep. You should be feeling refreshed in the morning."

"Did you learn that in your Care and Feeding of Wizards class?" he asked.

She cocked her head. "You laugh, but familiars are taught exactly that. It's part of our job."

He sobered. "What about the care and feeding of familiars?"

"We learn to take care of ourselves," she replied, dropping her gaze and paying a great deal of attention to cutting a bite of her steak.

"Why can't it be mutual?" he persisted.

She gave him that hard stare, like she figured him for crazy or an idiot or both. "The wizard–familiar relationship is codified the way it is for very good reasons. You'd do better to stop fighting the world and work within it. If you want to restore House Phel, then you can't be at war with the Convocation. You need to resign yourself to the power dynamic of our relationship. I have."

"Have you, though?" he asked with soft insistence. He'd begun to see through her shifting moods and masks of apparent poise. Jan had treated her with contempt, and that had hurt Nic as much as anything. *Familiars have no rank, kitten,* he'd jeered at her, an obvious hit to her pride, the humiliation clear in her face. She loathed being powerless, no matter what arguments she managed to force through her lips. He understood because he'd hate it, too.

"I don't want you to take me back to House Elal, if that's what you're asking," she said, ducking the actual question. "Papa would punish me—and punish Maman—and then he'd be forced to turn me over to the Convocation for more discipline and retraining and..." Her voice broke a little, but she covered it quickly with a flash of bared teeth and a swallow of wine. She shrugged, setting her glass down. "Remember that I'm practical. If I can't be free—which was clearly an empty-headed fantasy to begin with—then I'd rather take my chances with you in the swamps of Meresin. Which is, by the way, why you need to bond me."

"Explain that part," he said, seizing on it as the easiest to grapple. "I understood that once the proctor determined that you carried my child, then you… I—that is, we…"

She regarded him with clear amusement. "That I belong to you. It's all right to say the words. That's an objective reality. Also," she continued when he opened his mouth to argue, "while it's true that I belong to you now in the eyes of the Convocation, regardless of all else, not everyone obeys Convocation law. There are plenty of landless or houseless wizards not in the Convocation. Maybe they're from an exiled branch of the family, or they could be a spontaneous reappearance of high-potential wizardry from a happy recombination of old, forgotten bloodlines." She toasted him with her glass. "The ambitious among them sometimes attempt to claim an unbonded familiar. Once a familiar is bonded to a wizard, they belong to them until the wizard's death. A good thing, too, as otherwise wizards would be attempting to steal each other's familiars all the time."

Or familiars would be free to leave a wizard that abused them for a happier partnership, Gabriel reflected. "That's what your Jan assumed—that I was a rogue who'd abducted you."

"He's not my Jan, but yes. And *you* run the risk of someone else grabbing me and doing exactly that unless you bond me."

"You weren't worried about that in Wartson," he pointed out.

"I was sent—I went there because there aren't wizards in Wartson. If no one could sense what I am, I had a chance of living like any ordinary person."

"Aren't there spontaneous reappearances of high-potential familiars, too, if that happens with wizards?"

"Yes, but they don't live long. My point is that I'm not safe in Convocation lands unless you bond me. Why do you think I've lived the last years either at Convocation Academy or in House Elal?"

"I didn't know you had, but if asked to guess, I would've said it's because they—wrongly—view you as valuable property that must be kept locked up."

"Valuable property that could be stolen," she corrected. "No one expects a familiar to be so stupid as to try to escape the long arm of the Convocation," she finished, so bitterly that he wanted to pull her onto his lap and cuddle her.

"I think I can protect you well enough," he said instead. "I promise you that much."

"Gabriel." Finished with her plate, she pushed it forward and leaned her folded forearms on the table, regarding him earnestly. "There is no reason not to bond me. Just do it already."

"There is a good reason. Several, in fact." He returned her regard gravely.

"Do tell," she replied with considerable exasperation.

Finding he'd cleaned his plate—and that he was too full to stuff in another bite—he stacked his plate on top of hers. "Because you disliked the idea of being my familiar so much that you took an enormous chance in order to escape me," he explained patiently. "You told me, repeatedly, that you don't want to be married to me, so it stands to reason you don't want to be bonded to me either."

"What I *want* doesn't matter," she replied, not bitter this time, but sounding frustrated that he didn't get it.

He reached across the table and put his hand on hers. Her

magic simmered against his touch, beckoning. If only it meant she wanted him like he wanted her. "What you want matters to me."

"Then why didn't you release me back in Wartson when I asked?"

He should have. Making himself relinquish the sizzling warmth of her skin, he released her hand and raked it through his hair. "Because I was afraid you'd fall prey to the hunters again. If you don't want to be with me, I'll accept that—but I want you to be safe."

She pounced on that. "Well, I won't be safe until I'm bonded."

"What about with your family? You'd be safe with them. You were before."

She pressed her lips together, shaking her head slowly. "They can't protect me indefinitely. That's part of why I had to do the Betrothal Trials. If I'd stayed with House Elal as an unbonded familiar, especially one of my power, I would've had to live as a virtual prisoner. I'd have been under guard at all times to prevent my abduction. It's not any kind of life." She shifted restlessly, gazing out the window at a freedom that could never be hers. "There are no good alternatives for someone like me."

"You had a plan," he said, sitting back in the chair and watching her closely, "for the Trials. You said it wasn't because of me that you ran, but something about being tied to me made you decide to take the risk of escaping. I can't possibly permanently bond you to me, knowing that. Unless you can convince me otherwise."

She sighed, gaze still on the drizzling sky. "Just bond me already, Gabriel. You don't have to know everything about me."

He shook his head. "No. I won't do it unless you're willing."

"I *am* willing," she protested, gesturing to herself. "Look at me. Here I am, begging you to bond me. You want to talk about the pregnancy? All right. I feel fine. I don't feel anything yet, but the Oracle Heads are never wrong. You want to know why I ran? I had a chance, I took it, and the plan fell through. But we didn't know about the hunters, so it was a doomed plan regardless. I can't be free. I'm already yours, so let's just tie this up with a bow and move on with your plan to restore House Phel."

She was convincing. She also didn't mean it. The terror of the trap shone in her green eyes. He recognized that emotion, dreading something so much that you want to get it over with as quickly as possible. He didn't want her to live in fear—but he also couldn't be the blade she wielded against herself. Setting her free now wouldn't save her, but he could take one step to help her feel more like a person, not a slave.

"Are you done eating?" he asked, waving a hand at their empty plates.

She opened her mouth, closed it again. "There's apple pie, but I can't stuff in another bite right now."

"We'll have it for dessert tonight. Let's take a walk." He stood and went to the packages, sorting through them.

"A walk?" she repeated as if he'd suggested flying over the sea.

"An errand," he clarified, finding the package he wanted and triggering the sealing mechanism the saleswoman had showed him. "Some fresh air and exercise to help us digest this excellent meal."

"I had enough fresh air to last a lifetime on that benighted barge," she grumbled as she stood, sounding more like her sardonic self. "What is that?" Her expression of astonishment and growing delight did his heart good.

He shook out the cloak and, moving behind her, draped it over her shoulders. Because he couldn't resist her entirely, he brushed a kiss over her temple, inhaling the scent of wine-spiced roses. "A warm cloak. I keep my promises, Nic."

She ran reverent fingers over the emerald-green velvet and the white fur trim, sealing the front closure with a light touch. "Ophiel make," she commented, turning to face him.

"In House Phel colors." She looked incredibly beautiful in it, as he'd imagined. The deep green brought out her eyes, and the shadowfox fur lining set off her dark hair and vivid complexion.

"And very expensive," she finished. "I can guess how much this set you back."

"I'm not poor," he told her. "Yes, House Phel has a long way to go to reach the wealth of the High Houses, but I can afford to outfit my lady wife according to her station and beauty."

Nic narrowed her eyes at him. "Then your finances are better than Elal spies uncovered."

He allowed a mirthless smile. "As you've noted, I have ways of concealing information from even prying Elal spirits."

"You continue to surprise me, Lord Phel." This time, when she said it, she didn't spit his title like an epithet. She sounded respectful, possibly impressed. "But the rest of me is hardly presentable."

"A quick errand, then we can come back and follow your schedule of hot baths, naps, and meals."

"You laugh, but you'll see. It will do you good."

"I am not laughing," he assured her, and offered his arm. "Shall we, Lady Phel?"

Her lips pursed, poised with a tart reply, but she withheld it, and allowed him to escort her out of the room.

# ~ 17 ~

IT HAD BEEN a day full of turbulent emotions, and she had drunk rather too much wine for an empty stomach. Both of those factors had to account for the almost giddy pleasure of strolling with Gabriel in the—quite chilly—pelting rain, and her lack of ability to put two thoughts together.

She just really had no idea what to make of him. The wizard was a fascinating contrast of ruthless certainty and soft sentimentality. She saw how appalled he'd been at Jan's firm use of Daniel. And this nonsense of not bonding her unless she was willing. Why couldn't he be a normal wizard and take the decision out of her hands? She'd already practically begged him to do it. At this rate, she'd be forced to admit her feelings, that she loved him with all the irrevocable and desperate intensity of the most melodramatic familiar in the cheesiest tragic romance. Another pitiful Lyndella, pining for Sylus to make her whole.

She'd hoped to preserve her pride by nobly submitting to being bonded, but no. The man just *had* to have her willing—and he had no idea just how willing she was.

It was lowering to find that she barely cared about controlling her own life anymore. Everything in her longed to belong to him. Her familiar nature had kicked in hard, overriding all of her notions of living without him. If he tried to take her back to House Elal, he'd probably find her running down the road after him like an abandoned puppy.

That would be the final humiliation, following this seemingly endless string of them. Having Jan sneer at her and savor his superiority had been an especially stinging cut. One day she'd be used to it. Maybe.

"This is the place," Gabriel said, stirring her from her increasingly dour thoughts.

She glanced at the sign. *Iblis Locksmiths.* Gabriel was taking her to get the cursed collar removed. Swallowing hard, she forced back the tears that stung her eyes.

"I found this place earlier, and the locksmith says he can release the collar," Gabriel said, tilting his head to see her face, no doubt wondering at her sudden emotion. "I was under the impression that any Iblis wizard could do the work, but we can look for another."

She took refuge in being arch. "The place is a bit shabby, but it will do, I suppose."

His lips quirked in a half smile, not fooled by her attitude in the least. He knew how badly she wanted out of that collar, and he'd gone to the trouble of scouting for an Iblis wizard to do it. *What about the care and feeding of familiars?* His question echoed around her head. That had been the problem with Gabriel from the beginning. He was far too kind to her—and she had no defense against it.

He held the door for her, and she entered the shop. The Iblis wizard briefly looked up from a workbench littered with the parts of a disassembled safe, the door hanging crookedly open. "No unescorted familiars allowed," he barked, returning his attention to his project. "Narlis—get rid of her."

A woman old enough to be the locksmith's grandmother, wearing a fancy metal collar, stood up from her stool in the corner. "Master, there is a wizard with her."

The Iblis wizard glanced up in irritation, frowning at Gabriel. "Ah, it's you. I expected you sooner."

"We stopped for lunch," Gabriel replied smoothly, ushering Nic forward with a hand on her back.

"Well?" the Iblis wizard demanded. "I can't remove a collar I can't see or touch."

Nic reached to unfasten the cloak, but Gabriel was there first. "Allow me," he murmured with a warm smile, deftly triggering the magical fastenings. He draped the cloak over his arm, and Nic began unwinding the cloth she'd wrapped around the hunters' collar. The Iblis wizard came around his bench, studying the ugly thing.

"I see." He nodded knowingly at his fellow wizard. "You can't go with this kind of low-quality metal. See how it's messed up her pretty skin? And it's too heavy for her frame—the weight has bruised her collarbones. One that's properly fitted won't do that. You only use one like this to punish her. That's fair enough, as it's not easy to keep the young ones in line. Not like my Narlis here." He jerked a thumb at the older woman, sitting on her hard stool in silence. "She's too decrepit to refuse anything, though it's not like she's got much juice in her, regardless."

"Are you able to remove the collar?" Gabriel asked tonelessly, as if bored, but the garrulous wizard was getting on his nerves. Nic could hear it in his voice, see his horrified compassion in the way he gazed at the wizard's familiar.

"Oh, sure. You just need to pick out a replacement. For a familiar this pretty, you want a collar of gold, like Narlis is wearing there." He noted Gabriel's brooch. "Or silver. I can make you a lovely silver collar for her, exactly sized, with your house design." He peered at the crest. "What house are you, anyway?"

"House Phel," Gabriel replied coolly. "Just remove the collar. I don't need another."

"Phel?" He scratched his chin. "I've never heard of House Phel. Is it new?"

"In a manner of speaking. The collar?"

The Iblis wizard had to be a low-level—not surprising for one running a small shop in this backwater harbor town—but he was also unusually dense not to notice how Gabriel's magic intensified in the small room. Nic expected silver to begin to rain from the air. She put a hand on Gabriel's arm, the muscle there tense, and gave him a smile. He relaxed minutely, acknowledging with a slight nod. "Get it done," he told the locksmith, stepping back to give him room.

The locksmith grabbed Nic by the shoulders, turning her to face a bright mage light as if she couldn't understand verbal instructions. Once he had her positioned, the wizard seized the collar, turning it ungently. It scraped painfully over her raw skin, but Nic steeled herself to show no reaction. Gabriel didn't need any more incentive to lose his temper with this lout. "Where are you?" he muttered at the collar. "Ah. Gotcha.

Whoever sealed this meant it to stay," he told Gabriel, "until the maker released it."

"Then it's beyond your skills?" Gabriel sounded increasingly dangerous.

"Your lucky day, Wizard Phel. I happen to know this maker and his tricks. You came to the right locksmith. Narlis!"

The old woman stood creakily and shuffled over to lay an arthritically gnarled hand on the locksmith's shoulder. A burst of metallic-tanged magic spread heat over Nic's throat, and the collar fell free. Being freed of the weight of it, metaphorically and physically, had her nearly sobbing in relief. Gabriel drew her back against him, arm wrapped protectively around her, as if he understood.

"Go back to your stool," the locksmith snapped at the older woman, who shuffled away, sagging from even that small magic drain. Gabriel observed it, too, and for a moment Nic thought he might cause trouble, but he said nothing.

"Here you go, darling," he murmured, draping her in the cloak again, fastening it and drawing up the hood, as if it might protect her. He passed the locksmith a few coins—an exorbitant price for such a small job. Nic considered advising Gabriel that it was too much, but she really wanted out of there.

The Iblis wizard took the money, held the collar out to Gabriel.

"No." Gabriel's lip curled in distaste. "Dispose of it."

"Your loss is my resale." The locksmith cackled. "Good punishment collar, as I said. You sure you want to give it up? I can key it to you, so you're the only one who can put it on her—or take it off. Better bond that one quick, lest someone else be tempted to take her off your hands." He licked his lips. "Tasty morsel, that one. I have an idea who you stole her from."

"I paid you well," Gabriel replied, voice soft with menace. "To ensure your silence, remember?"

The Iblis wizard held up his hands. "I won't tell anyone. I'm just saying I have a lovely selection of collars here." He swept a hand at a display case of the things, from simple to garish. "Or, like I said, I can custom design something. Nothing shouts legal ownership like an expensive collar."

Gabriel turned his back and guided Nic out of the store. "I should've picked a better place," he growled in annoyance. "I'm sorry you had to endure that asshole."

"They're probably all the same," Nic soothed him. "Those minor wizards are so riddled with jealousy that they try to lord it over anyone weaker than them. Did you see how he needed his familiar for even that simple task? I bet he's no more than a three on the MP scale. Barely a wizard at all."

"Was that woman his… wife?" Gabriel asked hesitantly.

"With that age difference? Not likely, especially since she was unbonded. No, probably she belonged to another Iblis wizard in his family—maybe his grandfather or a great-uncle, judging by her age. He'd have inherited her. That's the only way a wizard like him would get a familiar, even an aged one."

"She should be living out her last years in comfort, not slaving in a shop for her grandchildren." Gabriel sounded angrier, silver sharp in the air.

Nic shrugged, trying to downplay the situation, though it had bothered her, too. "Some families allow their familiars to retire when their wizards die; some don't. Just like some families put their older livestock out to pasture and others keep them in harness until they die."

"Please stop," he bit out savagely, "comparing yourself to livestock."

She gave him a look, showing him her scrupulously closed lips.

He snorted a humorless laugh. "How did he know I hadn't bonded you?"

"Even a minor wizard can sense that," she replied promptly. "Didn't you sense Jan's seal on Daniel?"

He nodded reluctantly, getting that lip-curled expression of distaste again. "And Narlis didn't have that. I didn't know to look for it, but I get what you mean. I take it you can sense the bonding?"

"Yes. We have the same ability that way. I can recognize most magic just as well as you can."

"Then why can't you manipulate it like I can?"

She tapped her forehead. "My brain never developed that extra something, for whatever reason. Basically, we all start the same, but wizards go one step farther. No one knows why familiars don't develop into wizards, but they just... don't. Believe me, people tried to force it. There was a lot of dissecting of familiars and experimentation on them in the bad old days before the Convocation stepped in and put a stop to it."

Gabriel had a hard look on his face. "I didn't know that."

"History of the Convocation 101. Mostly a lot of pennant-waving about how glorious the Convocation is and how lucky we are to be protected by it." She snorted.

"Why isn't Narlis bonded?" he asked after a moment of quiet thought.

"Likely the Iblis wizard is too low level to do it. Besides, who would steal her? And if she ran, where would she go? No one's going to take in a dried-up familiar, especially if her house is willing to keep her."

"Your world is a harsh place," he commented.

"It's your world now, too," she reminded him. "And now you understand why you need to bond me," she added.

"No." He said nothing more, just the firm negation.

*Fine, then.* "Have it your way," she gritted through her teeth. "But the next time a wizard asks you why you haven't bonded me, say that you're waiting to do it in the House Phel arcanium, in the tradition of your family. Don't elaborate. Be mysterious."

His dark expression cleared with relief. "They'll believe that?"

"Yes. That's why Jan assumed you were a traditionalist," she explained. "It's a little odd, but wizards capitalize on being odd."

They'd reached the inn, the interior lobby warmly comforting after the brisk weather and nasty encounter with the Iblis wizard. Nic would've gone through much worse to be rid of the collar, though, so she counted it a good outing. The innkeeper greeted them cheerfully, saying that he'd had the broken glass cleaned up as requested. Gabriel thanked him and ordered a second bottle of wine, tipping him generously.

"But I don't necessarily need an arcanium to execute this

bonding," Gabriel said in a reluctant tone once they were in the privacy of their room. "Is that correct?"

"Correct. It's a power thing. An arcanium helps if you're a low- or mid-level wizard. But with your power and mine, we can do it right now." Nic shed the lovely cloak reluctantly. It outshone even the one she'd left in Elal, perfectly configured to be both deliciously warm and comfortably light. "Or in the morning, when you're rested."

"No," Gabriel decided, still sounding stubborn and snarly. "I like the idea of the traditional ceremony in the House Phel arcanium. Someday," he added, "if you're willing."

"Gabriel Phel," she said, tempted to stomp her foot—or kick him. "I'm willing now. Just get it over with and then there won't be any questions."

"No, you're clearly *not* willing, so stop lying about it!" he fired back at her. "Didn't we agree not to lie to each other?"

Taken aback by his vehemence, she shrugged that off. She wasn't lying, exactly. There were many shades of willingness—and she was as willing as she'd ever be.

He took a breath. "I can handle questions. I'm going to take a bath if you're sure you don't want to go first?"

"No. You seriously need a nap," she bit out, then relented. "And if you go first, I can linger in the tub as long as I like."

Abruptly, he grinned, changing moods in a blink. "Aha! You're not as selfless as you pretend to be."

She couldn't help smiling back. "Not in the least. You should know by now that I'm exceptionally high maintenance. Acquire an expensive familiar and you can expect to keep paying, you know."

"I can live with that," he said quietly, going over to the many packages he'd brought back from his shopping and scouting spree. Opening one, he grunted in satisfaction and handed her a silk case. "It might not be the exact stuff you like," he said awkwardly, "but it was the most expensive they had. And the saleswoman said it's a complete kit. With a crème, too, for your skin." He rubbed his own neck in demonstration, his gaze going to the bruises on her collarbones. "The other packages are all for you, too."

He hesitated, some thought making him awkward still, then he shrugged and went into the bathing chamber, closing the door behind him.

Nic checked the contents of the kit: high-end House Aratron cosmetics, hair balms, and lotions. Even a bottled grooming imp from her own house. She sighed in pure delight. Apparently, she hadn't needed to tell Gabriel she liked her luxuries. Going through the other packages, she felt like it was her natal day. Two lovely gowns, plus two more sets of clothes suitable for riding. A warm robe to go over the old nightgown Missus Ryma had given her.

Also, three books, brand new from the House Calliope presses, one of them by her favorite author—how Gabriel had guessed, she didn't know—and a set of embroidery silks, linens, and needles.

The man didn't miss a trick. *What about the care and feeding of familiars?* A burst of emotion made her heart actually throb in her chest. She was doomed.

Pouring him a generous glass of wine, she knocked on the bathing room door, going in when he called for her to enter, though he sounded wary. He watched her approach with something close to apprehension, surrounded in rising steam, his muscled arms braced on the sides of the large soaking tub. He'd dunked his head, so his silver hair looked darker, the black streak less startling, and water beaded on his impressive chest.

She handed him the wine, heroically keeping her eyes on his and not peeking any lower, tempting though it was. *You've seen it all before*, she reminded herself, but understood for the first time why Gabriel didn't find that to be a valid argument, either. "Thank you," she said, keeping it sincere and simple. Otherwise, she might start babbling.

He raised a single brow. "For?"

She held up the book by her favorite author. "How did you know?"

"Vale told me." He said it very seriously, but his lips quirked. "I heard you telling him that you wished you had a book to read while you soaked in your hot bath."

Ah, of course he'd heard that. The amazing part was that he'd listened. "Vale didn't tell you Lady Stewart is my favorite novelist."

"How can you be sure?" He sipped the wine, watching her over the rim with darkly amused eyes.

"Vale is very smart, but he is not a reader of fiction. Everyone knows horses prefer nonfiction."

"There is that." His wizard-black gaze simmered with some heated thought. "I saw that you had many books by Lady Stewart in your tower room, back at House Elal. When I asked for the bookseller's newest books, hoping maybe you hadn't read them yet, I recognized the name. You haven't already read it, have you?" He looked momentarily stricken.

"No, which makes the gift even more delicious, but even if I had already read it, I would've enjoyed rereading it. So, thank you—for the books, the clothes, the embroidery silks… everything. You thought of everything." She'd repeated herself, sounding like an idiot in the wealth of emotion.

"Surely not *everything*," he replied softly, with a quirk of a smile, but not laughing at her. "But I hoped to supply at least a few things that might bring you a measure of happiness."

The man was impossible. "You don't need to be concerned about my happiness," she said, waving the book at him wildly, losing her good intentions in her frustration.

"I disagree." He gazed at her steadily, immovable as a rock.

"What is this, Gabriel?" she asked.

He looked from her to the book and back. "Is that a trick question? I'm sticking with 'a book' as my answer."

"Why are you giving me gifts? Why are you being so…" She couldn't articulate all of the aggravating things he was being, how he was eroding her defenses, deepening her Fascination, and turning it into… She ended up finishing in a strangled sound of frustration.

"I'm courting you," he explained patiently. "In Meresin, if we find a person we want to marry, we give them gifts to please them. I suppose it's also a more primitive urge, demonstrating that we can and will provide a good life for our prospective spouse."

"*Gabriel!*" She made an epithet of his name, glaring at him in impotent exasperation. "How many times must I explain this? I am already yours. You don't need to convince me of anything."

"Now there, you are unequivocally wrong—and you're lying to me again." He sounded more weary than angry. "How can we get anywhere if we're not honest with each other? Especially about this."

She clutched the book in both hands, not sure if she wanted to hit him over the head with it or fling herself into his arms. Possibly both, except the book would get wet. "What do you want from me?" she asked instead of answering his impossible question, hearing the plaintive tone in her own voice.

"I think you know that perfectly well," he replied, finishing his wine. "I'll get out so you can begin your long, leisurely soak with your new book."

"No, stay. I didn't mean to truncate your bath."

"If I stay in here any longer, I'll fall asleep," he said with a wry smile. "So far your prescription is right on track. The nap is next—and inevitable. Go gather your supplies, and I'll get out."

"No." She set the book aside where it would stay nicely dry and picked up a fluffy towel. "I'm here already, so I might as well help you dry off." She eyed the pile of bandages on the floor. "And I should check your wounds. How do they feel?"

"The hot water burned like fire," he admitted, "but they're better. I can deal with them myself."

"On your back? I don't think so. Get out, then." She paused, considering, then gave him a seductive smile. "Unless you'd like me to get in?"

"I absolutely do not want you to do that." He looked away from her, and she wrestled the twin stings of disappointment and rejection. She waited, but he didn't move.

"Did you change your mind?" she finally asked.

He flashed her a look of irritation, black eyes chilly with it. "No, I'm waiting for you to leave so I can have some privacy."

"I've seen you naked before," she pointed out.

"That doesn't mean I want you to see me naked now."

"Do you want me to turn my back?"

"You're not going to leave, are you?"

"I can step out and come back, but I really should check your wounds." She indicated the pot of Inytta's healing salve. "You were clearly thinking along the same lines. It's pure stubborn foolishness to—"

"Fine," he gritted out, interrupting her. "Turn your back."

Suppressing a smile, she did. Nothing stopped her from watching him in one of the many fine mirrors in the elegant bathing chamber. House Byssan did excellent work, and Gabriel's reflection shone as true as life—clearly revealing his erection before he snatched a towel to wrap around his hips. *Oh ho!* Not so uninterested in her offer after all. And yet he'd still refused. *Hmm.*

He turned his back to her and perched on a vanity chair, spine stiff. "All right, you can look."

Refining her strategy, she moved to him and dried his back and shoulders with long, caressing strokes of the towel. He stayed rigidly unmoving, but the cool silvery shimmer of his magic curled around her in response. Lifting his hair, she dried his neck beneath it, then draped the towel over his shoulders and used a smaller cloth to blot his hair. The inn had a set of House Aratron hair potions for guest use, so she put a dab of their oil in her palm, rubbed her hands together to warm it, then worked it into his scalp.

The tense line of his shoulders dropped, and he made a small sound of pleasure, then quickly swallowed. Enjoying herself, Nic massaged his scalp, working the oil through his hair, but also exploiting the pressure points to relax and seduce him. She would demonstrate her willingness if that was what he needed.

"Did you learn this in school, too?" he asked in a gruff voice.

"No, Maman taught me this. Whenever we had to wash my hair, she'd do this for me as a treat. I was the only one of my friends who didn't loathe having her hair combed out." Nic picked up a comb from the inn's supply and drew it through his shining silver hair. The black streak grew all from one circle, a lone cluster of hairs dark as a moonless night. "How did this black streak happen?"

He grunted. "It's the reverse. My hair used to be all black, but I messed up experimenting with moon magic one night and accidentally turned it all silver, except for that one spot."

She shook her head at his recklessness. Truly, it was a wonder he hadn't killed himself "experimenting" with such powerful magic, completely unsupervised. She finished combing out his hair, leaving it in a smooth sheet of silver almost as flawless as the mirrors. Then she discarded the damp towels and picked up another dry one and came around to his front. Patting the towel over his face, she stroked down to his thickly corded neck, amused by the wariness leaking into his relaxed expression. "What were you trying to do?"

He huffed a humorless laugh. "I'd read a spell that turned moonlight into a reflective shield, so I could go unseen. I didn't execute it correctly and saturated myself instead."

The wry admission made her smile. "Stand up."

"Why?" Suspicion fully dominated his face now.

"I can't reach your wounds very well with you sitting in a chair," she pointed out, quite reasonably.

He made a humming sound, but stood, immediately turning his back to her.

She slipped around in front of him, stroking the towel over his chest and pretending she didn't notice his erection tenting the towel around his hips. Drying his chest hair to a silvery shine, she followed the treasure trail down, happily anticipating what she knew she'd find.

He seized her wrists in an implacable grip, stopping her. Looking up at him through her lashes, she made her face a picture of innocence. "Problem?"

"This is not my back," he said, his voice hoarse.

"No, it's your front, and most delicious, too," she purred, dropping the towel and splaying her fingers over his hard abdomen.

"Nic," he said in a warning growl. "Stop this."

"You don't like me touching you?" She stroked her fingers over his skin. So soft, with all that delicious muscle beneath. Her magic bloomed at his nearness, rising to coil with his.

But Gabriel's grip on her wrists only tightened. "I'm not having sex with you."

She leaned in and pressed a kiss to his bare chest, moving to flick her tongue over one of his nipples. A groan of need rumbled through him. Then he jerked her wrists up, stretching her to her toes as he stared into her face, wizard-black eyes focused on her mouth.

"I mean it," he informed her in a tense voice. "I won't use you this way."

She rubbed against him, almost in the right position to slide his length between her thighs—if not for that inconvenient towel. "It's not using me if I'm willing. That's my point.

Gabriel. I *am* willing."

He closed his eyes as if in pain, inhaling deeply. Then he shook his head sharply and set her away from him. "I don't think you know."

Nic stared at him, stunned, and more than a little angry. "Are you telling me I don't know my own mind?" *Which, actually, is a valid point, given the Fascination…*

Gabriel tightened the towel around his hips, heaving a sigh full of frustration—sexual and otherwise. "Maybe it's me who doesn't know. But I'm understanding more all the time of how this wizard–familiar power dynamic works. It's clear that your Convocation Academy carefully taught you that it would be your role to serve me. The care and feeding of your wizard. Offering yourself for sex is part of that, isn't it?"

She opened and closed her mouth, feeling like a stranded fish. "It seems like you've been taking care of me, too," she said, grabbing onto that argument.

"Yes, because that's what partners do," he replied without missing a beat. "*That* is what I want from you, to answer your question, in case you're too stubborn to acknowledge it. I won't participate in anything else."

"Don't you want me?" she demanded, fists on hips. Catching a glimpse of herself in the mirror, she winced. She looked like a waif washed up on the beach. She should have staged her seduction much better. "Maybe after I bathe. I'll put on something pretty and—"

He held up a hand to stop her. "Don't bother because I'm not going to let you manipulate me."

Her breath froze in her chest. Had she been trying to do that after all? She hadn't been consciously using her wiles on him, but… *If you want to have influence over your wizard master, then you will find sweetness gets you much farther than sarcastic words and dour moods.* Maybe Gabriel was right that she'd absorbed more of the shoulds and shouldn'ts for familiars than she'd realized. "Gabriel," she said, her voice hushed with horror at herself, "I didn't mean to—"

His forbidding expression immediately softened. "That was harsh of me." He raked a hand through his damp hair, disordering her careful work. "I know you're not trying to manipulate me."

But it was more true than he knew.

"It's just that…" He trailed off, seeing something in her face. "I won't use you, Nic. Not for sex, not for magic, not for anything. I *do* want you. Even if you put on those cosmetics and a pretty dress, I couldn't want you more than I already do." He gestured to his erection with chagrin. "It was foolish of me to try to hide that from you. But wanting you isn't enough."

"No?" Humiliation boiled into something hotter. "It was enough for you when you planted your seed in me. Remember that *you* engaged in the Betrothal Trials. Willingly," she added, spitting out the word.

"I know that," he ground out, "and believe me, I regret that night with everything in me."

*Oh. Ouch.* That revelation shouldn't hurt so much. She regretted that night, too, didn't she? After all, she'd wrecked her life, her relationship with Papa and her entire house to escape it. To escape him. She opened her mouth to tell him so and found she had no words.

Gabriel scrubbed the heel of his hand over his forehead. "I didn't mean that how it sounded."

"Don't apologize for being honest," she managed to say.

He cursed viciously, then caught her hand, holding it in both of his, holding her gaze with his. "I'm saying this badly. If I've learned anything since I was thrust into being a wizard, it's that I have to control the magic, or it will control me. With you..." He shook his head at himself. "The magic and the sex seem to intertwine."

"I know," she breathed. "For me, too."

He nodded, as if she'd confirmed something for him. "I don't know where the one stops and the other starts. Until we figure it out, I'm not taking that risk."

"What risk?"

He regarded her somberly. "That anything I do could make you like Daniel or Narlis."

"I wouldn't be."

"Are you sure?" He searched her eyes. "Something scared

you enough that you ran."

The man was too perceptive. And she still wasn't discussing her reasons. "Have it your way," she said evenly.

He winced. "Nic, I—"

"May I at least salve your wounds?" she interrupted.

Hesitating only a moment, he nodded, then turned his back. "Yes, please."

As she smoothed the salve over the remarkably healed wounds—all closed with nicely pink flesh—she commented. "We'll need someone to take the stitches out soon."

He grunted in agreement. "There's a healer in Meresin who can do that."

"How long before we get there?" There. Having a perfectly natural conversation.

"Two days should get us there," he replied in the same conversational tone. Weren't they just so polite?

"Thank you," he said when she finished, his expression grave as he faced her again. He looked tired, and she kicked herself for testing him when he needed sleep so badly. Lifting a finger, he caressed her collarbones where she knew the bruises glared with purple sullenness. "I'm sorry for this, for everything you've had to go through."

Throat going tight, she nodded, not trusting her voice.

He feathered his fingers over her cheek. "I didn't mean to make you unhappy," he said, searching her face. "I wanted you to enjoy this evening, and now I've ruined it."

She took a deliberate step back, unable to bear either his touch or his sympathy. Pasting on a bright smile, she picked up her book. "Not at all. I have my new book, plenty of wine, an endless supply of hot water, and clean clothes to put on. I'm happy as a fire elemental in a bale of hay."

His mouth quirked ruefully. "Should I expect to be burned to ash in my sleep?"

"Never," she promised, summoning a flirtatious smile. "I'd wake you up first, so you'd suffer more."

He let out a laugh. "Enjoy your bath. Linger as long as you like."

"I intend to," she replied lightly.

Neither of them moved.

"Go sleep, Gabriel," she said gently. "I'm fine. Really."

With a nod, he left her to it. As Nic assembled her supplies for the bath and to dress after, she wondered when, exactly, she'd fallen in love with the wizard.

# ~ 18 ~

"WE'RE GOING TO need another horse," Nic told him, "or an elemental-powered wagon." She surveyed her packed bags with a dismayed frown that did nothing to diminish her loveliness. He almost regretted buying that riding outfit for her, because the deep burgundy color made her beauty that much more vivid, especially her luscious mouth, and the tailoring—guaranteed by Ophiel magic to fit her figure exactly—emphasized every enticing curve he'd forbidden himself from touching.

She'd also left her hair down, the curls gleaming from the attentions of her grooming imp, and in the soft morning sunlight, she looked more delicious than the pastries they'd devoured for breakfast.

"Gabriel, are you listening?" She assessed him with a practiced eye. "Maybe you need more rest."

He nearly leapt at the suggestion. He wanted nothing more than to stay in the solace of the inn with her forever. Though he also couldn't trust himself in such close quarters with her a moment longer. Her magic curled around him, filling his head with the heady scent of rose-spiced wine, and his own magic constantly reached for her, wanting to take more and more. He shook his head to dispel the insistent craving.

"No, you're not listening to me?" She lifted a raven-black brow.

"No, we don't need another horse," he replied. "And I'm not buying one of those wagons."

"Well, you bought so much other stuff that I don't think we can fit all of this on Vale, even if we both walk."

"What I mean is, there will be three of us, so we'll need *two* more horses, so that we can each ride one. Three horses ought to be sufficient to carry the packs, too, if we distribute them evenly."

"Three horses," she said flatly. "Gabriel Phel, do *not* tell me you're contemplating what I think you are."

Amazing, really, how well she already knew him. He nodded. "We're taking Narlis with us."

She folded her arms, looking at him like he'd lost his mind. "You cannot steal another wizard's familiar."

"Why not?" He pressed the glyph to summon help to carry their bags.

"To begin with, because it's against Convocation law."

"I find I'm not all that fond of many Convocation laws," he remarked.

"Second, that Iblis wizard will hardly just let her go."

"I'll buy her from him."

"Gabriel!" She gaped at him in shock. "You can't buy and sell people in the Convocation."

"You could've fooled me," he growled. "That's exactly what's going on with familiars—it's just dressed up as something else."

"Still!" She actually stomped her booted foot, managing to look adorably elegant doing it.

"Fine, fine. Then if she's so free to choose, I'll invite her to come live in Meresin, where she'll be offered the comfort her long life deserves. Isn't that what you told me—that she'd likely leave him if only someone would take her in? I'll take her in."

"That Iblis wizard won't let her go easily," Nic warned.

"Let him try to stop me," he replied on a snarl. "I hope he does. I'd love an excuse to smack that weasel around."

"You're impossible."

"I didn't like the way he touched you," Gabriel said, fingers curling into fists at the memory. "Or the way he looked at you. Or the foul things he said. I'd like to wrap every one of those collars around his neck and strangle him with them. Though that brings up a fair point—if Narlis is wearing that collar, how do we get the Iblis wizard to take it off of her?"

"She won't be." Nic dismissed that problem with a dash of her hand. "That was a show collar, for demonstration. Like I said, most collars really are just for show and not functional." Her fingers drifted to the bruises at her throat and collarbones, only adding fuel to his anger.

"Good," he grunted. "Then there's nothing stopping us."

"Only good sense," she retorted. "What about Daniel?" she demanded. "Are you planning to save him, too?"

"What happens if you separate a bonded familiar from their wizard?" he asked. He'd been saving that question. Good of her to provide the perfect opportunity.

She held up a hand, ticking off her points. "One: even more against the law. Two: the wizard will pursue and will pull no punches. Jan would be within his rights to kill you, for example. Three: Daniel would fight you to get back to Jan. And—"

"Even if he hates his wizard?" Gabriel interrupted.

"You are not hearing me on this," she replied with some frustration. "When I say it doesn't matter how we feel, I mean that literally. Happy or unhappy, hate or love, familiars crave their wizard masters. That's four: he would waste away and eventually die without Jan."

Hmm. "That's documented?"

"Remember what I told you about the bad old days and experimentation on familiars? Yes, that was tested, too."

"It seems that if the bond can be forged, it can be broken," he argued. "Regardless, Narlis isn't bonded, so she's free to come with us."

Her tempting mouth curving into a smile, Nic came toward him, hips swaying hypnotically. He wrested his gaze up to her face as she lifted a hand to caress his newly shaved cheek. That grooming imp *was* handy. "This path leads to trouble," she said softly. "And won't help you restore House Phel."

"Maybe not." He laid a hand over hers. "But I have to be able to live with myself, too."

A line formed between her brows, eyes snapping with impatience, all softness gone. "You can't save every familiar, foolish wizard."

"Not one by one, but it's a start."

"A start to what?" she asked with growing suspicion.

"Change." A knock came on the door, and he kissed the furrow between her brows before going to answer it.

"You can't change the entire world," Nic called after him. He only grinned at her and let the pair of young people in to gather their bags. Nic was correct that it was a lot of stuff, but it had pleased her, at least a little. He'd go to a lot more trouble than that to alleviate the bitter grief that still haunted her face when she wasn't putting on a show for him.

"Let's go see someone about a couple of horses," he said, bringing her cloak to her.

She let him fasten it around her shoulders but glared at him balefully. "If you're determined to bring Narlis with us, a wagon would be even better."

"No. I don't want to be beholden to anything Elal."

"Stubborn wizard. I knew when I read your dossier that you were exactly the sort to dash yourself brainless trying to fight the Convocation."

He trailed a finger over her cheek. "So intelligent and insightful. And yet you didn't summarily dismiss such a foolish wizard."

"Clearly I'm not as smart as you think," she replied with asperity, moving away from his touch.

AN HOUR LATER, they'd returned to the inn with two new

horses to share Vale's burden. Nic perched happily on an elegant white mare, lightly dappled with gray, and with a mane and tail like glossy slate. Predictably, Nic had argued that the mare was too pricey, but she was perfectly sized for Nic's stature, and the pair of them had immediately fallen in love. She hadn't even protested all that much, though she'd made dire promises about taking a hard look at the House Phel accounts in the future, reviewing his expenditures, and creating a budget.

The other mare was a gentle bay with a smooth stride and an even temperament that should work well for Narlis.

With their copious luggage distributed between the three horses, Gabriel walked, leading Vale, Nic following behind on her mare and leading the one for Narlis. Gabriel had tried talking Nic into waiting at the inn for him to return with Narlis, but she flatly refused, insisting her place was by his side, in case he needed her assistance. When he argued that he could best the Iblis wizard without breaking a sweat, she'd called him arrogant and overconfident—then suggested that an abandoned, unbonded familiar left to kick her heels alone at an inn could be abducted.

And that had done it.

They reached the shop, Gabriel burying his deep distaste along with the urge to simply throttle the asshole wizard. "Stay on your horse," he told Nic, feeling he needed to remind her, even though that had been a condition of her coming along.

"Yes, master," she sang out cheerfully, simpering when he glowered at her.

He grabbed the door handle of the shop and found it

locked. Physically as well as magically. Stepping back, he stared in the darkened windows, confounded.

"It might've been smarter to acquire the rider before the horse," Nic noted sardonically.

"She's a solid mare," he replied without looking at her. "We can always use more good horses in Meresin."

"Good livestock is always valuable," Nic agreed, beaming at him innocently when he glared over his shoulder at her.

"Is this you being helpful?" he asked.

She blinked in false surprise. "But you told me—in no uncertain terms—that you didn't need my assistance."

He grunted, lifting his gaze to the second story, wondering if the wizard and Narlis lived above the shop.

"She won't be up there," Nic said at his elbow.

"Why aren't you on your horse?" he ground out.

"Because I dismounted," she confided, smiling sweetly. Then she tapped a gloved finger against her chin, pretending to think. "If only there were a way for you to make me follow your orders… Oh! I know. You could—"

"Stop." He sighed out his exasperation, fighting not to laugh at her mischief.

Nic's eyes sparkled knowingly. Though she had the hood of her cloak down on the chilly, overcast, but so far rainless day, the white fur ruff framed her striking beauty perfectly. "Narlis almost certainly lives out back," Nic told him.

"Out back?"

"I don't condone this enterprise, but I don't care to linger in this town either. Iblis isn't the type to keep his familiar in his quarters. She'll have a space in the carriage house at best, stable or kennel at worst." She lifted her brows at his shock. "Livestock."

"I hate this," he muttered, going back to gather up the horses' reins, leading them down the row of shops and looking for an entrance to the alley behind.

"It's exhausting fighting the world," Nic agreed.

"You would know," he shot back, then regretted it. "I'm sorry," he said, though she looked thoughtful, not upset.

"No, you're right. I did find that out, the hard way." She had her hands tucked inside her cloak since he was leading the three horses. "That's part of why I gave up."

*Ouch.* "Nic, I—"

"No, no." She extracted a hand and waved him off. She never did seem to want his sympathy. In fact, she actively rejected it. "I'm in a mood this morning. Don't mind me."

She picked up her pace so she was leading the way, and he followed after, knowing full well that their conversation of the afternoon before was the cause of her mood. Oh, she'd been perfectly charming company, alternately playful and solicitous. As promised, she'd soaked in the tub for hours and emerged looking like Lady Veronica Elal again—tightly swathed in the warm robe he'd bought her.

And she'd also retreated behind that wall of polite formality, her manners beyond reproach, no sign of the sensual woman who'd nearly succeeded in seducing him despite his better judgment.

He had to lengthen his stride to keep up with her brisk pace as she walked purposefully down a winding path behind the shops. He'd expected loading docks and so forth, but the rear side of the shops were residences. Several stories tall, most had expanses of windows, porches, and balconies to take advantage of the view of the harbor and ocean. He'd never have guessed they were there, but Nic seemed unsurprised.

"Have you been here before?" he asked, catching up with her, feeling quite sure she said she hadn't.

"Never. Why?"

"You knew about these residences being back here."

"Don't they do this in Meresin? This is pretty standard for the Convocation. Shops face the street, then residences are on the quiet side, away from traffic and commerce." She pointed to a row of rooftops on the downhill side, occasional stairways leading down. "Those will be the stables, kennels, and carriage houses, bordering the next street down."

They reached the back of the locksmith shop, the residence there looking equally dark. "Could be he left town," Gabriel noted. Hopefully the bastard wouldn't renege on the secrecy Gabriel had bought.

"Iblis said he knew the maker of the collar," Nic said. "It was a hunter collar. Therefore, the Iblis maker that our lowly locksmith knows has a business relationship with the same Convocation folks who sent the hunters."

"I paid him for his silence," Gabriel reminded her, following her down some steep steps and leaving the horses tied above. He had a bad feeling about the situation, though.

Nic shrugged. "The Convocation will probably pay him even more. They no doubt consider me a renegade. Even if they didn't feel they needed to make an example of me—which they undoubtedly do—there are few things the

Convocation fears more than an uncontrolled familiar."

He caught her arm. "Why?"

She frowned up at him. "Why what?"

"If familiars can't do magic on their own, why does the Convocation have so many laws to control them? What could possibly happen if familiars were allowed to simply run around on their own, without wizard masters?"

"Because, we—" She broke off, considering. "I guess I don't really know. I never thought about it that way."

"Something to think about, then."

She gazed at him, green eyes wide and thoughtful, lips parted as if she might say something more. "I will."

He released her arm before he succumbed to the temptation to kiss those inviting lips.

"None of that changes what is, however," she added. "And that is that the Convocation will want to retrieve me. At any cost."

"All the more reason to get you safely to Meresin."

"They'll never find me in all those swamps," Nic declared, shooting a triumphant fist in the air.

"You really are in a mood," he muttered.

Nic changed her raised fist to an obscene gesture, smiling broadly in counterpoint. He just shook his head. The Iblis locksmith's carriage house and stables, unlike the residence, had its doors open to the busy street. An Elal wagon stood halfway out, being loaded with supplies. Narlis included.

The old woman sat shivering in the back, wedged between a couple of casks—with not even a blanket. As Nic had predicted, she wasn't wearing the collar anymore. Small mercies. The Iblis wizard had his back to them, officiously railing at a boy staggering under the weight of a trunk. Probably loaded with collars for Convocation Center. Gabriel fingered the hilt of his sword. It would be child's play to simply drive his blade through the wizard's liver and leave him there in the street to rot. Most satisfying.

Nic put a hand on his arm, her face completely serious, all hint of mood and mischief fled. "Don't do it," she said quietly. "You joke, but starting wars with other houses, even one that's second tier like Iblis, will only jeopardize what you've been working toward."

"I don't care about—"

"Don't you?" she cut in, giving him a hard look. "We've both sacrificed for this future you've planned. If you destroy House Phel's prospects now, you'll take me down with it. Is that what you want—for the momentary satisfaction of murdering a wizard not worth even your passing attention?" She leaned in, her scent hothouse sweet and somehow redolent of summer heat even in the chill air. "There will be other battles to fight. Bigger, harder, more important. If you're serious about change, if you plan to take on the Convocation, then don't tip your hand now."

He considered her words and nodded. "Iblis!" he shouted.

The wizard turned, bobbled, mouth gaping in surprise. Then he pasted on his obsequious shopkeeper's grin, no doubt hoping Gabriel hadn't guessed his planned betrayal. "Wizard Phel, what a pleasure. Decided on a collar for your pet after all? I'm afraid I'm off on an errand, so a custom job is out of the question, but I do have a nice supply of premades here. Boy!

Put down that chest."

Tempted to pick up the chest of collars and chuck it into the sea, Gabriel caught Nic's warning look and reined in the impulse. "No, I'm here to take Narlis off your hands."

The Iblis wizard paused, face blank with incomprehension. "Narlis?"

The woman jerked at hearing her name from the wizard's mouth. "Yes, master?"

He waved her silent, his greedy gaze going to Nic, licking his lips as actual drool threatened to escape. "A trade?" he asked tentatively, as if hardly daring to hope.

Gabriel's fingers twitched at the thought of the man putting his hands on Nic. "Never," he vowed.

"She's not really yours," the Iblis wizard replied in a wheedling tone. "They'll be after you for stealing her. A trade is in your best interests." His hard gaze traveled over Nic. "I know exactly how to deal with her."

"He'll never agree," Nic said in a quiet sing-song. "You're wasting your breath."

As usual, she was right. "Narlis!" Gabriel called. "Would you like to come with us? I'm offering you a comfortable home, the retirement you deserve." The woman cringed back between the flanking casks, shaking her head wildly.

The Iblis wizard pointed at his familiar, expression gloating. "See? She doesn't want to go with you."

"Let me talk to her," Nic urged, and Gabriel nodded.

"You can't steal another wizard's familiar," the Iblis wizard continued ranting, pushing into Gabriel's face. This wouldn't end well. "Is this what you do?" he demanded. "You travel around and steal unbonded familiars from honest wizards? I'm reporting you to the Convocation and—"

"Don't," he growled. Drawing his magic to him, he leaned in to loom over the shorter man. "Or I will cauterize your tongue and insert it up your ass where you keep the rest of your head."

The Iblis wizard gaped at him, blanching and stuttering. Behind the man, Nic was helping Narlis down from the wagon, talking quietly to the old woman the whole time. Catching his eye, Nic nodded and turned the woman toward the steps leading up to the horses.

Unfortunately, the Iblis wizard turned just then. "Hey!"

Gabriel thumped him on the crown of his balding head, and the man dropped like a sack of grain. The boy who'd been helping load the wagon gaped, eyes bulging, then turned and ran.

Nic threw Gabriel a look of utter exasperation.

"Oops," he said, unable to suppress an unrepentant grin, striding over to join them.

"I thought we discussed this," Nic hissed. Narlis hobbled slowly to the steps, lifted a foot with painful deliberation.

"I didn't kill him," he countered.

Narlis, leaning heavily on Nic, pulled herself up the one step.

Gabriel looked at the steep column of several dozen steps remaining. Narlis lifted a foot slowly to the next step. "Gran," he said, "forgive me the impertinence." Lifting the woman gently into his arms, he carried her up the steps. It was like carrying a shivering sack of dandelion fluff. Nic raced ahead of them to ready the horses.

Narlis blinked cataract-fogged eyes at him, lifted her gnarled fingers to his cheek, and patted it. "You're a good boy," she said.

"I try."

"That's all we can do, try." Her blue-veined eyelids drifted closed.

"She's not going to be able to sit a horse," he said to Nic when he reached her.

She only nodded, having the grace not to say she'd told him so, leading the horses as she walked beside him. "The Elal wagon shop, then?"

"Will someone there recognize you?"

She pursed her lips, wrinkled her nose. "Possibly. Is that the real reason you didn't want to get an elemental-powered wagon?"

"It's another reason, but I definitely don't want to be beholden to Elal."

"More than you already are," she pointed out saucily.

"True. I wonder if they'd give me a wagon in lieu of your dowry?"

She rolled her eyes. "Papa showed me the contract. If they offer you that deal, *don't* take it. In fact, I wouldn't mention who *you* are, just in case."

"Because your father hates me?"

"No, actually." She slid him a look. "Papa said you had balls and deserved a chance to rebuild House Phel. He encouraged the match."

Gabriel didn't know how to feel about that. If your hated

enemy approves of you, what does that mean about the sort of person you *are*?

"We'll have to buy Narlis warmer clothing, too. Maybe a couple of blankets."

At the sound of her name, the old familiar opened her eyes again and smiled at him vaguely. "You're a good boy," she said.

"I'm not sure she even knows who I am," Gabriel said quietly to Nic.

She had a worried turn to her mouth. "You were right to steal her away."

"Did you just admit that I was right and you were wrong?" he asked, a smile tugging at his own lips.

Nic glared at him. "I never said you were wrong. I said it was a bad idea, and it still is. Trouble is going to follow us on this one."

"Let it follow," he invited. "We can handle it."

Nic muttered something about impossible wizards.

IN THE END, Gabriel parked the bleary Narlis with Nic at a high-end Ophiel dress shop, which Nic wryly identified as well beyond the Iblis locksmith's means, even if he had been inclined to dress his familiar well. While Nic picked out warm clothing for her "granny," Gabriel paid good coin—pretty much the last of it, too—for a comfortable wagon, powered by a fast and fresh Elal-branded elemental. While it stung to put coin in Elal's pockets, Gabriel comforted himself that he'd be getting a good chunk of that treasure back in the form of Nic's dowry.

Or, rather, Nic would be getting it. If she couldn't find her way to being his willing partner, he'd settle that fortune on her and help her find some kind of life. Where, he didn't know. Maybe back in Wartson, ironically enough. He'd have to find a way to ensure her safety there, but that should be possible. And then there was the child. Could he talk Nic into living near House Phel, where he could keep an eye on her and visit the kid?

It was all such a miserable mess, and he had no idea how to solve it. So, he kept his sights set on getting them all safely to Meresin. In his head, he knew being home wouldn't magically solve the tangled knot of problems, but his heart disagreed.

And his heart was where most of the trouble started and ended.

Narlis mostly napped, warmly tucked under a pile of blankets in the silently gliding sled—he'd gotten the kind that powered over any kind of surface, knowing that would be useful in Meresin—the third horse behind it, Nic riding beside him on her mare. Vale pranced along with refreshed energy, clearly pleased to be shed of bags. It was good for the gelding to carry only Gabriel's weight again, but he regretted that he'd lost the opportunity to ride double with Nic.

He shook his head at himself. No—that was a good thing, as he didn't need to be tempted more than he already was. What was he going to do about her? It was a puzzle with no easy answer.

"Gnats?" Nic asked, raven-wing brows arched. "Biting flies? You keep shaking your head," she clarified when he frowned in confusion.

"I think it's too early in the year for those yet," he said. "It's still freezing at night, at least inland."

"Ah." She nodded knowingly. "So, which problem is gnawing at you, then?"

"Take your pick."

"Maybe we could discuss it," she offered, a hitch of uncertainty in her voice. "This is something I could do, as your wife."

He raised a brow, interested that she seemed to be trying a different approach with him. Her cheeks flushed with high color, though that could be the brisk weather. "What do you mean?"

She flashed him an annoyed look, much more in her usual character. "I was raised to head a High House. I know Convocation politics. I certainly know House Elal and my father inside and out. There must be a strategy to resolve all of this—a kind of reset to how things would have been if I hadn't been such a ninny and tried to escape."

"Don't call yourself that. You had good reasons. I understand that now."

She snorted at that, then was quiet a bit. "Let's consider this. The wisest option—and the best for the future of House Phel—would be to turn me over to the Convocation to be disciplined, retrained, and—"

"No."

"Hear me out. If you—"

"No. We just got that collar off of you. If any hunters pursue us, I'm killing them all, not blithely handing you over to be—"

"Gabriel!" She spoke his name sharply, and loudly enough that Vale swung his head to look at her in mild dismay. "Sorry, Vale. Gabriel, I have no desire to be handed over to the hunters either. Thank you for your passion on my behalf. What I'm saying is, *you* could take me to Convocation Center. We'd face the council and accept their judgment. I take my lumps, learn my lessons, and you assert your rights when I'm done. Then we have a nice, public wedding with pomp to please everyone. You bond me so they know I'm duly controlled, and we go to Meresin to devote ourselves to rebuilding House Phel."

"Your *lumps*," he repeated. "Do you have any idea what they'd do to you?"

"Some." She shrugged as if it didn't matter, though her face looked pinched. "I'm tough. They won't want to do anything that will harm the baby, so they can't hurt me too much."

"Not physically," he said darkly, remembering the Convocation proctor's words. *Even an experienced wizard may lose control of a recalcitrant familiar. You will need to be assisted by our Convocation trainers to ensure that she is properly subdued.* "But I bet there are mental techniques."

"House Hanneil does have methods," she admitted, staring off down the trail. They'd had the road to themselves for some time, other traffic thinning to nothing, the width and quality of the road diminishing along with it. Almost no one who wasn't from Meresin traveled in this direction. "Gabriel…" She firmed her lips. "What I'm saying is, it would be easier, for both of us, just to let them do it. They can make me happy with my lot. I would be content, understand?"

The image of a happily obedient Nic smiling mindlessly turned his stomach. "No. You can't possibly want that."

"Maybe I do," she argued. "You know me by now. I might never be content otherwise. I'm ambitious and impatient. I don't follow orders well. I'm not… I don't have the right makeup to be a familiar, not a good one, not as I am. I should've been a wizard." Her voice was growing increasingly agitated. "If not for my stupid brain"—she thunked the center of her forehead—"I would've been exactly right for that life."

"And what would that have been like?" When she frowned at him, he persisted. "Tell me how you envisioned your life as a wizard."

"I would've studied magic, developed my own spells. I'd have helped my father, eventually become Lady Elal, and helped run all our lands and businesses."

"You can do all of that, with me, in House Phel."

"Familiars can't execute spells," she reminded him pointedly.

"You can still study magic. You know far more than I do about using an arcanium, for example. There's nothing stopping you from developing your own spells. We'll combine our magic to execute them."

"I thought you were too noble to use my magic?"

"I won't *use* you. I *will* work with you. We can combine forces. You can still be head of a house, run its lands and businesses. You can be exactly right for that life. But it has to be what you want."

# ~ 19 ~

NIC TRIED TO picture this life Gabriel described—and it looked surprisingly close to what she'd envisioned at the beginning of the Betrothal Trials. Except that she'd planned to seize power gradually, through manipulation and guile, exert her influence to create a place where she could make choices about her own life. Of course, all that had depended on having a wizard master she could hate enough to conspire against, possibly hurry along to his death.

She couldn't hate Gabriel. She never had been able to, and she couldn't, especially now that he freely offered what she'd planned to take. It was still galling, that he'd have to give it to her—and he'd retain the power to take it away if he chose—but that was still better than the alternatives. She clearly wasn't doing a great job of resigning herself to her fate as a content and biddable familiar if she was contemplating having a Hanneil trainer do it for her.

No, Gabriel was right. That would be the worst possible fate. She'd rather be miserable and know her own mind than blissfully no longer herself. She shook that thought away.

"Gnats?" he asked with a slight smile. "Biting flies?"

"Cute," she acknowledged. "So, if you're not going to turn

me over to the Convocation, that leads us to the next knotty problem: that Iblis wizard and awful Cousin Jan are going to report that I'm with you."

"I'm expecting as much. I'll explain that, by the Convocation's own laws, you belong with me."

"It won't be that easy. If you don't turn me over to the Convocation or my family, you could well have a war on your hands."

"I'm willing to face that eventuality, because I'm not risking what they'd do to you."

She appreciated that he wanted to protect her, but she knew a great deal more about the Convocation than he did. One wizard could hardly fight off their combined forces. "Can House Phel withstand a war—against very likely overwhelming odds?"

"We'll find out," he replied grimly. "If it comes to that, I'll accept the consequences."

"Gabriel, I don't want to be the reason you end up at war with the Convocation."

"Don't worry about that." His expression hardened into granite lines. "I have my own reasons."

And though she pressed him, he wouldn't say more.

THE LANDSCAPE CHANGED as they rode toward the rising sun, the hills flattening out and growing less rocky. The trees grew taller and more graceful, their network of branches overhead showing the green fuzz of budding leaves. Birdsong filled the morning air and flowers bloomed amid the lacy ferns and tangled grasses of the undergrowth.

They'd spent the night at an abandoned cabin, which hadn't been exactly comfortable, especially since they gave Narlis most of the blankets. The old woman had been quiet, not saying anything except that Gabriel was a good boy. Nic privately worried that, though Narlis hadn't been bonded to the Iblis wizard, the separation from close connection to the wizard's magic had eroded her reason. The stories certainly liked to show as much. When Lyndella was abducted by Sylus's nemesis, she'd gone mad, locked in a cell while Sylus searched frantically for her. When he finally found her, she was too far gone. Lyndella died in his arms, insane and broken beyond repair. Then Sylus used all his magic wreaking revenge on his enemy, killing himself, but taking his nemesis with him. Thus ended the tragic tale of Sylus and Lyndella.

When Nic described those stories to Gabriel, he only shook his head in disgust. "Aren't there any tales where the wizard and familiar triumph and live happily ever after?" he demanded.

Nic rolled her eyes. "Believe me, there are plenty of those, and they're even more obnoxious."

"Why obnoxious?"

"Don't get me wrong, I loved those books—read every one I could get my hands on, especially when I was younger—but after a while in the Convocation, you figure out that very few wizard–familiar relationships are based on love. Or rather," she amended, "it's not the hearts-and-flowers kind of love." Maybe it was more this grinding, burning, endless craving she felt for Gabriel. Unhappy thought.

"What kind of love is it, then?" Gabriel watched her so intently that she wondered if he'd gathered something of her thoughts from her expression.

"One-sided," she replied crisply, knowing he wouldn't drop the subject at that, but still unwilling to explain just how fully he held her heart in his grip. Just because he hadn't clenched his fist to crush it yet didn't mean he wouldn't if he knew what kind of power he held.

"Because familiars hate their wizards too much to ever love them," he said with certainty.

Surprised enough to glance at him, Nic wondered how he'd decided that. He caught the look and nodded to himself. "I understand. I saw your parents, remember? Your father treats your mother with apparent affection but controls her ruthlessly. And poor Daniel, he could never love someone as cruel as Jan."

*Daniel the spaniel.* He did love Jan, with hopeless devotion, but Nic didn't tell Gabriel. They rode in silence after that.

THE PATH GREW narrower, the foliage lusher and denser, and the air warmer—and dense with moisture. It felt soft, nourishing in a way, not cutting like the coastal humidity. Nic shed her furry cloak, still almost too warm in her velvet riding habit. By midafternoon, she realized that the sound of the horses' hooves had changed. Peering down, she saw that the surface they traveled was higher than the surrounding ground, which seemed to be all grasses, but that wasn't ground between the tall stalks, it was water.

"Are we in a swamp?" she asked incredulously.

Gabriel flicked her a wryly amused glance. "After all of your needling remarks about Meresin being a swamp, I don't understand how you can be surprised."

"I guess I thought people were exaggerating," she supplied weakly. How did they build here? Maybe she should've given more credence to Gabriel's warning remarks about the state of House Phel itself. "Do you live on boats?" *Please not a barge…*

He laughed. "Not exactly. But you'll see. We'll be at the house before much longer."

He *did* live in a swamp. Nic eyed the occasional glimpses of water, no longer finding the lush foliage so lovely now that she knew there wasn't any solid ground. Some ratlike creature *swam* through a set of reeds nearby, and a sense of vertigo swept her, even though the trail they rode remained stable.

"Besides," Gabriel continued, "to say 'swamp' is a misnomer. This is technically a marsh."

"Charming." She studied the raised path, finding she felt steadier keeping her eyes on it. "The road is magically kept dry?" If so, maybe there was hope for dry ground in her future.

He shook his head. "No, just physically built up. Though water magic does occur at low levels among much of the population of Meresin, and people use it to wick away moisture, to keep their homes dry."

Interesting. "Has anyone been keeping track of the Phel family tree over the last few generations?"

"You mean anyone besides Elal spies?" he asked blandly.

A flush heated her cheeks as she recalled the extensive dossier on Gabriel's parentage and the various branches of the family. A sudden thought occurred to her along with that. "Gabriel, do your parents live at House Phel?"

He lifted a brow. "Yes, why?"

*Shit.* "What about extended family—cousins and so forth?"

"All at House Phel," he confirmed. "Or nearby. That's traditional, isn't it? Where else would they be?"

"I don't know, on farms. Didn't you say you grew up farming? How do you farm in a swamp, or marsh, or whatever?"

"Why are you upset all of a sudden?" He frowned at her.

Because she hadn't mentally prepared to meet his family. She'd slept in an abandoned cabin and had been wearing the same clothes for two days. She probably looked no better than that swimming rat. "What will your parents think of me?"

"They'll think you're lovely."

"They'll think I'm a mess," she corrected. "And they'll hate me for trying to escape. If I'd succeeded, I would've ruined you, destroyed the future of House Phel, stolen their grandchild, and—"

"Nic," he interrupted, holding out a hand and nudging his horse closer. Because she couldn't refuse him, she put her hand in his. He squeezed it, the silvery-cool calm of his magic spreading through her, soothing and sweet. "They don't know. I told them we might not return for a couple of weeks, and it's been about that long."

Weeks? She frowned. "What did they think we'd be doing?"

He lifted a shoulder, wry and resigned. "I didn't know. I guess I imagined spending time at House Elal. Parties and receptions. Convocation society stuff. I figured you'd want time for friends and family to travel for the wedding, and more time afterward to say farewells. I didn't know your traditions and wanted to accommodate you in whatever they were."

She stared at him, feeling stupid and stunned at once. And unreasonably furious. "Why are you so kind?" she demanded.

He blinked at her. "Shouldn't I be?"

"No." She yanked her hand away and waved it in the air. "Your soft heart will lead you into trouble. You need to be hard and merciless if you're going to survive in the Convocation."

"Meresin isn't in Convocation territory," he pointed out.

"It will be if you want House Phel to be a High House again. Or, if your house is a boat, maybe you can row it to a new place that *is* in Convocation lands."

"It would be a bit big for that." He grinned and pointed.

The tunnel of trees opened onto a vista of blue sky and bluer lake, surrounded by green grass. On the far side of the glassy lake, a large white house sprawled, perfectly reflected in the water. Colorful gardens tumbled around it, with groupings of chairs and tables scattered throughout. The center section of the house was graceful, with steps leading to a balustraded porch, tall columns supporting several tiers of balconies. From there, wings branched in random profusion to either side, hints of more gleaming through the foliage.

It was decidedly not a swamp.

"That's House Phel?" she asked faintly, just to be sure.

Gabriel was watching her, an odd expression on his face. Nerves? "Yes. I know it's not as grand as what you're used to—and a great deal of it is still in miserable disrepair—but we're making it livable again. I promise your room will be perfectly dry," he added with a quirk of a hopeful smile.

He was actually worried she wouldn't like it, so she managed to produce a smile to reassure him. "It's beautiful," she told him honestly. "Like no house I've ever seen."

"Like a cottage compared to a castle," he agreed.

"Not that so much, but it *is* completely indefensible," she pointed out, worrying about war more than ever.

"We're not sitting ducks exactly," he replied with a smile. "Look, they've sighted our approach." He pointed to a banner rising on a center pole from the roof. The House Phel crest—a silver moon shining on still water, set on a deep-green background, the same shade as the foliage around the house—fluttered in the golden afternoon light. Increased activity showed on the porch and lawn, people streaming out, clearly arranging a reception.

"I need to stop and fix myself up," Nic told Gabriel. "Indulge my vanity, please."

"You look beautiful," he said, "but I understand the desire to make a good first impression. We'll find a place for you to dismount and fix up."

"Something with dry ground to stand on," she specified, only half in jest.

He grinned at her so broadly that she realized he'd been enjoying yanking her chain over this. "You forget who you're with." He waved a hand at a marshy patch beside them, the water sifting away to reveal a hummock of grassy earth. "I promise to always provide you with dry ground," he said, holding her gaze, and it ended up coming out like a solemn vow, the moment humming between them.

Nic broke the tension first, guiding her mare to the freshly dry spot and dismounting. Gabriel dismounted too, stretching his legs while she rummaged through her bags in the sled for her cosmetics and the precious grooming imp. Narlis still slept, so Nic left her in peace. Setting the imp to work on her hair, she checked her makeup in the mirror that had come with the kit. One thing about grooming imps was that, unless you had a wizard to direct them, they tended to exhibit a sense of humor with cosmetics. It was wiser to do them yourself.

"All right, that's as good as it's going to get," she declared, belying her words by dabbing a bit more concealer on the bruises at her throat and collarbones. They were better, but still regrettably ugly. And impossible to miss.

"You're not hot in that velvet riding dress?" Gabriel frowned dubiously. He'd changed into a clean shirt, crisp and white, and left off the leather vest and cloak. The shirt lay open, revealing the silver glint of chest hair against his darker skin. She'd love to taste him just there, in the hollow of his throat. "I bought you some lighter gowns to wear."

She had to drag her thoughts from the fantasy of licking him up like chocolate. "Those gowns would be much cooler, but one is linen and the other silk," she explained, "which means they're dreadfully wrinkled."

"Get one out," he urged with a mischievous smile. "The purple one."

"There isn't a purple one," she argued, knowing exactly which one he meant and digging for it. "It's mauve."

"It should be pretty with your eyes, whatever color it is," he said, turning his back while she undressed.

It definitely felt cooler to don the mauve linen, which immediately molded itself to her figure. The full skirts were as horribly wrinkled, as she'd feared, however. "You can look now," she told him. "It's lovely—thank you for it—but as I feared, the wrinkles are—" She broke off on a gasp as the wrinkles vanished, a faint hint of steam wafting through the air. "Well, that's a handy trick."

"I have a few," he replied with a slight smile, though his expression was tight with some suppressed emotion, his eyes dark with it, his magic a keen-edged heated silver, lingering still. His dark eyes dipped to her generously displayed bosom before he wrenched his gaze to her face again. "You looked lovely before, but now you're dazzlingly beautiful."

"Thank you." She searched his face, wanting to say something but not sure what it would be. Ever since he'd laid out his terms on not using her for magic or sex, he'd seemed to be waiting for her to make some kind of decision. But she didn't know what she could say that she'd hadn't already said.

"Ready to cross the finish line?" he asked.

She nodded and mounted her mare. "Is the steam another self-taught spell?" she asked, choosing a safe topic of conversation.

"Not really. It's a standard trick, just another version of wicking water in and out of household objects. Most everyone in Meresin can do it to some extent. No one thinks of it as magic."

"Though it *is* magic."

"I know that now," he answered wryly.

"That's why you remained oblivious to your magic for so long," she realized. "You were probably moving water away from you out of habit for a long time, as so many here do."

He nodded. "We almost never need to make water *appear*, so that ability came as a major shock."

"I'll bet you were a good farmer," she speculated. "Your fields always getting the right amount of moisture."

"Yes." He sounded introspective, almost sad. "I thought I had a talent for it."

"In point of fact, you did."

His lips quirked in a smile that didn't reach his eyes. "Not the same thing. But yes, it took a drought to wake me up to what I really was. Even then, it took a while to reconcile myself to it."

"You don't like being a wizard?"

"I never wanted this," he admitted. "At first I felt like a monster. After I got used to having magic, and began to learn all the ramifications... There's a lot of responsibility that came with it."

It couldn't have been easy for the young wizard, facing building an entire house from practically nothing. "We're quite the pair," she said, trying for a teasing tone. "You're what I wanted to be, and I—well, I guess you never wanted to be a familiar, so it's not quite parallel."

"I might've been happier as one, though."

"Don't be ridiculous. No one *wants* to be a familiar."

His lip curled. "You don't have to say it—I'm acutely aware of how the Convocation oppresses familiars and relegates you to a life of essential bondage."

"I wasn't going to say that," she replied quietly, taken aback at his brusque summation.

"No, because you don't want to admit that's what's happening," he replied easily, "that even your own family would see you brutalized rather than free."

"Wrong," she retorted. "I know—far better than you do—the realities of my station in life, to have my beloved papa go from cherishing me as his heir one day to treating me like yet another Elal export the next. To have assholes like Cousin Jan sneer when I have ten times his MP scores." *To crave Gabriel so much that I could never leave him, even to save myself.* Furious with herself, she dashed away the unwanted tears. Great, and now she'd ruined her makeup.

"I apologize," Gabriel said quietly. "I didn't mean to upset you. It's just that, sometimes you seem like you excuse the Convocation for how terribly familiars are treated."

"No," she replied, hearing the bitterness in her own voice. "I just don't expect a wizard to understand."

"That seems dramatically unfair," he said, staring ahead. "I've tried to understand."

"*You* have, yes." Which still bewildered her. "But if I'd become a wizard, I don't think I would have. I'd have happily seized the power and no doubt used my familiar equally as terribly."

He cast a curious glance at her then, lips quirked in disbelief. "No, you wouldn't. You like to pretend that you're so practical and hard-hearted, but you have a depth of compassion in you, Nic. You feel everything so deeply—probably that's why you developed such a hard shell. But that shell is a construct, not who you truly are."

His words struck hard at that vulnerable part of her, so much so that she had no reply. Especially if she didn't want to meet all of House Phel looking like a sodden and sniveling fool.

"What I meant was," Gabriel continued after a while, as if the emotional exchange hadn't occurred, "outside the Convocation, a familiar could go undetected, right? An advantage of not having this"—he tapped the center of his forehead as she had earlier—"is the magic doesn't go anywhere if you don't use it. No spontaneous deluges or moonlight layering the floor with silver while you sleep."

She did a double take, a watery laugh escaping her. "Did that happen?"

"Yes." He gave her a look of combined chagrin and curiosity. "I never told anyone else about that. It's weird, isn't it?"

"Definitely weird," she agreed, smiling as he made a face at her. "I don't know of any other wizards of your power who went untrained for so much of their lives, though. In the Convocation, by the time wizards mature to the point of active manifestation, they already know the basic disciplines to control it."

"Figures."

He sounded so glumly annoyed that she felt she needed to offer something in return. "It's not true, however, that familiars can just live like a nonmagical person. Not the potent ones, anyway. The low-potential familiars—and the low-potential wizards," she added, thinking of Dary, "are fairly common and use their magic unconsciously or not at all, like many of your people in Meresin. But the high-potentials, they face dangers besides abduction."

She was skirting the edges of secrets she'd been resolved not to tell him—and was also unable to summon that resolve anymore. Somewhere along the way, she'd stopped being able to think of him as her enemy. The Fascination, no doubt, taking over her better sense. She couldn't help herself—she *wanted* to tell him. He intuited as much, watching her with alert curiosity now. She let out a sigh, giving up one more line of defense. "Remember that I told you how there are good reasons for the wizard–familiar power dynamic?"

He nodded cautiously.

"A familiar can't vent their own magic, so it builds up inside us. It's like, well, a swamp. There's no channel cut for the magic to flow into, so the ground all around gets mushy and stagnant."

"Swamps—and marshes—aren't necessarily stagnant," he began with some indignation. "That's a common misperception. The truth is that—"

"You can teach me all about it someday," she interrupted, eyeing the rapidly diminishing distance to the house. Now that they'd broached the topic, she didn't want to leave it hanging. He deserved to know this about her, and if she had the opportunity to remember the good reasons she'd kept it from him, she'd lose her courage. He'd treated her well, and she could do this one thing for him. "The analogy is unimportant. The point is that the magic bottles up unless vented, and since familiars can't do it on our own, we need a wizard to do it for us."

"What happens if it isn't vented?" he asked, catching on now, wizard-black eyes fixed on her.

"We basically go crazy," she admitted. "An ungoverned familiar is a danger to everyone. The more powerful the familiar is, the greater the chance of disaster. That's why a wizard must bond and control their familiar, Gabriel. I didn't go into the Betrothal Trials only because I had no good options. I also don't want to lose my sanity." So she traded free will for her mind—not a wonderful trade, but that was the way of life.

"I see." He nodded, considering, but unconvinced, judging by his expression.

"There's a reason there are so many stories of familiars succumbing to madness," she persisted.

"What was your plan in Wartson, then?"

"Ma—My contact there was supposed to provide me with that answer."

If he'd had ears, he would've pricked them up. "Someone was to meet you in Wartson?"

"I'm not a complete idiot," she informed him crisply. "Yes, I was to have help—including financial—that didn't manifest." And why hadn't it? She worried about Maman. It had to be that Papa had kept her sealed in feline form all this time, so she'd been unable to execute the rest of her plan. Nic wished she had a way to contact Maman to find out for sure.

"We're almost there," Gabriel said, breaking into her thoughts. "Ready to run the gauntlet?"

It *looked* like a literal gauntlet, with a long row of people in festive dress lined up to greet them, hopefully with not actual weapons to strike her. At the front stood a man and a woman, much the same age as her own parents. "You go ahead and say hello first," she told him, feeling the nerves again, "and I'll wake Narlis so she's not alarmed by the crowd."

"Narlis has been awake for a while," he said with a knowing smile. "No reprieve for you there—but you shouldn't need one, since you have nothing to fear from these people."

She glanced back at the sled and, indeed, Narlis was sitting up, gazing around with a beatific smile, her white hair in a disarranged halo. Nic returned her gaze to Gabriel, giving him her brightest society smile. "I'm not afraid."

"I never imagined you were," he replied blandly, reining Vale in. The gelding, scenting home, reluctantly pranced to a halt. Gabriel swung down and handed the reins off to a young girl who ran up. He tousled her hair affectionately as she wrapped her arms around his waist in a hug. He sent her off with a quiet word and came around to Nic, who was adjusting her gown so she wouldn't flash any of the assembly as she dismounted. The disadvantage of changing into the lighter gown.

Taking her by the waist in his big hands, Gabriel lifted her down with easy strength. "I asked the kids to take care of Narlis, too, along with the horses and baggage, so you needn't fret about her."

"I never fret," she assured him breezily, restraining a remark about how he'd disposed of all the livestock in one breath.

"No, you're far too regal and intimidating for that." He tucked her hand into the crook of his elbow and led her to his parents. "Mom, Dad—may I present Lady Veronica Phel, formerly of House Elal, now lady of House Phel and my wife."

*And familiar*, Nic added silently. Gabriel was a stubborn man. Even knowing what he should now fully understand about her nature, he refused to accept the inevitable.

"Veronica," Gabriel's mother said with a broad smile, pulling her into a crushing embrace, rocking Nic from side to side with it. "You'll call me 'Mom,' I hope. Or Daisy if you're more comfortable with that. Oh!" She pulled back, wiped tears away, and gripped Nic's hands. "We are just so excited to meet you. And the baby!" She pulled Nic's arms wide so she could scrutinize her belly, clearly quite flat in the fitted linen. "You're not showing at all."

"Mom." Gabriel slid his hand under the fall of Nic's curls and set it on the small of her back, firm and steadying with its silvery-cool tendrils of magic. "Nic's only a month or so along, remember? Most women wouldn't even know they're pregnant at her stage."

Daisy studied them both with shrewd brown eyes. "Then are you sure? I know you promised us that your spell would ensure that she—"

"The Convocation has these oracles that know. They're never wrong," Gabriel spoke over her words rapidly, though not swiftly enough. Dark suspicion stirred unwanted in Nic's heart. It was against the rules to use magic to affect the outcome of the Betrothal Trials, but Gabriel had already demonstrated that he'd break Convocation law without hesitation—and those were the ones he knew about.

"How about we let the poor girl set foot inside the house before we interrogate her, hmm, Daisy?" Gabriel's father, who she would have known for his relative anywhere with his same build and bulk, held out a hand. "I'm Gabriel Senior, which gets confusing. Everyone calls me GF—middle name is Fayne."

"All right, GF, Daisy," Nic replied with a smile. Their informality and easy affection struck her as strange, but also oddly relaxing. "Please call me Nic, as Veronica is a mouthful."

Gabriel raised a brow at her, and she gave him a sweet smile, fully aware it had annoyed him that she'd made him wait so long to use her nickname. How desperately she'd clung to the least formality to wall him out of her heart. All to no avail.

"Now let me hug on my boy!" Daisy exclaimed, flinging herself at Gabriel and holding his face to kiss him on both cheeks, then scrutinizing him with sharp eyes. "You were gone so long," she added reproachfully. "*Much* too long. You know we can't do most of what we need to without you. An entire wing sank again. You look tired. Have you been eating right?"

"We've been traveling, Mom," he said, gently prying her fingers off his face. "And it's winter in Elal still. It makes travel slow."

She sniffed. "You know I worry. You could have—"

"Enough, Daisy." GF put a hand on her shoulder and drew

her away. He hugged Gabriel, pounding his back. "Our troubles have waited this long. They can wait another day. Good to have you home, son."

"What troubles?" Gabriel asked. "Besides that wing. My fault—I shouldn't have set to work on it with the possibility that I'd be leaving again so soon."

"The levees," Daisy inserted. "I told you they wouldn't hold, and they don't. Not without your wizardry."

"The new levees are leaking a little," GF allowed. "Nothing that can't wait to be fixed."

Gabriel frowned. "The orchards."

"We lost some saplings," GF admitted.

"Almost all of those orange trees," Daisy nearly wailed. "And they were so *expensive*."

Nic winced internally at that. At least she and Daisy were kindred spirits so far as bookkeeping went.

"Don't fret, Mom," Gabriel said, sounding weary indeed. "I can go now and—"

"Absolutely not," GF interrupted, clapping his son on the shoulder. "Acting now won't bring back what's lost. Tomorrow is soon enough. Enjoy your party. Let your mother feed and fuss over you."

"Yes." Daisy rounded on Nic with enthusiasm. "Your new wife must be introduced to everyone. Where is Lexia? I *told* that girl to be here and do her brother the honor of a proper welcome, but she can't be bothered."

"She'll be around," Gabriel said soothingly, running light fingers over Nic's hair and giving her a questioning look. She nodded that she was fine. Homesick and lonely, wishing she could bolt, but fine. *Not* afraid. *It would've been like this with any house you went to*, she told herself. *Likely worse.* Gabriel gave her a reassuring smile. "And I think there are plenty of other people waiting to greet Nic." He glanced pointedly at the line of people.

"Oh!" Daisy threw up her hands as if she'd forgotten. "The receiving line. What you must think of us, Lady Veronica."

Gabriel's parents whisked her into a seemingly never-ending parade of faces, names, and complicated familial connections to Gabriel—all explained in detail and immediately lost in the next introduction. True to his word, Gabriel shadowed Nic without fail, though GF and Daisy flanked her, taking over the actual introductions. The members of his extended family were all so proud of Gabriel—he was clearly the center of their universe—and they greeted her with varying degrees of apprehension and curiosity. A real life Convocation familiar! A couple of people declined to touch her, opting to bow instead. More than one person asked her to perform a magic trick, demonstrating that none of them understood much about familiars and wizards.

Nic began to understand the lacunae in Gabriel's understanding more and more. She also marveled at the apparent complete lack of rank within the family. Other than the respect accorded to Gabriel and his parents, nobody seemed concerned with status—hers or theirs.

Finally, they made it through the—many!—adults and were working their way through the teenagers when Daisy darted off, returning with a young woman who was all gangly legs and sharp elbows. She blushed shyly, pulling her dark hair around her face to hide a complexion scarred by acne.

"Selly, don't slouch," Daisy tsked. "Shoulders back and head high, please."

The young woman lifted her face obediently, her taciturn smile one Nic recognized as identical to one of Gabriel's pained expressions. "My daughter, Seliah," Daisy declared.

Nic fought the urge to look over her shoulder at Gabriel, to see if he had the experience now to recognize the obvious in Seliah. High-potential magic, probably water and moon also, given the way she felt similarly silvery cool to Nic. And she had to be in her midtwenties, which made her a familiar. One who'd been struggling with the ravages of her untapped magic, too, by the look of her.

"It's lovely to meet you, Seliah," Nic said, offering a hand. "I have a sister back at House Elal, so I'm so glad to know I'll have one here, too." Nic swallowed the impulse to mention her grooming imp could help with the acne scars—the little devils at least loved to take care of blemishes without direction—as she knew it would only make the girl more self-conscious.

Seliah shook her hand without meeting her gaze, or saying anything.

"Be polite, Selly," her mother warned, and her daughter mumbled something—then turned and literally ran away, her gait disjointed and awkward.

"I despair of that girl," Daisy said, throwing up her hands in dismay. "Here she is, twenty-four years old with the manners of a child, and a poorly raised one at that. I don't know *what* is wrong with her."

"She'll find her way," GF said staunchly, and with such firm affection that Nic's heart warmed for the man. "I'll go talk to her."

"Oh, don't bother." Daisy waved her difficult daughter away. "We're here to celebrate Gabriel coming home. And getting to know our new daughter, of course. You have such lovely skin, dear. And your hair!" She reached out to touch it, testing the texture between her fingers, and Nic had to fight not to pull back. "Maybe you can teach Seliah some of your tricks for prettifying. At this rate, she'll never find a husband." She patted Nic's belly. "It's a good thing *you* are providing us with a grandchild. Otherwise, I'd despair of ever being a grandmother!"

Nic managed a smile and stepped out of reach. "I'm so thirsty," she said to Gabriel.

Taking his cue—with a knowingly sympathetic lift of his brows—he offered his arm.

"Let's take care of that."

# ~ 20 ~

GABRIEL STEERED NIC to a small table under a blossoming tree, some distance from the main hubbub of his family. With only a pair of chairs, that should fend off visitors for a bit. Nic had her chin high and face impassive, all cool lady of the Convocation, which meant she felt overwhelmed. He couldn't really blame her. After the formal grandeur of House Elal, his family seemed as ramshackle and graceless as the mostly ruined house.

He sent one of the kids running for refreshments and sat, grateful for a moment of peace for himself also. Nic was quiet, gazing out over the gathering. She looked so tempting in that gown, softer than usual, her skin creamy enough to lap up. If he'd realized the gown would show so much of her full breasts, he might've rethought. As it was, it was all he could do not to stare—and fantasize. Nic seemed oblivious, possibly brooding about something. He imagined he could sense smoke burning hot through her wine-and-roses magic.

"I apologize for my mother," he said. When Nic glanced at him with a raised brow, he added, "I know she can be a bit much."

"She's fine, Gabriel. I imagine she's been through a lot of

changes also these last few years."

"Insightful of you. She's been fretting about what you'll think of the house and the family. We all feel like a bunch of farmers playing dress-up still." He offered her a smile, but she didn't return it, her eyes smoldering dark green. *Ah.* She wasn't overwhelmed or brooding about his mother's ways: She was pissed off. And he could guess why. *Shit.*

"Tell me, Lord Phel," she said softly, "what other Convocation rules have you broken?"

Internally, he cursed his mother's loose lips, but he kept the smile on his face, hoping against hope that Nic was thinking of something else. "Are you going to tell me that House Fruits and Vegetables owns a monopoly on orchards?" he teased.

Her eyes flashed with fire, the gold flecks burning through the green. "What happened to not lying to me?"

He opened his mouth, afraid to his very soul, not at all certain what he was going to say. Just then, two boys and a girl ran up, giggling and staring at Nic so hard they barely managed to deposit the pitcher of lemonade and platters of food on the table.

"Is it true you can turn into a giant black cat?" the boy asked in a rush. The other two burst into renewed giggles, clearly fellow instigators of the question, no matter who'd been elected—or blackmailed—into asking.

"Yes," Nic replied, baring her teeth in a wicked smile and curling her fingers into claws. "And if you're naughty, I'll get you with my finger-length, razor-sharp claws." She pretended to swipe at them, and the kids ran off, shrieking. "I shouldn't have done that," she mused, seeming surprised at herself.

"They'll recover—and now they have a good story to tell." Gabriel poured her a glass of lemonade. At least his hand was steady. "It's not Elal Summer Red, but we grow our own lemons and sugar cane, so it's fresh."

She took the glass from him and set it down, drilling him with that hard stare. "So, what spell did you use to ensure I'd get pregnant that night?"

He tried to look surprised, knew he was failing miserably. "Ah, what do you mean by—"

"Don't *lie*," she spat. "We both know what I heard your mother say. And I've been thinking back to that night, how confident you were with your *six or seven attempts*." She drawled that last with biting sarcasm. "You *knew*. Tell me how you did it. I know you don't have any Refoel healing magic—unless you cheated on your Convocation scores, too."

"I didn't *cheat*," he fired back, "on anything."

"You did something to ensure you'd win your supposed gamble. Tell me."

He drained his lemonade, resigned. "I used a moon-magic spell to ensure fertility."

She regarded him with a look that shredded him. "How is breaking the rules not cheating?"

He fought the urge to squirm in his chair. "The Betrothal Trials rules state that only House Refoel may unlock a familiar's fertility and that a wizard may not consult with any Refoel healer to enhance their own fertility, and that any wizard with healing magic must succumb to temporary suppression of that magic in order to not influence the fertility of either wizard or familiar. I don't have any healing magic, nor did I consult with anyone from House Refoel."

She held his gaze a moment longer, hers remote. Then she rubbed the furrow between her winged brows as if it pained her. "Gabriel, it's still cheating."

"Not exactly. I—"

"No, Gabriel," she shot at him, eyes blazing. "Don't you get it? You just lost your claim to me. Not only have you lied to me from our first meeting, you used fertility magic to skew the Betrothal Trials. The Convocation already wants to see you fail, and you just handed them the perfect excuse to strip you of everything. You'll forfeit your house status, the betrothal application fee, me, my dowry, *and* your heir. All because you think you're smarter than the Convocation."

She lunged to her feet, and he snagged her by the wrist. "I don't think I'm smarter than the Convocation," he bit out. "Do you have any idea how those ridiculous rules read? They offered you up like a lamb to the first butcher with a sharp-enough knife, and you're defending them!"

Nic yanked her hand from his grip but leaned down—unfortunately offering a dazzling display of her lush cleavage—hissing as her eyes blazed furious fire. "Don't you dare pull the high-and-mighty act, Gabriel Phel, for you were lined up with your knife and fork ready, happy to eat that tender lamb to further your interests. You moan and whine about not wanting to be a wizard, but you're building up a nice little empire here with your fruit trees and your adoring subjects. You criticize the Convocation for how it treats familiars, you scorn collars with righteous disdain, but you were happy enough to trap me with your child."

"Why shouldn't it have been me?" he demanded, guilt fueling his own anger. "So far as I knew, you'd put yourself on the auction block so you could find a good husband, which I had every intention of being. But that's not what you wanted, was it? Speaking of lies, *you* never had any intention of following through. You didn't want me—and that's why you ran."

"You're right," she spat, curling her fingers into those claws again as if tempted to use them on him. "I had a particular sort of wizard in mind, and it was not the likes of *you*." She spun to storm off, turned back. "Where is this room I've been promised? I'm done here."

He pushed to his feet, taking her arm. "I'll escort you."

"Just hand my leash to someone else." She tried to jerk away, but he held on. "Stay and enjoy the party for the heroic son returned home with a precious grandbaby for his mommy to spoil."

Setting his teeth against a biting retort, he strode for the house, keeping a firm hold of Nic. Far too much of a lady to make a scene, she gave up fighting him and strolled alongside, even nodding and smiling at the greetings sent their way. "I don't want your company," she said through gritted teeth.

"Well, you're getting it," he replied under his breath. "We're having this out, once and for all."

"And then what?" she inquired with sugar-coated spite. "Too bad you didn't buy one of those Iblis collars to chain me with."

He looked down at her, at the furious beauty of her, both

stung by that remark and impressed by her spirit. "That was unfair and you know it."

"Gabe," his mother called, waving them over. "Where are you going?"

"Nic is exhausted," he lied cheerfully, enjoying the mute fury on her face, especially as he was sure no one else detected it through her composed expression. He winked broadly, working it. "Pregnancy, you know. She needs a nap." He made that last remark particularly pointed, and her eyes glittered with the promise of retribution.

"Oh, of course. How inconsiderate of me. Perhaps we'll see you later at dinner. Or breakfast, if you prefer to sleep the night through." She eyed Gabriel with maternal longing. "Will you be back down, or…?"

"We'll see. Would you send up a tray to leave outside the door?" He glanced at Nic, who was resolutely avoiding his gaze. "I think we're both worn out and… peckish."

"Of course. Lady Veronica, do let us know if you need anything at all. We tried to make your rooms as nice as possible, but, well…" She waved a hand at the rambling, half-ruined house. "We are provincial, as you can see."

"I'm sure it will be lovely," Nic unbent enough to say, giving his mother a warm smile. "I'm sorry to have to leave such a wonderful party when you went to so much trouble to make me welcome."

"Oh." His mother waved that off, but she blushed. "It was no trouble. Don't give it another thought—I know how it is when you're carrying."

"Thanks, Mom," Gabriel said, bending to kiss her cheek.

He guided Nic up the steps and across the wide porch, trying to keep his pace slow enough that he didn't look like he was marching her there. She pulled at her arm in his grip, but he didn't release her.

"Let go of me," she hissed under her breath. "It's not like I have anywhere to run to."

She had a point, so—though he had to fight the fear that he would indeed lose her if he let go—he dropped her arm.

"Low blow," she commented, "to blame the pregnancy, as if I'm fainting away from your manly seed in my womb."

He managed not to wince. "I needed an excuse my mother would readily believe—or would you prefer to be still down there, being interrogated about your health and force-fed nutritious food?"

She didn't reply, making a show of studying the house's foyer and grand staircase, but he thought she had to suppress a glimmer of amusement at his words. Her humor was never far from the surface, even at her most pissed, so perhaps there was hope for them yet.

"This way." He led her up the stairs, then up another set, to the top floor. They walked in silence through the sitting area, and he opened a set of double doors, gesturing her in. Pausing to shut the doors and lock them—manual bolts at House Phel, though he could change that, now that he knew what to buy—he took a moment to draw a deep breath and rein in his temper. He'd known this moment would come, but he thought he'd have more time to… what? Charm and seduce her, he supposed.

When he turned, he found Nic had gone to one set of the

glass-paned doors that lined the far wall and opened onto the balcony that ran along the back of the house. "It's private," he told her, opening the neighboring set of doors and going out. "No one will disturb you out here."

She opened her own doors and moved out, her expression so neutral he had no idea what she was thinking. "There's a river," she said.

"Yes." He gazed out, too. It was a pretty view, he thought, with the gardens sloping down to the river and the dock. Hoped. He'd wanted her to like it. "I thought you might want a quiet place to read or sew, where you won't be bothered."

Without comment, she went back inside, exploring the large sitting area, perusing the shelves of books without comment. She went through the connecting doors to the bedchamber, the attached bathing chamber.

"We don't have indoor plumbing," he said into her silence. "So for now we'll have to have hot water brought up for your baths, but there's plenty of that to be had, obviously. And we can begin acquiring whatever magical conveniences you like. Just make a list."

She eyed him, quitting the bathing chamber again. "Only one bed," she commented.

"Yes. Recall that when I designed these rooms, I thought we'd be returning as husband and wife."

"Which we are."

"I thought there'd be a wedding," he clarified.

She shrugged as if that didn't matter. "We can have a wedding ceremony now if that will make you feel better. I really don't care."

"Nic, I—"

"Spare me your noble excuses, Gabriel." She began pacing, surveying the details as she went. Paused by the table for two by the fire, set with a pair of wineglasses. "These rooms are very nice. Well suited for me and the things I like."

"I'm glad you approve," he replied cautiously, not sure where she was going with this but sure it was nowhere good for him.

"Tell me, when did you begin preparing them?"

He swallowed the sigh of resignation. "When I received the notice announcing your Betrothal Trials."

She nodded, unsurprised. "Not only desperate, but confident. You picked me out and made a solid plan to achieve your goal. I assume you added details after we met while you waited for the inevitable news that you could pick up your purchase?"

He decided to let that one go. She had a right to be angry, and he'd take the hit. "Yes. Much of the house is not comfortable. I wanted you to be happy, and I thought this suite could be a refuge for you. I'm not sure that particular crime can be counted against me."

"Not a crime, no, but it points to a pattern. You're a determined man, aren't you?"

He folded his arms, bracing himself. "Yes. I have to be. I have responsibilities."

"To all these people." She waved a hand in the air. "I see that. It's good to know."

"What are you getting at, Nic?"

She spun and paced toward him, not stopping until she

stabbed him in the chest with one finger. "Do you want to know why I ran from you, Lord Phel? From *you*, in particular."

He folded his hand over her painfully poking finger, holding her hand against his heart. *Finally.* "Yes. Tell me." He braced himself for the worst.

"I did have a plan." Her eyes narrowed with keen malice and deep regret. "I reviewed all the applicants and used my power of summary dismissal on the ones I knew I wouldn't be able to manipulate. When I saw yours, I thought, 'Hmm, desperate upstart with no competition in his family. He'll be some wide-eyed, dewy-fresh wizard that I can manipulate until I consolidate my power. Then I'll run his life, and no one in his family will have the wit to know I'm doing it.'"

"I see." He considered that with some relief, that it wasn't *him* she hated. Her strategy made sense, and he admired her wily intelligence. "You weren't far off the mark. It could've worked."

"With *you*?" She jerked her hand away and plopped herself in a chair by the window, gripping the arms so her knuckles whitened. "I knew from the moment you walked into my tower room that you'd be as easy to push around as a boulder. Worse, I—" She broke off, looking away from him, firming her lips. "I knew my only hope was that your seed wouldn't take, that it would be someone else. I should have saved myself the trouble of hoping, because I never stood a chance, did I?"

He wanted to go to her. He also knew she wouldn't accept comfort from him. So, he stood there, awkward and ashamed. "If it makes any difference," he said quietly, "I apologize. I was thinking only of winning."

"Yes, well." She gazed steadfastly out the window. "That's why you've been succeeding, against all odds. You couldn't know I didn't want to be won by you."

That hurt, considerably more than he expected, though it was hardly news. "I'll release you," he said, not exactly on impulse because he'd been mulling the possibilities over the long journey home. She at least met his eyes again. "Whatever it takes to make you safe, I'll do it. I'll take you back to Wartson, finance your life so you can raise our child in peace, find a wizard to bleed off your magic."

"And the hunters? My family? The Convocation?" She ticked the points off on her fingers.

"Obstacles to be overcome," he replied stubbornly. "You said it yourself: I succeed against the odds because I'm determined. I'll find a way to make this happen. I owe you that."

She smiled slightly, though her eyes remained sad. Then she shook her head. "That's not what we're going to do."

No? He hadn't expected her to dance with joy, but he had thought she'd agree.

"You *do* owe me, Lord Phel," she said, holding his gaze. "Make no mistake there. You owe me, and I'm claiming the debt: you will give me what I want."

Cautious, not liking the bite in her voice, he nodded. "Anything within my power."

"You're going to bond me as your familiar. We—" She held up a hand to stop him when he started to argue. "Hear me out. This *is* what I want. We can have that wedding ceremony if you wish—tell your family that we wanted to have another for them to share in, I don't care what excuse you use—and you will bond me so no one can take me away from you. That is the least you can do for me."

He went to her, kneeling on the polished wood at her feet, and took her hands in his. "I know you don't truly want that," he said hoarsely. "I'm offering you freedom, which shouldn't be mine to give anyway. Since it seems to be, I'm giving it freely. Take it."

She tugged a hand loose and brushed his hair from his face, that strange sadness in her eyes. "You don't understand, Gabriel. I can never be free of you. It's too late. Even if you sent me to the other side of the world, I'd find a way back to you."

"You would..." He didn't think she was saying she loved him, or that she wanted him. She looked far too unhappy for that. "I don't understand."

"I know." She trailed her fingers down his cheek, tracing the line of his jaw. Her anger seemed to have evaporated, leaving a misty sadness like wilted roses. "You are, in some ways, that naïve wizard I supposed you to be—though far from dewy fresh and wide-eyed."

True. He'd lost any naïvety in those terrible days while he tried to stop the deluge he'd started and couldn't control. "Not for a long time now."

"Remember when I told you about the power imbalance in wizard–familiar relationships?"

"Of course. That's why I don't want to use you. I won't—"

She put a finger over his lips to silence him. "Familiars bond to their wizards, whether we want to or not. We call it

Fascination, and it's in here somewhere." She lifted her finger to tap the center of her forehead, leaving a cool and lonely spot on his lips where she'd touched him. "I felt it from the beginning. I hoped that if I ran, I could escape the bond before it formed. I didn't want to become like Maman, and she didn't want that for me either, which is why she helped me."

The pieces slid into place with heartbreaking clarity. "She was to arrange the contact in Wartson but couldn't because your father put her in cat form."

Nic held up her palms. "Maybe? I have no way of knowing, but it seems likely. I know she wouldn't have abandoned me if she had any choice. Gabriel, you must promise never to tell anyone that she was the one."

"I won't tell a soul." He could only imagine what they'd do to the self-possessed and graceful Lady Elal for such a crime. "If I hadn't come after you, would you have succeeded in freeing yourself of this… compulsion?"

"I don't know. I was working very hard not to think about you. Remember that copper snake bracelet you asked me about—that you thought I never took off until I did? I would press the fangs into my wrist to try punish myself out of longing for you."

He didn't know what to say. The idea of her hurting herself to try to escape him, like an animal chewing off its paw to free itself from a trap was unbearable.

"It's a moot point because we didn't figure on the hunters. No matter what, they would've brought me back and eventually given me back to you, and I would've bonded to you anyway. At least you saved me suffering all of that. I don't have any choice in this, so all you can do for me at this point is make me yours, so I can't be taken from you."

He stared at her, trying to make sense of it all. "I don't want to take away your choice. I acted wrongly, I know, but I never intended..." He trailed off at her vigorous head-shaking.

"I keep telling you that what I want literally does not matter, not even in my own mind. It's all very clear to me right now. You broke Convocation law by cheating the Betrothal Trials, which means they'll try to take me away from you. If you haven't bonded me, it will be easier for them."

Setting his jaw, he searched for an alternative. "We have time. We'll send word to your family that you're safely here. No one needs to know if—"

She hissed with impatience. "Open your eyes, Gabriel! The Convocation will be coming for me. My father will be coming for me. Wizard Iblis will lodge a complaint. These things won't go away. You must act to consolidate your resources, and *I* am one of those resources. You said you only thought about winning, well—think only about that now. I've said I want this in every way I know how. What can I say to convince you I'm willing?"

Gabriel rubbed his forehead, trying to think of a way around the knot of problems. What kind of willingness did he want from her? The thought immediately sprang to mind of the fantasy he'd nurtured, that they'd have a partnership, a real marriage.

"What?" she asked, searching his face. "You thought of something. Tell me what to say and I'll say it."

"I don't want you parroting words to me," he replied

sharply.

"How do you know that I would be?" she demanded. "I may be utterly Fascinated by you, but I'm not an empty-headed ninny. Give me some credit."

He couldn't help smiling. "No, that's the last thing you are."

"Just tell me," she urged. "Both of us, being completely honest."

# ~ 21 ~

"IT'S FOOLISH," HE said, not quite meeting her gaze, reluctance in his voice. "I—" He broke off, then threaded his fingers through hers. "I'm embarrassed to say the words," he admitted.

"Gabriel," Nic said with deliberate asperity, "I can't know what you're thinking unless you tell me. Even if I'd been a wizard, I don't have that much House Hanneil in my blood."

He didn't smile at her attempt at levity. It was a poor joke anyway. It would take a lot more than that to lighten this fraught tension between them. Gabriel had his magic tightly wrapped around him, only a few questing tendrils making it past his control. Her own heart thudded with a fear unlike any she'd ever known, something tied to feeling so emotionally exposed and vulnerable.

"I poured my heart out to you," she reminded him. "You know I can never leave you—never will want to."

He grimaced. "I know, I just—" He met her gaze, something in his face as raw and vulnerable as she felt. "I want you to *want* to be with me."

Her heart skidded to a clenching stop. "I do want to," she whispered. "I explained that—"

"Not like that!" She blinked at the outburst, and he shook his head. Blew out a breath. "I carried your miniature with me."

Frowning at the change in topic, she shrugged. "I know. I saw it in your belongings. I figured you'd carried it in case you forgot what I looked like."

He laughed hoarsely. "Not possible. What I'm saying is that it wasn't your dossier that decided me. I saw your portrait and I felt… drawn to you. Then I met you, and it seemed like we connected. That night, it seemed hopeful. I rode away in the morning thinking that—in time, of course—we could have a real marriage, that you might come to…" He trailed off, searching her face as if expecting derision.

"Love you?"

He flinched at the way she laid it out there. "Yes. I suppose so."

"Let me set your mind at ease, then," she said, adding a smile she hoped looked genuine. "I do love you."

The pained hope in his wizard-black eyes nearly broke her heart, as did the cynicism that quickly followed. He pushed up from the floor and sat in the other of the set of chairs. Everything in these rooms were in sets of two and spoke more clearly of his ideas of their marriage than any of his words. So many thoughtful touches, so revealing of how little he'd known about what he was getting into with her. It pained her to imagine him riding away with hope in his heart while she prayed to never see him again.

"I don't see how it's possible for you to be in love with me," he said, rubbing the back of his neck. "I'd like it to be true, but I can't get away from the suspicion that you're telling me what I want to hear."

"That's how the wizard–familiar relationship works," she explained as gently as she could. "This is what I've been telling you. I didn't understand it myself—or I didn't want to believe it was true—until I met you and felt the Fascination begin to form. Maman explained it to me, that I had a choice to either succumb to it or try to escape it."

"And we know what you chose: escape. You didn't want to feel this way then, so how can I welcome it now?"

"I don't know what to tell you, Gabriel," she replied, mastering her frustration. "Will it help if I tell you I regret my decision to run? I do. I had a beautiful wedding gown ready, one I would've been delighted to wear. I could've married you with every appearance of joy, told you that I loved you, and you would never have known different."

"I don't regret that you ran," he bit out. "I needed to be educated, to know more than the appearance you would've offered, to know different."

"Did you? I'm not convinced." Maybe if she'd gone along with the program, they would've both been happier. "I love you with all my being, but now you'll never believe in it."

His eyes hardened. "Because that's not real love."

Nic shrugged, trying to look more carefree than she felt. "What is 'real' love? I don't think anyone even knows. It's a word we use to describe a feeling that can't be put into words. And we use the same one for all kinds of love: for parents, children, horses, good wine, friends, favorite authors, chocolate cookies. Are you in love with me?"

She'd surprised him with that question, and he took a moment to consider it. Some women might've been offended that he didn't immediately respond with protestations of love, but she appreciated that he gave it serious thought. "I don't know," he admitted. "I think I could be, but I also feel like it would be… wrong."

"Wrong?" she echoed. "In what way?"

"Would you say your father loves your mother?"

*Ah.* "Yes. He does love her. And she loves him. What you saw between them was…"

"Unsavory," he finished. "I was horrified to witness that, Nic—and that's tied up in how I feel about loving you. I don't want us to pretend with each other. I not only loathe the lies, I think they're dangerous. If you ever love me, I want it to be because of me, not because of some enchantment that forces you to."

"I understand." And she did, all too well. Unfortunately, that left her in the position where if she explained that she did like him for himself, it would ring false. "So where does that leave us?"

He regarded her with somber resolve. "You've made an excellent case that I must follow through on what I got us into. I'm willing to do this bonding, but on one condition."

He could set all the conditions he liked, and she'd have to agree, but she nodded anyway. "And that is?"

He held out his hands, waiting for her to place them in his. She did, and he folded hers in his cool silvery grasp, holding her gaze. "I don't want you to be my servant." When she opened her mouth to argue, he raised a brow. "Hear me out," he said, throwing her earlier words back at her. "You have to teach me the bonding ceremony anyway, so we're going to figure out how to make it reciprocal. We'll be partners or nothing."

*Only him.* In purest exasperation, she burst out, "It doesn't work that way!"

"Has anyone tried?"

"I don't know. I doubt it. This is a centuries-old tradition for a reason. I certainly can't promise to abide by your ultimatum—it might not be within my control."

"All I ask is that we try," he replied evenly. "Let's set the question of love aside. I think we've built something of a friendship?"

"I suppose so." She considered saying more but left it at that.

"Let's continue to build that relationship, then—and we can't be friends unless we're equals."

"I don't think that's necessarily sound logic."

"It is for me," he replied, that implacable look in his face.

She regarded him dubiously, then sighed. "I really don't think it will work."

"What's the worst that can happen?" he asked, bending his head to brush kisses on her fingers, sending silvery shards of desire through her.

"I can think of a *lot* of terrible outcomes, actually," she said in a very dry tone.

He laughed, relief and genuine humor in it, breath shivering over her skin. She loved his laugh—the real one—and it made her want to kiss him, to take that laughter inside of her, a ripple of moonlight on water to gaze on when she lost hope.

"I have a condition, too," she said, and he lifted his head warily, bracing for it.

"Anything that's in my power," he promised again. Did he know how that made her heart turn over? Probably.

"Oh, this is." She gave him her most seductive smile. "I want a real marriage—with sex. No more of this refusing to 'use me that way,' either."

The storm of warring emotions crossing Gabriel's face might've made Nic laugh if she wasn't so intent on getting her way in this.

She stood and slid onto his lap while he was still stunned and trying to work out a reasonable defense. "I thought we'd start with a kiss." As she leaned in to take her kiss, he caught her by the shoulders, holding her away from him. She glared at him. "What?"

He searched her face, looking for something. "I don't think this is a good idea."

"Why not? It's not as if we have to worry about me getting pregnant." She pressed against his grip, the yearning deep inside pushing her to make contact with his very tempting mouth. "We agreed we're doing this—wedding, bonding, the whole commitment."

"Yes—as friends."

"Friends have sex," she purred. "And you said you wanted me."

He groaned as her bosom made contact with his chest, wizard-black eyes on her mouth as he licked his lips. "I do want you. You know how much."

"Then take," she invited in a sensual murmur. "Have."

His grip faltered, and she dove in, but he dodged the kiss, turning his head to the side and wrapping his arms around her. Clever of him, though not entirely effective as she now lay with her breasts crushed delightfully against his hard chest, his strong neck available for kissing and biting—which she proceeded to do. His magic coiled silver through hers, his groan of passion a rumble of distant thunder, his body heating as she poured fire to set him boiling. His arms tightened, holding her close.

"Gabriel, please, I liked having sex with you. All seven times."

"I liked it, too," he breathed.

"And I'm assuming you'd rather I didn't have sex with anyone else?"

His embrace tightened into granite. "Out of the question."

"No need to growl." She wriggled, and he released her enough that she could frame his face in her hands. "I feel the same. A familiar can't demand fidelity of their wizard, but I feel secure in requesting this?"

"You're my wife," he ground out, insult in his expression. "Fidelity goes without saying. I don't care what the rest of your foul Convocation society believes."

"So that leaves us having sex with each other, which is arguably one of the happier benefits of our alliance. I'm not willing to give that up because you're intent on punishing yourself."

"I'm not—" He broke off, blowing out a breath, leaning his forehead against hers. "Nic," he said, his voice ragged. "I *cannot* do that."

"You *can*," she insisted. "Do you want me to get on my knees and beg?"

"No." He thrust her away from him, actually picking her up and depositing her in the other chair. Looming over her, he glowered, hands clenched into fists. "I don't want to be like *them*," he nearly shouted at her.

He sounded upset enough to cool her ardor. "Like who?"

He pressed his lips together, shaking his head. Rejecting whatever image haunted him. "*Wizards.*"

"Gabriel," she said, as patiently as she knew how—which, admittedly, wasn't much. "You *are* a wizard. You cannot deny who you are."

"Maybe I can. I know more now."

"You know more, but you've also taken on more." She waved her hands at the party outside. "You're lifting this house out of a swamp. You have all those people out there, with shining eyes fixed on *you* to raise them up, too. You have orange trees to save!" She shot a finger in the air, going for a triumphant finish, if only to lighten his mood.

"We lived fine before," he replied, a stubborn set to his mouth. "We don't need orange trees. Not at this price."

All right, then. Time for some tough love. "It's too late to change your mind," she pointed out remorselessly. "You are in this now. The Convocation won't let you go back and disappear into your swamps. And I—*we*," she corrected, laying a hand on her belly, "are in this with you."

"Do you think I don't realize that?" he demanded, sounding desperate, a wild look in his eyes.

"Nothing has changed, Gabriel," she insisted. "You accepted this responsibility before. You came to get me because you had a plan. Get a familiar, restore House Phel."

"That was before I met wizards like that Iblis one, Jan, even your father," he shot back. "I keep seeing Jan in my head, yanking on Daniel's collar, and how *adoringly* Daniel gazed at the man brutalizing him. Seeing your mother, protesting, but unable to truly disagree. Even the Elal wizard at the border—she treated her familiar like he was nothing." He drew himself up, black eyes shadowed with self-loathing. "If that's what I'll become, I want no part of it."

She laughed. Laughed in his face, watching the surprise, hurt, and annoyance follow in rapid succession. *Better.* "Oh, please!" she finally got out. "You are so far from becoming any of them that the notion is simply ridiculous."

"Maybe to you."

"You have already had sex with me, and you haven't become like that."

His face set in rigid lines, he looked away from her. "I'm not so sure. Regardless, I have to set some boundaries for myself where you're concerned. Can you understand that?"

"Of course. Discipline is a key skill for both familiars and wizards. Sex has nothing to do with it."

"It does for me." He paced away from her.

"Gabriel. Sex is a physical release, nothing more."

He gave her a hard and curious look. "Is this you pretending to be *practical*?"

She ignored the sarcasm. "Yes. I *am* practical—and sex is physical. A thing of the flesh, no more.

"Do *not* lie to me," he snarled.

"I'm not lying!" she retorted in the same tone.

"Then you're lying to yourself." He strode to her, seizing her hands and yanking her to her feet. His magic coiled around her seductively, and he raked her with a gaze so full of desire the breath caught in her throat. "I remember that night," he crooned, black eyes roving to her exposed bosom with palpable heat, "even if you pretend not to. What passed between us was far more than physical."

"Maybe for you." She'd tried for arch, but the words came out breathless.

Smiling mirthlessly, he pulled her arm around his waist, snugging her against him with a hand pressing against the small of her back, his cock hot and heavy against her belly. Leaning in, he brushed his lips over her cheek, not quite a kiss, but as if caressing her with his breath. The tidal pull of his moon magic tugged at her, and she moaned. "You felt something, too," he murmured. "I think that's part of why you ran. You were afraid of this powerful thing between us."

"That's what I've been telling you." Through the haze of desire, a hint of panic fluttered. He had pried her hard shell open, and through that crack, long-banished dreams were leaking in. Romantic fantasies of things that could never be.

"No. You're still lying. To us both." The hand at her back wound in her long hair, pulling gently but inexorably, so she lifted her chin, yielding to his strength, exposing her throat to his sensual not-quite kisses. "You blamed it on being a familiar, on this 'Fascination,' but I think it's more. You want me."

"I *said* I wanted you," she protested, panting and squirming against him.

He released her hair, balancing her until she was steady on her feet before letting her go. "Then why are you afraid of me?" he demanded. "The truth."

When she gaped at him, unable to keep up with the sudden reversals, he trailed a finger over her cheek. "Nic, I can sense it in you. Even when you're melting for me, the fear is there. At first, I thought it was because of how your other suitors treated you. But that's not all of it, is it?"

"I don't know about that." She managed a bit of her usual insouciance. "They were right bastards."

He smiled slightly, then immediately sobered again. "Nic… I can't bear it if you're afraid of me. And I think you'll always be afraid of me if I hold all the power in our relationship."

Sighing heavily, she threw up her hands in surrender. Hadn't she known from the first moment she saw him that he'd be stubborn as a rock? "Fine. Where is your arcanium?"

He blinked, thrown off balance. "Why?"

"Because you won't be happy until we see if we can do the bonding reciprocally. So let's try it. Regardless of the outcome, we'll have the answer, and we can move forward with information in hand, rather than speculation."

He shook his head. "We need to study, to plan. There might be some spell books that—"

"Gabriel," she interrupted firmly. "If we get this to work—your way—it will be unprecedented."

"So far as you know."

"So far as I know," she allowed, "but I do know what's in the books, and nothing like what you're proposing is. Time and study won't help. Even if it would," she said, holding up a hand to forestall him when he opened his mouth to protest, "time is a luxury we don't have. The hunters or my father's people could arrive at any moment. I need to be bonded by you before then, one way or another." Had Lyndella needed to cajole Sylus into bonding her? No. He'd masterfully bonded her despite her pleas and protests—to which she'd ultimately submitted with delight.

*Of course, Lyndella also died broken in mind and body.*

Gabriel was scrutinizing her, far from persuaded. "Are you pressing this because of sex?"

She gave him a saucy grin. "There are worse reasons."

"There are better ones, too."

"I can't abide suspense, how's that for a reason? Let's get this over with already." He still looked unconvinced, so she laid a hand on his chest, letting him see her very real fear. "I *am* afraid. You do see that in me. But I'm afraid of many things right now, and losing myself to you is no longer my greatest fear. I *really* don't want the Convocation to take me."

He grimaced in resigned accord, covering her hand with his. "All right." He gave her a quelling look at her squeal of triumph. "There is, however, a problem."

"Only one?" she asked lightly. "At least we've whittled them down."

He breathed a laugh. "I have no idea where the arcanium is."

# ~ 22 ~

NIC GLARED AT him in frank incredulity—and more than a little irritation. "You *said* back at the inn in Ophiel that you didn't want to consider doing the bonding there because you wanted to do it in the House Phel arcanium!"

"No," he corrected, feeling pedantic even as he said it, "I said I liked the idea of a traditional ceremony in the House Phel arcanium." He essayed a smile, though it faltered in the face of her outrage. "And I do like that idea."

She made a low sound that might be a growl. "You are impossible. Fine. We'll do it here."

"No." If this didn't go as he hoped—if Nic came out the other side of the bonding ceremony like puppyish Daniel—then he didn't want that memory to taint these rooms. She would still be his wife and mother of their child, and they could—*would*—build a life together, regardless of their eventual power dynamic, as she so coldly put it. It had become glaringly obvious that he wouldn't be able to keep his hands off of her much longer.

"Why not?" She fisted her hands on her hips. "We're private. Between us, we have the power. You're just dragging your feet. Honestly, Gabriel, this delay is worse torture for me than getting it over with."

She'd been like that their first night together, too—insistent on getting the bedding over with while he wanted time to get to know each other. Her fire to his water. They would make a good team if they could be true partners. A big if.

"I'm not delaying," he promised, "it's just that... We're trying something new, yes? And you say the arcanium will help focus power, so I'm all for every bit of help we can get."

She eyed him. "*If* the arcanium even exists."

"It does." He held up hands to fend off her argument. "I'm sure it exists, because books on the house reference it, just not specifics of its location."

"Well, no, they wouldn't," she mused. "As I told you, wizards are cagey about their arcaniums. It would be in a mostly inaccessible location, all the better to keep it secret and private. The Elal arcanium is at the top of a tower. I feel I should note at this point that House Phel has no towers."

"Not anymore, anyway," he conceded.

"Exactly. The arcanium could've fallen into the swamp ages ago."

He raised a brow at her. She really did love to needle him about the Meresin landscape.

"Don't get me wrong," she continued hastily, observing his expression. "The parts of the house that you've restored look remarkably good." She swept her hands at the graceful rooms. "And I appreciate that you've installed me in the best section of it, but don't think I haven't noticed how much of this place—especially the wings farther from this core section—looks like it was sunk in a swamp until just recently."

"That's uncomfortably accurate," he conceded.

"I'll bet you haven't even been through all of it," she speculated with a canny expression.

"Well, submerged in swamps and all," he pointed out sardonically. "Though, really, this area is a marsh. See, the difference—"

"The point is that I'm not swimming to some underwater arcanium, Gabriel," she interrupted, giving him an arch look. "Full stop. Swamp, marsh, bog, lake, I will not—"

"*Lake.*" The thrill of the answer filled him with excitement. "I know where it is. Where it must be."

"Please don't tell me it's in the lake." She looked so aghast that he couldn't help laughing.

"*Under* it." He took her hand and pulled her toward the doors.

"What? *No!*"

"I promise you won't have to swim."

She was dragging her heels, so he paused at the doors. "Trust me?"

Searching his face, she sighed. "I do trust you, Gabriel."

She meant it, he realized, and that trust, more than any of her other assurances, settled his mind. Maybe she couldn't love him of her own free will—but trust was something else, something he'd earned, and he'd value that accordingly. If they could build on that trust, maybe she'd stop being afraid of him. Brushing his fingers over her cheek, he bent to kiss her, savoring the taste and feel of her, red wine and roses, redolent and dizzying, as he hadn't let himself before.

"Or," she whispered against his lips, "we could go to bed.

Lots of sex."

"We don't have the luxury of time, remember?"

"I meant days, not hours," she argued.

"And you don't want to live in dread."

"True. What if I promise not to dread? Sex, then a long, lovely nap. A hot bath after. Much better than some dank, damp, waterlogged arcanium."

He laughed, taking her hand and opening the doors. "I'm surprised that someone who hates water likes baths so much."

"Cold water," she clarified, dragging behind him. "I hate *cold* water. So, unless that lake is heated..."

"I'll keep you warm," he promised with a wink.

"You sure are frisky all of a sudden," she commented sourly.

"I'm excited," he agreed. "I think this will work."

Fortunately, his family was all still out on the lawn, enjoying the party and the warm spring evening without them. Even so, knowing it would be better not to run the risk of being noticed, Gabriel led Nic down the back stairs to the kitchens. He found a lantern, and a candle for it, which he lit with a match. "Don't look at it like that," he said when she wrinkled her nose disdainfully. "It does the job."

"Until the candle burns out," she retorted.

"Aha." He grinned at her and led her to the cellars. "There are *more* candles."

She muttered about the smell and speculated darkly about the worse conditions to come, but she followed along more or less willingly. When they reached a round door set into a wall that was, admittedly, beaded with moisture, she gave him an incredulous look. "Seriously? No. Gabriel, do *not* open that—"

He muscled the round door open, the hinges stiff and creaking but operational. He gestured to the round, stone-lined tunnel beyond. "Not flooded," he noted.

"You didn't know."

"I did. Water wizard, remember?"

Gingerly, she peered inside. "There's water in the bottom, though."

"Hold this." He handed her the lantern, then picked her up and stepped over the threshold. "Pull the door shut, would you?"

"So they'll never find us, ensuring we die down here. Great idea," she grumbled, pulling the door shut anyway.

Chuckling at her, he strode down the tunnel, the ankle-deep water splashing and echoing off the rounded, moss-covered walls.

"Why can't you just wick the water away?" Nic asked, gaze focused ahead. "Then I could, you know, walk by myself."

He nuzzled her temple. "What's the fun in that?"

"Who are you and what have you done with my grumpy wizard?"

"I'm not that grumpy," he protested. "And why spend magic on drying out a tunnel when it's passable as is and I'm wearing waterproof boots?"

"Now there would be an excellent House Phel export," she mused. "We could ally with Ophiel to make waterproof clothing."

"Good idea, Lady Phel."

She snorted, still looking ahead. "I don't love that we have no idea how long this tunnel is."

"I know how long it is," he reassured her.

That got her attention. She swiveled her head to look at him. "You've been here before."

"How else could I know it was here?"

"You might've said," she snarled with purest exasperation.

"I thought I did," he replied mildly.

"Why don't we skip the riddles, and you just tell me why you think the arcanium is at the end of this tunnel?"

"When we were kids, we'd dare each other to explore the ruins of House Phel," he explained. "Depending on the time of year—you'll understand when you let me explain marshes to you—we could explore the cellars. Of course, we found this tunnel."

"Of course you did," she replied drily.

"It goes under the lake," he added, "which, as kids, we thought was really neat."

"Explains why water is dripping from the ceiling."

"Only a few drops here and there. The tunnel finishes at a dead end, which I always wondered about."

"Because why go to the trouble of building a tunnel under a lake that goes nowhere."

"Exactly." He grinned at her. "Unless you wanted to hide a secret room at the end of it. We're water wizards. What better place for our arcanium than under water?"

"A nice, dry tower that's closer to the moon," she retorted, but he could tell he'd gotten her interested in the possibility. They were nearing the end, the lantern showing the smooth stones that pinched into a V. Nic eyed it. "Looks like a dead end, all right."

"There must be a way to open it."

"Must there?"

"Yes—to get into the arcanium."

She sighed. "Gabriel, it's entirely possible that whoever built this tunnel planned for it to go somewhere eventually, but they got tired of it. Maybe they ran out of funding. Or a very practical Lady Phel put her foot down and said that building a tunnel under a lake was asking for trouble."

"Why was the practical person a woman?" he asked, amused by her, even as he scrutinized the join of the walls.

"Some things you just know." She shifted in his arms, holding the lantern higher. "Gabriel, my only love, can we go back upstairs now? Seriously, we can do the bonding anywhere. It won't take long, and then we can move on to more productive pursuits. Drier ones." Her stomach growled. "Supper would be welcome."

It would've been nice if she'd called him her only love in a less sarcastic tone, but he still liked the sound of it. "I know there must be a way in. We need to do it this way, Nic, I feel it in my bones."

She sighed. "Well, that's probably your wizard's intuition," she conceded. "So we should heed it. Maybe it's a door that can be opened with moon magic, since the water part is already handled. You'll need to draw on my magic, too." When he frowned at her, she tapped the middle of his forehead with a gentle finger. "Arcanium equals wizard plus familiar. The key to this particular lock likely requires a blend of both."

Much as he hated it, that made sense. "Can you just give

me some?"

She rolled her eyes. "Not something *I* can actively control, else I'd be a wizard, too. You're already in physical contact with me—and you drew on it before—just do that."

"I wasn't really thinking about it then," he admitted.

"Exactly, because it's intuitive. Your magic is always reaching for mine without your conscious control." She put her finger over his lips. "Don't apologize. That's how we're built. Think about how my magic feels to you—is there any aspect that makes you want to consume it?"

*If she only knew.* "You feel to me like the best red wine," he told her hoarsely, holding her gaze, her green eyes catching the candlelight so they seemed to glow. "Infused with roses, warm and spicy. Sometimes I want nothing more than to drink you up."

Her full lips curved into a smile. "That might be the nicest thing you've ever said to me." She cupped the back of his neck and pressed her mouth to his. "Drink of me, Gabriel."

He couldn't resist her, not with her magic thickening the air and her lush body so warm in his arms. She opened her mouth to him, full of the flavor that beguiled him, her magic flowing thick and hot as blood, twining with the vines of his moon magic and blossoming there, crimson petals velvet and redolent.

Moon magic twined out of him, the silvery light overwhelming the lone candle's glow, tendrils finding purchase in the cracks between the stones. A grinding sound filtered into his perceptions.

"Gabriel," Nic breathed. "Look."

The tunnel had somehow spiraled open. Beyond it lay the most extraordinary room he'd ever seen.

Stepping inside, he set Nic down on the perfectly dry, gleaming tiles, which spun in a dizzying pattern of silver and myriad shades of blues and greens somehow evoking the swirl of moonlight on water. Stone walls inlaid with silver runes framed sheets of thick glass, the water beyond them deep blue, growing lighter nearer the surface. An enormous round lens of glass—or crystal, given its luminosity—sat in the center of the ceiling, focusing the last golden light of evening on a circle formed by the tiles, an echo of the window above.

Nic whistled low and long. "Impressive. I take it all back. This was worth even wading through freezing water to get to."

"Did you just say I was right and you were wrong?" he asked, wondering why they were both speaking in hushed, nearly reverent tones.

"Not in so many words," she replied, flashing a smile.

"So I noticed. I also feel I should point out that you didn't even touch the water *I* waded through, so you don't know what temperature it was."

"Yes, I do," she muttered darkly. "I could feel it even from your towering height. Besides, plenty dripped on me from the tunnel ceiling, and that was so frigid it burned."

He laughed softly, turning to take in the space, the various cabinets against the walls between the windows. Strange tools hung in orderly rows, the uses opaque. And… "Is that a bed?" He frowned at it.

"Pretty standard for an arcanium," Nic agreed, strolling to

it and examining the posts. They, like the frame of the bed, appeared to be made entirely of silver. "Though this is an extraordinary specimen. Pure silver if I don't miss my guess. You said moon magic is tied to silver. If you needed quick cash, you could sell this thing for a small fortune—though I doubt we could get it through the tunnel without dismantling it beyond repair. Besides, it's likely far more valuable here to amplify your incantations. Those will yield enduring income, as opposed to a one-time cash infusion."

"Amplify my incantations," he repeated. "I thought maybe it was here for naps, like in between spells."

Nic slid him a look that was both knowing and pitying. She pointed to the feet of the bed. "Wheels, so it can be rolled beneath the moon window there." Plucking up a chain he'd taken for a bit of silver decoration, she rattled the attached cuff meaningfully, directing his attention to similar chains on the other posts. "To bind your familiar," she explained.

He couldn't quite look at her, aroused by the images that sprang to mind, appalled by the implications. "For sex," he realized with dull horror. He was like those other wizards, no matter what Nic said, because some deep-buried part of him had come to slavering life at the possibilities.

"Sex and pain are both excellent for building and releasing magic," she agreed with a nonchalant shrug. "Almost all wizard–familiar relationships are sexual for that reason. Surely you knew that."

"How can you sound so matter-of-fact about it?" he asked, focusing fully on her. With the dimming light filtering through the shifting water, her vivid beauty was softened, her sharp eyes shadowed and mysterious, her hair like blackest night. The image of her lying naked on a bed of that hair, chained to the silver bed, gripped him even as he tried to banish the thought.

She smiled, knowing and sensual. "Because it's a fact of Convocation life, Gabriel," she answered gently. "Wizards receive extensive training in ways to extract maximum power from their familiars, so I don't know the particulars, but there are always rumors. And novels," she added.

"So, even your parents—" He cut himself off before following that path to its end.

Her smile widened. "Naturally, one doesn't like to envision one's parents engaged in such activities, but it's another reason the arcanium is private." She closed the distance between them, sliding her palms up over his chest. "No one will ever know what you do to me in here," she purred.

He gripped her wrists, hard enough that she blinked in surprise, even as she melted against him. "I don't understand you," he whispered. "This isn't some game. I could hurt, maim, or kill you, and you wouldn't care?"

"Familiars get hurt all the time," she replied, "but wizards aren't going to carelessly maim or kill one of us. We're far too valuable for that. Besides, Convocation law protects—"

"Don't quote Convocation law at me," he snarled. "I'm *never* going to do anything like that to you."

She lowered her gaze meaningfully to his grip on her wrists. "You already are."

He released her as if burned, staggering back a few steps. "I don't believe it has to be that way."

"It doesn't and it does." She followed, hips swaying, her skin somehow glowing, as if the arcanium infused her with light. "I've tried to explain—the flow of power follows certain patterns. Because the wizard uses the familiar's magic as well as their own, the combined force can be a great deal to control. These are simply tools to help you contain and focus my magic productively."

"To *use* you effectively," he bit out.

"I know you don't like to think of it that way, but yes."

She reached for him, and he stepped back, warding her off. "Those other suitors... If they'd won you, you would've let them do *this* to you." He flicked his gaze to the bed.

Her expression hardened with her habitual exasperation, along with something darker. "There wouldn't have been any 'letting' about it. That's the life I was born to, Gabriel. Once I received the verdict that I would be a familiar, never a wizard, I knew that what I wanted no longer mattered—with one salient exception."

"The Betrothal Trials," he whispered.

"Yes. At least I was able to exercise my summary dismissals there, select my suitors—if only by process of elimination. Believe me, there were applicants that would have been much worse. Unfortunately, the most cruel are often the wealthiest, and if I'd been sold to the highest bidder, I stood a fair chance of belonging to a wizard who would've made my life a living nightmare. I know you don't care for my father, but I'm lucky that Papa didn't need the money that would come from such a sale—and fortunate that he loves me enough to spare me that fate."

"Did you..." He cleared his throat, gaze wandering the arcanium and landing reluctantly on the bed. "Did you think I would be cruel to you—was that why you were afraid?"

"No." She edged closer, and this time he stayed steady for her as she wrapped her arms around his waist, laying her cheek against his chest. Lightly, he folded his arms around her. "No, Gabriel," she repeated quietly. "I was afraid because I knew I'd give you everything, deny you nothing, and enjoy every moment." She tipped her head back, chin resting on his chest, eyes glowing as if with moonlight. "No regrets," she told him firmly.

Unable to resist her, he lowered his head to brush her lips with his, sweet and lingering. "I don't ever want to hurt you," he whispered against her mouth, barely audible, even to himself.

"We don't have to worry about it now. All we have to do tonight is the bonding. And look—the moon is shining down on us. Surely that's a good omen."

She was right. The sky above the moon window and the lake surface had darkened. Somehow, they'd ended up in the circle directly beneath the moon window, and the bright moonlight showered over them, argent and potently stirring his magic. Nic's magic hummed beneath, a wine-red harmony pulsing with his.

"Here in the circle?" he asked.

She nodded. "It's your arcanium, your intuition we're following, but I think so."

"It's *our* arcanium," he corrected. "And yes, this feels like the focal point."

"You'll need a knife," she told him.

He tensed, wary. "What for?"

"Another tool, Gabriel," she said soothingly. "Don't worry—my tail will grow back."

"What?" he gasped in horror, and she burst out laughing.

"I'm teasing!" Her laughter became a shriek of giggles as he picked her up and kissed her firmly.

"No teasing," he told her sternly.

"Yes, master," she said humbly, but with a smirk.

He set her on her feet again. "Seriously, Nic. I'm nervous enough as it is."

She patted his arm. "Don't be. This is pretty simple. Then, once it's done, you can spoil me by supplying me with wine while I soak in a hot bath."

"Not that you're obsessed with hot baths."

"Not *obsessed*, no."

He took a breath. "Any blade will do?"

"Given your magic, I'd go with a silver one. That cabinet ought to hold some."

It did: drawers of blades in all sizes, some clearly ceremonial, others looking like they might be used to butcher animals. What sort of people had his ancestors been? Shoving that thought aside, he picked the most ceremonial-looking dagger—an athame with a handle made of shining obsidian—the double-edged blade wickedly sharp. When he turned back to Nic, she'd shed her clothing and stood naked under the moon window, arms upraised as she turned in a slow circle, hair spilling down her back as glossy black as obsidian, moonlight silvering her perfect curves.

Noticing his regard, she lowered her chin and smiled at him. "The moonlight feels good. I like it."

"Do you have to be naked?" he asked gruffly, wanting to toss the athame away and ravish her sweet body.

"It's traditional," she replied sweetly. "And since neither of us has done this before, I think it's best to stick to the rules, much as you disdain them."

"I'll strip, too, then."

She shook her head. "No—you stay clothed. We're drawing lines of power here."

"No, we aren't," he said with firm determination. "We're making this a partnership." Going back to the cabinet, he selected a second athame, twin to the first—speaking of a good omen—and stripped off his clothing. Returning to naked to Nic, he handed her one athame, which she regarded with bemusement.

"What am I to do with this?" she asked, almost—though not quite—rolling her eyes at him.

"Whatever I'm doing with this one," he replied. "Reciprocal."

"You really are impossibly stubborn."

He grinned at her tone. "Something you've known from the moment you met me," he reminded her.

"True," she sighed.

"What next?"

"The familiar kneels."

"Then we both do." Taking her hand, he steadied her as they knelt in unison, facing each other within the circle, the moonlight shivering like frozen sparks over his skin, potent and arousing. "Do you feel that?"

"Yes, through your magic, I think," she replied in the same reverent tone. "Now, wrap your magic around me as you wind your free hand in my hair."

"Show me," he whispered hoarsely.

Leaning closer to him, the tips of her stiff nipples brushing his chest, she wound his hair around her hand. "Lucky yours is long enough for this," she said, wetting her lips, eyes fulgent. "If you had short hair, I don't know how we'd produce a mirror effect."

She'd said that, that first night, about how she couldn't cut her hair. Was this why? He imitated her, winding the long, silky length of her curls around his hand, trying to ignore the way he hardened at the feel of her. He'd been at half-mast or more for hours anyway, so the rush of blood came with excruciating intensity.

"Wrap your magic around me, too," he coaxed her, sending the water and moon-magic tendrils to embrace her as they always longed to do anyway.

With her gaze fastened to his, she released her magic, allowing it to suffuse the space between them with the heady, rich scent of roses. As it had when they'd made love that night, the magics intertwined, filling the other's spaces. This would work, he felt sure of it.

"You have to pull," she whispered. "Drink me in."

He did, feeling the rush of her essence filling every internal pore. "Is that enough?"

"More than," she breathed, a smile of utter sensuous delight illuminating her face. "Now kiss me, and as you do, cut off my hair."

Though he'd suspected, remorse spiked through him at the thought. "Your beautiful hair."

"It will grow back," she promised solemnly. "Take my power with the severing of my hair, wizard, so that I may be bound to you while you live."

"Then you do the same. Take my power with the severing of my hair, beloved familiar, so that I may be bound to you while you live."

"Gabriel," she gasped, eyes widening. "That isn't—"

"Do it," he ordered ruthlessly, willing to force at least this. Fastening his mouth to hers, he took it with a drugging kiss, their magic flaring into a blazing silver inferno where water fed the flames and billowed with steam. Her grip on his hair dragged his head back, a searing counterpoint to the driving need to drown in her kiss.

He waited for her athame to bite at his hair before setting his own to hers, mourning the loss of the glorious length of it. But she was right—it would grow back. And, for better or worse, she would belong to him now, irrevocably and for all their lives. He would be with her to watch it grow—to watch their child grow in her belly and beyond—and the thought filled him with an emotion so incandescent he had no words for it.

As the last of his hair came free, and as the thick tail of hers came away in his grip, the magic leapt to a keening new level, as if the water transcended to something beyond even steam, and moonlight solidified, chiming as it fell on the tiles.

They shuddered in each other's arms as the magic gripped

them, forging the bond that resonated through realms he hadn't imagined. Nic let out a cry, the sound guttural and sexual, her mouth feeding on his with fierce need, her body slick against his. He needed to bury himself in her with a ferocity that seemed to come from beyond him. "Is it done?" he asked, almost begging.

"Yes," she said on a moan. "It's done. I'm yours."

# ~ 23 ~

GABRIEL BROKE THE kiss, and Nic nearly wailed her frustration. He stared down at her, eyes wild. "Be more specific," he demanded. "Did it work?"

"I'm definitely bonded to you." And she was, the silver links of his magic firmly connected to hers. "We'll have to experiment to determine how reciprocal it is. Our magics work differently, so if you are bonded to me, it won't be in the same way."

He dipped his chin in a crisp nod. "All right, let's conduct some experiments. We can—"

"We can start tomorrow," she interrupted firmly, deliberately sliding against him, using the movement to tantalize that cock thrusting hot and hard against her belly. "Tonight," she purred, pursing her lips to draw his gaze, "we celebrate."

His expression softened with yearning. "Is that traditional?"

Breathing a laugh, she shook her head, so light without the weight of her hair. His silver locks curled with unruly abandon around his face, freed of the length. "I don't care, do you?"

"No," he replied, considering. "I don't think I care. I want you, Nic, more than I can bear."

Her whole body shivered with anticipation. "Take, Gabriel. Have."

"Yes." His mouth quirked in a smile as he showed her the bundle of her severed hair. "Can I keep this?"

"I believe it's traditional," she answered on a laugh.

"We can't defy tradition." Setting the hair carefully to the side, he laid his athame beside it. She laid her own prize—shorter but glittering silver—and athame beside hers. They made a picture, blending with the pattern of the arcanium floor. Gabriel smoothed his hands over her shoulders, drawing her attention as he gazed at her.

"Do I look awful?" she asked.

He shook his head, then nodded judiciously. "It's a bit ragged. It could use some trimming."

She brushed away the single lock of black hair falling into his eyes. "I suspect likewise for you. Something else for tomorrow." She slid her hands into his silking curls, pulling him down to kiss her. "Take, Gabriel," she said for the third time. "Have."

He followed her down to stretch beside her on the floor. "Here?"

"It's good for the arcanium. Sex magic will infiltrate the spells laid into the walls, refreshing and reenergizing them."

"I'm not sure that's a good thing, given what my ancestors may have been like." His gaze strayed to the silver bed.

She caressed his jaw, drawing his eyes back to hers. "Good and evil lies in our intentions and actions, not in the tools we use. You and I will need all the tools—and power—we can muster if we're going to fight the Convocation."

He closed a big hand over her breast, enfolding it and teasing her taut nipple with a rough palm so that she arched her spine with a gasp. "Is that what we're going to do?" He said it more musingly than asking the question, his mouth drawing on her other nipple, wrenching a strangled cry of longing from her.

"The wages of breaking the laws," she panted. "You made your bed, wizard. Now you must lie in it."

"So long as I'm not chained to it," he said with a half smile, watching her face as he trailed his hand down her body, tracing her curves, then sliding up the inside of her thigh as she spread her legs for him. Beyond willing. Desperate for his touch.

"Not unless we're enjoying being chained to it," she corrected, losing her saucy attitude as his silvery touch caressed her slick folds. "Oh, Gabriel," she sighed with needy pleasure.

He levered himself between her thighs, slipping a hand beneath her hips to position her. "I'd rather lie on you," he murmured with a wicked smile that went tight as he pressed into her.

She moaned, low and long as he filled and stretched her. It felt like yesterday and forever since he'd been inside her. So long since he'd marked her with his magic, so indelibly that it had settled into her bones and blood, forever calling her back to him.

And him to her.

Her hips lifted as she welcomed him in, bringing him home, wrapping him in her magic as his flowed into and out of her, surging with a silvery tide that eroded all her doubts and fears.

This was right. This was meant.

Back and forth.
Water and fire.
Silver and crimson.
Wizard and familiar.

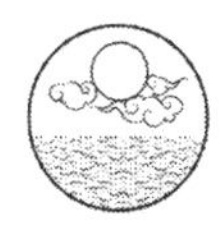

A LONG TIME later, Nic lay on her back, head pillowed on Gabriel's arm as she gazed up at the silvery light sifting through the lake water and flowing through the moon window. "There's something you should know," she said, hating to ruin the moment, but knowing Gabriel wouldn't appreciate that she'd kept mum even this long.

"What?" he asked sleepily, reaching over to stroke her with a long caress that made her want to purr.

"You won't like it," she warned him.

"Tell me," he prompted, not unconcerned but… trusting. He trusted her, she realized, to tell him what he needed to know, like it or not.

"Seliah is a familiar."

He stayed quiet so long that she might've thought him asleep except for the sharp brightness of his magic, stirring restlessly. "I won't ask if you're sure," he finally said, "because you would know. Did you sense it the moment you met her?"

"Yes. I'm sorry I didn't say so sooner, but…"

"But we had things to work out." He pulled her tighter against his side, sighing heavily. "After all these years, I can't imagine a few hours or a day will change much."

"No, but we will have to help her, or she'll continue to decline mentally."

"It explains so much," he murmured, almost to himself. "She was always so bright, so talented. All the way into her late teens, and then… it was like a shadow fell over her."

Nic nodded, understanding the metaphor exactly. "I know you don't trust the Convocation, but they can help her."

"No." He relaxed his tightened arm. "Only as a last resort," he amended. "You and I will try to help her first."

"All right," she agreed, surprised at herself, snuggling closer against him. "Something else for tomorrow."

"Tomorrow." He kissed her forehead, and they lay like that long enough that it began to feel like forever. Perhaps, like happiness.

The story of Gabriel and Veronica continues in
*Bright Familiar*

# TITLES BY JEFFE KENNEDY

## FANTASY ROMANCES

**BONDS OF MAGIC**

*Dark Wizard*

*Bright Familiar* (June 2021)

*Bonds of Magic #3* (October 2021)

**HEIRS OF MAGIC**

*The Long Night of the Crystalline Moon*

(in *Under a Winter Sky*)

*The Golden Gryphon and the Bear Prince*

*The Sorceress Queen and the Pirate Rogue* (April 2021)

*The Winter Mage and the Dragon's Daughter* (August 2021)

*The Storm Princess and the Raven King* (December 2021)

**THE FORGOTTEN EMPIRES**

*The Orchid Throne*

*The Fiery Crown*

*The Promised Queen* (May 2021)

**THE TWELVE KINGDOMS**

*Negotiation*

*The Mark of the Tala*

*The Tears of the Rose*

*The Talon of the Hawk*

*Heart's Blood*

*The Crown of the Queen*

**THE UNCHARTED REALMS**

*The Pages of the Mind*

*The Edge of the Blade*

*The Snows of Windroven*

*The Shift of the Tide*

*The Arrows of the Heart*

*The Dragons of Summer*

*The Fate of the Tala*

*The Lost Princess Returns*

**THE CHRONICLES OF DASNARIA**

*Prisoner of the Crown*

*Exile of the Seas*

*Warrior of the World*

**SORCEROUS MOONS**

*Lonen's War*

*Oria's Gambit*

*The Tides of Bára*

*The Forests of Dru*

*Oria's Enchantment*

*Lonen's Reign*

**A COVENANT OF THORNS**

*Rogue's Pawn*

*Rogue's Possession*

*Rogue's Paradise*

## CONTEMPORARY ROMANCES

*Shooting Star*

**MISSED CONNECTIONS**

*Last Dance*

*With a Prince*

*Since Last Christmas*

## CONTEMPORARY EROTIC ROMANCES

*Exact Warm Unholy*

*The Devil's Doorbell*

**FACETS OF PASSION**

*Sapphire*

*Platinum*

*Ruby*

*Five Golden Rings*

**FALLING UNDER**

*Going Under*

*Under His Touch*

*Under Contract*

# EROTIC PARANORMAL

**MASTER OF THE OPERA E-SERIAL**

Master of the Opera, Act 1: Passionate Overture

Master of the Opera, Act 2: Ghost Aria

Master of the Opera, Act 3: Phantom Serenade

Master of the Opera, Act 4: Dark Interlude

Master of the Opera, Act 5: A Haunting Duet

Master of the Opera, Act 6: Crescendo

*Master of the Opera*

**BLOOD CURRENCY**

*Blood Currency*

# BDSM FAIRYTALE ROMANCE

*Petals and Thorns*

Thank you for reading!

# ABOUT JEFFE KENNEDY

Jeffe Kennedy is an award-winning, best-selling author who writes fantasy with romantic elements and fantasy romance. She is an RWA member and serves on the Board of Directors for SFWA as a Director at Large.

Books in her popular, long-running series, The Twelve Kingdoms and The Uncharted Realms, have won the RT Reviewers' Choice Best Fantasy Romance, been named Best Book of June 2014, and won RWA's prestigious RITA® Award, while more have been finalists for those awards. She's the author of the romantic fantasy trilogy with St. Martin's Press, The Forgotten Empires, which includes The Orchid Throne, The Fiery Crown, and The Promised Queen. She also self-publishes the romantic fantasy series Bonds of Magic, Heirs of Magic, and Sorcerous Moons.

Jeffe lives in Santa Fe, New Mexico, with two Maine coon cats, plentiful free-range lizards, and a very handsome Doctor of Oriental Medicine.

Jeffe can be found online at her website: JeffeKennedy.com, every Sunday at the popular SFF Seven blog, on Facebook, on Goodreads, and pretty much constantly on Twitter @jeffekennedy. She is represented by Sarah Younger of Nancy Yost Literary Agency.

jeffekennedy.com

facebook.com/Author.Jeffe.Kennedy

twitter.com/jeffekennedy

goodreads.com/author/show/1014374.Jeffe_Kennedy

**Sign up for her newsletter here.**

jeffekennedy.com/sign-up-for-my-newsletter

Made in the USA
Las Vegas, NV
11 November 2023

80647837R00240

An Evangelis
for the 21S

# Till the NETS Are Full

DOUGLAS JACOBY

**Till the Nets Are Full**
An Evangelism Handbook for the 21st Century



Original edition (Shining Like Stars) 1987. Revised 1990, 2000, 2006, 2010, and 2018.

ISBN: 978-1-948450-00-3.



Printed in the United States of America.



Interior layout by Toney C. Mulhollan and cover design by Roy Applesamy of Toronto, Canada.

Illumination Publishers titles may be purchased in bulk for classroom instruction, teaching seminars, or sales promotional use. For information, please email paul.ipibooks@me.com.

Illumination Publishers cares deeply about using renewable resources and uses recycled paper whenever possible.

**About the author:** Since 2003 Dr. Douglas Jacoby has been a freelance teacher and consultant. With degrees from Duke, Harvard, and Drew, he has written over thirty books, recorded over 600 podcasts, and spoken in numerous cities in 120 nations around the world. Douglas is also Adjunct Professor of Bible and Theology at Lincoln Christian University.
For information about his work, speaking schedule, and teaching ministry, view his website at www.DouglasJacoby.com.

There is a free ebook version for all purchases of the hard copy of this book for your personal use. Go to www.ipibooks.com for details.

## Books by Douglas Jacoby

*A Quick Overview of the Bible*

*Answering Skeptics*

*Campus Core*

*Chariots of Fire*

*Compelling Evidence for God and the Bible*

*Exodus: Night of Redemption*

*Foundations for Faith: Old Testament Survey*

*Jesus and Islam*

*Life to the Full*

*Principle-Centered Parenting*

*The Faith Unfurled: New Testament Survey*

*The Lion Has Roared*

*The Spirit*

*The Ultimate Bible Quiz Book*

*Thrive! Using Psalms to Help You Flourish*

*What Happens After We Die?*

*What's the Truth About Heaven and Hell?*

*El Espíritu*

*La Aljaba*

*Verdadero y Razonable*

# Contents

Preface to the Updated Edition 9

Part I

## Do Not Be Afraid

*Challenges for the heart*

1. Where Are You Hiding? 12
2. The Mission 15
3. The Lifeblood of the Church 21

Part II

## I Am Going Fishing

*Fishing in our neighborhoods, at work and in school*

4. From House to House 29
5. God's Ambassador at Work 39
6. The Goose That Laid the Golden Egg 47

*More challenging arenas*

7. Reaching Our Families 54
8. All Things to All People 65
9. The Ultrareligious 73

Part III

## Put Out into Deep Water

*Teaching the lost*

10. Studying with Non-Christians 84
11. Guard the Gospel – Series A 101
12. Guard the Gospel – Series B 125

# Contents

13. Guard the Gospel – Series C 149
14. Old Testament "Guard the Gospel" 179
15. A Medical Account of the Crucifixion 182

*Grounding new believers in the Word and the mission*

16. Grounding New Christians: Thirteen Follow-Up Studies 186
17. In the Hall of Tyrannus: Effective Group Bible Discussions 201
18. A Fountain of Life: Fourteen Studies and How to Lead Them 207

PART IV

DON'T STOP NOW!

*Conclusion*

19. Translating the Challenge into Action 231

Appendix A: Bringing Back the Stray 234
Appendix B: Harnessing Technology for Effective Outreach 237
Index 240
Bibliography 243

# *Preface to the Updated Edition*

The first edition (blue) of *Shining Like Stars* was published in 1987. Substantial revisions were made for the 1990 (yellow) edition. In the same way, massive editing preceded the release of the millennium (spiral bound) edition in 2000. By 2005, once again it was clear that a revision was in order. This version is an update to the "fifth edition"—and with a new name. As always, please consider it a work in progress.

If you have read any of the earlier versions, you will notice a host of changes. Some are significant corrections of a theological nature. As my understanding of God's grace has deepened, I have seen many deficiencies in the earlier editions, especially in their overly mechanical approach to evangelism and reliance on human wisdom. Other changes are simply the cutting away of the superfluous or the polishing and sharpening of the dull. A good amount of new material has also been added, in part to set forth the rationale for personal Bible studies with nonbelievers, and in part to clarify a number of unfortunate impressions from certain sections of the earlier versions. In short, a new edition was sorely needed.

Further, we (my publishers and I) wanted to craft a book that would speak to the broader Restoration Movement, namely the Christian Churches and Churches of Christ. (Not to say the book will be of no use to those in other faith traditions.)

## How This Book Can Help

This is a manual on personal evangelism. It is challenging. It is practical, with dozens of in-depth studies to be shared with non-Christians and also young Christians. Through the past thirty years it has helped tens of thousands worldwide.

A book cannot change your heart—that's between you and God. You'll have to make a personal decision to face reality head on and make the appropriate changes. But if your heart is right, the book can help you in several ways:

- It will challenge you to overcome shyness and live boldly for the Lord.

- It will draw your attention to opportunities God is giving you every day to reach out to those around you.
- It is brimming with effective study materials you can use to help your non-Christian friends come to faith, and new believers grow in their faith.

**Three Books**

This book is admittedly the word of man (1 Thessalonians 2:13). It can only point us to the master evangelist, Jesus Christ, suggesting a number of possible approaches as we share the life-giving news with outsiders. The only book with *real* authority is the Bible itself. And yet as has been said, for many people, we who are Christians may be the only "Bible" they will ever read, and the only "Jesus" they will ever see (2 Corinthians 2:14–16). Therefore my hope is that *this* book will ground us more deeply in *the* book so that our lives will truly be *a* book known and read by all.

As Christians called to fish for people (Mark 1:17), may we drink deep of the Holy Spirit, who always insists on making Christ known!

Douglas Jacoby
Marietta, Georgia

PART I

# DO NOT BE AFRAID

> Jesus... got into one of the boats, the one belonging to Simon, and asked him to put out a little way from the shore... When he had finished speaking, he said to Simon, "Put out into the deep water and let down your nets for a catch." Simon answered, "Master, we have worked all night long but have caught nothing. Yet if you say so, I will let down the nets." When they had done this, they caught so many fish that their nets were beginning to break. So they signaled their partners in the other boat to come and help them. And they came and filled both boats, so that they began to sink. But when Simon Peter saw it, he fell down at Jesus' knees, saying, "Go away from me, Lord, for I am a sinful man!"... Then Jesus said to Simon, "Do not be afraid; from now on you will be catching people." When they had brought their boats to shore, they left everything and followed him (Luke 5:1–11 NRSV).

Jesus taught his followers that they were destined to influence the world by calling men and women to follow him. Those who understand the holiness of the one calling them, the enormity of the task, and the reality of the Lord's presence can only fall down in awe, fear, praise, gratitude, prayer, and determination.

First things first. Chapters 1 to 3 of this book deal with our life decision to face our fears and embark on our mission—or, in some cases, return to it.

# 1
# Where Are You Hiding?

I believe that you, the reader, want to serve God and make an impact on the world. People don't buy books on evangelism unless they want to be evangelistic. Yet all of us can slip into a careless, inattentive state. We neglect the very things which mean the most to us. A husband neglects the wife of his youth, children fail to appreciate the one who brought them into the world, a disciple slips in showing gratitude to the God who saved him or her.

**Hide and Seek?**

When it comes to evangelism, many of us do more than merely neglect it: we actively *hide* from it. Are you hiding? Adam and Eve hid among the trees in the Garden. Moses tried to hide behind his brother Aaron, while Saul hid among the baggage. Even Peter, in a moment of weakness, denied Jesus and hid himself among the guards around the fire.

People hide not only because they are confused about the facts or unsure of what to do. They also may hide because they are unwilling to face reality.

This book is written for those who are serious about evangelism. We heard the call to discipleship as we were making our decision for Christ. At baptism, we said, "Jesus is Lord"—a lifelong promise to obey his word, follow in his steps and be fishers of people. But how are we really doing in our own evangelism? Are we hiding?

Jesus said, "You are the light of the world. A town on a hill cannot be hidden." At times don't all of us hide our light? He continued, "Neither do people light a lamp and hide it under a bowl. Instead they put it on its stand, and it gives light to everyone in the house. In the same way, let your light shine before others, that they may see your good deeds and glorify your father in heaven" (Matthew 5:14–16). This passage is simply the Great Commission in another form.

Have you been hiding? And if so, where? What are your excuses, who are you trying to hide behind, or what trivial thing is distracting you from your mission? (Or is your conscience clear?) Let's agree to come out into the open. We have nothing to hide and we certainly do not want to hide from our mission.

### Is God Calling Me to the Mission Field?

"Okay," you think, "no more hiding. I'll come out into the open. But I know what this means. I'll have to throw in the towel on my degree, my job plans—everything!—and move overseas. Maybe preach to the pygmies..." This form of self-delusion does at least sound somewhat glorious. But such thinking is flawed, for the mission field is not just "over there"; it is right here! If we aren't ready to strike up conversations with those around us, invite them to share in our lives, our faith, our Lord—how is it suddenly going to become easier if we move to a foreign country, with all the extra challenges such a move entails?

No, if we're not striving to be fishers of people here, we are simply not ready to go to a foreign field. The truth is, we are always surrounded by fields "white/ripe for harvest" (John 4:35). God is in fact calling every one of us to the "mission field." It may well be in Africa, Asia, or somewhere behind the "bamboo curtain." More likely it is in our own country. The point is to be ready, all the time. Ready to "go anywhere, do anything, give up everything" for the cause.

I remember a time in my life when I thought missions meant only *foreign* missions, and the more foreign the better! The enormous continent of South America, with its hundreds of millions caught in dead traditional religion or misguided zeal, captured my imagination. I began reading the Bible in Spanish, even trying to pray in Spanish. So when I was initially invited to join a mission team to London—you know, English-speaking England—I didn't react well. "London? That's not glorious enough," I was thinking. "They speak the same language as we do (almost). Would I really be laying it all on the line if I went there? I hope I'm destined for a higher calling," I mused.

And yet London was awesome! I was proud to be on the mission team—and wish more of us were excited about being on "mission teams"! I rapidly became an Anglophile. I have watched the inspiring film *Chariots of Fire* fifteen times! Everything British was better, and in a funny way I secretly became ashamed of being so "American." I even tried to change my accent. (As easily as the leopard changes its spots, to use the idiom of Jeremiah.) "Hank the Yank," they called me, and many others of us too. We meant well—but how we stuck out! As things turned out, I ended up living abroad for twelve years—in England, Sweden, and Australia.

The point is, you can serve the Lord anywhere. Preach in your own country, or move somewhere else. That is, if you are convicted that the Lord has a plan for your life, that he has sent you on a mission. And the alternative?

Hide. (Is that what you're doing?)

# 2
# The Mission

In the last chapter we were asked a question: "Where are you hiding?" In this chapter another vital issue receives our attention: the mission. Often in the Word we read of people *sent* on missions: Jonah to Nineveh (Jonah 1:2), Isaiah to the Israelites (Isaiah 6:8–9), Saul to the Amalekites (1 Samuel 15:18–24), Jesus to the earth (John 1:11–13). Are you clear on your mission? This means commitment to God, living your life for him (2 Corinthians 5:15).[1] This means doing great things for God, praying grand, global thoughts, not puny, parochial prayers! And this means thinking, believing, dreaming, living, and dying heroically. As Horace Mann remarked, "Be ashamed to die until you have won some victory for mankind." And as the apostle remarked, "Grace to all who love our Lord Jesus Christ with an undying love" (Ephesians 6:24). Undying love—you're in it for the long haul, disciple. True zeal is more than skin deep. It is not a costume you don every Sunday. God's claim on our life is total, not partial. Have you compromised your mission?

### Slain by a Fierce, Wild Beast!

Deep in our hearts many of us have always suspected this is the way it must be—if there is a God, his Word is true, and we are to follow him. Ever since I was a little boy I knew (from Sunday school) that we were supposed to live for God. I heard about people who sold everything and lived in poverty—and something in my soul responded, "I should live that way, too." There was a certain attractiveness to the grand old hymns, waxen candles, and walks through cemeteries, thinking about God. Even confirmation classes intrigued me! And I still remember the words of a song I heard when I was six or seven years old:

> I sing a song of the saints of God,
>     patient and brave and true:
> They toiled and they fought and they lived and they died

for their own good Lord they knew.

And one was a doctor and one was a priest
and one was slain by a fierce, wild beast;
And there's no, not a reason, no not the least
Why I shouldn't be one too![2]

My conscience was mildly haunted by the words of that song for another twelve years—especially by the thought of being slain by a beast! Could there be something so worth living for that it was also worth dying for? The words remained in my heart, until I began to consider the Bible more seriously. Looking back now, I believe I was just waiting for a chance to become committed. (Maybe you were, too!) When I met men and women who lived as committed a life as the one they taught (and sang) about, the old chords were set vibrating, and I knew that my quest, in one sense, was at an end.

The world is looking for a cause, something to live for. People rally behind one cause or another, but seldom with the clarity and resolve of Christ. It is up to us to show them that Jesus Christ is worth living for. And dying for, if that is what we are called to do. It's all part of the mission.

## Holiness an Option?

Is holiness an option? Is the mission only for those who feel comfortable with it, or are we all called to "fish" (Luke 5:4), to "gather" (Luke 11:23)? In these days of "church of your choice" and "nonjudgmentalism," is this level of commitment just one more jaded theme we could just as well do without? Or is this not the narrow path that Jesus walked, and which he bade us come and walk as well? The Hebrew writer was definitive: "Make every effort to live in peace with everyone and to be holy; without holiness no one will see the Lord" (Hebrews 12:14). The Scriptures are clear: Holiness is no option. Let the world mock, and let the religious world defend its shallow piety with theology Felix would have applauded (Acts 24:25). Lukewarmness is not an option, because God, the holy God, is not an "option." God commands us to be holy because he is holy (1 Peter 1:15–16; Leviticus 11:44-45, 19:2, 20:7).

It should be no surprise that the Holy Spirit makes us holy.

The Spirit flows through our veins, a transfusion of life and determination coursing through every artery and capillary. The person who claims to have the Spirit must live a holy life, or the game is up! By their fruits you will know them (Matthew 7:20). Without holiness no one will see the Lord (Hebrews 12:14).

Although in time the emphasis on holiness declined, especially after the legalization of Christianity in the 300s, God never lowered his standard. Striving for holiness continued unabated, even among the rank and file, for nearly three centuries before the early church finally cooled off. This is not to say that there were no true Christians during the extended period of apostasy that began in the fourth century. Their lives shine out, yet it is as lamentable that they were called "saints"—aren't all Christians to be saints?—as they were exceptional (as opposed to normal).

Consider the second-century sermon called 2 Clement. Clearly, at this time, there was still a concern for holiness: "What assurance do we have of entering the kingdom of God if we fail to keep our baptism pure and undefiled? Or who will be our advocate, if we are not found to have holy and righteous works?" (2 Clement 6:9b). Reading the "Church Fathers" (the patristic writers), can be enormously beneficial, affording clearer insight into how the original church evolved into the confused state of modern "churchianity" and bringing us closer to the radical spirit of our earliest brothers and sisters in the faith.

We read in Romans 12:11, "Never be lacking in zeal, but keep your spiritual fervor, serving the Lord." *Fervor* is the Latin word for "seething, heat; ardor, passion." The verb *fervere* means "to boil." This fervor, energy, or heat, is the difference between pulseless, morbid religion and vibrant, vital faith. No amount of explanation about how a corpse is really "alive" is going to convince anyone with eyes in their head. Living faith has a pulse because it is energized by the very Spirit of God (James 2:26).

### "When You're Hot, You're Hot"

"When you're hot, you're hot. And when you're not, you're not," the saying goes. God's word demands that we be hot, not cold or lukewarm. The success of the mission absolutely depends on it!

"To the angel of the church in Laodicea write: These are the

> words of the Amen, the faithful and true witness, the ruler of God's creation. I know your deeds, that you are neither cold nor hot. I wish you were either one or the other! So, because you are lukewarm—neither hot nor cold—I am about to spit you out of my mouth" (Revelation 3:14–16).

These words are addressed to a church that used to be hot, but had slipped into the self-satisfaction of lukewarmness. Sadly, only a few decades later this church seems not to have repented. Other churches that received letters in Revelation 2–3 were still in existence (like those in Ephesus and Philadelphia, for example), but the second-century writers sent no letters, as far as we know, to the church of Laodicea. It seems this first-century church dwindled in faith and in numbers, ultimately vanishing off the screen.

Jesus Christ looks not just at heart (our faith and intent), but also at deeds. "Holy" and "hot" are nearly synonyms when it comes to commitment. (Technically speaking, we are pressing the analogy. In Laodicea, as in our homes today, hot water and cold water are both good. It's the lukewarm that triggers a response of disgust.) Religious experiences are no substitute. Truly spiritual people don't gather "miracle" stories and seek after a spiritual buzz (Colossians 2:18); they do the work of God (Matthew 7:21–23).

Can you honestly say that you are "hot" for God, his word, his will, his people, his plans? You can if his mission runs in your veins.

### "Inwardly Boiling"

Over a billion people on our planet claim to be Christians, despite the fact that their "pulse" is impossible to locate. The result: dead faith creating dead weight in dead churches. Imagine your friend asking you to go and check a pot of water on the stove.

"It should be boiling by now," he says.

You check it swiftly dipping in your finger (just to be safe), only to feel tepid water. "Still cold!" you reply.

"No, it should be boiling by now," he returns; "please go back and check again."

You check once more and feel only lukewarm water.

What would you think if he said, "I know it's hot; it must be boiling. Yes, it must be '*inwardly* boiling'"?

What if he persisted in spouting off slogans like "What counts is heart, not heat," and "Lukewarm water needs time to 'mature,'" wouldn't you eventually come to question his sincerity, or his understanding of words such as "hot," "cold" and "boiling"? He then further defends his doctrine: "No water is perfect"; "All water has the right to seek its own temperature"; "Being nice is what counts, not being hot"; or perhaps "The warming up is more important than the heat." The theology of lukewarmness continues to blossom: "We truly believe in inner boiling," and "Judge not water's heat," and finally, "Hot-water-only groups are too exclusive!" Would you not be right to accuse him not only of illogic but also of special pleading (that is, deliberately ignoring aspects that are unfavorable to his point of view)?

So it is with holiness. The commitment of discipleship is nonnegotiable. The fervor of spiritual zeal is defined by God, not by human beings. No one has the right to dilute holiness, then say, "It's good enough."

### Fake versus Real Zeal

Zeal can be faked. Showing up at church—even smiling, clapping, saying "Amen"—may fool others, but it cannot fool God (Galatians 6:7). He knows whether we are about his mission or not.

Do you have a zeal that's real, or are you the "hype type"? Still confused about what God thinks about faking dedication, feigning devotion, falsifying discipleship, fudging holiness? The tale of Ananias and Sapphira (Acts 5:1–11) reveals the heart of God on this matter. When this couple pretended to be more committed than they were instead of being honest, we read that they were lying to the Holy Spirit (v.3) and testing the Spirit of the Lord (v.9). God the Spirit is offended when, instead of allowing him to make us holy, we make a farce of faith. No more showy, shallow, sham religion!

How can we claim to be God's people when we are lacking in zeal? Many people lack the truth, and yet sometimes are just as zealous in their religion as real Christians are (Romans 10:1–2). Zeal does not mean loud "Amens" and boisterous behavior, but being filled with the Spirit of God and modeling the walk we talk about. After all, as Mark Twain said, "Few things are harder to put up with than a good example." When people see that kind of zeal, they will know it's real.

Never, ever forget who you are and whose you are. True Christians are *a holy people on a holy mission in a holy church serving a holy God.*

## Notes

[1] Much of the material in this and the following chapter has been adapted from chapters 12 and 13 ("A Zeal That's Real" and "The Spirit Insists!") of *The Spirit: Presence & Power, Sense & Nonsense* (Spring, Texas: Illumination Publishers, 2017).

[2] Lesbia Scott, 1929.

# 3
# The Lifeblood of the Church

Evangelism has been described as the lifeblood of the church of Christ. It is a major part of our mission here on earth and deserves our time, energy, and wholehearted labor. At this point, it should be clarified that mission and purpose are different things. Our *purpose* is to enjoy our relationship with God and make it to heaven; our *mission* is to change the world. (When mission and purpose become confused, spiritual burnout is not far away.) As vital as evangelism is—yes, the very lifeblood of the church!—it is not everything. As with physical life, blood is vital, but so are the heart that pumps it, the organs that draw from its supply, and the brain that regulates the whole. Are you clear about your purpose? About your mission? And about the difference between the two?

The mission is twofold. We are called to preach the Word and to help the poor. Although ultimately one's spiritual condition, not one's medical or economic situation, is what counts, still we are called as the people of God to both facets of the mission. True Christians love the poor, especially their poor brothers and sisters (Galatians 6:10). True Christians also love the lost and share what they have found with them. It is unrighteous to neglect one or the other.

Let's zero in on our evangelistic responsibility. Just as Jesus sent his disciples out to preach the Word and to minister to the needy, so the Spirit sends us today on the same twin mission (Mark 3:14).

### Message, Mission, Ministry

World evangelism is our consuming passion as disciples. It was the will of God in the first century, the mountaintop mandate of the Lord Jesus, and the lifeblood of the New Testament church. The situation is no different today! While we humbly realize that our generation is probably not the last in human history, you never know. We may be living in the final epoch. (1 Thessalonians 5:1) Thus, surely our common goal must be to bring Christ to every nation—to saturate the earth with the gospel in our lifetime, by all means possible.

Our first-century brothers and sisters, moved by the Holy Spirit, caused quite a stir when they preached the radical message of the gospel. The Spirit insists that we work together to turn the world upside down.[1] How do we know that? Because the Spirit inspired the entire Bible. Europe, Asia, Africa, Australia, the Americas—the entire world!—can be and must be evangelized if we, as God's children, are to be faithful to our Father's wishes. On this there can be no compromise. Nor should we ever leave our "great work" in order to negotiate with the critics (Nehemiah 6:1–14).

I am privileged, as an international traveler and Christian speaker, to have preached in some 125 nations, and keep up a vigorous correspondence with thousands of men and women globally. (Not that I don't enjoy sharing about the Lord in my home country.) My teaching ministry is a thrill, a joy, an honor, and an all-consuming passion. You may not be an international evangelist, but that doesn't mean you don't have a *message*, a *mission*, and a *ministry* right where you live. All Christians have the message (the gospel), a mission (to make Jesus known, through word and deed), and are "in the ministry" (a royal priesthood, in the words of 1 Peter 2:9). We should resist lingo that equates being "in the ministry" with having a highly visible gift set, or being on church staff. The lingo is faulty because the underlying theology is faulty.

Hopefully you don't have to be *told* to share your faith before you do so. The good news is so "good" that it is contagious, explosive, and nearly impossible to contain (Jeremiah 20:9). As someone has said, "The Spirit of Christ always insists on making Christ known" (see John 15:26).

**We're Outta Here!**

How determined are we to follow the Spirit and to refuse to tolerate unspirituality? Years ago (in the '70s, in fact), my brother and I were driving down the East Coast of the United States, attending various Christian conferences. The first message at one conference we had registered for was on the topic of evangelism. The speaker began by describing evangelism as a "talent" or "gift." The experts, according to this man, had calculated that only ten percent of Christians can be expected to evangelize, since for ninety percent of us, it is not our gift.

But there is a difference between gifts and commands. For example, we are all commanded to encourage others (Hebrews 3:13), yet some have the gift of encouragement (Romans 12:8) and will find that what may be hard for others is relatively easy for them. While it is true that some of us find some of the commands easier to obey than others, we must never minimize a command into an option under the claim that "it's not my gift"! Evangelism is not an option. After all, in Ephesians 4:11, the gift is not evangelism, but evangelists—the leadership position.

As the conference speaker was droning on, I thought of the ten lepers (in Luke 17) and how only one returned to thank Jesus. (Yes, only "ten percent" returned to Jesus to show appreciation for what God had done in their lives. The "ten-percent rule" applied here, though not as meant by the speaker!) After the talk, I turned to my brother, Steve, and said, "I'm outta here!" We walked out, since we were not interested in explaining away the Great Commission or consoling ourselves about our lack of commitment.

How about you? Are you hanging out only with those who have low expectations for world impact? Are you attracted to a fellowship that says, "I'm okay; you're okay," "Judge not," and "Lukewarm is acceptable"? Putting it another way, do you count the hours that go by between times of sharing your faith, or the days? How often do you share your life with friends in your home? (Acts 5:42; 1 Thessalonians 2:8). The Holy Spirit is not a spirit of timidity, but one of power, love, and self-discipline (2 Timothy 1:7). The next time a thought of compromise starts to "lecture" you on why you do not have to obey the Great Commission, just say, "I'm outta here!"

### The Acts of the Spirit

Probably the place where God has most clearly shown his will that all disciples be evangelistic is the book of Acts. The title "The Acts of the Apostles" is something of a misnomer, since only Peter and Paul receive significant coverage in this book. Many scholars contend that Luke's second volume could be called "The Acts of the Spirit," since it is the Holy Spirit who essentially serves as "Director of Evangelism" and "Chief Empowerer of the Christian

Movement." This is key in understanding the plan of Acts. In our lives we have no more powerful advocate in evangelism than the Holy Spirit himself. Let's examine a few of the ways the Spirit assists us.

After Pentecost, first-century Christians were not interested in concealing the gospel—only in revealing it. When the church was scattered in the Great Persecution after the martyring of Stephen, many shared their faith—not just the top leaders! (Acts 8:1, 4). Acts records the birth and growth of the church during its first three decades. Several aspects of the explosive expansion of the church are noteworthy:

- The bold proclamation of the message
- The universal opposition met with by the church
- The rapid growth of the fledgling movement

Since the same Spirit empowers us today, is there really any reason not to expect a similar working of the Spirit in our own lives? Why not study Acts with an eye on the spirit of the Christians as the Spirit impelled them to take the Word to a lost world?

### Boldness Booster

Timidity has never been the way of the Spirit! The Spirit will help us to change any area of our life necessary in order for us to become effective evangelistically. Have circumstances gotten you down? Are you not as bold lately as you have been in the past? If so, claim the power of the Spirit as the early Christians did when under great pressure: "Now, Lord, consider their threats and enable your servants to speak your word with great boldness" (Acts 4:29). Was that prayer ever answered? (Would God let any prayer like that go unanswered?)

> "After they prayed, the place where they were meeting was shaken. And they were all filled with the Holy Spirit and spoke the word of God boldly" (Acts 4:31).

A miracle? Perhaps. (The shaking is immaterial.) They sincerely desired boldness, prayed a prayer for boldness and emerged from that prayer meeting bolder than ever! Coincidence? Hardly! God is waiting and willing to fill with his Spirit any of us who need to grow in the area of boldness.

## Spirit-Directed Outreach

The book of Acts shows just how involved the Holy Spirit is in the enterprise of evangelism.[2] Let's take a quick tour through Acts and notice how often the Spirit is mentioned in connection with outreach:

- Through the Spirit Jesus briefed his apostles, explaining the kingdom of God and preparing them for the mission soon to commence (Acts 1:2).
- The Spirit would empower the Christians systematically to evangelize the world: first, the city; then, the outlying towns and villages; finally, faraway lands (Acts 1:8).
- The Spirit brought the international crowd together to hear the good news of Jesus Christ (Acts 2:5).
- The Spirit filled the praying Christians with evangelistic boldness (Acts 4:31).
- The Spirit equips obedient disciples to speak even in the face of opposition (Acts 5:27–32).
- The Spirit made it clear that racial divides are no obstacle to the kingdom of God (Acts 8:14–17).
- The Spirit advised the early missionaries where to preach and when to move on (Acts 8:29, 39).
- The Spirit encouraged the church, leading to numerical growth and spiritual sobriety (Acts 9:31).
- The Spirit made it dramatically clear that we are to focus on the central elements of the gospel, not the peripheral ones, when the Gentiles were ushered into the kingdom (Acts 10:44–48, 11:12–18).
- When the Spirit and faith fill a person, many people are brought to the Lord (Acts 11:24).
- The Spirit conceives missionary plans (Acts 13:2) and sees them through (Acts 13:4).

- The Spirit sometimes blocks missionary plans (Acts 16:6–7).
- The Spirit places leadership, particularly eldership, over those who have been led to Christ (Acts 20:28).

Surely we can be confident that the same Spirit has been working in our lifetime to bring down walls of communism and apartheid, thus opening the door to the evangelization of our world. Jesus concluded the Great Commission by saying, "I am with you always, to the very end of the age." Is it not through the continuing work of the Spirit that his promise is being fulfilled?

## The Spirit Changes Hearts

The Spirit works with us in our evangelism. We do not need to rely on our own wisdom but must rely on the power of the Spirit (1 Corinthians 2:1–5). According to John 16:8, the Spirit convicts the hearts of non-Christians. The Word is the sword of the Spirit (Ephesians 6:17). Here is the world evangelism plan in a nutshell:

- The Spirit changes the hearts of followers of Christ.
- Disciples of Christ preach the Word wherever they go.
- The Spirit works through the Word to change the hearts of nonbelievers.

## Conclusion

The early church took the Great Commission (Matthew 28:18–20) to heart and made a concerted effort to implement Jesus' command to preach the gospel.[3] They obeyed the Great Commission because they understood the Greatest Commandment (Matthew 22:37ff). Love for God comes before love for the lost, and when the order of the commands is reversed, skewed theology and lopsided lives result. Understanding the intent of the master evangelist, the apostles saw most of the territory around the Mediterranean evangelized within their lifetime. Inroads were made deep into Africa, Asia, and Europe. In the following centuries, before the legalization of Christianity in 313 AD, the fledgling faith continued to expand, the message being carried nearly worldwide—in some form at least—in the following millennium.

Sadly, although the original nuclear church exploded into

action, it later slackened. Worldliness and materialism crept in. Soon Christians failed to forge unity. Instead, they "forged" it—only in pretense, as powerful leaders used their weight to intimidate their opponents or those who might see matters differently. Amazingly, within a few decades of the legalization of Christianity, the persecuted church became the persecutor —torturing and killing those who would not conform to official church doctrine. The slide into the spiritual Dark Ages was rapid and drained the true church of its lifeblood.

Yet today again the Spirit of God is moving in the world so that the torch is being rekindled. The truth is being proclaimed. Disciples are being won to Christ, and these disciples are training new disciples. Are you part of this great conflagration, in your heart of hearts?

Evangelism is the lifeblood of the church. Let's preach the Word and pray for God to saturate the earth with the message. We leave the results to him. (It is not our job to control outcomes; those we leave to the Lord.)

## Notes

[1] The phrase "turned the world upside down" comes specifically from Acts 17:6 (RSV). Technically, the verb means "to upset" (disturb, as in the sense of disturbing the peace) more than to "upend." When the Latin Vulgate translation was produced, Jerome chose the word *concitant,* which means simply "rouse, stir up." The same word is found in Acts 21:38, referring to "the Egyptian." Thus the phrase is a negative, not a positive one.

[2] Much has been made of Acts 17:26–27, which in the NIV was originally translated "From one man he made every nation of men, that they should inhabit the whole earth; and he determined the times set for them and the exact places where they should live. God did this so that men would seek him and perhaps reach out for him and find him." Is it true that God *directly* determines where people live—125 Main Street (as opposed to 127 Main Street)—in order to place them in proximity to disciples? God's providence is awesome and evident everywhere. But when Acts 17 is preached this way we are not talking about providence, but a subtle form of predestination.

The theological problem is that if God has determined where those who will be saved live, and when they will be there, then he has *de facto* consigned others to situations in which they will not have an opportunity to respond to the gospel. Then there is the textual problem. The RSV, among many good translations, renders Acts 17:26 more accurately in this instance than does the NIV. We read, "And he made from one every nation of men to live on all the face of the earth, having determined allotted periods and the boundaries of their habitation" (RSV). There is an allusion here to Deuteronomy 32:8. Paul is not talking about local geographical predestination, but rather God's *providence.* Fortunately, the current (corrected) NIV translation of Acts 17:26 reads, "From one man he made all the nations, that they should inhabit the whole earth; and he marked out their appointed times in history and the boundaries of their lands."

[3] Technically speaking, the intentional effort to evangelize the world began with the First Missionary Journey (Acts 13), eighteen years after the resurrection.

PART II

# I AM GOING FISHING

> Simon Peter said to them, "I am going fishing." They said to him, "We will go with you." They went out and got into the boat, but that night they caught nothing.
>
> Just after daybreak, Jesus stood on the beach; but the disciples did not know that it was Jesus. Jesus said to them, "Children, you have no fish, have you?" They answered him, "No." He said to them, "Cast the net to the right side of the boat, and you will find some." So they cast it, and now they were not able to haul it in because there were so many fish…
>
> Simon Peter went aboard and hauled the net ashore, full of large fish, a hundred fifty-three of them; and though there were so many, the net was not torn (John 21:3–11).

When we have the attitude of Jesus Christ, we will naturally and sincerely hold out the word of life, above all in the major arenas of our personal witness: neighborhood, workplace, and school. These are the focus of chapters 4 through 6.

Afterward we will explore three rather more challenging arenas. Chapters 7 through 9 cover evangelism at home, with foreigners, and with the extremely religious.

It is God's will that all Christians be fishers. Because, wherever they are, whatever the time or circumstances, there are people. It's what Christians do.

# 4
# From House to House
## *Neighborhood Evangelism*

There is a direct link between selflessness and evangelism. Selfish people, like selfish children with their toys, do not "share." But when we have the attitude of Christ, we naturally hold out the word of life. As Paul wrote,

> "Do everything without complaining or arguing, so that you may become blameless and pure, children of God without fault in a crooked and depraved generation, in which you shine like stars in the universe as you hold out the word of life" (Philippians 2:14–15).

When we hold out the word of life, we will "shine like stars." What is essential is the heart of a servant, not an attitude of entitlement (Philippians 2:1–11). What a contrast this creates with the surrounding society! When we have the attitude of Jesus (Philippians 2:5), our "default mode" is to be evangelistic. Yes, I know we're *commanded* to "go." And yet I have found that most Christians, when they are at peace with God, feel loved and respected by their leaders, and are growing spiritually, *automatically* share their faith with others. All the king's horses and all the king's men couldn't stop them.

Outside the home, the three major arenas of personal witness are neighborhood, workplace, and school. The early Christians let their light shine publicly, as well as "from house to house" (Acts 5:42). In considering the goal of evangelizing the world, or even just a city, the importance of neighborhood evangelism cannot be overestimated. This is where the majority of the people may be most easily reached. This is the largest evangelistic "field"—dwarfing by comparison any college campus or workplace.

## Relational Evangelism

At the outset, let me say that most Christians are not *naturally* good at relationships. We struggle. We need help. There is a simple reason for this: (a) We have come out of the world, (b) in the world people are generally poor at relationships, and (c) conversion does not immediately alter this deficit. Growth in Christ is a *process* which requires effort (Philippians 1:25; 2 Peter 1:5–9). It takes time! In the meantime, all of us have to struggle to become more relatable, less self-conscious and more patient with our fellow humans. (I do. Don't you?)

In this chapter we will focus first on single adults, then on married adults. In reaching these two groups effectively, it is obvious that different approaches are necessary, owing to the diversity of needs and outlook.

## Reaching Single Adults

Let us define the "single adult" as follows: someone who is not a teenager, not a student and not retired. (These categories have their own special needs, which will be touched on later.) Typically, they are in their twenties to thirties, working and without family responsibilities. Nothing else about them is typical (race, income, social background), except that they are at that stage in life where they may be the most "open" to the gospel. They are young enough to accept new ideas, available enough to study the Bible frequently, and flexible enough to adjust relationships, residence and whatever else is necessary to change in order to serve God more fully.

Furthermore, older, more "stable" people are commonly reached through relationships previously established with single adults, as opposed to direct invitation from an unknown Christian. In combination, these factors obviously make the evangelization of this group of people both urgent and strategic.

So how do we effectively go about it? Single adults can be met in a number of ordinary ways. Use your time wisely and invite people while at work. How about restaurants or recreational facilities? Trains, planes, buses—generally any mode of transport has potential. The most important key is to start conversations. The majority of Christians undergo a quantum leap in evangelism if they simply set their minds to start conversations. If you are looking for a formula, try these steps:

*Smile; establish eye contact.* People will usually warm to you as you warm to them.

*Start talking.* Any subject will do. Be friendly. Most people would rather have someone interesting to talk to than sit in silence or pretend to be busy.

*Say something "spiritual."* I don't mean, "Brother, art thou redeemed?" Turn the conversation to spiritual matters. If you mention something about your religious activities, or your reading, or your faith, and the other does not "pick up" on it, that may well be a clue that they are not interested, at least at this point in their life. If their interest is piqued, then keep sharing. Do let the other person talk, however! No one enjoys a chatterbox.

*Invite them in.* Maybe it will be an invitation to a church service. More effectively, how about an invitation to coffee, lunch, a party, or a sports activity?

The beauty of this method is that anybody can do it. It all starts with conversation—an effort to communicate, to reach out.

Once I conducted an experiment. I decided to meet as many people in a day (and invite them to church) as possible. The only rule: I would not strike up conversations "out of the blue." I pledged to meet them "naturally." I started conversations while standing in lines, eating at restaurants, walking in the park, and so on. A few times I even managed to strike up talks with small groups of people. All these interactions took time, and by the end of the day—in which I did most of the things I normally did, including errands—I was tired! Yet before I retired that evening, I had invited forty-eight men and women; nearly all were single adults. That was an eye-opener. It began with a decision!

### Evangelistic Keys

Let me offer some keys to effective evangelism of singles:

*Group evangelism times.* Get a small group of Christians together after work or on a weekend day to share their faith, then to have a meal together.

*Have follow-up parties together.* So many contacts, not followed up on, slip through the cracks. "Strike while the iron is hot." Follow-up needs to be emphasized—never forget that evangelism is not simply inviting people, but teaching people the gospel and winning "as many as possible" (1 Corinthians 9:19).

*Set up personal studies.* It is important to set up personal studies,[1] as many and as quickly as possible. Not only is this important for effectiveness, but it is also important for the morale of the group. The sooner the Christians are involved in studies which make progress, the more encouraging an experience it is for them. The leader should keep track of the more receptive people being studied with and the progress that is being made.

*Friendship and fun.* Two further ingredients that make for effective evangelism are friendship and fun. Don't underestimate the importance of having a good relationship with someone you are studying with. In fact, if a non-Christian has several good relationships in the church before becoming a Christian, it will both help them to make the right decision and also serve as a source of security and stability in the first few months as a Christian. Get your whole Bible discussion group reaching out to each of the visitors, especially to those who are progressing well. Remember that you're asking people to make decisions that will radically change their lives—they need to know that you care.

*Prayer.* Pray for your ministry to grow. Keep a prayer list for your own personal devotional times. Pray as a small group. Pray with others over the telephone. Have the occasional early morning or late night (or all-night) prayer time. Set up prayer chains, or times of prayer and fasting. Seek other ways to rely on the Lord as you hold up one another's arms.

*Activities.* In line with the idea of friendship and fun, activities of all sorts really help to make a group Bible discussion fruitful. Some Christians may not be able to get many people to come to a Bible study, but they certainly know how to get someone to come to a party! Here are some suggestions for activities that have worked well in the past:

- Dinner/Barbecue before Bible study, or apart from the Bible study. If you can, have an international dinner or one that focuses on one particular nationality. Have food, music, and clothes from that country—perhaps even a slide show.
- Show a movie after the study.
- Camping—go to the country with visitors for a night or two. This is easy for singles and is great for developing relationships with people who are moving along well in

personal studies.

- Housewarming Party—when you move into a new apartment or home, have invitations printed and put them through the doors of all your neighbors, immediate and not so immediate. You'll be amazed at how many show up.
- Ordinary Party—at your parties use all available talent to the full. Many churches are blessed with a lot of musical talent. It is not uncommon at our parties for these brothers and sisters to give off-the-cuff displays of their "skills and thrills." It definitely negates the idea that church is a place for people who have nothing to offer!
- Sports and games of all kinds are useful activities.
- Use public holidays—they are great occasions to get people together.
- Wine and cheese parties. Once we even organized a *nonalcoholic* cocktail party. I was the bartender! A huge number turned out. (Yes, we were up front that there would be no $C_2H_5OH$!)

Hopefully these ideas will get your creative juices flowing. Singles like fun, spontaneity, and creativity. You will be effective if you can be a pacesetter as far as social life goes. Few people will have a busier social life than a Christian, and in particular a single Christian.

### The Difference

A main difference between singles and marrieds is the amount of free time singles have. Their interests are not "divided" (1 Corinthians 7:33–34). They are able to meet for meetings and studies much more often than family men and women. This is especially true of singles under forty.

A word also ought to be said about some of our older singles. Most in their forties and above, or in some larger ministries, their fifties and above, will appreciate not being included with the twenty-somethings! (If you don't understand why, ask one; he or she will not hesitate to tell you!) Friendship is based not just on common interest, but also on common position: position in life, social circumstances, cultural background, and so forth. We should seldom expect an older single to keep the same pace as someone twenty years younger.

## Reaching Married Adults

By virtue of their age and experience in life, evangelizing among married adults often, but not always, requires a different approach from that which we have looked at so far. The biggest enemy of the married adult is a complacency of sorts. It is that feeling of having in some sense "arrived." They have a spouse and a job, are raising (or have raised) a child or two—and do not need *your* advice about how to live, thank you very much! This is especially the case if you don't have an impressive job (in their eyes), or a spouse and children of your own. "What do you understand about life, anyway?" they are probably thinking.

In reaching this group you're at an obvious advantage if you yourself are a married adult—particularly if your marriage is healthy. (Make sure you are praying every day as a couple; hold each other accountable to some goals; find a couple to help you, with whom you can open up.) Whether you are married or not, a high premium is placed on qualities such as patience, sensitivity, tact, and hospitality, as well as overall exemplary lifestyle. You'll be evaluated at the workplace, in the home and in the neighborhood. More than with singles, students, or teens, you have to *earn* the right to teach this group of people the gospel. This makes sense, when you think about it, because married adults carry more responsibility than singles. A decision for Christ affects not only themselves but also their spouses, families, and careers. When the future of your family is at stake, you want to be sure of what you're getting yourself into!

On the other hand, being married isn't a biblical requirement, nor should singles be pressured to marry if this is not God's path for them. Both Jesus and Paul taught clearly that the preferred path for singles is lifelong celibacy—for those who have the gift (1 Corinthians 7:7; Matthew 19:10–12).

The rewards of perseverance are great indeed. This group carries a healthy maturity and stability into the church. It is from the ranks of married adults that elders are raised up. Because of generally higher incomes, this group may also be valuable as financial contributors to the church. And they are often the ones who'll reach more married adults!

## Suggestions

Here are some suggestions for effectively evangelizing married adults:

*Open your home.* As the Apostle Paul writes, "practice hospitality" (Romans 12:13). Have marrieds over for meals; let them see you in your home—the Christian family is a great drawing card and a reflection of how "together" your life is. Moreover, it shows them that you value their friendship and their openness to the gospel.

*Don't overdo it.* This is especially important at work. Again, you need to win their respect. Mistakes have been made all too often by overzealous young single adult Christians who have tried to preach too much too fast to too many. (Ever done that?) In Mark 4:33 we read that Jesus was considerate, teaching people "as much as they could understand." What your married coworker needs to see in you is a reliable, cooperative employee (or employer). This will earn their respect and pave the way for later instruction in the gospel. (This is a similar principle to Peter's counsel in 1 Peter 3:1–6.)

*Respect their priorities.* Spouses, children, and jobs are priorities. Don't make unreasonable demands on their schedules. Once a week may be the most you'll initially be able to study the Bible with them. One of the challenges in reaching out to this group of people is to get into their schedules, which between jobs and family are busy. Make appointments well in advance, even two or three weeks if possible.

*Have activities for families.* While some of the suggestions for singles (above) will work, family activities make allowances for a broader range of ages, and of children's ages. Don't plan too far into the evening. (Remember, those kids may need to go to school the next day. And the parents will need to get them ready in the morning.)

*Childcare.* At group Bible discussions, as well as at activities, make sure facilities are available to take care of children unless it's an activity for everyone. If you can, do your best to take the children off the parents' hands and give them a good time. You'll have won some valuable points with them. The more children a family has, the less available time they will have for "spiritual" activities and the more often the sickness of one child will keep a parent at home. (Remember when you were sick as a child? Who did you want—a babysitter or your mother?)

*Be helpful.* Look for ways to help out. Married people are accustomed to being in a world that is so hectic that very few people make the time to help others. This is a great arena in which to let our light shine. If you're perceived as interfering, though, hold back.

*Seek wisdom.* For example, do not project false costs. Exaggerations of biblical passages pertaining to the cost of discipleship are particularly undesirable when applied to this group, because the damage will be greater. "To become a Christian, you're going to have to give up your job and stop spending time with your family" are false costs. Wife, children and jobs are biblical priorities (Ephesians 5:22–6:8; 1 Timothy 5:8; Colossians 3:22–25). Much sensitivity and understanding need to be exercised in counting the cost with married adults. Obviously, this does *not* mean watering down biblical standards. You may need to sit down with your married adult friend and help them work out a reasonable schedule that will place their priorities in balance. The next section, on what demands will be made on the married adult Christian, should be helpful with this.

### What Can Be Expected?

We have discussed at some length the limitations that can hamper married adults and the implications for effectively reaching out to this group. These limitations apply to all married people, Christians as well as non-Christians. What can be reasonably expected of married disciples? How can they get involved evangelistically? Here are some ideas that may help.

*Work out a schedule.* Go through the individual Christian's schedule, making sure their priorities are considered. Priorities are as follows:

- **Relationship with God**—ensure that regular quiet times are scheduled into their routine. Given most people's busy schedules, this probably will need to be in the morning. But don't legislate; personal devotions are between the individual and God, and the Bible doesn't lay down concrete rules for how to do this.
- **Relationship with family**—the married adult's most important earthly relationships are with spouse and children, in that order.

- **Relationships in the body and church attendance**—schedule in church meetings, group Bible discussions and time spent in one-another relationships. If you add to these time spent at work, it becomes clear that time available for meeting and studying the Bible with people is limited.
- **Special note:** When working with seniors, the priorities are the same, but how they are expressed will be different. Health considerations may make attendance at church services and activities difficult. Never doubt that seniors have good hearts. Yet the complications of life, including many of the routine tasks that younger persons perform without any difficulty, require extra consideration and sensitivity. These same principles apply also to physically challenged Christians, regardless of age.

*Evangelism in the workplace and neighborhood.* Encourage married adults to see the workplace and neighborhood as their personal ministry. Encourage them to be the best neighbors and best workers they can be. Emphasize reaching out to people in these places and having vision for them to become Christians. Things may move more slowly than in a singles ministry, so encourage the Christians to be patient.

*Evangelistic lifestyle.* Encourage them to develop an evangelistic lifestyle, inviting people while shopping, traveling on public transport, etc., making the most of every opportunity.

*Group evangelism with singles.* From time to time, encourage married adults to go out with the singles in group evangelism times. This may well be feasible on Saturday afternoons, for example.

*Bible studies.* Challenge them to strive to have at least one person they're studying the Bible with. If you are too busy to share your faith, you are too busy—you may be gaining the world and losing your own soul! Come to an assessment of how many people an individual can study the Bible with effectively without abandoning their other legitimate priorities. Bear in mind that effective studying involves time for relationship building as well as time for personal Bible study. If you're mentoring a married adult, love them enough to ensure that they are involved in following up with and studying the Bible with someone.

## Conclusion

In this chapter we have looked at some of the ins and outs of community evangelism. We've seen its importance and examined the specifics of working with two major groups in the community: single adults and married adults. One last suggestion: Draw a map of your neighborhood or a diagram of your apartment building that includes at least twenty houses or apartments that are near yours. Write in the first and last names of all your neighbors living in these places. If you do not know the names, develop a plan for finding them out. Turn this map or diagram into a prayer and planning list for reaching out. Then proceed, with prayer and genuine concern, "from house to house."

It is clear that community evangelism must be the major emphasis in our thrust to win the world for Christ. This is where the majority of the people are! We must devote ourselves to evangelistic principles and practices that are effective with people in the community, in order to make this one of the strong points in our ministries. Only then will we "win as many as possible" (1 Corinthians 9:19). Only then will the nets be full.

### Note

[1] The rationale for personal evangelistic Bible studies is laid out in chapter 10.

# 5
# God's Ambassador at Work

*Workplace Evangelism*

If we were to take to heart the lesson of the last chapter, and became proficient only in ministry to our neighborhoods, we would probably have more people to follow up with and study the Bible with than we have time. And yet there is another phenomenal arena for daily evangelism. It is the workplace. In fact, in the book of Acts (God's evangelism textbook!), we see all sorts of men and women—working class, upper class, every class—being won to the cause of Jesus Christ.[1]

## The Ambassador

Imagine it: You're sitting in your den watching the nightly news. Dinner is in the oven, and you have just stopped for a few minutes to rest. Your feet are propped up on the coffee table, and, wouldn't you know it, the phone rings... On the other end of the line is an official-sounding voice saying your name in an official-sounding way. Then you recognize the voice. The same voice you just heard on the nightly news. No mistaking it. It is the President. *The* President! "We were wondering if you would consider assuming the office of Ambassador to Switzerland?"

Even though few of us will ever receive the offer of an ambassadorship from our country, all of us have received an even more important offer:

> "We are therefore Christ's ambassadors, as though God were making his appeal through us. We implore you on Christ's behalf: Be reconciled to God" (2 Corinthians 5:20).

This is a really big-time ambassadorship—not just between two countries, but between heaven and earth. As God's ambassadors, we have the responsibility of bringing to the world around us his message of reconciliation. Most don't even know that they are at war or that they are in need of reconciliation with God. Enter

*Mission: Possible!* We get to tell them with our words, with our commitment, with our lives, with our love.

Specifically, you are God's ambassador at your workplace. Granted, you do not have a special parking place with a neatly lettered sign: Reserved for Ambassador. But you are one all the same.

Sharing your faith at work is multifaceted. It can be confusing, discouraging, exciting, terrifying, and much more. But one thing it is not is optional. Before ascending to his Father in heaven, Jesus was clear about the mission he was placing into the hands of the disciples and those the disciples would bring to him throughout the ages: you and me, specifically. No sealed envelope with an encoded message. No MP3 player that will self-destruct in five seconds. Just the word of the Son of God and no chance of misunderstanding:

> "Then Jesus came to them and said, 'All authority in heaven and on earth has been given to me. Therefore go and make disciples of all nations, baptizing them in the name of the Father and of the Son and of the Holy Spirit, and teaching them to obey everything I have commanded you. And surely I am with you always, to the very end of the age'" (Matthew 28:18–20).

As clear as the mission was the promise: "I am with you always, to the very end of the age." Well, guess what: The age isn't yet over. Granted, it is a long age, but it will not be over until Jesus returns in the same way that he left.

As you walk into work every day, remember Jesus' promise, "I am with you always." That means "I am with you now!" "You are not alone." "You are my specially chosen ambassador; together we will get the job done."

## Being Real

Sharing our faith does not always mean verbally telling someone about Jesus or the church. Our daily lives—actions, reactions, interactions—share much about who we are and whom we imitate. The Word "becomes flesh" once again as we live it. The fruit of the Spirit in our lives produces the seeds for others to know God. In order for people to desire our way of life, we must come across as real people, not plastic or stained-glass religious versions of human beings. Sometimes we are so aware of needing to be a good example that we become tense and rigid. We are afraid of making mistakes and of admitting them when we do.

The truth is that people who work with us day in and day out will see us sin. Accept it. Then deal with it in a righteous way that will help them to learn how they should be dealing with sin too.

We must learn to relax and to be friends to people. We cannot wait until someone totally cleans up his or her act and becomes a disciple before we affirm the good things we see in their lives. Friends convert friends. That is healthy, but it is not necessarily easy for most of us.

Because of the gossip, bad language, dirty jokes and complaining attitudes of those around us, we want to withdraw. What a tightrope we sometimes seem to walk! As disciples we must be discerning and learn to balance the following two scriptures:

> "I have written you in my letter not to associate with sexually immoral people—*not at all meaning the people of this world* who are immoral, or the greedy and swindlers, or idolaters. In that case you would have to leave this world" (1 Corinthians 5:9–10, emphasis added).

> "But among you there must not be even a hint of sexual immorality, or of any kind of impurity, or of greed, because these are improper for God's holy people. Nor should there be obscenity, foolish talk or coarse joking, which are out of place, but rather thanksgiving. For of this you can be sure: No immoral, impure or greedy person—such a man is an idolater—has any inheritance in the kingdom of Christ and of God. Let no one deceive you with empty words, for because of such things God's wrath comes on those who are disobedient. *Therefore do not be partners with them"* (Ephesians 5:3–7, emphasis added).

Paul says that we obviously need to associate with people who are worldly, but we should not become partners with them. We are not to purposefully place ourselves with people who corrupt our hearts and minds. If this is happening at work and we have already spoken up, we will need to make wise choices. We may no longer be able to sit with certain people at lunch when they persist in improper talk, but we can still seek to be their friends. Learning to *engage* but not to *indulge* is the goal. To "associate with" but not to be "partners with"...

## Taking Advantage of Opportunities

Paul wrote to the disciples in Colossae,

> "Devote yourselves to prayer, being watchful and thankful. And pray for us, too, that God may open a door for our message, so that we may proclaim the mystery of Christ, for which I am in chains. Pray that I may proclaim it clearly, as I should. Be wise in the way you act toward outsiders; *make the most of every opportunity.* Let your conversation be always full of grace, seasoned with salt, so that you may know how to answer everyone" (Colossians 4:2–6, emphasis added).

Since we are paid to work for our school, hospital, store, studio, or company, and not paid to share our faith, we must be responsible and discerning on the job. We cannot spend long periods of time studying or talking about the Bible with others. But God does give us opportunities here and there to share. We must have keen spiritual eyes and open, receptive hearts so the Spirit can move us, as he did Philip, to take advantage of an opportunity for the sake of the kingdom:

> "Then Philip ran up to the chariot and heard the man reading Isaiah the prophet. 'Do you understand what you are reading?' Philip asked.
>
> 'How can I,' he said 'unless someone explains it to me?' So he invited Philip to come up and sit with him" (Acts 8:30–31).

When people "invite" us into their lives audibly, or simply by showing need, we must be ready with conversation that is "always full of grace, seasoned with salt, so that [we] may know how to answer everyone." Just as children have specific and rare moments of "teachability," so do adults. Our daily walk with God should be others-focused enough that we recognize these moments.

## Being Bold

Grace and patience are Christian virtues, but these should never be excuses for not being bold. Patience does not negate boldness. Patience has to do with trusting God for right timing. Boldness has to do with trusting God and saying what needs to be said or doing what needs to be done, no matter what the consequences. In our natures we tend one way or the other, toward patience or toward boldness. Or could it be more accurately stated: toward cowardice or toward insensitivity? The cross always calls us to the center of God's will: neither to the right nor to the left.

Most of us do not want to rock the boat in our work situations. We are afraid that if we do, we will fall out (or be thrown overboard). I can remember sitting at the table in the teachers' lounge and wondering when or if I should say something. Although I knew all the teachers pretty well, I was actually a "substitute"—not really one of them. Was it really my place to speak up when I felt they were being unprofessional and maybe even cruel in the way they talked about a student? At that point I decided just to be a positive example. But since then I have felt that I should have said something—not to the whole group at once, but privately to the individuals I knew personally.

In another situation, I was working with two teachers and a parent to put on a middle-school talent show. We had fewer students try out for the show than we had anticipated. So the kids were asking one of the teachers, "Is everybody who is trying out going to be in the show?" Since she thought they would not feel as special if everyone was going to be in it, she wanted to lie and say, "No. Everyone will not be in it."

I said, "But that's lying. There is a way to respond that is not lying. You can say, 'Those of us on the committee are the only ones who need to know how many are chosen.'"

She said, "Yeah. That's good."

Since it was natural for her to lie in such a situation, she simply didn't think about how she could respond in a truthful way.

Boldness in expressing our convictions about God, Jesus, the Bible or our church is imperative. How often, though, have we been like Peter? In the inspiration of the moment with Jesus he says, "Even if I have to die with you, I will never disown you" (Matthew 26:35). Then that very night he swore, "I don't know the man!" (26:74).

During our prayer times in the morning, or when we are together with our Christian brothers and sisters, we, like Peter, say to Jesus, "Even if I have to die with you, I will never disown you." Then, in the press of the day and the embarrassment of the moment, we shrink back as if to say, "I don't know the man!" Sometimes Jesus just doesn't seem to fit in our workplaces. In fact, that is why he was crucified: He just didn't seem to fit. Are we ashamed of him? Are we too cool to be associated with him? Too afraid to be thought of as strange or as a goody-two-shoes?

Lord, we believe. Help our unbelief!

## How to Be More Effective Through Your Job

I will now close this chapter, having shared tried-and-true wisdom on workplace evangelism,[2] with some of *my own* practicals on how to become an even more effective ambassador at your workplace.

*Be punctual.* Come on time, or even slightly early, and leave on time. Do not "stretch" breaks or lunches without your employer's permission. This is really a matter of integrity, and how we do in this area creates powerful visible and subliminal impressions. Disciples need to be completely above reproach (Daniel 6:3).

*Don't be "overrighteous" at work*—to borrow that unusual expression of Solomon's (Ecclesiastes 7:16, NIV). Go easy on the crosses and religious paraphernalia. No need for showy prayers before the office lunch. (Not to say don't pray!) Avoid religious terminology, "church" jargon especially. ("I had a mega-awesome quiet time this morning.")

*Control your work hours.* Excessive overtime and working weekends and evenings will, for most disciples, be detrimental. How can you share effectively if you are weak spiritually?

*Be cheerful.* A positive disposition is appreciated by all. Remember, we do not shine like stars when we argue and complain (Philippians 2:14). Negativity darkens our countenance and example.

*Don't waste time.* On the job, the Christian must make sure to stay focused, complete their assignments in a timely manner, and in short, do what they are paid to do. Computer games—watch out! Some time ago I erased every computer game from my hard drive. I asked myself, "Am I paid to become an expert 'minesweeper' or solitaire player, or to follow my boss's instructions?"

*Be patient.* Professionals cannot always drop everything and come along with you, even if you are an exemplary employee. Don't become despondent. When someone is booked this weekend, ask about next weekend; even ask about next month. High achievers will seldom have an empty schedule; they have planned ahead. So should you!

*Do not be intimidated.* Beware of overestimating the confidence of the professional. Underneath the tough exterior is often a hurting individual. The marriage may be unraveling, the children may be resentful, the job may bring only hollow fulfillment. He or she needs you—not vice versa. Sure, anyone can learn from others, but we're talking about learning the gospel here.

*Be a listening ear.* Most men, especially, have no really close friends to talk to—least of all about family, marriage, or spiritual matters. Be available, but do not be pushy.

*Do not be underemployed.* While the spiritual effects of being underemployed are not as significant as those of being unemployed (see 2 Thessalonians 3), still a subtle erosion of character may be taking place when we are not "stretched," or maximizing our God-given talents. Look for ways to upgrade your job situation. One caveat: never jeopardize your spiritual condition or your family relationships in doing so. It isn't worth it.

*Network with Christians in similar professions.* You will benefit from such a network of support relationships. Why reinvent the wheel? You can learn from their experiences.

## Conclusion

Our workplace affords us many opportunities to reach the lost. To borrow a phrase from the US Army, "It's not just a job, it's an adventure!" May we truly bring honor to God as his ambassadors in the workplace.

## Notes

[1] Knowing how much we desire to be effective at work, and not feeling the need to "reinvent the wheel," I asked permission from my former publishers (DPI) to adapt a chapter on evangelism from Sheila Jones' *9 to 5 and Spiritually Alive.* This powerful book offers counsel on successful Christian living in many aspects of the workday, including a number of chapters on sharing our faith. Afterwards, I will conclude with some of my own suggestions for effective workplace evangelism. Thus chapter 5 is an adaptation of Chapter 5 ("God's Ambassador at Work: Sharing Your Faith") in Sheila Jones' book *9 to 5 and Spiritually Alive* (Woburn, Mass.: Discipleship Publications International, 1997).

[2] Sheila Jones' book has many excellent chapters on evangelism. Most relevant to the subject of *Till the Nets Are Full* are chapters 5 (on sharing your faith at work, much of which we have just read), 6 (relationships with male coworkers, a great help for all women in the "professional" world), 8 (about how to have an encouraging commute), and 9 (entitled "What If I Do Not Like My Job?").

# 6

# The Goose That Laid the Golden Egg

## *Campus Evangelism*

Campus ministry may be described as "the goose that laid the golden egg." A large number of leaders in growing churches around the world were met and converted during college years. And many of those not actually converted in college were converted and trained in the ministry by those who were. Yet as time has passed, it is easy to neglect that "precious bird." College ministries tend to flourish when talented men and women devote themselves *exclusively* to that work.

Campus ministry presents a golden opportunity for reaching younger persons—people who may be in their prime in terms of openness to the gospel, who have many years before them, and who are well positioned to affect others for Christ by virtue of their placement in the university setting. Tens of thousands have become Christians during their college years, and a great number of these have gone on to enter various fields, including full-time Christian service, and affect countless others.

And yet, although the fruits of campus ministry have been so great, some congregations in university cities are not prioritizing campus ministry. This chapter urges us not to neglect "the goose that laid the golden egg."

### Convictions

For ten years I served as a campus minister, heading up outreaches at some twenty universities—in London primarily, but also in Sydney, Birmingham, Stockholm, Philadelphia, and Washington DC. Campus ministry is truly rewarding, for many reasons, including the openness of the students, the relative simplicity of their life situations, and their vibrancy and vitality. My principal convictions about campus ministry are few and simple.

*First, students need to flourish academically.* While it is true

God in his providence has put them on the college campus to win others to the cause of Christ, they are also there to study. God is not honored by substandard work. This means campus ministry must be elegant and streamlined, not clogged with multiple meetings and complicated programs that interfere with study time. Today's students often have to work part-time jobs as well, which means that a lack of planning on the campus minister's part can make it difficult for them to succeed.

*Second, students need good communication with their families.* In an era when so many family relationships are already distant or strained, we do students a disservice when we fail to encourage them in relationships with parents, who have often sacrificed so much for them to study. Christian students should be the most grateful students on campus!

*Finally and obviously, students need to grow spiritually.* Just as discipline is crucial for academic life, discipline is crucial for spiritual life as well. In my experience, I see that students deeply desire to live sacrificially; they admire those who embody the high ideals of Christ in their lifestyle.

When young men and women receive encouragement and support from their leaders in these areas—academics, family relationships, and spirituality—they will flourish evangelistically as well. Students love to hold discussions, and Christian students will find the urge to talk about Jesus Christ irresistible.

As I look back through the years, I realize how much I have learned from my mentor in the ministry, Douglas Arthur. (Once a rather critical television program described us as "accomplices." I prefer the term "partners.") Maybe one reason I am such a big believer in campus evangelism is that I became a Christian while a college student. In fact, Gary Knutson and Douglas Arthur knocked on *my* door only a day after I entered university! (I think God knew I was ready. Only seven weeks later, I was baptized into Christ.) Just as I have learned a tremendous amount from Douglas, let me invite you to do the same. The rest of the chapter is the evangelistic strategy this man taught me in our campus years together, especially in Boston and London.

## In the Beginning

The beginning of the year is perhaps the most critical time in the life of an academic ministry. If it is handled well, it can ensure lots of evangelistic personal Bible studies—and hence a good number of new Christians throughout the year. If it is handled badly, opportunities will be lost that can never be recovered. Since this is such a crucial time, you need to begin your work before the beginning of the academic term.

### Before the Beginning

One good idea is to have a college leadership planning session before the year begins. Ideally, have a mini-retreat; go somewhere overnight as a group. This is the time to:

- Establish who will be in which group Bible study.
- Discuss where and when group Bible studies will meet.
- Plan special activities for the campus ministry (retreats, play days, etc.).
- Make sure all the students are involved in good one-another relationships (prayer partners, discipleship groups, etc.).
- Have a time of Bible study, prayer, and fellowship with a view to developing unity among the leaders of the campus ministry.
- Encourage students to get into the dormitories around the campus at the earliest possible opportunity—it's a good strategy. Frequently, dorms and other facilities are open several days before the first day of classes. Christian students might move in early, get themselves settled and then begin helping others, building friendships through serving.

### Two Terrific Weeks

Many college ministries limit themselves to slow growth by mishandling the first two weeks of the year. During those precious few days virtually everyone is looking for new friends. There is an openness to new relationships that will soon begin to fade dramatically.

Christians must resist the urge to spend large quantities of time with one or two apparently receptive people. Meeting the masses is the need of the hour. Some students will benefit from setting personal goals for making new acquaintances. (E.g.,

"Today I will reach out to ten new people.") It is terribly difficult to keep track of all those new names and faces, so keep some kind of record. Lots of good evangelism time can be wasted by lack of good recordkeeping.

In your first few minutes of conversation, mention the Bible discussion that you attend. If people are receptive they will pick up on it immediately. In this way you may get many visitors coming without issuing a single invitation. Take special note of those who seem open, and try to see them daily. The key in the first two weeks is not spending a lot of time with them, but making the time you do spend exciting.

Be creative in devising ways to double up on your appointments. For example, if John in Room 14, Frank in Room 62, and Sam in room 53 seem open, plan on meeting them all from 9:00–9:30 for a grand Star Wars competition or the "Minnesota Fats" grand pool championship of the dorm.

Keep the interactions short, sweet, and consistent, and continue to meet lots of new people each day. During the first week don't take time to study personally with people; just get them to the Bible studies or Christian activities. In the second week, study only with the most responsive people and keep on meeting new people. By making the most of these precious days you will surface the maximum number of open contacts.

## Residence Halls

If the Garden of Eden was the paradise for humankind, then dormitories are the Christians' evangelistic paradise. They provide the best environment imaginable for seeking and saving the lost. Next to having a campus minister, having students in the dorms is the most obvious asset a campus ministry can have. Often students are encouraged to live off campus, to get out of the dorms. I think this is often bad counsel. (In my own university years, I lived eight of my eleven years in the dorms—the payoff was enormous.)

The Apostle Paul was not afraid of leaders in his society and neither should we be. The resident advisor, or R.A., is the most immediate symbol of authority most dorm residents face. It is important that Christians develop good relationships with the R.A. before the Bible studies begin. Then if anyone complains, you'll be seen as a friend and not as "that religious nut" in Room

18. Further, don't be intimidated by the R.A.s—countless times they have turned out not only to be "allies," but also have become Christians. Respect their authority, just as you strive to cultivate good relationships with all authorities in your life. Most residents get to know few people outside of their dorms, classes, and clubs. In the university setting, you will typically encounter a number of small cliques, with only shallow interaction between groups. Our challenge is to get to know people in as many groups as possible, thereby expanding the number of people we can invite in a personal way.

Clubs, student government, and sports are good ways of developing friendships, but you must be careful not to flood your schedule with activities that may be evangelistic "dead ends." Ideally, you want to find a number of varying activities on a casual basis. The challenge is to become genuinely interested in things that interest other people, while never losing sight of the fact that the activities are tools and not ends in themselves.

### Meals

Everyone likes to eat. Fortunately, in a university setting people are generally eating together with dozens, and often hundreds, of other people. Mealtimes are superb evangelistic opportunities. Regardless of how hectic the pace of life becomes, we must all take time to eat—which means that *everyone* has time to meet people, at least while we eat. Even during final exam times we can keep our evangelism going by simply scheduling our meals with other people. The key is planning, and not just doing whatever comes most easily. Whether it is two or three meals you eat each day, plan to make them count. If you don't have someone to sit with, you can look for a group of people that you have never met before and join them.

### The Classroom

Everyone has a favorite place to sit in a classroom. Many will sit in exactly the same seat for the entire term. Many Christians deny themselves that luxury; through the course of the semester they move around the room, getting to know all the little groups in the classroom. It is a bit like Dungeons and Dragons; you enter various chambers, and in some you'll find beasts and in others princes or princesses looking for what Jesus came to offer.

There is much to be said about your example in the classroom. Here are some suggestions about how to increase the brightness of your light.

*Come early to class*—a person rushing in late is a nuisance to everyone. If you are early you can chat with other students before class.

*Do your homework*—confused Christians make for timid ambassadors. Gain people's respect academically, and they will listen to you about more important things.

*Initiate with professors*—this will help you learn the material and feel more confident in class. It will also give you a chance to invite them to church.

*Be joyful*—Demonstrate the peace that passes understanding—let people see your joy even in hard times and they will begin asking "Why?"

## Community/Commuter Colleges

In this situation, most students do not live in dorms (residence halls); some colleges do not even have housing available. That does not stop the work; it simply redirects it. It means that the focus of evangelism shifts to the classes, cafeterias, and common rooms. The group Bible studies may take place at lunchtime as well as in the evening, in classrooms or in the homes of Christians who live near the campus. Becoming a recognized student organization is helpful in all college ministries, but it is especially important in a commuter college setting.

## Conclusion

College ministry is a challenge and an opportunity like no other. It's a challenge because you stay under constant scrutiny. There is no retreating—only shining like stars all day, every day. It is an incredible opportunity for the same reasons. Never again will you have such easy access to so many people on a consistent basis. Not only that, but you are reaching out to people who may well be at the height of their receptivity to the gospel.

If you're a student, rejoice and enjoy it. If you're a leader in the church, find men and women to devote themselves to this most fruitful of harvest fields. Whatever your situation regarding college ministry, make the most of it. Let us not neglect the goose that laid the golden egg.

For more practicals on campus ministry, see *Campus Core*. This book can help students in four ways: growing in confidence, especially that "to fish for people" on campus is appropriate; doing well academically—an area that affects conscience as well as credibility; engaging with professors, fellow students, and course subject matter (advice is offered for over fifty different classes); and figuring out their future (Should they go to graduate school? Is full-time church work a good path? And so on).[1]

### On to More Challenging Arenas

All of us want to win our own families. We yearn to make an impact on the world. And we would give anything to have the boldness and confidence of Jesus in the presence of the "ultra-religious." Accordingly, chapters 7 to 9 will discuss reaching our families, foreigners, and those who believe they receive direct guidance from God.

#### Note

[1] Douglas Jacoby, *Campus Core: How to Have an Impact on Campus, Get Good Grades, and Figure Out Your Future* (Spring, Texas: Illumination Publishers, 2016). The book will be of interest not only to university students, but also to high school seniors, parents of students, and campus ministers.

# 7
# Reaching Our Families
## *Relational Priorities*

"And whoever does not provide for relatives, and especially for family members, has denied the faith and is worse than an unbeliever" (1 Timothy 5:8 NRS).

This chapter is primarily focused on reaching our children for Christ, although the principles also apply generally to sharing the gospel with other family relations. If we are going to reach our families, we are probably going to have to rethink relational priorities.[1] To help you think about the subject, please work through the following short exercise. Take a moment to reflect on your most important relationships. Consider the following: husband or wife, children, the church, the lost (those who do not yet know God), and of course the Lord. Arrange them into their order of importance—that is, starting with the most significant relationship. (Single parents, in this exercise, for simplicity, do *not* include your former spouse/partner.) In terms of your God-given Christian responsibility, which feels most important... next most important... and so on?

1. ____________________

2. ____________________

3. ____________________

4. ____________________

5. ____________________

It may come as a surprise to some that there actually is a divine order of relationships. Did we perhaps think that all relationships are equally important, apart from our relationship with God? They aren't.

### Divine Order

We harm our families, and the church family, when we disregard God's wisdom, his divine sequence. Let's begin with what we all agree, on paper at least, to be our most important relationship. We are pretty confident that you placed the Lord in the number one position. And this is right:

> "Hear, O Israel: The LORD our God, the LORD is one. Love the LORD your God with all your heart and with all your soul and with all your strength" (Deuteronomy 6:4–5).

If we love him with all our heart, there can be no one we love more. Both testaments agree that the Lord God is to be the ultimate recipient of our love and devotion. (In the New Testament, see Matthew 22:37, Mark 12:30 and Luke 10:27.) Are we really loving God with our whole heart? And do our children see us putting God first? Don't think they aren't watching. They know whether father and mother really believe what they claim to at church. The kids know what we really love most. And if we are reaching out to parents or older relatives, we must not be confused. They can tell whether our religion is skin deep, or whether we are really living out what we profess.

Clearly, God comes first, according to Scripture, and this has big implications for how we spend our time. Failure of husband or wife (but more typically the husband) to actively seek the Lord has a detrimental effect on the children. How can the family be godly if the leader of the family is taking them in an ungodly direction? (Luke 6:39). Yes, the Lord is first, and others second:

> "Love your neighbor as yourself" (Leviticus 19:18b—also Matthew 5:43, 19:19, 22:39; Romans 13:9; Galatians 5:14; James 2:8).

Our neighbor includes family members and non-family members, and it is true that sometimes we have to choose between loyalty to Jesus and loyalty to blood relatives (Matthew 10:34ff; Luke 14:26). God always comes first. And yet even if the Bible teaches that we are to put God before our families, we are still to put our families before all other persons.

One of the most challenging verses in the entire Bible

addresses those believers who presumptuously expect the church to take care of their aged relatives when it is in their own power to help them:

> "And whoever does not provide for relatives, and especially for family members, has denied the faith and is worse than an unbeliever" (1 Timothy 5:8, NRS).

Of all the family relationships, the Bible has the most to say about the marriage relationship. In fact, there is far more in the Bible about husbands and wives, including marriage principles, than there is about children or parenting advice. As Paul says,

> "In this same way [as Christ loved the church], husbands ought to love their wives as their own bodies. He who loves his wife loves himself. After all, no one ever hated his own body, but he feeds and cares for it, just as Christ does the church—for we are members of his body. 'For this reason a man will leave his father and mother and be united to his wife, and the two will become one flesh.' This is a profound mystery—but I am talking about Christ and the church. However, each one of you also must love his wife as he loves himself, and the wife must respect her husband" (Ephesians 5:28–33 NIV).

This famous marriage passage stretches from Ephesians 5:21 to 5:33. It is thirteen verses long, while the parenting passage that follows is only four verses long:

> "Children, obey your parents in the Lord, for this is right. 'Honor your father and mother'—which is the first commandment with a promise— 'so that it may go well with you and that you may enjoy long life on the earth.' Fathers, do not exasperate your children; instead, bring them up in the training and instruction of the Lord" (Ephesians 6:1–4 NIV).

Why is there so much more biblical material, especially in the New Testament, on marriage than there is on being a father or mother? We believe that's because the better the marriage, the better the parenting. Part of parenting, after all, is showing your kids how to love the one you promised to love and be faithful to "till death do us part."

Spouse comes before all other human relationships, and

that includes children! So often, in the world, once the babies begin to arrive, husband and wife grow distant from one another. But if the Bible makes anything clear, it's that the husband-wife relationship deeply affects the children.

This relationship is prior to and more important than the parent-child relationship. When we favor a child over our spouse, we are undermining the basis of security that the child needs in order to grow up with a sense of well-being, confidence, and trust. Worse, if we are not respectful toward our spouse, that disrespect will affect how our children relate to the opposite sex! Of course we are not saying that we should neglect the basic needs of a defenseless baby in order to see to our marital pleasures and whims. There are those who abuse their children. God will not countenance such sin, and his penalties will surely be severe. Having made this qualification, spouse still comes before children, and the children need to know this.

A secular psychotherapist visited a house-church meeting in our home a few years ago. I was encouraged to hear her response after I asked her opinion about the key to well-behaved children. She replied, "It's the marriage." I nearly said "Amen!" It was reassuring to hear biblical wisdom coming from a professional counselor.

Of course, parents naturally take care of their children (2 Corinthians 12:14), so children immediately follow spouse in the divine order. We are to favor our own children over "church friends" and the lost, even though fellowship with other Christians is vital, and outreach to the unsaved is also essential. We would encourage you fathers to spend individual times with your children every week, if at all possible. It may be less necessary for mothers to have scheduled time with each child, as they tend to spend more time with the children in a variety of settings anyway (homework, driving them to activities, and so forth).

So far, based on the biblical evidence, we have arrived at the following relational priorities:

GOD
SPOUSE
CHILDREN

But what about everybody else—those *not* in your immediate

family? We can distinguish between believers and nonbelievers, not because this is a convenient division, but because the Bible makes this very distinction. For example, consider Galatians 6:10:

> "Therefore, as we have opportunity, let us do good to all people, especially to those who belong to the family of believers" (NIV).

Other versions, instead of "the family of believers," read "the household of faith" (HCSB, NAS), or "the family of faith" (NRS). The Apostle Paul is referring to the church family.

Who are your church family? They come next in the sequence, *not* the lost. Paul made that clear. He is certainly *not* saying that we shouldn't try to be a light in the community, share the gospel with others, or "push" ourselves to be outgoing, even to the point of initiating with strangers. What he is saying is that we are to honor our spiritual family—our brothers and sisters in Christ—above outsiders.

Nor is Paul saying that it is okay to ignore the lost in the name of church obligations, any more than it is legitimate to ignore children for the sake of spouse. It is not a matter of cultivating the higher priority relationships and ignoring the others; all must be pursued *simultaneously*. But when push comes to shove, when a decision must be made, the priorities are clear.

Please don't misunderstand. Evangelism is a command of Christ that applies to all believers. The book you're reading, as a book on evangelism, is well founded, biblically speaking. And yet the New Testament emphasizes relationships with fellow Christians—"one-another relationships"—*far* more than reaching out to the lost. Could it be that if we focused more on our one-another relationships (exhorting one another, speaking the truth to one another, serving one another...), evangelism would take care of itself?

Once again, we are obligated to reach out to insiders and outsiders alike. And yet there is a ranking: insiders first, then outsiders. Also, as we saw, in a number of passages the immediate family takes precedence over others (1 Timothy 5:8). Another reason the church comes between family and the lost is that the church family is ultimately an extension of our own nuclear families, in all their dynamics and patterns of interaction. A spiritual congregation with strong nuclear families will display a tight-knit fellowship. And that is bound to be attractive to outsiders.

Putting it all together, the ladder of earthly relationships looks like this:

1. GOD
2. SPOUSE
3. CHILDREN
4. THE CHURCH
5. THE LOST

## Counterproductive Counseling

Remember this order; it is integral to good parenting and also to good evangelism, both of which respect the divine sequence. Unfortunately, it is often not respected, even though there are loads of scriptures to back it up. For example, instead of focusing *(up the ladder)* on God [1] when my marriage [2] is hurting, I am tempted to pour my life into others *(down the ladder)* [3, 4, 5]. It is usually easier to work a rung or two down the ladder than to focus on the real issues. If anything, an improvement at a *higher* level will benefit relationships lower down. The human tendency to focus *downward* instead of respecting the divine order is counterproductive, and leads to confused and unhelpful counseling when we are trying to advise others.

To illustrate further, our children may be acting out, and through various incentives or disincentives I may try to change their behavior [3], when the real problem is between me and my spouse [2]. Or church relationships [4] may be suffering from disunity, resentment, and gossip. And yet the preacher is mostly concerned with bringing in new members [5]—oblivious, one wonders, about the dysfunctional quality of the fellowship the newly evangelized are joining. There are times, we believe, when we should "clean our own house" before inviting the neighbors over.

The human tendency is to look at the surface, not to go to the source (1 Samuel 16:7, etc.). If you are running a high fever, putting ice on your skin is not the ultimate solution. We must probe deeper and understand the cause of the fever. If steam and blue smoke are pouring out from under the hood of your car, the problem is not with the tires or the sun visor—it's somewhere under the hood. In the same way, God's word tells us where to look:

- If the marriage is struggling, look one level *up*. Take an honest look at your spouse's walk with God—and also at your own.
- If the kids are acting out, look *up*—at the marriage!
- If the church is not a happy place, look *up*—at the nuclear families it comprises.
- If the lost are not being attracted to the community of faith, look a level *up*—how are relationships in the body of Christ?

In other words, trying to build an evangelistic ministry is not going to work—or at best, it will see only short-term growth—unless we appreciate biblical relational priorities. Evangelism without sensitivity to these crucial truths is likely to become mechanical, shallow, and counterproductive!

## Summary

We must recognize the basic truths that flow from the divine ordering of relationships:

- All relationships depend, ultimately, on one's relationship with God.
- When children arrive on the scene, couples must make the conscious decision to prioritize their marriage relationship.
- Kids observe the spirituality of and interactions between Mom and Dad, and are deeply shaped by them.
- The church family is merely an extension of the nuclear families of the church, especially the families of principal leaders.
- While our mission is to seek the lost to help bring them to Christ, this must not be raised above the biblical imperative to excel in one-another relationships.

## A Word to Those in Special Circumstances

Some of you are single parents and some of you are married to someone who is not a Christian. Let me say a few things about your situation, because I recognize it presents some special challenges. Since single parents have to do the work of two, extra patience is required. The two-parent family is God's ideal, and yet thousands of committed, vibrant disciples have been raised by single parents. In other words, as challenging as your situation is, never accept that obstacles are insurmountable. A few ideas:

- Pray daily with your children. When possible, join with another family for devotionals.
- If remarriage is a possibility, pray for it patiently. Don't let your frustration affect your judgment.
- Although television, computers, and video games have their place, beware the temptation of letting them become a "babysitter." Instead, encourage your kids to invest in friendships, sports, schoolwork, chores and reading. Do you really want advertisers and liberal programmers conforming your children to the pattern of this age? (Romans 12:2).
- Do not associate with grumblers and complainers (Proverbs 22:24–25). The world is filled with people who will offer you a false sympathy, one that fosters a critical spirit rather than a Christlike one.
- When you drop off your kids to your church's children's ministry, make sure they already have a positive, giving spirit. Cooperate with their teachers, accepting their feedback. Children's ministry is a privilege, not a right.
- Finally, when you are tired—perhaps after a long day—don't "tune out" when your kids need you. Yes, they need you to go "one more lap." You are serving as both mother and father to them!

As for those whose spouses are not disciples, you face yet another set of challenges. Whether you are a man or a woman, 1 Peter 3:1–5 applies. This passage teaches that your character is more decisive in winning over your mate than your words. A few practicals:

- Resist the temptation to make subtle "digs" at your mate, whether in direct conversation or in your prayers. Don't be manipulative. Pray for a gracious spirit. (The Proverbs will prove faithful friends!)

- When you speak about your spouse to others, be positive. Remember, he/she does not have a "voice"; your brothers and sisters in Christ are likely forming their impressions of your mate through your words. Never, ever speak ill of your spouse in the presence of your children. (This will undermine their respect for you.)
- Strive to coordinate schedules as much as possible, giving advance notice whenever possible. Sometimes this means that when there have been sudden changes in plan, you will need to stand at your spouse's side (e.g. the last-minute prayer meeting or church party).
- Never, ever argue, raise your voice at your spouse, or lose your temper. Your mature example in Christ, not childishness, will change his/her heart.
- When you do sin, be quick to confess and ask for forgiveness both from your spouse and your children. Show them that you know you need God's grace and are grateful for it.

For both single parents and those without Christian spouses, character issues are of the essence, more than external behavior. Pray for a pure heart (Proverbs 4:23).

**Other Family Members**

Some of us are not old enough to have children (or grandchildren) of our own. If this is the case, it is more likely that we have a number of relatives still living: siblings, parents, uncles, aunts, cousins and perhaps grandparents. To win them, here are a few valuable principles.

- Family members cannot be rushed. A stranger may become your friend and make their decision for Christ in a period of weeks or months. With family members, who know your weaknesses (and strengths) well, months and years are often the time units we should be thinking in.
- Keep up regular communication with them, whether by mail, telephone, email, or personal visit, depending on the relationship and the time of year. The exact frequency of contact is probably less important than its consistency. Keep

them up to date with what is happening in your life!

- Forgetting birthdays and special occasions in the lives of our family members can make them think they are not important to us anymore since "finding God." This impression is to be avoided! Write down the key dates in your calendar, and remember them.
- If they are religious, seek opportunities to pray with them. There is no harm in it, and it not only shows your heart for God but also brings you closer together emotionally.
- Often it will be less awkward if an outsider studies the Bible with your relatives, especially siblings and parents. Though the message may be the same, it will be heard differently, with less defensive ears. Choose someone you trust, and be helpful, yet resist the temptation to interfere.
- Ask them for advice. Your relatives are trained professionally as accountants, chefs, business people—each has an area of expertise. People feel special when their counsel is solicited. But do not limit the advice to just the professional—ask for feedback (more than input) in the area of family and marriage. For example, ask, "How do you think my children are doing? What do you see in their characters?" Or perhaps, "Dad, when you were at this stage in your life, how did you feel when Mom...?" "Do you have any tips for me?"
- Introduce your friends to them, not just the ministry staff of your local church. Talk about your friends in their absence. Then, when your family happens to meet them, they will have more of a sense of connection.
- Share with them any books on marriage and parenting you have found helpful. (Not, "Here, you really need to read this," but "I have found this helpful for me. I know I have a lot of things to change. Are you interested in reading it?")
- Pray for your relatives every day. The persistent prayer (Luke 18) will not fall on deaf ears.

**Conclusion**

Christians are called to love and serve the people of the world. Above all, this includes our own families. After our spouses, out of all the family members we most long to see baptized into Christ, our children are closest to our hearts and at the head of the list. To win them, to "impress" them, we will need to live differently, to talk differently, to schedule differently. If we follow the priorities laid out in this chapter, we will build healthier churches; our children will not resent us, but rather covet the secret of our joy and spirituality; and evangelism will be enhanced as outsiders enter the happy and emotionally healthy[2] family of believers.

Whether you are counseling others (Romans 15:14), sharing your faith with outsiders (Colossians 4:5–6), or simply enjoying Christian fellowship (Philemon 7), keep the "ladder" of relationships in mind. It will help us better love our spouses, parent our children, and build godly families and godly churches.

Of course merely reading this chapter will not change anything. You have got to have your own conviction. So, what decisions have you recently (say, in the last ten or twenty minutes!) made about family evangelism?

## Notes

[1] This chapter is an adaptation of chapter 5, "The Ladder of Priorities" in *Principle-Centered Parenting* (Spring, Texas: Ilumination Publishers, 2017), which itself is an adaptation of chapter 7, "Impress Them on Your Children," in the millennial (3rd) edition of *Shining Like Stars*.

[2] Highly recommended: Peter Scazzero's *The Emotionally Healthy Church* (Grand Rapids: Zondervan, 2003), ISBN 0-310-24654-7.

# 8
# All Things to All People
## *Foreign Evangelism*

God's will is that all nations receive the gospel through Jesus Christ (Galatians 3:8). This means world evangelism. World evangelism can take place "here" (wherever you live) or "overseas"—that is, where indigenous churches will reach out and make a difference. This chapter concerns not so much the need to take the gospel to foreign lands as the need to reach foreigners who happen to be in your own country.

My wife and I have a deep love for things international. When we go out to eat, we rarely eat at a "western" restaurant (I'm talking about American or Continental food, not Texas fries or buffalo burgers from the "chuck wagon"). We prefer Asian—and the spicier the better! Our children were born in three different countries, none in the country where we now live. We have many friends from Africa, Australia, and Latin America. My love of languages naturally draws me to any country where English is not spoken (which is *most* nations). We quickly turn to the international news section of the paper before any other section. (For me, even the crossword has to wait for the international news!) And in our marriage, it is not clear who is the "foreigner" —is Vicki (the Briton) the foreigner, or am I (the American) the outsider? To tell the truth, it depends on where we are at the time, as we have relatives on both sides of the Atlantic.

From the perspective of the citizens of some two hundred nations, it is *you* who are the foreigner! We all tend naturally to view our own nation as the center of the universe, don't we? Most maps are drawn with the nation of production of the map squarely in the center. The Chinese called their land the "Middle Kingdom"—all others were outside. Similarly, the ancient Romans named their primary body of water the "Mediterranean" —from *media* (middle) and *terra* (earth)—meaning the water in the middle of the earth. For the ancient Greeks, those outside the kingdom were barbarians—simply because they weren't Greek!

This is the human tendency.

Part of being a citizen of heaven (Philippians 3:20), in my opinion, is overcoming this natural form of geographical prejudice. At the end of this chapter I will give you some ideas on how better to retain an international focus and awareness. For the time being, our concern is the evangelization of foreigners in your own country. I have personally studied with people from nearly one hundred nations, and the Lord has enabled me to bring many of them to a saving knowledge of the truth. Part of this I attribute to evangelism and prayer, part of it to my genuine interest in things foreign. Do you have a love for "foreigners"?

The evangelization of foreign nationals is of crucial importance as we labor to win the world for Christ. Many countries do not allow foreign missionaries, but it is harder to prevent their own citizens from sharing the gospel with their countrymen. While it is true that churches ought roughly to reflect their geographical setting demographically, it is also true that we must not ignore the alien in our midst. Through our study of the Scriptures and our outreach to these people, we have discovered several invaluable principles of effective outreach.

In the following pages, we will discuss the language barrier, the importance of friendship, the need to ascertain motives, "counting the cost," and our own need to be more aware of the world we live in.

## Language

Revelation 7:9 describes a truly "international scene":

> "After this I looked and there before me was a great multitude that no one could count, from every nation, tribe, people and language."

God has never intended for language to be a hindrance to people who are seeking to know him. Today God has provided his written word in almost every known language. A "language barrier" should never be an excuse for not reaching out to people from other countries.

When evangelizing foreign people, it is important to realize that most of them know some English, at least enough to find their way around. Foreigners usually understand more English than they can speak, so you should not be afraid to speak to them in English. The most helpful thing you can do is to speak *slowly*, clearly articulating each word (especially the consonants) and avoiding rare idioms and difficult words. And be patient—they will take a little longer to understand what you are saying.

In reaching out to foreigners, it helps to know a few phrases of their language, and to be willing to learn more. Foreigners are elated when they meet someone who can speak a bit of their language. Phrases like "What is your name?" "My name is..." "Where do you live?" and "Hello, how are you?" are great icebreakers in starting conversations. It is well worth learning these phrases in the languages of the main national groups in your own city. A learner's attitude on your part is also helpful as you begin studying the Bible with those for whom English is a second language. Your interest and humility in learning their language will, in turn, encourage their interest and humility in learning about God.

In studying with people who know little English, it is important to get them a Bible in their own language. Contact your nearest Bible society or Christian bookshop. This gives them a greater trust that what you are teaching them is correct (Acts 17:11). It also allows them to do their own personal study, which will be essential for them to develop a genuine and lasting faith. When you study with someone who knows little English, be sure to read each passage at least twice. Ask simple, specific questions.

For Luke 13:1–5, for example, don't ask, "Do you grasp the import of Jesus' utterance? Is damnation the ineluctable result if one neglects the precepts of the Almighty?" Come down to earth! Use simple vocabulary. Try sentences like "What happens if you don't change?" Frequently ask the question Philip put to the eunuch: "Do you understand what you are reading?" (Acts 8:30). As you study, use fewer scriptures than usual in each study, but spend more time carefully explaining each passage. If you are thorough, much of the language barrier can be overcome.

It is exciting to know that open people will respond even if they understand only a little English.

### Friendship

A second consideration is friendship. "A new command I give you," Jesus said. "Love one another. As I have loved you, so you must love one another. All men will know that you are my disciples, if you love one another" (John 13:34–35). As we have discussed, it is important to deal with the language barrier as we reach out to foreigners. Yet we must never forget the most powerful tool Jesus gave us for bringing people to him: love, the universal language.

As we study God's word, we can see that loving friendship is the key ingredient in his plan for reaching foreigners. We can see this in John 4 as Jesus befriends the Samaritan woman, in Luke 7 as he dines with Simon the Pharisee, and in Luke 19 as he meets Zacchaeus. Jesus was known as "a friend of tax collectors an sinners" (Matthew 11:19). When we love people in a way they have never been loved before, then they will know that there is a God who loves them. If we are to win foreigners to Christ, we must be their best friends.

The magnitude of the decisions to be made makes this event more important. It is amazing to think that within a few weeks or months after meeting someone, you may be challenging them to give up smoking, drinking or sexual immorality, or to change their job, schedule, or travel plans. You will probably be challenging them to leave behind their family's religious beliefs, no matter how devoutly or sincerely held. These are hard decisions for anyone to make, especially for someone hundreds, or thousands, of miles away from home, facing a strange land and culture, and perhaps with little or no previous exposure to the gospel. We need to be people's best friends so that we can encourage and persuade them to make these kinds of decisions.

Friendship is also important because foreigners tend to form close-knit communities or cliques when away from their home nations. Deep friendships with Christians are crucial in helping them stand up against opposition.

Friendship is vital for winning foreign students, because often they are in the West on scholarship from their own countries, and easily feel much more pressure to please professors and parents than to seek God. Only through a close friendship can you persuade a busy student to make time in their schedule to consider becoming a Christian.

Generally, foreigners are quite open to friendship, once you have gained their trust. There are several ways to do this. You need to show a willingness to listen to them and understand their problems. Be willing to take time to get to know them. Keep up with current events in their country. Try to learn a little bit about their country and culture. These are excellent ways to start building common ground.

Sharing a meal together also can do wonders for a friendship, especially a home-cooked one. And, yes, be prepared to try any exotic cuisine. Quite often foreign styles of cooking are not only edible, but delicious! And even if they aren't, you are sure to win points by making an effort to try them out. Let us strive to "become all things to all men."

Playing sports or games they enjoy, or going to a film, museum or cultural event can be helpful, too. And genuine compliments about home, clothing, appearance, or personal strengths can be encouraging, as well. Basically, being a friend to people from other countries is not much different from being a friend to anyone else. You need to love them and treat them as unique, special individuals.

### Motives

As we have said, we must do all we can to bring people to Christ. Yet in reaching out to people from other countries it is important to guard against wrong motives. This is a tricky enterprise, since "motives are weighed by the Lord" (Proverbs 16:2). It is possible for us to think that someone from another culture is interested in Jesus, when in reality their interest lies elsewhere.

Jesus, of course, was a master at reading people's hearts. "He did not need any testimony about mankind, for he knew what was in each person" (John 2:25). Jesus had that special ability to look into people's hearts and see what was really there. The same Jesus who compassionately forgave the adulterous woman left speechless the proud men who accused her (John 8). Jesus brought salvation to humble Zacchaeus (Luke 19) but stiff challenge to Simon the Pharisee (Luke 7). After feeding the five thousand, he told the people that they were more concerned with miracles than truth (John 6). Jesus was continually evaluating the motives of all those he came into contact with. He knew people; and in the same way, we need to be wise, especially when evangelizing foreigners. (Admittedly, we will not have the confidence and accuracy of Christ.)

All of us have had the experience at one time or another of reaching out to someone whose interest in Christianity sprang from impure motives. When dealing with people from cultures and backgrounds completely different from ours, we must be sensitive to the possibility that they might have mixed motives for becoming Christians. Improper motives reveal themselves in a variety of ways. Some people are interested in financial gain or solutions to their money problems (1 Timothy 6:9). Many foreigners have large debts to pay or families abroad to support, and some hope to find in the church an easy source of short-term cash. A warning sign that someone may be motivated by money is when they ask for financial help soon after meeting the church. In some cases this may be an expression of legitimate need, in others an indication of a hidden and less-than-noble agenda.

Sometimes people come to church hoping to make contacts to help them find accommodation, locate a job, acquire a visa, or sort out personal problems. If, after exposure to the gospel, they still seem more concerned with their problems than with God, we need to reexamine their motivation.

Foreigners may be more interested in learning English than in learning about Jesus. Study at a slow pace with people like this, and see if they are consistent in their personal prayer and Bible study, church attendance and changing their lives. Strong challenges generally sift out the people who are not serious about following Jesus.

Other times people come to church looking for relationships with the opposite sex. If you think this could be the case with someone you are reaching out to, challenge them.

Still other times people come to the church not because they are willing to serve God, but merely because they are lonely and want friends.

Ultimately, the way to deal with impure motives is to teach people Jesus and the message of the cross. As people learn, they will either fall in love with him and change their motives, or they will reject him.

## Counting the Cost

Surely part of "counting the cost" (Luke 14:25–34) with anyone is asking them to ask themselves *why* they want to follow Jesus. Don't rush. Ask about relationships in other countries. I once studied with a single man and baptized him. I found out weeks later that he had a fiancée. "I asked you before if you had a girlfriend, and you said no!" I remarked. "You asked about whether I had a girlfriend, not if I was engaged," he came back. Was this a result of a language gap, or a touch of deceit? Hard to judge!

Another helpful idea is to have someone from their home country—preferably Christians currently *in* that country—to have a conversation with them, even to "count the cost." Sometimes this costs me financially. I remember studying with one fellow, a dentist in his 30s, who desperately wanted to be baptized but insisted that his "old pastor" in his home country taught accurately about conversion. "Be my guest," I said. "You can phone him, I will pay." He took me up on my offer. Ten minutes and $50 later (time and money well invested), he said, "Douglas, you were right. I am in shock. He reacted just as you said he would. When I go back to my country, I need to help my pastor, too." This man was baptized into Christ soon after and is a strong, effective, married Christian to this day.

The main reason to let someone else assist you in your study with a foreigner is that you are at a distinct disadvantage. You think differently, use a different language, and lack the background necessary to easily enter the world of the man or woman you are sharing your faith with. Be humble. Don't just assume you understand.

### The World We Live In

In addition to considerations of language, motives, and so forth, you will enhance your ability to "connect" with foreigners by becoming more aware: internationally, geographically, and culturally. In closing, here are some suggestions toward those ends:

- Improve your geography! Christians need to be strong in this area if they are effectively to visualize and pray for the nations of the world. I have a large map in my study, with pins inserted in cities I have visited or spoken in. At my website I feature a different nation each week as a "prayer point." When I read of a land or city I am not familiar with, I look it up! There is a perpetual opportunity to learn. Maybe a new map or globe is the birthday or Christmas present you should pray for!

- Newspapers, magazines, and news broadcasts can be helpful. Avoid following only local news. The horizons of the disciple of Christ need to be broad. As the people of God, charged to pray for rulers and those in authority (1 Timothy 2:1), we will do well to become more aware internationally.
- Be more daring! Visit that Ethiopian restaurant. Befriend your neighbor from the Caribbean. Learn a few words of Japanese. Read a book about Mexico. One morning, pray for all the nations of the world! Reach out to an "alien." "Remember, at one time we too were foreigners and aliens..." (Ephesians 2:19).

## Conclusion

As we reach out to foreigners, we must be prepared to meet their special needs. We must overcome the language barrier through patience and study. We must love them even more than we love ourselves. And we must test their motives. Yet we must always remember that with everyone we reach out to, it is God who gives the increase (1 Corinthians 3:6–7). With his power at hand, we can convert foreigners and equip them to evangelize their own countries. The alternative: we can go there ourselves!

Let's truly become all things to all people (1 Corinthians 9:22).

# 9
# The Ultrareligious
## *Those Who Have a "Hotline to God"*

The ultrareligious[1] claim they have a personal hotline to God. They receive direct guidance from the Lord, whereas the rest of us carnal, unenlightened individuals must fumble around in the darkness. They may "speak in tongues," have "visions" or "prophesy." They are convinced, and this conviction includes a way of looking at the world that usually requires a partial deconstruction before the light of the gospel can fully enter.[2]

### Assumptions

Before we continue, I feel a conviction to make an important qualification. I have had a fair amount of experience studying with extremely religious people. Many of the principles in this chapter I have learned through the "school of hard knocks." I have made many mistakes, and I do not desire that you repeat them. Also, many personal Bible study topics are named, assuming you are familiar with them. I realize that the study series, *Guard the Gospel,* is not detailed until chapter 11, so in a sense this chapter is out of order. Yet because it deals with one of the more challenging evangelistic arenas, along with family and foreign evangelism, I prefer to include it here.

### Going on the Defensive

Sometimes Christians are on the defensive when talking with the ultrareligious: adrenaline surges, voice levels rise, arguments become hurried and emotional—in short, we come on far too strong. We may behave this way because we lack experience in studying with this sort of person, or because their questions are difficult to negotiate, or because we feel personally threatened. Perhaps we fear we may be "outclassed" by their claims of experiencing the Spirit. People sense such intimidation. It does not give the impression that we are confident of our position, and this can easily reinforce others' false sense of security. The solution: know your Bible, relax, be friendly and trust God. Realize that God is on your side if you are on his.

No one is saved by virtue of their claims to religious experience. Unbiblical theology, doctrine, and living put people into a precarious position in the sight of God. Don't kid yourself; sincerity does not make one justified in God's sight (1 Corinthians 4:4). If a person has not met Jesus on Jesus' terms of salvation, they are not prepared to meet their God. But if you have the truth, why be on the defensive? Why be intimidated?

## Avoiding the Cardinal Insensitivities

In our attempts to be confident, it is easy to be insulting. This is not wise, nor will it commend your position to the ultra-religious. Here are some of the "cardinal insensitivities":

- Arguing against experience. This is not only insulting, but illogical, since there is no way to prove that someone has not really had the experience they claim. The interpretation of the experience may be open to debate, but never the experience itself.
- Making fun of the ultrareligious position. Comments like, "If you are supposed to have the gift of healing, how come you still wear glasses?" are not likely to win points. Moreover, there were a number of people in the New Testament with the gift of healing whom God did in fact leave unhealed, or without the ability to heal certain others. Paul left Trophimus sick in Miletus (2 Timothy 4:20), told Timothy to drink wine for his stomach illnesses (1 Timothy 5:23) and himself had a thorn in the flesh that God would not remove even after three prayers for healing (2 Corinthians 12:8). My friend Jim McGuiggan helped me with my own tendency to poke fun. His gracious approach was much more effective than my own brusque and disrespectful tendencies.
- Harsh or sarcastic comments about the religious person's views. Sometimes believers bring out of the arsenal such retorts as: "You people are just like the Jonestown group. They were so gullible, they would believe anything. And look where they are now—the same place you're going!"

Other times overgeneralizations can be just as damaging: "Hey, remember that vision of the nine-hundred-foot tall Jesus Oral Roberts saw who told him to ask for more money? I bet your church just wants your money, too!"

- Prematurely judging a religious person not to be a Christian. Informing someone of your assessment that they are lost before you have studied the Bible together and have a good relationship is a common but foolhardy move. First, it is likely to backfire. Second, you have no right, especially in their eyes, to say such a thing to a fellow believer who has neither been tried nor found guilty. Third, you may undo all the good you have done and prejudice them against the things you still plan to study out.
- Denying the work of God in their life. God works in the lives of *everyone*, whether or not they are true disciples. One of the worst errors we can commit is to ascribe good deeds and sincere religious experience to the devil. One of my most haunting memories is turning away a sincere "charismatic" from baptism. We had studied many passages, and he was beginning to surrender many of his ultrareligious interpretations. He had come to the midweek service with a towel and a change of clothes. I asked him whether he still thought God had been working in his life. He replied, "I know I'm lost, but I just can't believe that God never had anything to do with me." David might well be a disciple today if I hadn't turned him away with my judgmental, *too* black-and-white attitude. God *can* and does work in everyone's life (Matthew 7:7; Acts 14:17; 2 Kings 5:1–15). David, forgive me.

Let us realize that, in the face of the insincerity of the religious world, we have more in common with many of the ultrareligious than we do with most other religious people. This kinship, so to speak, should be capitalized on. Remember, "reckless words pierce like a sword" (Proverbs 12:18). At all costs, let us avoid the cardinal insensitivities.

### The Friendship Factor

Without a solid friendship, you will convert only the most purehearted. Unfortunately, not all ultrareligious persons are

"Ethiopian eunuchs." The truth is hard to swallow, especially when your entire approach to spirituality is wrong and you are seeing that your friends are lost. Love and gentle instruction go a long way (2 Timothy 2:25). We need to apply verses like 1 Thessalonians 2:8 to the ultrareligious as much as to anyone else. Friendship begins with mutual respect. You are likely to be respected for your commitment to Christ, and you should particularly respect the rather "hot" religious person for their commitment too. Yet even if you don't respect the ultrareligious person's commitment, you should still respect them as a human being. Ask them to tell you about their religious experiences (meanwhile making careful mental notes for future Bible studies). Ask them to share in a prayer at the end of your study; there is no harm in your praying together, and it is likely to draw you closer.

Work on the friendship, balancing serious studies with more relaxed outings together. Eat together, stay in good touch, and allow the friendship time to grow. You will be surprised at what good rapport you will be able to develop after only the first meeting or two, as your relationship is based on mutual respect, love and (increasingly) Christ.

Finally, introduce your ultrareligious friend to Christians in your congregation who were converted out of a similar background. It will be conducive to their conversion and long-term stability to have more than one good relationship, and the older disciple will be able to help them through any difficult patches which may arise during the studies or afterwards.

If you want your studies with the ultrareligious to be fruitful, and not just an exchange of disagreements, remember the friendship factor.

## Evangelistic Personal Bible Studies

The personal Bible studies suggested below are only one possible way to help your friend. The units of the *Guard the Gospel* series (see next chapter) should be employed as needed, depending on the situation of the person you are studying with:

Jesus Christ—his character and dealing with people
Seeking God—getting serious about finding God
The Word of God—its absolute authority
Discipleship—with special emphasis on evangelism
Sin—specific sins and separation from God

The Cross—the motivating power in the Christian life
Repentance—a radical change in life
Baptism—New Testament baptism
Implications—of the NT teachings on conversion
The Church—the need to be invested in the body

Keep in mind the following principles if you want to be effective in your studies with anyone, and especially with highly religious persons:

- Patience: allow time for concepts to sink in.
- Logical flow: create a sense of continuity in the progression of studies.
- Flexibility: select studies that address the person's individual situation.

### Dealing with Religious Pride

As with all religious people with whom we study the Bible, pride must be confronted. Some important advice:

- Be firm. Jesus was more direct in dealing with proud religious people than he was with "sinners" (John 8:1ff; Luke 7:36ff).
- Temper challenge with friendship (relaxed time together). Play a sport or game with them. This can be useful in dealing with pride: Either it provides an *opportunity* to humble them (in something at which you are good), or an *outlet* for their pride (assuming they can beat you)! Play it by ear.
- Initially it may be good to offer to "disciple" the religious person. Teach them what you know about evangelism. Take them under your wing and begin a "discipling" relationship with them, teaching them the basic studies. As the studies progress, they will realize that they have more need of them than they thought!
- Offer to take them evangelizing with you.
- Go through a Bible study on self-righteousness with them. Useful passages might include Luke 3:7–11, 5:31–32, 7:29–30, 18:9–14 and 2 Timothy 2:19.

### The Issue: Repentance

Repentance is the main issue with any non-Christian, no less so with a religious person. Repentance has been watered down in the religious world. Biblical repentance, however, is a radical decision leading to a radical change in one's lifestyle. People who have repented are eager to know God, eager to spend time with others who know God, and eager to help others to know God. If an ultrareligious person claims to be saved but has never been devoted to God, committed to reading the Bible, active in sharing their faith, and so forth, it is unlikely they have ever repented. We must not water down the message! Their lives testify to their repentance (Matthew 3:8; Acts 26:20). Ultimately, God is the judge of whether they have repented or not.

Because this is the clear biblical focus, make repentance "the issue"—for it is! [3]

### No Baptism Without Repentance

A classic mistake young Christians make is "blowing away" their friends and family with the Bible's teaching on baptism. Such tactlessness seldom bears fruit, usually hurting the victim's short-term chances of turning to God, and cultivating the habit of using the Bible as a club instead of the fine sword of the Spirit that it is. But many not-so-young Christians make the identical mistake! The mistake, again, is the premature study of baptism. The power is not in the plan of salvation; the power is in the cross of Christ (1 Corinthians 1:17), so unless the message of repentance is clearly understood and responded to first, the biblical teaching on immersion will fall on deaf ears. And on top of all this, by "inoculating" them against the truth, you make it even less likely that they will ever grasp the apostolic teaching on salvation. And so a fundamental principle emerges: *Avoid the study of baptism with people who have not repented!*

### Further Advice

Despite the temptation to enter into an involved study of the Holy Spirit with an ultrareligious person in the early stages of your relationship with them, *don't!* You may need to go easy on the Spirit material until they understand they have been misled about discipleship. Also, adapt your studies to the ultrareligious, sharing verses or points that will be helpful in the future, once they realize where they stand before God. Aim to instill *principles*, but do not get into the major issues too early.

When I was a student at the University of London, a deeply religious man named Mohan, who lived in my dorm, began attending the group study in my room. For several weeks we studied the Bible with Mohan. He was a very knowledgeable neopentecostal. He spoke five languages fluently—as well as "tongues." He was also a postgraduate student in economics at the University of London, and he wanted *answers*. We met for twelve hours of intense study on the Holy Spirit, but Mohan still remained unconvinced.

One day he walked into my room and asked me if I would like to hear him speak in tongues. "Sure," I said, "go ahead." Mohan then used his "prayer language," hoping to convince me.

"Is that supposed to prove to me that you're saved?" I asked.

"Oh, you're not listening!" a frustrated Mohan said.

"Do you want to hear *me* speak in tongues?" I asked.

"Go ahead," replied Mohan.

"*Korobka dvyer karandashkuya, boomega okno*," I faked some words of Russian.

"Was that really tongues?"

"More than what you just did," I replied.

"Wow, I'm impressed."

Was this the turning point? No! Hours of Bible study on the Spirit did not do the trick. Nor did impugning his tongue-speaking ability. (I was still learning about the cardinal insensitivities!) What made all the difference? Going back and nailing down the fact that, according to what the Bible teaches on salvation, he was not a Christian. Two days later, Mohan, now a powerful man in the service of God, was baptized into Christ.

The moral of the story is simple: establish the fact that someone is not a true Christian *before* you dive into a study on the Spirit. Otherwise, if they still think they are a Christian, they will not be able to make sense of their experiences. (And don't expect them to jettison them all at once.) Once they have accepted their own lostness, they will be looking for—and will need—answers to their questions. Tie up all the loose ends *after* you have covered baptism.

## Order of Studies

Studies with the very religious may follow the normal sequence until after the baptism study, when it will be time to tie up the loose ends. The Feelings study is good to cover early (you will find it in chapter 13), but apart from that there is little need to cover the peripheral Holy Spirit topics. After discussing baptism, one or two studies on the Spirit will be necessary. Many neopentecostals will need separate studies on topics like tongue speaking, the purpose of first-century miracles, or other themes or difficult passages in the Bible.[4]

## Conclusion

There is no magic formula for converting the ultrareligious, but a working knowledge of the Scriptures, a measure of common sense, a lot of love and much prayer can make all the difference. Let's not be intimidated by those whose passion for God—however misguided—takes forms more unusual than that which we are used to. For while their "hotline to God" is something largely in their own fantasy, God's deep desire for their welfare and salvation is not (Ezekiel 18:32; 1 Timothy 2:4).

## Notes

[1] This category includes not only those convinced of mystical, esoteric, and not necessarily biblical experiences, but also those belonging to a number of non-mainstream groups: Jehovah's Witnesses, Mormons, et al.

[2] This chapter is a modification of Chapter 14 of my book *The Powerful Delusion*. The first edition (London Church of Christ, 1987) and second edition (London Church of Christ, 1990) are both out of print. They will not be reprinted. For more information on the working of the Holy Spirit, as well as an exposé of the more common forms of misunderstanding current in our religious world, see my book *The Spirit* (Spring, Texas: Illumination Publishers, 2017).

[3] There are far more people in the world who have been immersed for the forgiveness of sins than have scripturally repented. Many groups teach immersion for the forgiveness of sins (e.g. Christian Church, Apostolic Church, Mormons, Church of Christ, some charismatic groups, and numerous independent fellowships, yet hardly anyone teaches repentance as the Bible does.) Surely Christians ought to be known for their radical commitment, knowledge of the Scriptures, love for others and love for God rather than for their adherence to any one doctrine (e.g., baptism), regardless of how central it is in the scheme of things. Keep the focus on repentance!

[4] Here are some possible study sequences with four ultrareligious persons. The first (Mr. Breeze) is interested in little more than the good feeling he thinks the Holy Spirit can give him. The study series is as follows: *Discipleship*.

Is that all? Yes, for it turned out that Mr. Breeze, who was not following in the footsteps of Jesus (1 John 2:3–6), refused to admit that he was not a true disciple of Christ. He became quite uncomfortable when he read the verses on evangelism and saw that he hadn't ever really given his life to the Lord. In fact, in the middle of the study Mr. Breeze felt "led" to leave the room, and was never heard from again. (Not all people sort themselves out so easily, however, as we shall see.)

The second (Mr. Gust), another very religious person (though not living for the Lord) was impressed by the Bible knowledge of the Christian, and after admitting that he "could be doing more" to spread the Word and live as a disciple, consented to study the Bible. Here is the series covered with Mr. Gust: *Discipleship, The Word, Feelings, Sin, Repentance.*

Alas, things were going well, but then Mr. Gust found it impossible to accept that he (and his ultrareligious friends, whose Christian life was no more active or devout than his own) were not true disciples. In fact, at the end of the *Repentance* study he saw that he himself was lost, but became completely silent as the implications dawned on him. Then he changed his mind and said he was saved after all. He heartily thanked the Christian for helping him to "grow spiritually" much, and said he would like to continue the studies in the future—which he has yet to do. (The Christian wisely resisted the temptation to study baptism with Mr. Gust, who would have made that the bone of contention instead of repentance, and gone away feeling justified.) From time to time they pass each other in the street, and their relationship is cordial. Perhaps one day Mr. Gust will rethink his decision and seek out the Christian again.

The third ultrareligious individual, Mr. Wind, was a sincere, committed individual. He initially got caught up in the excitement of speaking in tongues, but after a year started to have some doubts. As far as he could see, however, there was no alternative to his ultrareligious fellowship, which has much more to offer than the dead denomination in which he was brought up. He met the Christian while the Christian was inviting people in the streets, and was interested in getting to know him better. These are the studies the Christian covered with Mr. Wind: *The Church, The Word of God, Feelings, Sin, Repentance, The Cross, Baptism (two studies), The Holy Spirit, Discipleship.*

As you may have supposed, Mr. Wind became a Christian after about four weeks of studying the Bible. The Christian started with *The Church,* making the study convicting, and challenging this ultrareligious man to get involved in a church where everyone seriously studied the Bible and shared their faith. From then on, Mr. Wind started attending all the services of the local church, which significantly accelerated his decision for Christ.

After the study of *The Word,* Mr. Wind was still talking about what he *felt* the Spirit was saying to him, and so the Christian thought the *Feelings* study would be appropriate. After *Sin* and *Repentance,* Mr. Wind realized that he was lost, and so the coast was clear to proceed toward baptism. To make sure his motivation was pure, however, the Christian first studied *The Cross* with him. *Baptism* was a welcome solution, and after one long study on *The Holy Spirit,* and another on *Discipleship* as a wrap-up, he was immersed. Now the Christian and Mr. Wind are doing some more in-depth study on the Spirit, so that Mr. Wind will be able to reach his religious friends.

The fourth man is Mr. Gale, who, shall we say, has been strongly influenced by the ultrareligious ideology. He speaks in tongues, feels he has been healed of a tumor, and is thought to possess the gift of prophecy, which he exercises on occasion. Mr. Gale was actually the one who invited the Christian to consider Christ! They hit it off from the start, but it was clear that Mr. Gale was not going to be easy to convince. These were the studies the Christian and Mr. Gale covered over a four-month period: *Discipleship, Feelings, The Word, Faith and Works, Sin, Repentance, Baptism (two studies), The Holy Spirit, The Miraculous Gifts, The Church, Speaking in Tongues, The Cross.*

From the very start, the studies were challenging. There was no tiptoeing around, because Mr. Gale was serious about his commitment to Christ. It wasn't until the *Faith and Works* study, which cleared up a lot of misunderstandings in Mr. Gale's mind, that he was prepared to visit church with the Christian. (He was involved in his own church five evenings a week, and felt that, even if they were "drooping" in their discipleship, they needed him, and that was where the Lord wanted him.)

Mr. Gale really appreciated the thoroughness of the *Sin* study. When the time came to study *Repentance,* however, the Christian was afraid that because he was so committed, he would not be able to see that he wasn't saved. But Mr. Gale had a pure heart, and thought that although he had not fully repented, he very much wanted to and asked the Christian to pray for him. After the *Baptism* study, everything fell into place; Mr. Gale did not put up any fight.

That is not to say that he had no questions, though! It took three more studies on the Spirit to satisfy his curiosity and to make it clear to him why the experiences he and his friends had claimed did not prove they were saved. (After the *Repentance* study, Mr. Gale realized that most of his ultrareligious friends were lost, but there were a few who were committed, and he was not so sure about these.)

The final study, on *The Cross,* helped Mr. Gale to be urgent in finalizing his decision, and he was baptized the very next day.

Although Mr. Gale would have been an intimidating fellow to many Christians, he was reached because someone saw in him a great potential and cared about him enough to spend hours and hours every week with him. (In the last week of their studies, Mr. Gale and the Christian studied nearly every day. Some of those studies on the Spirit lasted two or three hours!) Praise God that the Christian shared his faith with Mr. Gale, because already he has helped three of his friends to become Christians, and will soon be leading his own group Bible study!

What we must understand is that, although most of the ultrareligious are like Mr. Gust or Mr. Breeze, there are a great number like Mr. Wind and Mr. Gale. If we don't know the Bible, or if we are not willing to make them our friends, they may die separated from God.

PART III

# PUT OUT INTO DEEP WATER

"As for us, we cannot help speaking about what we have seen and heard" (Acts 4:20).

The third section of *Till the Nets Are Full* contains the bulk of the teaching material—nearly fifty studies you can share with those interested in Jesus Christ, as well as with new Christians. After chapter 10, on how to lead personal Bible studies, you will find three series of *Guard the Gospel* material. But that is not all! Chapters 14 and 15 contain even more valuable material for the disciple determined to hide the word of God in his or her heart.

Of course, no method is foolproof, and whether we are successful or not in our fishing is up to the Lord. He is the one in control of outcomes, not we. Yet success favors the prepared.

# 10
# Studying with Non-Christians
## *The Biblical Warrant*

A set of evangelistic personal Bible studies—does this have any biblical warrant? Shouldn't we just preach the Word and leave it to the Lord to bring our friends to faith? (John 16:8). Is there any reason our presentation of the gospel shouldn't happen in a single session? And what about the notion of "studies"—might this not be a humanistic approach to evangelism? These are the kinds of questions addressed in this chapter.

### Expecting Too Much?

If we expect people to go through a study series and make specific changes in their lives, are we not teaching salvation by works? Is this not "performance theology"? Not necessarily.

I do not doubt that it is tempting for us to "raise the bar" too high—to require more than the Lord himself requires.[1] But this is no better than expecting too little—or nothing at all, which is not uncommon in modern-day Christianity. A useful study is to examine the ministry of John the Baptizer. What did he require before anyone was baptized? Did he ever turn anyone away?

Actually, yes. Though we won't go into the scriptures at this time, please look them up and come to your own conviction. In Luke 3 many persons came to John for baptism, including the religious leaders. Before he baptized them, they confessed their sins—not necessarily exhaustively, but not vaguely, either. When they asked him what they needed to change, John was specific, with challenges appropriate for the various people who sought baptism. And yet one group apparently did not feel comfortable with such specific admission of guilt and need of repentance: the Pharisees. Although they were present in Luke 3, they rejected God's purpose for themselves, refusing to be baptized by John (Luke 7:29–30). The Baptizer, after all, he would have expected specific repentance. Many Pharisees had great difficulty seeing, and admitting, this need (Luke 5:32). Biblically speaking, it is wrong to expect too much, but it would also be wrong to expect too little (Luke 7:29–30).

## One-Shot Approach?

The traditional "one-shot" approach of exposing someone to the "whole counsel"[2]—everything needed in order to become a Christian—has an abysmally low success rate. We must discipline ourselves not to rush in our Bible studies with nonbelievers, but rather be patient. Most likely it will take time to bring them to an accurate understanding of the truth. The one-shot approach does not allow time to internalize the new concepts or process the far-reaching implications, which normally dawn on those studying the Bible for the first time. See Acts 17:2.

## One-Day Conversions?

"What about Pentecost?"—someone is sure to ask. "Didn't these people become Christians in a single day?" Now, I am pretty sure there were "first-timers" in the audience, and yet Peter speaks to them as persons who already know the facts about Jesus Christ (Acts 2:22). They know about Jesus' miracles and even about his death. It may have been their first time to hear an apostle speak, but it was hardly their first exposure to the gospel. These persons[3] have Judaism in common—which is a huge head start on many people in our modern secular society. Many may have stayed over in Jerusalem after Passover, which took place just seven weeks previously. And what about the preparatory work of John the Baptist? And the ministry of the Twelve, and of the seventy-two? Jesus himself had spoken to countless thousands (Luke 12:1) during his three years of public ministry. It seems most of the Pentecost crowd knew quite a bit about Jesus Christ, even before Peter began speaking.

As for the Ethiopian (Acts 8), this is a better example of a "one-day conversion." As a "God-fearer" (a Gentile attracted to Judaism, yet who had not submitted to circumcision—and in his case, one who never would!), he had previously been exposed to Judaism and had faith in God. He was reading, after all, in the book of Isaiah the prophet. He was seeking, and he was receptive. Philip preached the word, and the Ethiopian was baptized the same day. What was it that he needed to hear? He needed to hear about Jesus, and that is who Philip presented to him. At any rate, here is an example of someone who came to faith quickly. (And we all know many more in our own day.)

As for Saul of Tarsus (Acts 9), he had *plenty* of Christian background—when you consider his acquaintance with the faith he was determined to eradicate, the exposure to Stephen's message (Acts 7), the confessions he must have heard as he tried to force men and women to renounce Christ, the Damascus Road experience, and the miracle of regaining his sight. Saul encountered the Lord personally. In terms of knowledge and experience, Saul of Tarsus was well ahead of many who come to faith in our day.

In short, the "one-day conversions" of the New Testament are not normative. (And even then, it is clear in each case that God had been at work in their past, preparing them for the moment.) In my experience, many "one-day conversions" do not endure. I doubt we do people a disservice by encouraging them to take adequate time to prepare for the most important decision of their life.

## Specific Teaching?

In Ephesians 4:20–24, Paul reminds his audience of their conversion. As we read this passage, we too receive this reminder: that we were *taught*—to "put off the old self" and "be made new." In other words, there was teaching *before* conversion.

> "You, however, did not come to know Christ that way. Surely you heard of him and were taught in him in accordance with the truth that is in Jesus. You were taught, with regard to your former way of life, to put off your old self, which is being corrupted by its deceitful desires; to be made new in the attitude of your minds; and to put on the new self, created to be like God in true righteousness and holiness."

Similarly, in Acts 16:31, it was not enough for Paul just to tell the Philippian jailer to believe in Christ. He had also to preach the Word to him (v. 32). This was followed by baptism (v. 33) and of course a great deal of joy (v. 34), as this man and his family had come to a saving faith.

Now the Lord has not told us *how* to teach the lost, only *to* teach them (Matthew 28:19–20). That means we cannot make a hard-and-fast rule. The goal is that people accept Jesus as he is, as Savior and Lord (Acts 2:36, Colossians 2:6). This is not likely to take place, for most of us, without some helpful instruction. Perhaps this is why *every* person who becomes a Christian in the book of Acts does so through the agency of a human teacher. No one comes to Jesus on their own; everyone is taught. This is humbling. It also takes time. And it requires that we know our Bible!

## Personal Studies

A personal study is a session in which you *share* with a non-Christian. What are you sharing? Three things: the gospel, your faith, and your life (1 Thessalonians 2:8). You will talk about God's word. This is easiest with an open Bible (Acts 8:35, 17:11).

All of us want to lead others to Christ, and we know that our lives will never be more fulfilled than when we are sharing the good things we have received with others. We know that if we "instruct many," it's only a matter of time before we begin to "lead many to righteousness" (Daniel 12). Yet when it comes to studying with non-Christians, how often we fall short, not so much through sin as through ignorance! Some of us specialize in diplomacy, yet the message of Jesus is muddled or missing. Others know exactly what to say, but through errors in judgment invest all their time into people who simply are not willing to make Jesus Lord, or worse, turn off prospective converts through sheer insensitivity. This chapter aims at giving concrete help as to "what to say and how to say it" (John 12:49).

## When Should I Set Up the Study?

The answer is "As soon as possible." For a few people, that will be the first time you meet. For most, it will be after a few visits to a small group Bible study, or to church, or after a few spiritual discussions, perhaps in your home. It is important that the person feel comfortable with the concept of seeking God or at least growing spiritually through Bible study before you propose the idea of studying together. The "Oh, no, she's trying to convert me" reaction should most definitely be avoided. On the other hand, sometimes we let timidity or fear that someone might not be open cause us to delay unnecessarily. Perhaps the easiest time to set up a study is *immediately after* a group Bible study or a church service, or even after a good conversation. It is important not to let it go too long before proposing the study—otherwise he or she may become *too* comfortable in the fellowship. Friendship is also an important element for most people. It helps to have the beginnings of a good relationship—a certain degree of trust—before you begin studying.

### How Do I Set Up a Study?

That depends largely on who the non-Christians are. Some people, like the Ethiopian eunuch (Acts 8), are so wonderfully open that they could not care less how you propose it, and will certainly ask you to study with them if you do not hurry up!

Many religious people are more difficult to approach. You have to tiptoe around their religious pride long enough to win trust and dispel unsound thinking. It is essential to strike the balance between respecting their knowledge and challenging their life and doctrine. If people are committed, you might share with them the passages that have helped *you* to share your faith with others. Gradually, the impact of these scriptures on their hearts will, prayerfully, enable them to be more receptive to the things God wants to show them.

Other religious people are interested, but not exactly wide open. Sensitivity is of the essence; balance urgency with patience. Capitalizing on meetings or discussions is usually best. "What do you think about that verse the preacher used about seeking God? Maybe we could get together and study more about this topic." Or you might say, "He really got my attention when he was talking about *knowing* you're saved. My confidence comes through knowing the Scriptures. Would you like to get together and spend some time looking at some other verses?" Regardless of whom you are setting up a study with, there are three imperatives if you want to be as effective as possible.

- Be confident—never apologize for taking up their time. This is probably the most important thing they could be doing, so why apologize? If you are new to the Bible yourself, be humble, but don't put yourself down. People listen to confident teachers—with confidence based not on ourselves, but on the power of the gospel.

- Be relaxed—you know that a "no" answer to the gospel is an eternal mistake, but there is no point in conveying that to them, at least initially. Pray and assume the best, then calmly propose to start studying the Scriptures together.
- Be excited—in your efforts to be calm, don't be boring! We should have at least as much enthusiasm as the world does when they invite us to parties or events. Those things bring superficial thrills at best; Jesus brings peace and joy forever.

### How Many People Should Be Involved in the Study?

In my situation, it was one man studying with me. For many others, two or three others helped them come to faith. There is obviously no biblical rule here! Often it works well when three persons, including the non-Christian, meet together. That arrangement allows a younger Christian to learn how to study from an older one. The non-Christian also benefits from having more than one close relationship. For some, however, "Two is company and three is a crowd." If that is the case, then proceed with two but encourage one or two other Christians to make special efforts to get to know them. Too many people in the group, and it will be hard for the seeker to open up, since confidentiality is seldom found in crowds, and most people are less likely to speak up when they are surrounded by others who know more about the subject than they do.

### How Long Should the Study Last?

That depends on the topic and the other person. Most studies last thirty to ninety minutes. You want to allow enough time to discuss things thoroughly, but not so much that you waste time rambling. Resist the urge to explain the Bible from Genesis to Revelation when a person seems eager. These three tips will help you to keep the time reasonable.

- Give them the verses to read in advance—this will help them to feel secure in their understanding of the passages, as well as minimize the time you spend on basic explanations.
- Stick to the topic—if the topic is sin, don't get involved in a discussion of Armageddon. If it is the Word, don't get diverted into a debate on baptism. Learn to say, "We can talk about that later; for now, let's get back to our study."

- Let the Scriptures do the talking. Don't plead with your friend to accept your views about repentance; have the person read Luke 13:5 themself. Avoid the trap of arguments that are really smokescreens for disobedience. 2 Timothy 2:14 and 23–26 will help you. Of course, there are legitimate questions, even in the midst of a study, that deserve an answer. Always direct the discussion back to the Word, because that is where the power is.
- Although it's fine to teach from more than one book of the Bible, in general, try to keep most of the study in one book, when possible. Fewer verses is often better than more. Hopping around from proof-text to proof-text doesn't provide the best model for Bible study, and your friend may get the idea that the meaning of the Scriptures is always obvious, or that it's not necessary to study text, context, or content.
- You may want to begin and end with prayer. It will be easier for them to accept the truth when they believe that you too are a seeker after truth, someone who is trusting in the Lord in your own life.

## How Often Should We Study?

How often can you study? How available is your friend? Once a week is an ideal. Less than that, and some people absorb the information intellectually but struggle with making changes in their personal lives. Becoming a Christian is an incredible change for anyone. The transition cannot be made on the strength of a commitment that is inferior to that of an average member of a bowling league.

After you have had a number of sessions and the person's urgency is increasing, it may be possible to study every two or three days. Coming to church or group Bible studies is important, yet so is studying together. Aim to keep your friend growing on both fronts.

It is essential that people develop relationships in the local church and become accustomed to the weekly schedule of church meetings. If they spend time with the disciples, then feel free to study as often as they are willing. Discuss the frequency of meeting together after a study on Seeking God or The Word. I will often say, "Now, we can study as much as you like. I'm available to study a couple of times a week if you want. If you are not quite ready for that, we can start with once a week." Also, you can save a lot of time by establishing when the next study will be at the end of each session together.

Don't be afraid to study with someone every day. This often works out with singles, not so often with marrieds, especially marrieds with children. Yet even if someone is eager to study daily, don't rush. Haste makes waste. Be alert for possible wrong motives, and try to make sure the implications have sunk in.

## How Do I Know If They Are Open?

Titus 2:14 talks about people *eager* to do what is good. 2 Corinthians 7:8–11 talks about people *eager* to clear themselves. The following is a list of characteristics to look for in an open or receptive person.

1. They are willing to read the scriptures before you meet to study.
2. They deal with sin in their lives; they don't rationalize.
3. They take stands with family and friends.
4. They initiate with you (phone calls, email, etc.).
5. They attend church services.
6. They are beginning a consistent prayer life.
7. They are willing to spend time together outside of "study time."
8. They confess sins and struggles; they don't conceal them.
9. They change opinions when confronted with Scripture.
10. They understand the difference between your own opinions and the word of God itself (1 Thessalonians 2:13).

## When Do I Strongly Challenge?

This is another one of those delicate issues that call for perception and sensitivity. The biblical ideal is to challenge people with severity proportionate to their knowledge. Jesus was exceedingly strong with the Pharisees, calling them "hypocrites," "sons of hell," "snakes" and "blind guides," to name just a few epithets. Yet with those theologically less informed, such as the centurion (Matthew 8) and Zacchaeus (Luke 19), he was quick to reassure them of their place in the kingdom.

Some people never really need strong challenges. A simple encouragement or admonishment brings about immediate repentance or redirection. Others of us, in fact most of us, are not nearly so tenderhearted. We need a more dramatic form of correction. We must be friends like Jesus. He loved people and told them what they needed to hear (Mark 10:21). The best policy is to handle people with tender loving care, using as little force as necessary. If someone makes a mistake out of ignorance, that is one thing. It is an entirely different matter when people defiantly, "deliberately keep on sinning" (Hebrews 10:26). Our style ought to reflect the teaching of Jesus (Luke 12:47).

### When Do I "Shake the Dust Off?"

Jesus said, "If anyone will not welcome you or listen to your words, shake the dust off your feet when you leave that home or town" (Matthew 10:14). Jesus was unmistakably clear—there is a time to walk away. He mentions two very specific reasons that indicate it is time to part.

- "Will not welcome you"—this one is easy to identify but sometimes hard to accept. When family or close friends are totally closed we must resist the urge to keep "blasting away" until they "break." Invariably, our blasting causes them to harden rather than crack. If people are not willing to accept the Word, don't hurt their future chances—move on to others who are searching for the message.
- "Will not listen to your words"—there is a difference between listening and hearing. Virtually everyone can *hear* what we are saying, but fewer are prepared to *listen.* It can be difficult discerning when a person has stopped listening and has only begun to hear. One revealing sign is the inability or refusal to be consistent. People begin saying things like: "I know unless you repent you'll be lost, and I definitely haven't repented...but I'm still sure I'm saved"!
- "Backtracking" is another clear indication. People begin doubting the authority of the Word, the divinity of Jesus and even the existence of God, when previously these were not issues. We must try to help people through these difficulties, but if they persist we must be willing to walk away.

We must trust that God is in control, and that people go through some stages in their lives when they are more open than at other times. "Shaking the dust off" does not mean you have stopped caring or that you will never try again. It simply means that in this situation your time is better spent helping others who are searching. We err if we allow dozens to die lost who might have responded if given a chance, yet no chance was given because we stubbornly insisted on "casting our pearls before swine" (Matthew 7:6, Jesus' own strong words).

And yet always leave the door open. People change, and many times they come back months, even years later. So keep up the relationship. We mustn't only be interested in "quick" conversions. Some people take years. Yes, I have studied with people who became Christians in a week or less, and even in a day or two! But others have required years to become Christians. (And three men I studied with took ten to fifteen years each!) In short, "Treat people nicely on the way out, for they will certainly remember on the way back in!"

## When Do I Study Baptism?

Many a soul has been lost due, in part, to a premature study of baptism. Sadly, some of us have developed a reputation for "preaching baptism instead of preaching Jesus." Ironically, if by magic, starting today, baptism were completely optional and totally unrelated to salvation, that would affect the eternal destiny of less than one person in a thousand. The other nine hundred and ninety-nine would still be lost on the basis of the Bible's teaching on sin, repentance, and discipleship.

We must teach people that the road is narrow, not because of Acts 2:38 but because of Deuteronomy 6:5 ("Love the Lord with all your heart, soul...") and Luke 13:3 ("Repent or perish..."). Further, loving God and repenting of sin are far more intuitively obvious requirements for salvation than baptism. Don't rely on a baptism study to convict people about a lack of discipleship. If you establish their need for forgiveness beforehand, you will turn baptism into a joyfully simple solution rather than a doctrinal technicality of "your church."

## How Do I Count the Cost?

Jesus was confronted by the perfect convert (Luke 9:57), who said, "I'll follow you wherever you go." Jesus said, in effect, "Count the cost!" Jesus compared becoming a disciple with building a tower and said explicitly to "sit down and estimate the cost" (Luke 14:28). Counting the cost is biblical and essential to strong disciple making. It would be unethical to preach "Jesus is Lord" without spelling out in no uncertain terms what that confession really means. We must not bind unnecessary loads on people, but it is equally wrong to dilute the call to discipleship. The overriding question is *"Are you ready to make Jesus your Lord?"*

Once again, before anyone is baptized into Christ, it is our responsibility to follow Jesus' instructions in making disciples, as well as to keep our conscience clean. While we cannot judge the motives of the heart as God (alone) can, it is nevertheless our aim to help prospective Christians to truly repent. Without repentance, the baptism is not scriptural (Acts 2:38, 3:19). Jesus did not want people following him who weren't willing to count—and meet—the cost (Luke 9:57–62, 14:25–35; John 6:60–61, 66).

Following are a number of areas that may be helpful to cover as you "count the cost" with those considering baptism. Every person is different, and what needs emphasis with one person may not with another. Select from this list what applies to the person you are reaching out to, based on his or her unique situation and needs.

*Conversion:* They must be able to explain clearly to you how to become a Christian. Ask them about the "good Hindu"—do they understand that no one can go to heaven outside of Jesus Christ? (Or the "good churchgoer"...)

*Obstacles and challenges:* Ask them what they think the biggest challenges could be. Ask specifically about the temptations you covered in the Sin study (sex, worldly parties, laziness, selfishness), as well as aspects of commitment you know they may find difficult.

*Implications of repentance:* Ask, "What is the greatest difference you see between real Christians and others who are less committed?" They should answer, "The commitment, repentance, discipleship, evangelism," or something like that. Make sure they see how few really teach or practice biblical repentance.

*Implications of baptism:* Ask about the doctrine of "praying Jesus into your heart." Although the Bible never specifically says that someone must understand all the implications in order for baptism to be valid, people who have never followed through intellectually on the implications of the gospel will probably struggle, and are more likely to leave the Lord.

*Purpose and mission:* They should understand that while their purpose is to have a relationship with God and go to heaven, their mission is to seek the lost and to help the needy. Evangelism is for every Christian. Make sure they understand persecution is the inevitable result of preaching repentance (Acts 26:21; Luke 6:22–23; 2 Timothy 3:12). If the person about to be baptized hasn't done much evangelism or feels apprehensive, be encouraging. Share how it was difficult for you at first, and how the Lord strengthened you. Explain that God gives us all time to grow, and more is expected of "older" Christians.

*New Testament church:* Explain that we must attend only a church that follows the Bible. This means a church whose mission is to bring salvation to the world, a church that teaches salvation as proclaimed in the New Testament, and a church that teaches repentance.

*Attending church:* Make sure they know what the regular meetings of the church are. If your church leaders expect members to attend additional meetings (retreats, harvests, devotionals, etc.), tell them so. (This usually means a few extra days a month.) Talk about arriving punctually—really wanting to be at the meetings. (We get out what we put in.) Emphasize the need to be devoted to the "fellowship" (Acts 2:42), not rush off as soon as services are over. Christians who miss meetings tend to do poorly spiritually, and most of those who quit church have had a pattern of missing meetings. Make sure they see that the church is God's plan for Christians to stay strong, grow spiritually and joyfully fulfill God's purpose for their lives.

*Dating and marriage:* Since we can marry only followers of Christ (1 Corinthians 7:39), it stands to reason that we should date only disciples. The term "believers" in the New Testament always refers to true Christians, not persons with a nebulous, vague faith. A believer is a disciple of Christ. Dating non-Christians messes up our motives and theirs, and is extremely unwise. Since this is one of the areas in which the world has destroyed lives the most, we must be open to lots of input. God must be the center of our marriages. (See the follow-up study on Christian Marriage in chapter 16.)

*Giving:* All Christians are expected to support the work of the church (salaries)—Matthew 10:10; 1 Corinthians 9:14; Philippians 4:14–19. This is nothing to apologize for, so be sure to mention it. All Christians are also expected to give to the poor (Mark 14:7; Matthew 6:2; 1 Corinthians 16:1–2; 2 Corinthians 8–9). Proverbs 3:9 tells us to honor the Lord with our money. The money is God's; we are only stewards, and should manage the Lord's money well. Many people you study with have been undisciplined in their budgeting and spending; you will need to teach financial responsibility.

*One-another relationships:* Make sure they have one-another relationships, and there is someone who will be "showing them the ropes," especially during his or her first couple of years in Christ. Explain that there are follow-up studies you will want to do over the next few months. Stress the need to be open to advice.

*Taking a stand with family and friends:* Do they understand where their family members stand before God? Are they ready, like Cornelius, to reach out to them? (Acts 10:24). Are they willing to firmly (and lovingly) take a stand, share their faith with them, and hold to their conviction? Ask them how they would react if family opposed their decision for Christ. In the case of university or college students still officially living at home or receiving support from their parents, it is wise to make sure they have already communicated with their parents and know how the family feels about the decision. For minors, hesitate to baptize them if parents are opposed.

*Sacrifice and service:* Jesus left us an example of service (John 13). Service takes time, is humbling and often goes unnoticed (Luke 17:7–10). Are we willing to be servants? There are many opportunities for service, like (a) serving older members, including those with families; (b) volunteering for work parties as needs arise around the church; and (c) helping with the children's ministry, ushering, or whatever other duty we may be asked to assist in. It is commendable to look for opportunities to serve—even when we have not been asked. Emphasize the importance of coming to church ready to give (Acts 20:35).

*Lifelong decision:* Explain that it would be better not to be baptized than to take the step and then fall from grace (2 Peter 2:20–22). We "put the hand to the plow" for life. Explain that the confession made at baptism "Jesus is Lord" means just that!

Pray for wisdom so that you may effectively "count the cost." Again, this is just a rough guide to help you cover most areas. You will find some people with special backgrounds and problems, and for them Jesus becoming Lord will entail other issues not listed above.

**How Many Studies Should I Have?**

That depends on who you are and where you are in life. If you are a mother of two small children, then probably one, or two if you have Herculean strength. If you are a working man with family responsibilities, you may also be limited to one or two studies with your friends. An undergraduate student will probably find the time for two or three ongoing studies through most of the academic year. Graduate students differ enormously in regard to their available time. When I was studying theology, I often had five or more studies going at any one time. A close brother of mine was doing doctoral work in biochemistry and was in the lab eighty hours a week. I was constantly challenged as he insisted on maintaining at least one study at all times and consistently led people to the Lord.

I generally establish a pool of relationships, investing time and prayer in them all. Some people I meet on airplanes. Others I meet in the neighborhood, or in the gym, or through friends or family. When I am reaching out to a number of men, there are plenty of people to study with.

"I don't have time to share my faith" is perhaps the most glaring admission that we are not seeking his kingdom—that our priorities are completely out of line. If you are too busy to seek the lost and lead them to Jesus, it's not time that you need, but forgiveness! Jesus described it as "desires for other things"

(Mark 4:19) that choke our relationship with God. The question is not "Can I study with people?" but rather "How may I make the best use of the time the Lord has given me as I strive to have an impact on others?"

Guidelines are guidelines, and ultimately only you can make that decision as to how to share your faith. Before deciding, however, you would do well to arm yourself with a deep love for the lost, a sacrificial attitude, and a realistic appraisal of how much time you have. The number of studies you can "carry" at any one time can and will change.

### When Is It Best Not to Study?

When do you become a "Bible basher"? When is the double-edged sword more lethal than life-giving? It is when you become more concerned about getting through your teaching material than you are about getting through to the person's heart. There are times when the best thing you can do is say, "Let's not study today; let's just play some backgammon / go for a walk / have an ice cream..." This may especially be the case if every time you meet with your friend it is only for a "religious discussion." Have people into your home. Hospitality—sharing your life—is an integral part of evangelism in the New Testament. As the old saying goes, "People don't care how much you know until they know how much you care."

Oftentimes people simply need to know you can empathize with what they are feeling. Christian workers tend toward one of two extremes. They love either to have fun and hate the challenge of Bible study, or they love the "turn or burn" passages and see relaxation as a waste of God's valuable time, as the earth teeters on the brink of damnation. We must remind ourselves to strike the proper balance. When people feel burdened they need the most support and encouragement. Some of the things that cause people to be burdened are (1) negative reactions from family or friends, (2) feeling overwhelmed about repentance, (3) emotionally battling the implications of conversion, and (4) fear of not measuring up as a Christian. These are some of the most common obstacles people face, and we must be there to help them through.

## Answering Questions

Questions inevitably arise in the course of studying the Bible with another person. In fact, be a little suspicious of those who have no questions, who agree with everything you say. Anyone who interacts and wrestles with the Scriptures will be confused, puzzled, or even shaken by certain aspects of the Bible. The following are seven ways in which Jesus responded to questions:

- With an assignment (Matthew 9:13). Sometimes he gave his questioners "homework." Often the true answer to a question can only be grasped through personal involvement with the subject.
- With illustrations (Matthew 9:14ff). Here the Lord provided a series of great illustrations for his hearers to take away and think over.
- With Scripture (Matthew 12:3). Having a ready recollection of God's word (both testaments) will enable you to defend the truth, refute error and proclaim the good news.
- With a question in return (Matthew 19:17, 21:25). Questions, "hitting the ball back into their court," make them think!
- With a well-reasoned argument (Matthew 22:41–26). Here Jesus reasons from premises to (implied) conclusion using logic, a familiar but misunderstood Old Testament passage, and the presuppositions of his hearers. (In this case, the conclusion is inescapable: the physical descendant of David is divine!)
- With silence (Matthew 26:63). Sometimes there is nothing to be profited by answering, at least for the moment.
- With a moral challenge (John 8:9). Jesus answered their question in a way that sent them away thinking profoundly on the condition of their own souls.
- As always, with gentleness and respect! (See 2 Timothy 2:14, 23–26 and 1 Peter 3:15).

## Conclusion: The Key to Effectiveness

What is the key to evangelistic effectiveness? It isn't your style. It's not your perception. It isn't even your Bible knowledge. It's God working in the hearts of the men and women you are studying with (1 Corinthians 3:16). We are God's coworkers, but God makes it grow!

Prayer is the secret. Pray for wisdom for yourself (James 1:5) so that you may know how best to meet their needs. Pray for open hearts, because all the good logic in the world will not reach a single hard heart. We must become the best waterers and planters that we possibly can. But we must never forget the simple fact that God makes it grow. This realization is the secret to a joyful, productive life evangelistically.

## Notes

[1]As Edward Stillingfleet, Dean of St Paul's London, eloquently put it in 1659, "It would be strange indeed the Church should require more than Christ himself did, or make other conditions of her communion than our Savior did of discipleship... Without all controversy, the main inlet of all the distractions, confusion, and divisions of the Christian world hath been the adding of other conditions of Church-communion than Christ hath done."

[2] Acts 20:27, RSV. At Miletus Paul reminded them that he had shared with them everything they needed to know—but over a period of several years, not in "one shot"!

[3] Incidentally, since the Jewish counting system regularly numbers men only, it is a fair assumption that the three thousand were men only, as in Acts 4:4. This is not to say that women were not baptized on the first day of the church, only that the usual method of counting, in both testaments, was to focus on the men.

# 11
# Guard the Gospel
## *Series A*

*Guard the Gospel*[1] is a collection of personal Bible studies you can use to instruct your non-Christian friends. The lessons are also suitable for sharing with believers. This collection has been designed with three aims in mind:

- To provide a set of teaching materials for conveying the gospel to non-Christians.
- To instruct the young disciple in how effectively to teach the gospel to others.
- To confirm young Christians in their faith by reviewing the basic doctrines of Christianity. The series more or less follows the course of study they may have been taught when they became Christians.

The basic idea of the gospel message is easy enough to grasp, but it isn't always easy to teach the Scriptures to others. A sense of natural progression through the studies and the diplomatic touch take time for the young Christian to learn. In fact, aren't these areas in which even the most experienced disciple stands to learn a good deal?

Doubtless, through experience gained in bringing others to Christ, you will perfect your own method. That is good. These studies are intended only as *model* studies, and new believers, less skilled in effectively teaching the Bible, appreciate a working model. Later on they can branch out and retool the studies in accordance with their own personalities, preferences, and insights. This series has eleven units:

**Jesus I**
**Seeking God**
**The Word of God I**
**Discipleship I**
**Serving the Poor**
**Sin I**
**The Cross**
**Repentance I**
**Baptism I**
**False Doctrines about Conversion**
**The Church**

Note: the Roman numerals following some of the titles do not mean the study is somehow incomplete without a "Part II." They indicate only that there are further studies available in Series B and C.

Scriptures for suggested memorization are given with each study. Scripture memory is one of the most useful things we can do to put the word of Christ into our lives (Colossians 3:16). And yet it is not just for young Christians! Memorization is helpful for all Christians. (The clearest passage recommending Scripture memory is probably Proverbs 22:18.)

A number of "tips" follow each study. This material fleshes out the study "skeletons" at the head of the unit. Some passages ("extra passages") are not found in the box but may prove useful, and are provided to increase the scriptural information at your fingertips. (The study could be shared using *only* the verses and points in the box.)

---

## 1
## Jesus I: Jesus the Only Way

Who was Jesus? What was he like? What did he say? Most people today do not know the answers to such simple questions as these, because they have not been taught from the Bible. The impression they have of the Son of God is a sketchy and distorted one. The following study, taken from John and Hebrews, will blow away the fog and reveal the truth about Christ.

| | |
|---|---|
| • John 1:14 | God became man in Jesus (the incarnation). Jesus is God in nature. |
| • John 6:35 | Jesus is the bread of life. |
| • John 8:12 | Jesus is the light of the world. |
| • John 14:6 | Jesus is the only way to the Father. |
| • Hebrews 4:15 | Jesus was also human, tempted as we are, qualified to relate to us. |

### Tips

**John 1:14**—Tie this verse in with 1:1 to show that Jesus is God!

*John 2:3–17—Extra passage. Clearing the temple, Jesus shows us the burning passion for the righteousness of God that we should have. (See Psalm 69 to understand the reaction of the early disciples to Jesus' conviction.) Do you have this level of conviction about the Lord?*

*John 3:1–10—Extra passage. Jesus teaches the teachers!*

**John 6:35**—Jesus was not just a teacher of truth; he pointed to himself as the source of spiritual nourishment. Could any other man make those claims about himself? (This is one of the "I Am" statements.)

**John 8:12**—Jesus is light. Jesus taught truth from God so that we can see the way we should go. In the world there is disagreement about basic moral questions, and it is unfashionable to take a strong stand. Without Jesus we are truly in the dark.

*John 11:2—Extra passage. Jesus promises eternal life to his followers, because it is his to give. Later, his resurrection proved this to be no empty claim.*

**John 14:6**—Jesus is "exclusive." This makes sense, because the only way *to* God is *through* God—through Jesus. But don't all paths lead to God? No! Why would God want to confuse us with a tangle of different, convicting and contradictory "ways"? (P.S.: No *other* founder of a major world religion ever made such claims.)

*Luke 4:1–13—Extra passage. Jesus was tempted. We imagine Jesus to be a superman, invulnerable and gliding through life with perfect ease. But Jesus was tempted like us: desires of the flesh (4:3–4), materialism (4:5–7), pride (4:8–12). This was not a one-time temptation for the whole of Jesus' life (v.13). He lived a life of struggle with Satan (Hebrews 5:7).*

*Hebrews 4:15–16—Jesus is a sympathetic savior. Jesus understands our problems, because he both faced and overcame them all.*

*Hebrews 2:17–18—Extra passage. Having suffered all that we suffer, Jesus is merciful. He not only understands, but also helps us.*

*Hebrews 1:3—Extra passage. This passage sums up all we have learned about Jesus: he really is the "exact representation" of God's being.*

---

## 2
## Seeking God

This is a useful first study. In doing this study, you are essentially asking people if they are open to a change in their lives: to putting God first. A person's reaction to this study reflects their (current) openness to God. (You will probably want to skip this study in the case of someone who is already seeking.)

- Matthew 7:7 — Seek and you will find.
- Matthew 7:13–14 — The way is narrow, and only a few are seeking.
- Matthew 6:33 — The only effective way to seek is to seek God first.
- Acts 8:35 — Let another person help you understand the Bible.
- Acts 17:11 — Do your homework!

### Tips

**Matthew 7:7**—This is a great promise. God is a loving father, and he wants you to find him!

**Matthew 7:13–14**—If only a few *find* the way to eternal life, then only a few are truly seeking. How should we seek, then?

**Matthew 6:33**—Ask what sorts of things keep us from making this our top priority. (Friends, family, social life, job, studies, worry.) Now let's look at some good examples of people seeking God.

**Acts 8:26–40**—the Ethiopian is an example of someone "seeking first."

- Important man, great responsibilites, busy, yet still made time for God (Jerusalem trip).
- Seeking in the right place (Scripture).
- Was humble (asks for help).
- When he finds, he does not continue to "seek." It is time to act. It has been said, "When a sincere seeker finds what he has been looking for, either he stops seeking or he stops being sincere."
- He is a truly happy person afterward; he has come to know God.

**Acts 17:11–12**—the Bereans are another example of people "seeking first."

- Noble character—integrity.
- Enthusiastic.
- Seeking in the right place (the Scriptures).
- Read daily until they discover the truth.
- Not naïve (healthy skepticism).
- Respond to the truth and become believers.

*Matthew 13:44–46—Extra passage. Man in field stumbles across treasure. (Most of us are like him—not actively seeking truth). Three results: joy (the result of finding); sold everything (commitment); obtained the treasure (as always happens when people seek first). Merchant looking for fine pearls. (Some of us are like him—actively seeking the truth). Similar results.*

*Conclusion*

Close with an invitation to regular Bible study, encouragement to study the Bible daily, and the challenge to start attending church regularly.

---

## 3
## The Word of God I

This study is absolutely foundational. Anyone who truly accepts it has an excellent chance of becoming a Christian. Aim: to establish confidence in the Bible as the perfect and authoritative word of God, and to create an obedient spirit.

| | |
|---|---|
| • Hebrews 4:12–13 | Relevant (living) and active (dynamic). Surgery and pain. |
| • 1 Tim 4:16 | Life and doctrine both important. Then why are there so many opinions? |
| • 2 Tim 3:16–17 | Everyone will not accept the Bible and apply it. |
| • John 12:47–48 | Rejecting the Word = rejecting Jesus and salvation. |
| • Acts 17:10–11 | Right response: Read Enthusiastically, Asking questions Daily |

## Tips

**Hebrews 4:12–13**—The Word penetrates like a sword. Studying the Word is penetrating; like the penetration of any sharp instrument. This means that at times it may "hurt." Don't shy away from the challenges.

**1 Timothy 4:16**—Life and doctrine are important. Ask, "Why have people come up with so many interpretations?" Consider some of the reasons (no need to read every passage below, but you may want to write them down for your friend):

- Ignorance of the Word—Matthew 22:29; Hosea 4:6
- Personality cults—1 Corinthians 1:12; Acts 20:30
- Twisting Scriptures—2 Peter 3:16; Genesis 3:1
- Personal convenience—2 Timothy 4:3; Isaiah 30:10–11
- Human traditions—Mark 7:6–9; Colossians 2:8
- Additions to the Word—Proverbs 30:6; Revelation 22:18
- Unwillingness to obey—John 8:31–32; John 7:17

*Then ask whose fault it is that there are so many differing interpretations—God's or humans'? The word of God can be understood, and agreement can certainly be reached on the fundamentals of the faith.*

*Extra point if your friend is biblically literate: sound (healthy) doctrine (teaching) is teaching that makes us healthy spiritually. What makes us unhealthy? As with our diet, we won't be at our best when we consume lots of junk food and sugary drinks. Common unsound teachings and doctrinal systems (all of which are addressed later in this book):*

- *Signs & Wonders (fascination with miracles)*
- *Health & Wealth (prosperity theology)*
- *Fear & Fascination (end-times speculation)*
- *Messianic Judaism (a modern Christian movement that contradicts Paul's teaching in Galatians)*
- *Faith Alone (a Protestant overreaction to Catholicism)*

**2 Timothy 3:16–17**—The Word is both inspired and useful.[2] The following acronym provides even more reasons why people have departed from the Word and exited the narrow road: E̲asy way (2 Timothy 4:2–3; Isaiah 30:10–11; John 8:31–32), e**X̲**tra teachings (Proverbs 30:6; Deuteronomy 4:2, 12:32, 1 Corinthians 4:6; Revelation 22:18–19), I̲gnorance (Matthew 22:29; Hosea 4:6; Isaiah 1:2; 2 Timothy 2:15), T̲raditions (Matthew 15:6–9; Mark 7:6–9).

**John 12:48**—Remember taking exams? What if the examiner handed out the test early for all the candidates to study? Would you read it? Would there be any excuse for failure? Emphasize God's generosity and fairness in revealing the standard for judgment.

*Conclusion:*

**Acts 17:11**—For those approaching the Bible for the first time. The Bereans were eager to learn, and they trusted the Scriptures, not just Paul. Do you have such a noble character? Challenges:

- **R**ead every day (suggest what to read: the gospel of John, for example).
- Do so **E**nthusiastically.
- **A**sk questions; don't just believe what anybody tells you! (healthy skepticism).
- Study that Bible **D**aily. Make the Scriptures your foundation.

*2 Timothy 2:15— Extra passage. For those already studying the Bible and excited about it. Are you lazy in your Bible study? God says, "Do your best!" God wants skilled, reliable workmen. Time to step up your Bible study!*

---

## 4
## Discipleship I

Discipleship may come earlier or later in a study series, depending on the person. For someone from a Bible-oriented background, it will often be one of the earlier studies; for a less active person, wait until faith and commitment have grown. Try not to come on too strong, too soon. Tiptoeing around the pride of someone claiming to be "born-again" but lacking the attitude of Christ is the opposite error.

Discuss evangelism with your non-Christian friends as soon as they are able to understand it. It is only fair to bring up the subject, since evangelism will characterize their Christian lives when they make the all-important decision to follow Jesus Christ (Mark 1:38; Luke 19:10). Another reason to bring it up is that people are looking for mission in their lives, something to which they can fully and unreservedly devote themselves.

The study on discipleship can be used at different stages in a course of studies, according to the needs of each individual:

- Early on, with religious but uncommitted people.
- Early on, with committed people who need the challenge.
- With people who are progressing, but don't show keenness.
- As a wrap-up for everything else for less religious people.

| | |
|---|---|
| • Acts 11:26c | A disciple is a follower of Jesus. |
| • Mark 1:17 | Jesus came to save souls. |
| • Matt 28:19–20 | Chain reaction: disciples making disciples making disciples = church! |
| • Luke 9:23 | Self-denial at the heart of discipleship. Willing to push yourself? |
| • Luke 14:33 | Count the cost: our closest relationships, total surrender... |

## Tips

*The Call to Discipleship:*

**Acts 11:26c**—The word "disciple(s)" occurs over 200 times in the New Testament, whereas the word "Christian(s)" occurs only three times. The religious world prefers the "easier" term, doesn't it?[3] And yet in the Bible there is no double standard![4] There are numerous terms for a follower of Christ in the New Testament (disciple, believer, friend, brother, Christian, saint).

**Mark 1:16–20**—"Follow me" means Jesus came to save souls (Mark 1:38), and as we follow Christ we learn to save souls. Evangelism was for the apostles, but is it for every disciple today?

**Matthew 28:18–20**—the Great Commission

- Baptism for those who want to be disciples.[5]
- "Obey everything" implies teaching them to obey the "Great Commission" = Chain reaction!
- This collective of people is the church.
- "I am with you always"—in the Great Commission. (Otherwise, is he with us? See 2 Chronicles 15:2.)

*The Result of Discipleship*

The result of effective discipleship is seen in the explosive growth of the New Testament church. *Extra passages:* Acts 2:42, 47, 4:4, 5:14, 6:1,7, 9:31,42, 11:21, 24, 26, 12:24, 13:49, 14:1, 21, 16:5, 17:4, 12, 18:8, 10,19:10, 18–20, 26, 21:20. This is what happens when the church obeys the Great Commission. Stress that this picture of the church is *normal,* not exceptional or ideal. (Skimming through all these passages need not take too long, and is impacting and convincing. Alternatively, study Acts 8:1–4 and select just a few from the list.)

*The Cost of Discipleship*

**Luke 9:23–26**—Some things that may need to be sacrificed through the cross: independent spirit, self-indulgence and softness, impulses and feelings, overeating, sleep, etc. If we're ashamed to share about Jesus, he will be ashamed of us at the judgment. This is a matter of *salvation.* (End with a focus on verse 24.)

*Luke 9:57–62—Extra passage. Must understand cost, priorities (9:57–58); God comes first! (9:59–60); don't look back (9:61–62).*

**Luke 14:25–33**—"Total unconditional surrender"! If necessary, explain what it means to "hate" your family. The best clarification of 14:26 is 16:13. (Matthew 10:37, which is similar, has a different emphasis.)

*Concluding Challenges*

- Decide to put the Lord first in your life.
- Give the person you are studying with some evangelistic invitation cards.

- Make a list of whom to invite: friends, family, workmates, etc.
- Start evangelizing!

**Further Perspectives**

It is common for people who have not shared their faith before to feel that for them it is impossible. An encouraging study to overcome this is "Discipleship II: Excuses and Fear" (chapter 12).
Making the Discipleship study convicting:

- Be firm that there is no "double standard" in Christianity.
- Share about your own progress in evangelism—overcoming timidity, learning how to start conversations, the reward of knowing you have done the right thing, and especially of seeing your friends come to Christ.
- Share about your own congregation and its aims in evangelism. If your church is not growing, share your vision for how you would like it to change.

---

# 5
# Serving the Poor

Just as disciples of Christ are called to spread the word—to seek and save the lost—so we are also called to seek and serve the poor. Both are part of what it means to follow Christ. Some Christians know this and in fact live such a life. But all too often the world dictates our priorities; serving the poor becomes an afterthought. Or maybe it becomes something we "outsource." That is, though willing to donate money to worthy causes, we are not *personally* involved with the poor. In the same way, some people in the first century preferred to donate "in the name of" their parents, rather than actually take care of them in their old age (Matthew 15:3–6; Mark 7:5–13). How unlike Jesus this is. He interacted regularly with persons in all strata of society. In fact, he sought them out.

The study series in its present form has been used to help people become Christians for some forty years. We have occasionally emphasized the twofold mission (see, for example, pages 21 and 96). And yet never has there been a *single* study on the biblical imperative to serve the poor. We feel this is a glaring omission. It is difficult to see how one can claim to be a disciple while ignoring the hundreds of verses that deal with meeting physical needs, being generous, resisting one's own materialism, and helping the needy.

Once again, our mission as disciples is twofold: to preach the good news and to help the poor. Matthew 28 does not trump Matthew 25. The good news is more than just a formula about how to be saved. It is good news for the whole person. For God himself cares deeply about our "*whole* spirit, soul, and body" (1 Thessalonians 5:23).

In the early church, it should be noted, assistance to the poor was normally rendered within the church family. The "least of these brothers and sisters of mine" in Matthew 25:40 was usually interpreted to mean Christians, not outsiders. See also Galatians 6:10. This is not to say it is wrong to help outsiders, only to restore the New Testament emphasis. And when the church takes care of its own, the gospel is greatly enhanced; outsiders are attracted and want to be insiders. See also Acts 2:44–45, 4:32–37, 6:1–7.

The purposes of this study: (1) to highlight the biblical imperative to serve the poor; (2) to confront excuses that tend to isolate us from the needy; (3) to illustrate how such service is part of what it means to follow Christ.

| | |
|---|---|
| • Psalm 82:3–4 | Help the weak and the needy. |
| • 2 Cor. 8:9 | Jesus sacrificed position and status, connecting with the poor. |
| • Luke 10:29 | No excuses; anyone is potentially a "neighbor." |
| • James 1:27 | This is the religion that is acceptable to God. |
| • Galatians 2:10 | We ought to be *eager* to remember the poor. |

## Tips

**Psalm 82:3–4**—So many passages in the Old Testament urge God's people to compassion and action on behalf of the poor. See, for example, Isaiah 58. God's people are called to care because God cares (Exodus 34:6; Psalm 113, etc.). In Psalm 82 defending the needy is commended. But is this just an Old Testament teaching?

**2 Corinthians 8:9**—God's care is exemplified above all in the incarnation of Christ. That is, God became flesh—a human being—in Jesus Christ. He sacrificed position and status, connecting with the poor. In Jesus' lifestyle he reached out to people of every social stratum. In him there was no favoritism (James 2:1–13), nor should there be among his followers. Interestingly, this passage lies at the heart of Paul's exhortation to the Corinthians to have a heart for the poor—in this case, needy Christians in Judea. Caring for the poor is not only *Old* Testament doctrine, but a thoroughly *biblical* teaching.

**Luke 10:29**—Many know that they *should* love others. Both testaments teach we should love God first, our neighbor second. And yet we can redefine "neighbor" to the point that we're scarcely involved with the needy. Jesus challenged such thinking in the parable that follows: the Good Samaritan. As happens so often in the Bible, it is not the "insider" who "gets it." It is the outsider, which is why Jesus told the parable. The truth is, there are no valid excuses. Anyone is potentially a "neighbor."

**James 1:27**—Not all humans are equally needy. In Scripture there is a special place for the hurting—those who have suffered significant loss. Such persons include orphans, widows, foreigners and the oppressed. Our religion is unacceptable to God if we do not share this concern.

**Galatians 2:10**—The Apostle Paul is known as a powerful evangelist, taking the good news where it had never been proclaimed before and establishing communities of believers. And yet, like Jesus, he had a passion to change the world: to preach the gospel and to help the poor.

*Further passages on poverty and materialism:*

**Psalm 39**—Chasing riches is a vain pursuit. Don't be lured by the materialistic message of the world.

**Proverbs 19:17**—One of many passages noting that the Lord blesses those who remember the needy.

**Ezekiel 16:48–49**—Materialism numbs our social conscience and blinds us to the needs of others around us.

**Matthew 10:8b**—Since we have *received* freely, we ought also to *give* freely.

**1 Timothy 6:17–18**—While it is not necessarily wrong to be rich, those with wealth must be generous, not stingy. After all, Jesus said it is hard for someone who is rich to enter the kingdom of heaven (Matthew 19:23). To be balanced, however, all of us are called to share what we have, not just the rich (Acts 2:44–45, 4:32). Selfishness and materialism are not only a disease of the rich. They also affect the middle class, and even the needy themselves.

**Hebrews 13:5**—When we keep our lives free from the love of money, we will be in a much stronger position to be a source of spiritual and physical blessing to others.

*Some areas in which we can serve:*

Feed the hungry; visit prisoners; clothe the naked; adopt a child; encourage the aged; sell possessions and give to the poor; visit a country in the developing world; take your children with you on such a visit; assist in disaster relief; invite the poor into your home; fast and pray for the needy; comfort widows; provide medical care to the poor; reach out to refugees; etc.

*Concluding questions*

- Do you think the Lord is pleased with us when we always serve the poor at a distance? To what extent can giving money to a good cause substitute for active involvement?

- Do you agree with the statement, "People don't care how much you know until they know how much you care"?

- When was the last time you had a disadvantaged person into your home? Or ate in a poor person's home?

- Are you ready to study out what the Bible says about this essential topic? Be sure to read Luke and Acts, as poverty and possessions is one of the major themes of these books. See also Proverbs, as well as the prophets.

- Are there lifestyle changes you need to make as a result of this study?

*Note:*
In some of the ministries I have visited, people are not accepted as church members if they are unwilling to help the needy—to personally serve the poor. (Even poor members are expected to actively serve others.) Such outreach is not exclusively for evangelistic motives. Christians serve the poor whether or not this leads to their conversion. Few congregations, however, have such high expectations. If you have a conviction about these matters, please speak up. But first, study the Scriptures, come to your own convictions, and pray.

When loving the poor is part of our evangelism, our church life and our personal lifestyles, then the gospel message, lived out in the disciples of Jesus Christ, will make more sense to the watching world. It will be the good news today just as it was after the birth of Christianity.

---

## 6
## Sin I

The Sin study is a highly personal discussion. Most men and women will be much more open if this is a one-on-one as opposed to a two-on-one study. Everyone has sinned, and without specific conviction and specific repentance, there can be no conversion. The human tendency to rationalize and blame-shift must be confronted in love.

By the time you study sin with someone, you should have built up a good relationship—essential at this stage, because many of the things covered in the Sin study are challenging and personal.

It is tempting to go to one of two extremes when doing the sin study: too severe, or too soft! It needs to be convicting (John 16:8), but it mustn't become an interrogation session! (1 Peter 3:15). Don't say, "I'd better challenge their socks off, just to make sure." On the other hand, we must be careful that in our efforts to be diplomatic and considerate we do not tread too lightly, afraid to offend. God is not pleased with those who are soft on sin (Jeremiah 6:14). The right balance takes a lot of practice. If you are dealing with a person whose faith needs building up before making their decision, or with someone who likes the church but is not eager to change, a premature study of this subject could turn them off completely, or encourage them to rush into baptism without the faith and repentance to make the decision solid and lasting. The aims of the Sin study are to help people to:

- See themselves as God sees them: sinful.
- Realize they need forgiveness.
- Identify sins specifically, to enable them to repent.

| | |
|---|---|
| • Romans 3:23 | All have sinned, fallen short. |
| • Mark 7:21–22 | Jesus got specific about sin! |
| • Gal 5:19–21 | Sinful acts are obvious! |
| • James 4:17 | Making plans without considering God is sin. |
| • Isaiah 59:2 | Sin separates us from God. |

## Tips

**Romans 3:23**—Everyone has sinned and fallen short. Analogy: leaping across the Grand Canyon—even the best Olympic jumper, though certainly jumping farther than me, still falls woefully short! In other words, no one is good enough to make it to heaven on their own. Most people are willing to admit that they have sinned. This verse provides a palatable introduction to a potentially confrontational study. Ask them what they think sin is. Possible answers: breaking God's law (1 John 3:4), not doing what you know you ought to do (James 4:17).

**Mark 7:21–22**—We are responsible for our sin. It comes from our own hearts. Upbringing, environment, genes, and social pressure may all play a part in influencing us to do wrong, but ultimately the decision is ours. Go through the specific sins. Define terms where necessary. Discuss in detail such sins as sexual immorality (adultery, premarital sex, homosexuality, incest, lust, pornography, abortion, child abuse...), greed (materialism, selfishness), malice (grudges, refusal to forgive), deceit (lies, deceptiveness, poor work ethics), lewdness (language, dress, inappropriate entertainment), envy, slander, etc.

**Galatians 5:19–21**—Be as specific here as you need to be![6] Sinful deeds are obvious. You don't need a PhD in psychology to identify sin. Cover such specifics as debauchery, hatred, fits of rage, selfish ambition, and drunkenness. When going through a list, do not feel compelled to go into detail for each item. Tailor the scriptures to the individual. Define "entering the kingdom of God" (going to heaven). "Those who live like this": how many of these sins do we have to be actively indulging in to disqualify ourselves for heaven? Answer: only one. Note: Sometimes it may be helpful to ask your friend to write a list of their sins, for their benefit. If he or she feels comfortable sharing it with you, that's great; if not, take care not to be invasive.

*Ephesians 5:3–7—Extra passage. "Not even a hint": not only the action that is being condemned, but even the very appearance of evil. How do you respond when an off-color joke is told? People will try to talk you out of such a black-and-white position (5:6), but God expects a radical break from the world (5:7).*

*2 Timothy 3:1–5—Extra passage (excellent for religious people). Notice all the "lovers": lovers of themselves, lovers of money, without love, not lovers of the good, lovers of pleasure, not lovers of God. Ask: What do you love? Food? Comfort? "Form of godliness": this refers to religious people.*

*Romans 6:23—Extra passage. Though God wants us to enjoy eternal life, the wages of sin is death; we get what we deserve.*

*Revelation 21:8—Extra passage. Hell is real. Cowardice and timidity are sin; lying and deceitfulness can cost us our salvation.*

**James 4:13–17**—"Sins of omission," not just "sins of commission."

**Isaiah 59:1–3a**—Sin separates us from God, putting us in darkness. We're guilty (3a); our hands are dripping with the blood of Jesus. God is not an impotent old man (arm too short = arthritis; ear too dull = hard of hearing). Draw a picture of a person separated from the light of God by sin, thus putting him or her in the darkness. Ask, "Which side of the wall do you think you are on? Would you be saved if you died tonight?" Or course the honest answer is, "I'm in the darkness—I'm lost." If the person says they think they are right with God, you may

- Challenge them directly, asking them what makes them sure,
- Hold off, in the case of a religious person who is fairly committed (and perhaps has even had a "conversion experience" and dealt with obvious sins) and convict them in the repentance study, or
- Reply candidly, "I doubt that very much" in the case of someone who is obviously involved in sin. Go back and explain from the verses you studied.

*Conclusion*

Clearly, the human race's greatest problem is *sin*; our greatest need is *forgiveness*. Sin is against God—it is personal—and so he must decide to forgive us. Soon we will study the first step in receiving the forgiveness of our sins: *repentance.*

---

## 7
## The Cross of Christ

Jesus said that once he was "lifted up" he would draw all people to himself (John 12:32). The power of the cross to transform someone's attitude and life should not be underestimated! The aim: to produce conviction and gratitude for God's saving us in Christ. Note: ask your friend to read Matthew 26–27 in advance.

The heart of our message is lost when we rely on our own human wisdom, make baptism the main issue (1 Corinthians 1:17–18), or fail to focus on the cross. As Christians we should be moved by Christ's death. Make sure you have conviction when leading the study, and don't be afraid to show your emotions.

| | |
|---|---|
| • Matt 26:39 | Jesus had a choice, and he chose to die for us. |
| • Matt 27:46 | We are "Barabbas"! |
| • 1 Peter 2:24 | "Die to sins, live for righteousness" is our response to the cross. |
| • Medical Account | Read the Medical Account (found in Chapter 15). |
| • Acts 2:36–37 | The cross cuts us to the heart, producing a readiness to obey God. |

## Tips

*Introduction*

Christ died for our sins. Analogies:

- Soldier: A soldier dives onto a grenade about to explode. In dying, he saves his fellow soldiers from certain death.
- Train: The little boy was playing on the railroad tracks, unbeknownst to his father. By the time the father noticed him, it was too late: he looked with horror as he saw two passenger trains speeding toward each other from different directions; they were on a collision course! The only way to prevent the collision was to redirect one of the trains off onto another track, where the boy was playing. The father had to act fast—it was only seconds before the collision, but he loved his son! What did he do? He threw the switch and saved the passengers, but in doing so he sacrificed his little boy's life. God threw the switch. It was the only way to save us. He watched his son die for our sins. Yet most of the world carries on along its selfish course, unaware and unappreciative of the sacrifice that God made for us.

Matthew's account (shorter version, Mark 15:16–39)

- 26:36–46: Jesus is dreading the cross—prays for the right attitude.
- 26:66–68: Beaten, mocked.
- 26:69–75: Denied. Have you ever denied Jesus? (Luke 9:23).
- 27:26: Flogged.
- 27:27–31: Mocked, crowned with thorns, spat upon, beaten.
- 27:32: Crucified.
- 27:46: Abandoned by God. He bore not only the punishment due us, but also the actual *guilt*. He was separated from God (Isaiah 59:2, 2 Corinthians 5:21).

**Matthew 26:36–46**—Jesus had a choice: "drink the cup" or not; he chose to die for us.

**Matthew 27:46 (27:11–50)**— Like Barabbas, we don't deserve to be set free. Jesus bore our guilt.

**Medical Account**—Become familiar with the Medical Account, which is found in chapter 15 of this book. If necessary, practice reading it aloud so that when you share it with your friends it will "flow." But keep in mind that the early church probably placed more emphasis on the resurrection than on the cross. (Examine the speeches in Acts and notice the relative emphasis.) They certainly didn't "camp" on the goriness of the abuse Christ suffered.

*Our personal response to the cross:*

**1 Peter 2:21–25**—*Galatians 2:20; 2 Corinthians 5:14–15—Extra verses.* Die to sins and live for righteousness! Share your own personal response (leader of the study).

*Conclusion*

**Acts 2:22–38**—*Romans 5:6—Extra Verse.* You are a sinner; you crucified Christ, you don't deserve salvation. The Cross always produces commitment in an open heart. How are you going to respond? How *should* you respond?

---

# 8
# Repentance I

This is the key study! Do it well and the baptism study will be a cinch. Cover it lightly and you may be in for a long uphill battle! The purpose of the study: to clarify real repentance, clear away fuzzy thinking, and create a willingness to put God first. (Don't go directly into a baptism study! The NT teaching on baptism is not intuitive. No one appreciates it without having first come to an understanding of repentance.)

The aim of the study is twofold: To teach the meaning of biblical repentance, and to make it clear whether the person you're studying with has repented. In order to achieve the second aim, the study focuses on five simple questions that can be posed from the scriptures.

- Luke 13:5 — Repent or perish (only two categories of people).
- Acts 26:20 — Repentance is a decision leading to a radical change of lifestyle.
- 2 Cor 7:10–11 — Worldly and godly sorrow.
- Matt 5:29 — Radical attitude.
- Acts 3:19 — Times of refreshing come. Repentance is a relief, not a burden!

## Tips

**Luke 13:1–5**—Good alternate passage: 2 Peter 3:8–12.

**Acts 26:19–21**—Repentance is a change of heart/mind. It is a *decision.* It is followed by deeds—one's life must reflect the change. It can be done in an instant, though the effects last a lifetime. Notice that opposition tends to come from religious people when repentance is preached (26:21).[7]

Question 1:
*Have you ever had a significant change in your behavior? A time when everyone said, "What's come over you? You're different"?*

**2 Corinthians 7:10–11**—Analogy: *Speeding.* The officer pulls you over. Worldly sorrow—you're sorry you got caught. Good chance you will speed again. Godly sorrow—you're sorry you have broken the law, endangered lives, etc. In both cases you are sorry, but repentance comes only with godly sorrow.

Second analogy: *Pregnancy*: Your girlfriend gets pregnant. Worldly sorrow: sorry about the consequences. Start to use contraceptives instead. May have an abortion. Godly sorrow: will never be immoral again.

Godly sorrow produces a visible change in one's character (earnestness, eagerness to clear self, indignation, alarm, etc.) Thus we can tell whether one has repented or not.

Question 2:
*Are you eager to do the will of God, or do you have to be coerced?*

**Matthew 5:29–30**—Radical attitude toward sin (negative side). Zeal to do the will of God (positive side). Ask: Do you think someone who has repented would study their Bible diligently? Attend the church services? Share their faith with others? Serve the poor?

World's attitude: sin is OK in moderation. God's attitude: sin is wrong—deal with it drastically! Do you have a radically repentant attitude about ____ (be specific)?

Question 3:
*Do you have God's attitude toward sin? A radical aversion?*

Question 4:
*Have you repented in accordance with what the Bible teaches?*
We are almost always looking for a "No" answer. If someone claims to have repented, ask when. "Yesterday," "a few weeks after I met you," or "just now" are more likely correct answers than "when I was six years old," or "long, long ago." Go back over the study again if you need to. Emphasize how narrow the road is. Be sure to ask, for there are few religious people who have repented. Ask some probing questions about their life and about the lives of any religious people they may look up to. (Why do they accept that person as a brother or sister if they have never repented and become a true disciple of Christ?)

Question 5:
*How many people do you know who have truly repented?*
If someone answers that most churchgoers have repented, they probably haven't a clue about what you have just taught them. If they think that most people back in their "old church" have repented, again they have probably missed the point. (After all, did they teach them to obey the Lord? Did they hold them accountable?) Back up until they get it right! Be sure to ask them about where they think their friends and family stand.

**Acts 3:19**—End the study positively!

*Additional comments on Repentance:*

- Often as Christians grow to understand God's will more fully, or are convicted of sin, there is a tendency to doubt one's initial repentance. Remember: repentance is a change of heart—a decision—and a deepening walk with God in no way implies that one's initial decision was defective.
- Although the percentage is extremely small, there are some non-Christians who have repented. Yet if someone isn't living as a

follower of Christ—they aren't evangelistic and devoted to God—the chances are he or she has never repented.

- Sincerity is not enough! A person needs a sense of sin, not Bible knowledge alone.
- Your friend will doubtless start making life changes even before becoming a Christian. Yet keep in mind the Holy Spirit. If he or she could become holy without the Spirit—through sheer human effort—then there would be no place for God. Expect that some of the big changes will take place in the years and decades *following* baptism.

---

# 9
# Baptism I

Purpose of the study: to explain how we receive forgiveness for sins and become Christians. *Not* a study for anyone reluctant to repent. Be wise; delay the study until God has prepared their hearts for it!

Sometimes it may be wiser to do a preliminary study before plunging in to the Baptism unit.[8] With a religious person, the study may need to take place twice.[9]

| | |
|---|---|
| • Ephesians 4:5 | Baptism is a basic Christian doctrine—and there's only one. |
| • Acts 2:38 | Repentance + baptism leads to forgiveness and the gift of the Holy Spirit. |
| • Romans 6:3–4 | Participation in Jesus' death, not just a parallel. |
| • 1 Peter 3:21 | Baptism is essential for salvation. |
| • Acts 22:16 | The Bible is clear.[10] What are you waiting for? |

**Ephesians 4:4–6**—The Bible identifies the basic, essential doctrinal areas. Baptism is not one of the peripheral items!

*Let's look at baptism in Acts, then in the letters, finally in the gospels. We find in Acts that baptism is how people were forgiven of their sins. Here we see people being saved (present tense).*

**Acts 2:36–39**—Already believed (2:37), but still not saved. Must repent first, then be baptized for the forgiveness of sins. "Every one of you," "for all whom God will call" means no exceptions!

*Acts 8:26–38—Extra passage (Ethiopian eunuch). The good news includes baptism (vv. 35-36). "Down into the water" implies more than sprinkling.*

*Acts 16:33—Extra passage (Philippian jailer). Belief alone insufficient (16:31): must hear the word (16:32). Baptized in the middle of the night.*

**Acts 22:16**—(The Apostle Paul). Came to faith on the Damascus road. Fasted, prayed, alone three days (Acts 9:9). "What are you waiting for?... Wash your sins away..." (Urgency, cleansing).

*Next we turn to the letters, which are all written to Christians—those who have already been baptized (past tense).*

**Romans 6:3–4**—"Baptized into Christ" means baptized into (participating in) Jesus' death. Buried with him through baptism (participation), raised (participation).[11] Jesus' death: blood of Christ (Ephesians 1:7). "New life" = being born again.

*Colossians 2:12—Extra passage. "Burial" (Romans 6:4)—baptism is immersion. Faith in power of God, who forgives us of our sins.*

**1 Peter 3:21**—Floodwater symbolizes baptism (not vice versa!) The Bible never calls baptism "symbolic." It is not just a bath; the spiritual signi cance of baptism must be grasped. It is an *appeal* (RSV, Greek) to God for a clear conscience.[12] It saves by the resurrection (Romans 6:4; Colossians 2:12).

*Finally we turn to the gospels, where Jesus spoke a few times of how people would be saved under the new covenant (future tense).*

*Matthew 28:19—Extra passage. Baptism involves discipleship.*

*Mark 16:16—Extra passage. Belief + baptism = salvation.*

*John 3:5—Extra passage. Born again of water and spirit.*

*Conclusion*

Recap what happens at baptism. Repentance must come first, then baptism. Analogy: must put film in (nondigital!) camera first, then take the shot. The result of obedience to God's plan: forgiveness of sins (a right relationship with God) and the Spirit, which helps us to live with and for the Lord.[13]

---

## 10
## False Doctrines about Conversion

Begin the session with a summary of the New Testament teaching on conversion:

- Hear the message — Romans 10:17; Acts 11:14
- Believe — John 3:16; Acts 16:31
- Repent — Luke 13:3; Acts 3:19
- Confess Jesus as Lord — Romans 10:9; 1 Timothy 6:12
- Be immersed — Acts 2:38; 1 Peter 3:21

| | |
|---|---|
| • Gal 1:6–9 | False doctrine (teaching) is destructive. No one can alter the gospel. |
| • Ezekiel 18:20 | "Original sin" is a false teaching. |
| • Heb 10:26 | "Once saved, always saved" is a false teaching. |
| • James 2:24 | Salvation by "faith alone" is a false teaching. |
| • Rev 3:20 | Salvation through the "sinner's prayer" is a false teaching. |

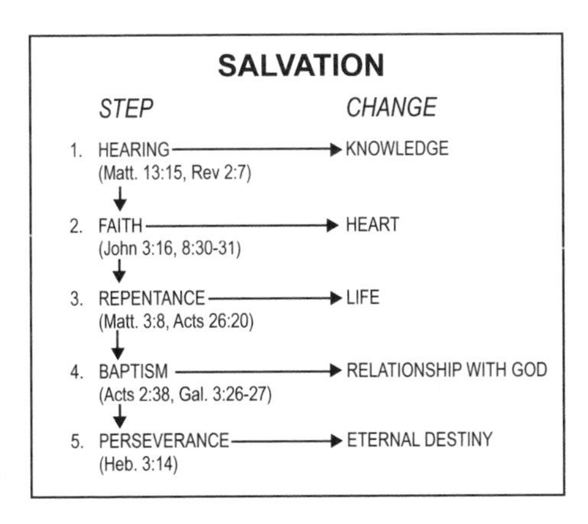


## Tips

**Galatians 1:6-10**—We need to take a stand, and not be "people-pleasers" (1:10). No one—religious leader, angel (see 1 Kings 13!), apostle—has the right to "update" the gospel!

**Ezekiel 18:20**—The false doctrine of infant baptism is refuted by this passage (guilt is nontransferable). Those who advocate infant baptism hold that baptism remits "original sin." Infant baptism is also refuted by Colossians 2:12 and Galatians 3:26–27 (personal, not proxy, faith is key in baptism). Moreover, it is impossible biblically to baptize babies because of the necessity of repentance. This false teaching was not officially endorsed by the Catholic Church until the early fifth century. The sister doctrine of "confirmation" is equally baseless.

**James 2:24**—The false doctrine of salvation by "faith alone" is explicitly refuted by this verse. John 3:16 shows faith as the basis of our entire response to the gospel. This must not be taken out of context. Consider all relevant passages. Refuted also by John 8:30–32; Hebrews 5:9; Romans 1:5, 16:26. For Protestants, "faith" has the general connotation of belief or mental assent; for Catholics, "faith" suggests works. Yet, as one modern theologian has suggested, the English word "allegiance" captures the impact of the Greek original.[14] Faith means faithful living.

**Revelation 3:20**—The false doctrine of "praying Jesus into your heart," or "accepting Christ," or "receiving Christ" was invented on the American frontier in the early nineteenth century! Examine this passage carefully, and its context! It is spoken to Christians, *already* saved (3:14, 22). "Be earnest and repent" means let Christ back into your life, not be converted initially. The passage mentions nothing about faith, confession, or baptism, as the readers are already converted.

*John 1:12—Extra passage. "Accepting" Christ is necessary for becoming a child of God (born again), but it is not sufficient. "Accepting" Christ biblically means accepting the words of Christ, receiving his message (12:48). Nowhere in the New Testament is there a record of anyone just saying a prayer and becoming a Christian!*

*Luke 23:39–43—Extra passage. The false doctrine of the thief on the cross: "The thief wasn't baptized, but Jesus said he would see him in paradise. What do you say to that?" Here's what you say to that:*

- *Mark 2:10: Jesus had authority during his earthly ministry to forgive sins.*
- *Romans 6:3–4: Baptism is a participation in Jesus' death, burial, and resurrection. The penitent thief could not have been baptized, as Jesus had not yet died.*
- *Hebrews 9:17: The new covenant (New Testament) was not yet in force, as Jesus hadn't yet died under the old covenant.*
- *Still, the passage does show God's willingness to save any and all, even at the "eleventh hour." God is good, and it is ultimately up to* him *(not* us*) to make exceptions.*

*Conclusion*

**Galatians 1:6–9** (once again)—A different gospel is no gospel. (See also 2 Corinthians 11:4.) Anyone preaching or following a different gospel is condemned. Doctrine does matter to the Lord! All these false teachings are condemned and condemning.

*1 Corinthians 15:1–2—Extra passage. We're saved by the gospel, and must firmly hold to it as it was taught by the apostles. Otherwise we believe in vain.*

---

## 11
## The Church

Aim: To encourage, inspire and teach God's plan for success as Christians. His plan is total commitment to the church, which is the body of Christ.[15]

| | |
|---|---|
| • Col 1:18 | Jesus is the true head of the body, or church,[16] which is his body. |
| • 1 Cor 12:21 | We're members of this body. We need the church; the church needs us. |
| • Heb 10:24–25 | Will avoid "swerving" if we spur others on and make the meetings of the church. |
| • Heb 3:12–13 | Daily encouragement prevents us from becoming hardened by sin. |
| • Acts 2:42 | Time capsule look at the early church. |

### Tips

**Colossians 1:18**—The church is not an institution, corporation, building or denomination, but the body of Christ. Not an *organization*, but an *organism.* As there is only one head, so there is only one body.

*Ephesians 2:19–20—Extra passage. The church is not a* building, *but is compared to one because God dwells in his people, the church. It is also a family (1 Timothy 3:15). As with a natural family, you must be born into it. At that time God becomes your father, and every other Christian your brother or sister. The church is the people of God. The church must base itself on the New Testament (NT apostles and NT prophets [Ephesians 3:5, 4:11]—i.e. their teachings) in order to have a claim to legitimacy. It is through obedience to his word that we submit to Christ.*

**1 Corinthians 12:12–27**—Analogy: church = human body. According to 12:13, we are baptized into the church.[17] According to 12:14, the church needs us, and we need the church. The goal (12:25) is that there be no division in the body, rather equal concern and love for one another.

*Romans 12:5—Extra passage. As in an earthly family, each member belongs to all the others. We're not our own! So surrender that independent spirit! We are interdependent, not independent (refusing direction) or dependent (refusing to take responsibility for our own decisions).*

**Hebrews 10:23–25**—To do well spiritually ("hold unswervingly"—analogy of car swerving all over the road) you need the church—this is God's plan. Attend all the meetings of the body you possibly can! Think in advance of how to meet the needs of other members of the body.

**Hebrews 3:12–14**—Personal involvement in one another's lives, lest sin cause anyone to forfeit salvation. We must persevere to the end (3:14). We are responsible for the spiritual welfare of our brothers and sisters in Christ. This entails openness (Ephesians 4:24), confession (James 5:16), counseling (Colossians 1:28), and daily encouragement (contact), as seen in many New Testament passages.

**Acts 2:42–47**—Ask, "What are the characteristics of a New Testament church?" (If people followed all these principles, what would the church be like?)

- Devotion to God's word, leading to a working knowledge of it.
- Devotion to the fellowship.
- Devotion to communion (See also Acts 20:7.)
- Devotion to prayer.
- A sense of awe and excitement!
- Generous with one another, both with money and hospitality.
- Growth of the body: not only spiritual, but also numerical. In the New Testament, this is the result of daily evangelism.

*Conclusion*

Urge your friend to keep coming to as many of the meetings as possible. Stress that we will do poorly spiritually if we do not take advantage of the opportunities to grow that God has given us in the church.

In the next two chapters we take this basic series two steps further.

## Notes

[1] In the 2000 version of this book, "Guard the Gospel" appeared in three series (Basic, Intermediate, and Advanced).

[2] Strictly speaking, this passage applies to the Old Testament Scriptures (see vv. 14–15), but by extension to the entirety of Scripture. For example, 1 Tim 5:18 quotes Luke 10:7 as Scripture. The point is that Paul's and the other inspired writers' view of Scripture was not limited to the Old Testament, but included New Testament writings as well.

[3] For example, consider the otherwise positive review of an International Church of Christ publication in *Pulpit Helps of Undivided Devotion* (May 1998): "The writing is very good, and the messages are biblically sound. Many of the writers frequently use denominational jargon such as the word 'disciple,' a term they use for Christian, or 'brother' or 'sister,' referring to a particular church member. Unless you are a member of this denomination, some of the terminology can get confusing." Christianity has lost sight of its founder when calling one another brothers and sisters and calling each other to be disciples is construed as jargon!

[4] The term "Christian" may have been, originally, a term made up by outsiders: Acts 11:26, 26:28; 1 Peter 4:16.

[5] Not to get hung up on semantics, we must still point out that, while one must certainly be willing to live as a disciple in order to be scripturally baptized, it is in one sense incorrect to speak of "baptizing disciples," insofar as baptism is only for the lost. Since we usually use the term *disciple* to refer to a true Christian, saying someone must be a disciple *before* baptism is illogical, as well as somewhat misleading.

John 4:1, at any rate, refers not to Christian conversion but to the pre-Christian baptism instituted by John the Baptist (though that term has specific denominational overtones, and "Baptizer" would be more accurate), and which (a) did not confer the Spirit, or (b) bring believers into a covenant with God. John's role (see Malachi 4:1–6) was to prepare the people for the coming of the Lord (Jesus), primarily through getting their relationships right with their fellow human beings.

[6] Other great passages: Ephesians 5:3–7: "Not even a hint." Not just the action, but the very appearance of evil is condemned. e.g., the club-party scene (1 Peter 4:4). In Revelation 21:8 we see that cowardice and lying are sin. (Not taking a stand, giving in to peer pressure...) 2 Timothy 3:2–5 chronicles the sins of religious people. Luke 18:9–14 is great for confronting self-righteousness. Finally, Romans 1:21–32 and 1 Corinthians 6:9–11 may prove helpful.

[7] Biblical repentance is not Catholic *penance* (something you do to atone for your sin), nor is it Protestant penitence (which stresses feelings of contrition over actions). Although true repentance involves feeling (see Psalm 51) and doing (Proverbs 28:13), it is not so much something you feel or do as it is a decision.

[8] A preliminary study on baptism, to get people ready:

a. Time perspectives in the New Testament (this explanation is useful for people who already have knowledge of the Bible):

- Gospels: look forward to conversion.
- Letters: look back at the Christian conversion.
- Acts: shows Christian conversion occurring in the present.

b. Two essential elements:

- Forgiveness: the Sin study shows that a person's iniquities separate them from God (recall the diagram showing the wall of sin). No relationship between God and a person can exist until sin is removed (Isaiah 59:1–2).

- The Spirit: a Christian is someone in whom the Spirit of God lives. No saved relationship between God and a person exists till the Spirit is given (Romans 8:9).

c. The Spirit. Receiving the indwelling of God's Holy Spirit cannot precede the forgiveness of sins (Habakkuk 1:13; Isaiah 59:1–2). Yet similarly, forgiveness comes through the spirit (Titus 3:5; 1 Peter 1:2). A contradiction? No. God forgives someone's sins and gives them the indwelling Holy Spirit simultaneously!

In the baptism study, rather than try to correct false doctrines, focus on the positive work the Spirit does in the life of a Christian.

[9] Be wise in studying conversion with a religious person. We have already warned against the premature study of baptism. Again, it is *essential* you study conversion only with people who are serious about their repentance. In Luke 3:7–9 we see John the Baptist turning away the self-righteous, insisting on "fruit in keeping with repentance" before anyone was baptized by him. When studying baptism with a *religious person,* you may want to split the material between two sessions. First study conversion from the book of Acts (Acts 2, 8, 16, 22). If for some reason your friend does not accept that baptism is essential for salvation, and especially if they think they don't need it themself, *do not* go on to the remaining passages. Do challenge them to consistently accept the Bible: the Scriptures are clear. Study Naaman's healing in 2 Kings 5—which yields some good parallels to the cleansing of baptism.

Focus on repentance, asking specific questions about changes made in response to the Word (righteous living, evangelism, etc.). If there is complacency, study repentance again. Only proceed if you are confident there has been a change of heart. Next time you study, cover the remaining passages and talk about the implications.

[10] Further baptism verses: Matthew 28:19; Mark 16:16; John 3:5; Acts 8:12–13; 9:18, 10:48, 16:15, 18:8, 19:5; 1 Corinthians 1:13–17, 10:2, 12:13, 15:29; Galatians 3:26–27; Ephesians 5:26; Colossians 2:12; Titus 3:5; Hebrews 6:2; 10:22.

[11] 1 Corinthians 15:3–4 shows that the gospel is the death, burial, and resurrection of Christ. Thus, being baptized is sharing in the gospel.

[12] The NIV rendition "pledge," which reflects evangelical theology, is far from certain. *Eperótama* is sometimes translated "answer," or (better) "appeal."

[13] It may be helpful at this point to "demystify" the work of the Spirit. Explain how God does not have impossible expectations; his Spirit enables us to follow him. In Ephesians 3:16 we see that the Spirit brings the power to live the Christian life. Indeed, God lives up to his promise to be with us in our mission to save the world (Matthew 28:20). Furthermore, in John 16:8 we see the role of the Spirit in convicting of sin. Nothing bizarre, however—remember, the Spirit works in our hearts through the Word (John 6:63), transforming our personalities to be Christlike (2 Corinthians 3:17–18). God wants us to grow spiritually all of the time. 2 Timothy 1:7 shows that the Spirit helps us in our evangelism.

[14] Matthew Bates, *Salvation by Allegiance Alone: Rethinking Faith, Works, and the Gospel of Jesus the King* (Grand Rapids: Baker, 2017).

[15] There is another approach to studying The Church which is also effective: trace the following themes in the book of Acts: (1) Boldness, (2) Persecution and (3) Growth. For each theme select verses from the book of Acts; proceed straight through for each of the three themes, and stress that these are characteristics of God's church.

[16] Church = translation of *ekklesia*; which means assembly or congregation. For example, in Acts 19 *ekklesia* is used three times of the illicit assembly of the

enemies of the church! (19:32, 39, 40).

[17] Moreover, we are baptized in the Spirit when we are baptized in water. The Spirit makes us members of the body of Christ.

# 12
# Guard the Gospel
*Series B*

Additional useful studies include:

**Jesus II**
**Sin II**
**Repentance II**
**Obedience**
**The Resurrection**
**Grace**
**Faith**
**Discipleship II**
**Baptism II**
**The Holy Spirit I**

Since this course builds on the material in Series A, several of the studies in Series A find counterparts in this series:

| *Series B* | *Series A* |
|---|---|
| Jesus II: Jesus in Action | Jesus the Only Way |
| Sin II | Sin |
| Repentance II: Self-righteousness | Repentance |
| Discipleship II: Excuses and Fear | Discipleship |
| Baptism II | Baptism |

Other studies cover entirely new, but nevertheless important material: Obedience, The Resurrection, Grace, Faith, and The Holy Spirit I. This last unit finds its counterpart in Series C, which is presented in chapter 13.

The material inside the box is recommended for memorization or identification.

---

## 1
## Jesus II: Jesus in Action

Whereas the Series A Jesus study is for those without a lot of Christian background, this study especially meets the needs of those who claim to know Christ. It is a challenging study because it focuses on Jesus *in action*. When it comes to describing the manhood and character of

Jesus Christ, there are a huge number of verses giving us a composite picture of the god-man in action.

As we will see, Jesus was a man of power! For first-timers hearing this study, there will be many surprises! (Note: the entire study comes from the gospel of Luke.

- Luke 24-4-7-11-12-13-23-2 (chapter sequence in study)
- *Agonidzesthai*
- Luke 23:34

## Points

**Luke 24:19**—After his death, people remembered Jesus Christ as a powerful man, not a sissy.

*In the following passages we get a mosaic picture of Jesus' life and his power.*

**Luke 4:1–4**—Power to resist temptation! Discuss several specific activities associated with "being a man." Real men don't follow the crowd at parties to show they can "hold their liquor"; real men go against the stream—when it's flowing in the wrong direction.

**Luke 4:28–30**—Authority! Taking a stand against prejudice, first message to hometown! They try to throw him off a cliff. If twenty or thirty men tried to throw you out the window, could you stop them? Clearly Jesus was no pushover! His authority was felt.

**Luke 4:33–37**—Speaks sternly to demon. I would have fled in terror!

**Luke 4:42**—Up early after a busy night. *Packed*, not *wimpy* schedule!

**Luke 7:14**—Against social convention when necessary. Imagine the guts needed to stop a funeral procession!

**Luke 11:37–39, 44–46**—Strong talk to religious leaders—as guest at a dinner party! Have you ever talked to anyone that way?

**Luke 12:49–51**—Jesus was focused and driven! What a radical message!

**Luke 13:24**—"Make every effort": Greek *agonidzesthai,* contend for the prize (the root of *agonize* in English). To follow Jesus you have to really "go for it"!

**Luke 23:34**—It takes strength to forgive. Any fool can harbor a grudge or take revenge, but it takes a real man to love and to forgive!

**Luke 2:34–35**—People reacted strongly to Jesus, because he was such a strong character. Is this the Jesus you want to follow? If so, you are destined to become more and more like him. Watch out!

# 2
# Sin II

This study covers in greater detail than Sin I a number of issues that may arise in the course of a personal Bible study with a friend. Whether or not all these areas are relevant to the life of your friend, or even to your own, you will want to gain a mastery of all the material in Sin II.

- Matthew 12:32
- Colossians 3:5–9
- John 6:66
- 2 Timothy 3:2–5
- James 1:13
- Revelation 21:8

## Points

1. Alcohol
   - There are cultural differences among countries. Drunkenness is the sin, not drinking *itself* (Isaiah 5:11; Proverbs 23:29–35; Galatians 5:21). In other words, though it is a dangerous substance, ethyl alcohol is not sinful *per se.*
   - 1 Corinthians 8:9; Romans 14:21—Do not cause others to stumble.
   - In the case of those who have been ensnared, it is probably wisest to counsel abstinence until the sin is under control. For alcoholics, permanent abstinence may be the best advice.

2. Discos, Drugs, Gambling
   - Titus 2:5, 8, 10—make the gospel attractive. Titus 2:7—be a good example.
   - Discos, clubs, and the like: Ephesians 5:3—not even a hint! No one should get the wrong idea!
   - Drugs: 1 Corinthians 6:20—taking care of the temple.
   - Gambling: Matthew 25:21—responsibility with what has been entrusted to us. As an institution, gambling hurts the poor, seniors, and minorities the most. Be careful.
   - Proverbs 3:9—honoring God with our money.

3. Smoking—10 reasons not to!
   - It enslaves (Romans 6:12; 2 Peter 2:19).
   - It is a bad example for others—(Luke 17:1–3a; Titus 2:6–10).
   - The smoker knows it's wrong, and wouldn't recommend it (Romans 14:23).
   - It hurts one's influence (1 Peter 2:12; 2 Peter 2:19): with non-smokers, smokers trying to quit, religious people.
   - It violates others' rights (Matthew 7:12; Philippians 2:4).

- It dishonors God with one's body (Romans 12:1; 1 Corinthians 6:20; 2 Corinthians 7:1; 1 Thessalonians 5:23).
- It takes years off your life (Ephesians 5:16).[1]
- It is a waste of God's money—bad stewardship (Matthew 25:21).
- It's a poor substitute for prayer as a means of dealing with anxiety (Philippians 4:6; 1 Peter 5:7).
- The Surgeon General has determined that smoking causes lung cancer, emphysema, and heart disease. (No scripture—see any cigarette packet!)

4. The Occult
   - Condemned in the Old Testament:
     a. Leviticus 19:31—Don't consult the mediums (Isaiah 8:9).
     b. 1 Samuel 28—Saul and the witch of Endor (1 Chron 10:13).
   - Condemned in the New Testament:
     a. Acts 19:19—Word spread as people gave up sorcery.
     b. Galatians 5:12—Witchcraft will keep you from heaven.
     c. 2 Thessalonians 2:9—Satan counterfeits miracles.
     d. Revelation 21:8—A serious sin—don't play around!

5. Sexual Sin
   - Living together (Genesis 2:24), even if not sexually immoral (Ephesians 5:3).
   - Premarital sex (Genesis 34 [Shechem] and Genesis 29 [Jacob]) wrong under both covenants.
   - Masturbation: address it. Importance of openness, both before and after conversion. Ask where is the person's mind while he or she is engaged in this act (Matthew 5:28).
   - Homosexuality: ask about it; don't be embarrassed to discuss. It is dangerous! (1 Corinthians 6:9; Romans 1:26–27; Leviticus 18:22).
   - Other useful passages:

| | |
|---|---|
| Genesis 39:9 | Habakkuk 2:15 |
| 1 Corinthians 6:9, 18 | Hebrews 13:4 |
| Exodus 22:16 | Matthew 5:28 |
| 2 Corinthians 12:21 | 2 Peter 2:14 |
| Leviticus 18 | Romans 6:19–21 |
| 1 Thessalonians 4:3 | Revelation 2:21 |
| Deuteronomy 22:20–22 | Romans 13:14 |
| 1Timothy 5:2 | Revelation 21:27 |
| Job 31:1 | 1 Corinthians 5:9–11 |
| 2 Timothy 2:22 | Revelation 22:15 |

6. Materialism
   - Proverbs 30:7–9—Seek the mean between poverty and riches.
   - Ephesians 5:5—Not even a hint of greed!
   - Gospel of Luke—This is one of his special emphases (over 30 verses).
   - Recommended reading: *Rich Christians Living in an Age of Hunger*, R. J. Sider.

*Theological Questions*

7. The Unforgivable Sin (Matthew 12:22–37)
   - The healing was clearly of God.
   - The hearts had become evil (vv. 33–37).
   - The unforgivable sin is a (intractably) hardened heart.

8. Original Sin
   - Psalm 51:5 is either literal or figurative. Compare it with Psalms 22:9, 58:3, 71:6—clearly it is figurative. Therefore Psalm 51 does not support the doctrine of original sin.
   - Romans 5:12 (key verse)—if it teaches that all are born *damned* because of Adam's sin, then 5:18 must teach that all are automatically saved by Christ's death. If so, where is there room for free will? It makes a lot more sense to say that on account of Adam's sin all are *potentially* lost (that is, if and when they sin—"because all sinned"), and that through Christ's sacrifice all are *potentially* saved.
   - Ezekiel 18:20 shows guilt is not passed from father to son.
   - Matthew 18:3, 19:14—children held up as a standard for disciples. Would he have done this if children were guilty and lost?

9. Prayers of Sinners—Are they heard?
   - John 9:31; Psalm 66:18—sin can keep God from answering our prayers, but God will always help us to find if we are seeking. (Matthew 7:7; Acts 10:4)
   - God hears our prayers (nothing escapes his notice [Hebrews 4:13]), but obviously a Christian can approach God in a way that a non-Christian never could.
   - Analogy: *servant vs. son.* The master of the house may grant a servant's request, though he certainly has no obligation to, whereas he will freely grant the request of his son.

10. Disfellowship,[2] Excommunication
    - Matthew 18:15–18—three steps in the case of someone refusing to be reconciled to another (quarrel, leadership problem, marital strife).
    - Titus 3:10—two warnings, then disfellowship in the case of a divisive person.[3] See also Romans 16:17.
    - 1 Corinthians 5:11—on the grounds of such sins as immorality, greed, idolatry, slander, drunkenness, swindling (serious sins).
    - Note: Idleness (2 Thessalonians 3:6–15) is not grounds for disfellowship, though it is grounds for a strong warning.

# 3
# Repentance II: Self-Righteousness

Sometimes people aren't moved by the Repentance study. Simply put, they seem unable to see themselves as sinners. Repentance II tackles the self-righteousness that characterizes so many religious people these days. (Besides, it is a major theme in Luke's gospel.)

- Luke 3, 5, 7, 13, 15, 18
- Luke 5:32
- Luke 18:9

## Points

**Luke 3:7–14**—John the Baptist insisted on a serious change.
- Rebuked religious pride.
- Instructed people to repent of selfishness.
- Expected repentance to lead to fruit.

**Luke 5:31–32**
- In repentance we must see ourselves as lost.
- Jesus always preached against *self-righteousness.*

**Luke 7:29–30**
- We surrender our way to *God's way* in repentance and baptism.
- John the Baptist *held off* the Pharisees from being baptized—they had not repented.
- They had thus *rejected God's purpose* for themselves: an incredible waste of talent and influence.

**Luke 7:36–51**
- Pharisaical self-righteousness: "comparative religion"—comparing yourself to others.
- Gratitude, love, and commitment abound when we see ourselves as lost.

**Luke 13:1–5** (may omit if already covered in the basic study)
- *Repent or perish.* Any other option?
- It's either one or the other: they either *have* or *have not* repented.

**Luke 13:6–9**
- God is patient with us.
- Yet he expects change.

**Luke 13:22–30**
- Make *every effort* (repent).
- Repentance is a matter of *salvation.*

**Luke 15**—Three parables on repentance: skim over.

**Luke 18:9–14**
- Are you confident of your salvation? Are you a Pharisee?
- Keeping track of your good deeds?
- Self-righteousness will condemn us!

---

## 4
## Obedience

This is an excellent study for a religious person, perhaps even as a first study. What an enormous theme in both testaments! Much of the religious world waters down obedience, preferring "easy believism." They talk about "grace," "faith alone," "judgmentalism" and "acceptance." The Obedience study sets the record straight.

- 1 Samuel 15
- 2 Samuel 6:1–7
- 2 Kings 5:1–15
- Matthew 7:21–23
- John 14:15, 23–24
- 1 John 2:3–6

### Points

*Old Testament teaching—Let's examine three people under the old covenant.*

Saul—**1 Samuel 15** (selected)
- 15:1–3: Saul is asked to obey a specific command.
- 15:7–9: Saul only *partly* obeys the command.
- 15:12–31: He puts up quite a fight before admitting he has sinned. Rationalizations!
- Conclusions:
  a. Partial obedience is disobedience!
  b. Selective obedience is disobedience!
  c. It's possible to be completely deceived about whether or not we have been obedient.

Uzzah—**2 Samuel 6:1–7**
- God views disobeying his word as serious!
- Sincerity does not remove guilt (1 Corinthians 4:4).
- Does this sound unfair? David thought so too, until he learned what God's word said (see 1 Chronicles 15:12–15).

Naaman—**2 Kings 5:1–15**
- 5:10: God's word is plain and straightforward.
- 5:11: Beware an emotional reaction to God's word.
- 5:11: Surrender preconceived ideas.
- 5:12: No, there are *not* any alternatives to doing what God says.

- 5:13: We need help to be objective and reason things out.
- 5:14: God blesses obedience.
- 5:14: *Approximate* obedience is insufficient (five dips in Jordan, or seven dips in Pharpar).
- 5:15: We learn to appreciate and reverence God once we actually begin to obey him.

*New Testament teaching: Let' see what Jesus and his followers taught about obedience.*

**Matthew 7:21–23**
- These people were religious, active, and possibly sincere—but lost.
- Only those who obey God will make it to heaven.
- It's possible to believe that you have a saved relationship with God yet not be saved at all.

**John 14:15, 23–24**
- Obedience isn't just part of the old law; Jesus and the New Testament discuss obedience again and again.
- Love and obedience are virtually equivalent.

**1 John 2:3–6**
- 2:3: You can be sure of your salvation if you're living as an obedient disciple of Jesus.
- 2:4: If you claim you know him but are disobedient, you are a liar.
- 2:6: We must follow Jesus' lifestyle! Obedience is a central part of Christianity.

*Conclusion*

As we see, obedience was not rendered optional by the cross. It has always been crucial for a true follower of God. What has been keeping you from obeying?

---

## 5
## The Resurrection

This study is useful for bringing people to faith who are open to believing but just need a little "evidence." The resurrection receives a considerable amount of attention in the gospels and is a major theme in the sermons of Acts.[4]

- 1 Corinthians 15:19
- 1 Corinthians 15:17
- 1 Corinthians 15:6
- Matthew 28:13
- Acts 17:31
- Acts 1:3
- Flow chart (be able to reproduce it)

## Points

*A Historical Event*

Opening passage: 1 Corinthians 15:3–8, 11–19, 32. The resurrection is *crucial* to the entire Christian message. It is "of first importance," as Paul says. Then he insists that Christ *appeared* to many people. He provided "many convincing proofs" (Acts 1:3). As Paul maintains, Christianity is a historical religion, based on historical events. The resurrection is a real historical occurrence, just like the Second World War or the building of the pyramids. The whole Christian faith stands or falls on this single issue. If Christ was not raised:

- Preaching is useless.
- Christians are liars.
- Christian faith is useless.
- Our sins are still unforgiven.
- The dead have no hope of salvation.
- Christians are the most pathetic people in the world.
- We might as well seek pleasure, since life is so short.

*Setting the Scene*

- Read one of the gospel accounts of the resurrection of Jesus (Matthew 27:26–28; Mark 15:15–16:14; Luke 22:63–65, 23:26–24:12; John 19:1–20:28).
- Explain that the claims of Jesus stand or fall on the resurrection.
- If Jesus *didn't* rise from the dead, then what *did* happen? Perhaps you will find the diagram below helpful for your friends. It shows all the possibilities:

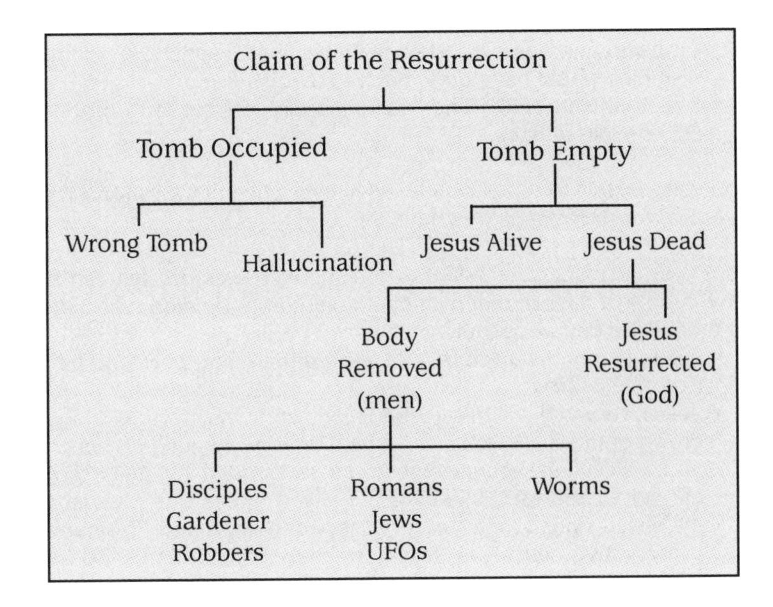

No lazy thinking—you can't just say, "I don't believe it!" and fold your arms. If you deny the resurrection, you must believe that:

- Jesus was buried and stayed buried,
- Jesus never actually died, or
- His body was removed from the tomb.

Let's see if any of these assumptions hold water:

"Jesus was buried; Jesus stayed buried."—If you think this, you also think that

- They looked in the wrong tomb on Sunday morning, and
- Hallucinated the risen Christ.

*Taking these one at a time...*

"Wrong tomb!"—Do you really believe that:

- None of the disciples could remember where Jesus had been buried, not even Joseph of Arimathea (he owned the tomb and put Jesus in it himself, by the way).
- The Romans guarded an empty hole?
- Yes, that's what you're claiming!

"Holy hallucinations"—Their emotions overcame them? Some contradictions in your claim:

- John 20:19—The disciples were not even expecting the resurrection. Thirsty men see water: Yes. Dejected disciples see Jesus: No.
- Acts 1:3; John 20:35—The disciples were skeptical and needed "many convincing proofs." No hysteria here.
- Acts 2:31—They knew the corpse was the issue. If Jesus' body (and surely it was around *somewhere)* had been shown them, the disciples would have gone back to the fish trade.
- 1 Corinthians 15:6—The "hallucination" appeared to more than 500 people at once?

It is as easy as this to reject conclusively the notion of the "wrong tomb." The actual tomb of Jesus was definitely empty.

"Jesus was just unconscious" (swoon theory)—Yes, he felt refreshed after a couple of days in that nice cool quiet tomb. He didn't die. *Really?* Well then, logic demands that:

- Jesus *lied* to his disciples. He tricked them into believing he rose from the dead.
- Jesus survived all this: exhaustion, clubbing, torture, flogging, crown of thorns, beating (by which time he couldn't lift his cross) and crucifixion: around six hours suspended by nails through his wrists and feet, bleeding. Finally, a spear was plunged into his chest, right to the heart. Wrapped in linen and 75 pounds of preservative ointments, he lay in chilly conditions for 36 hours. *Would you like to try?*

- John 19:32—The same executioners who broke the legs of the thieves *mistook* Jesus for dead. And the spear-thrust to the heart was a little too soft?
- When Jesus revived, he was strong enough to get up, unwrap himself, roll away the large stone, overpower the guard, walk several miles on pierced feet, and be calm and casual in front of his disciples.
- Are you prepared to stand up for these claims? If Jesus didn't die, you *must.* Let's face it: Jesus received enough punishment to kill him several times over. Indeed, *Jesus was dead on the cross.*
- Someone removed the corpse—the disciples did it, or someone else beat them to it. In other words, you think that:
  a. The disciples were deceitful, or
  b. "Someone else" had both the motive and the means to make off with the corpse.

*How likely are these propositions?*

- Anxious apostles: Rather than lose face, the disciples staged the whole thing (Matthew 28:11–15). In other words:
  a. The apostles lied, going against the teaching of their master.
  b. They changed from cowards (John 20:19) to commandos!
  c. Acts 4:20—They refused to come clean, even when they were threatened and later beaten, and most of them put to death for their deception.

No, the story just doesn't add up. The disciples did not move Jesus' body. Then who?... "All kinds of people (other than apostles) might have done it," you claim? Hold on just a minute. If the body was stolen, then the disciples either lied or hallucinated, and we've already ruled out those possibilities! We could stop here, but instead let's point the accusing finger at some suspects.

- Guilty gardener: *Motive:* if he was *against* the disciples, he'd have given the corpse to the Jews. If he'd been for them, he would have ended their needless persecution. Either way, no motive for a theft. *Means:* He overcame sword and shield with spade and pruning scissors!
- Thoughtless thieves: *Motive:* Ah! Must be something pretty valuable in there for a guard to be posted. Even so, is anything worth breaking Pilate's seal and risking punishment? *Means:* Assume they killed Joe Soldier. When disappointed by their find, would they, could they, have eagerly removed 220 lbs (100kg)—including corpse, graveclothes, and ointments—of a dead man?
- Rebellious Romans: Christianity turned Jerusalem and the Roman world upside-down! Can you think of any reason why the authorities would want to encourage civil disorder?
- Jealous Jews: Again, what motive would there be? The Jews were the last ones on earth who wanted the people to believe the Christians' "lie." If they had taken the body, they would have been

the first to produce it.

- Sorcerous saucers: (Yes, people have claimed this!) Kind creatures "beamed him up" (Scottie). Let's agree that science fiction is exactly that!
- Ravenous worms: Do you get the feeling that we're running out of convincing ideas? Did worms eat the body over a short weekend?

*Conclusion: Jesus Rose from the Dead!*

In the light of all the evidence, doesn't it take *more* faith *not* to believe in the resurrection than to accept it as true? Truly, Jesus rose from the dead! This is the only explanation that makes sense of all the facts, including Jesus' repeated prediction that he would rise on the third day. It is also the best explanation for the incredible transformation in the lives of the early disciples, as well as in the lives of his disciples today.

If the resurrection of Jesus Christ from the dead actually took place, then we have "good news and bad news." The good news is, when Jesus returns, you too will be resurrected and have a chance to live eternally with God.[5] The "bad news" is, you have to change. See Acts 17:30–31. The resurrection means we are under the obligation to *repent*—each and every one of us.

---

## 6
## Grace

A good companion unit to the Obedience study, Grace will be especially helpful for (a) religious people with a twisted understanding of grace, (b) all who are having difficulty forgiving themselves or letting the past go, and (c) followers of Christ who are flagging in their strength.

The Apostle Paul appreciated God's grace perhaps more than any other man of his day, and he tells us that's why he accomplished so much (1 Corinthians 15:10). Since it's essential for us to understand the concept of grace and to teach it clearly, we choose Paul for a balanced understanding of grace.

- Ephesians 2:8
- Titus 2:11
- 1 Corinthians 15:10
- G.R.A.C.E. (learn acronym)

### Points

**Ephesians 2:1–10**

- We are dead to God in our sins. When we live the way the world wants us to, or follow our own desires, we become objects of wrath.

- Because of grace (God's love for us), we can be saved. We don't deserve it, but it's free for us as a gift if we accept it.
- It's through our faith in Christ that we're saved.
- God's love motivates us to do good works.

**Romans 5:6–11**

- Definition of grace: God loving us enough to allow Christ to die for our sins when we were his enemies. Acronym: God's Riches at Christ's Expense.
- We were lost sinners deserving only punishment, but he sent Christ to suffer in our place.
- Through Jesus' blood we are saved from God's wrath (blood must be shed for forgiveness [Hebrews 9:22, 28]).

**Titus 2:11–14**

- Grace means salvation for us.
- God's love leads us to purify ourselves from sin; we won't take advantage of God's grace.
- Since grace overcomes passion, it isn't a license for sin (Jude 4). Grace isn't cheap—it cost Jesus his life.

**1 Corinthians 1:18–25**

- The cross is God's powerful solution for sin.
- Without an understanding of God's love, the message of the cross will be foolishness to us.

**2 Corinthians 5:14–21**

- Christ's love demands a response! (See 1 Corinthians 15:9–10.)
- Jesus bore our sins to the extent that he became sin, or a sin offering.
- God's love motivates us to live for him, and to speak for him.

**1 Corinthians 15:9–10**

- Though it is not true that we are saved by working hard, it is true that those most affected by God's grace are God's hardest workers!

---

## 7
## Faith

Like Obedience and Grace, the Faith study is intended "to comfort the disturbed and to disturb the comfortable." It is also beneficial when studying with an atheist who is tempted to dismiss God and religion because of the "practical atheism" he or she has seen in churchgoers.

- Practical atheism
- Psalm 14:1

- Hebrews 11:1
- Hebrews 11:6
- James 2:22
- James 2:24
- Martin Luther

### Points

**Psalm 14:1**

- Faith isn't just an option, it's an attitude of the heart.
- You can be religious and yet still be a *practical* atheist. (Do you live as though there's a God?)

**Hebrews 11:1**

- Faith isn't just "believing in something you know isn't true anyway"!
- It's not just a leap into the dark. (It's a leap into the light!)
- It is spiritual *certainty.*

**Hebrews 11:6**

- It is *impossible* to please God without faith.
- We can and must believe that God exists.
- He is there, and we will find him if we earnestly seek him.

**James 2:14–26**

- Faith without actions is useless.
- Striving to be righteous: deal with sin.
- Striving to have a relationship with God: prayer, Bible study.
- Striving to help others: church, evangelism, caring for the needy.
- Faith is complete only when it is *active* faith.
- Abraham's faith and actions worked together. In Genesis 22, God knew Abraham had true faith only at the moment of obedience (22:12).
- No one is justified by faith without deeds (James 2:24).
- Note: Because of his belief in "justification by faith alone" and "once saved, always saved," Luther (1500s) rejected the entire book of James. He also rejected Hebrews, since this book repeatedly states that it's possible to lose our salvation. (Luther disagreed.)

---

## 8
## Discipleship II: Excuses and Fear

An excellent follow-up to the basic Discipleship study, this unit removes excuses and inspires prospective disciples to face and overcome their fears. The study centers on five great men of God and how the Lord helped them to become powerful men of God. The study is especially helpful for people who are timid by nature.

- Exodus 4:13
- Judges 6:15
- Jeremiah 1:6
- Isaiah 6:8
- Luke 5:10b

### Points

Moses—**Exodus 3–4**

- 3:10–12: feeling of insignificance
  a. Moses is given an important mission.
  b. Moses thinks God has got the wrong guy!
  c. God is *with us* in our evangelism.
- 3:13: lack of knowledge
- 4:1: fear of rejection
- 4:10–12: lack of eloquence
- 4:13–14: reluctance to obey
  a. This is the real issue!
  b. God is angry with our excuse-making!

*(Moses, already eighty years old, goes on to become a bold leader in God's kingdom!)*

Gideon—**Judges 6:11–16**

- 6:11: fearful (threshing in the winepress at a time when God needed men of courage to rise up).
- 6:12: "Mighty warrior": God sees his potential.
- 6:14: "Go in the strength that you have": don't worry, just do your best.
- 6:15: Gideon claims he's too insignificant and unimpressive to follow and obey God.
- 6:16: God will be with you!

*(Gideon repents of his fear and excuses and rescues his nation from the enemy—powerfully and bravely!)*

Jeremiah—**Jeremiah 1:4–8**

- 1:5: God has a mission for our lives, too.
- 1:6: Excuse of youth (see 1 Timothy 4:12).
- 1:8: God rejects Jeremiah's excuse.
  a. God commands us not to fear.
  b. God is with us! (God plus one is a majority!)

*(Jeremiah spreads the word for forty years, even though most people reject him, and becomes one of the greatest prophets of all time!)*

Isaiah—**Isaiah 6:1–8**

- 1:1: He has an awesome vision of the awesome God!
- 1:5: "Woe is me!"

   a. Isaiah sees God in all his glory.
   b. He realizes his own lostness.
   c. He realizes the lostness of everyone else.
- 1:6–7: Experiencing God's forgiveness transforms our lives.
- 1:8: Then and only then are we ready to go and spread God's word.

*(Isaiah too goes on to have a tremendous impact on his generation!)*

Peter—**Luke 5:4–11**
- 5:5: Peter is willing to take Jesus at his word.
- 5:6: Incredible result—God's word is powerful!
- 5:8: Peter realizes who he's dealing with; knee-deep in fish he comes to Jesus, realizing his own sinfulness.
- 5:10: Jesus encourages Peter to evangelize.
   a. He commands him not to fear.
   b. "Catching people" (HCSB)—evangelism.
   c. Jesus assures him that he "will" be effective.
- 5:11: We too must pull our fears and excuses up on the shore, and actively obey Jesus Christ!

*(Peter ultimately confronts his fears and fulfills Jesus' prophecy of martyrdom [John 21:18–19].)*

Additional figures: King Saul, Queen Esther, Ezekiel...

*Concluding Challenge:*

Peter and the others did great things for God because they gave up their excuses and stepped out on faith, despite their fears. You can do the same! God will change you, be with you and enable you to do great things for him.

---

# 9
# Baptism II

For the Series A study, see Chapter 11. This unit is a twenty-part mini reference work, and will supply you with a plethora of angles on, illustrations of, and reasons for baptism!

- 2 Kings 5:1–15
- Hebrews 11:30
- Mark 16:16
- Galatians 3:26–27
- John 3:5
- "Lifeline"
- Justin Martyr
- Shepherd of Hermas

1. The Lifeline

You can make a "lifeline" just before the conversion study, or at least find out the facts ahead of time (when your friend thinks they became a Christian, whether they were baptized, whether they were "saved" before baptism, etc.). Include such items as when they:

| | | | |
|---|---|---|---|
| *i.* | *were converted* | *viii.* | *became a Christian* |
| *ii.* | *received Christ* | *ix.* | *were born again* |
| *iii.* | *came to believe* | *x.* | *repented* |
| *iv.* | *were forgiven of sins* | *xi.* | *were confirmed* |
| *v.* | *joined church* | *xii.* | *were immersed* |
| *vi.* | *were infant baptized* | *xiii.* | *were "Holy Spirit" baptized* |
| *vii.* | *received the Spirit* | *xiv.* | *were truly saved* |

Even though many of these items may appear redundant, it is amazing what people will say to you, sometimes placing them all at separate points in time! Draw a timeline. Have the person enter the relevant event/experiences, with dates. Then draw your own lifeline. Show that belief and repentance came before your conversion, and that all God's blessings came at the point of baptism (nos. i, ii, iv, v, vii, viii, ix, xii, xiii, xiv).

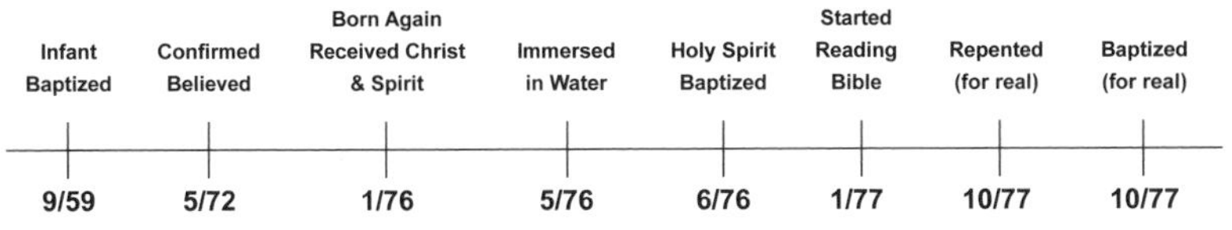


The lifeline is useful because sooner or later you will need to find out how the religious person views their "conversion." This will prevent them from "revising" their story in light of the new information they will have learned through your study of conversion.

2. Paul's conversion

Paul believed (Acts 22:10), confessed (22:10), fasted (9:9) and prayed (9:11) for three days (9:9), obeyed (22:10–11) and repented, and still was not a saved man. He was *not* saved on the Damascus road, contrary to the teaching of virtually all denominations.

3. "Three lists"

Take a piece of paper and divide it into three columns. Write at the heads of the columns:

*Infant baptism "Optional" believer's baptism "Essential" baptism*

Now go through the conversions in Acts and place each in the appropriate column (or two, if more than one view seems tenable from the single passage). The results are striking, with the vast majority of passages falling into the third category. This is not to imply that in the New Testament babies were baptized or baptism was optional—only to show how unlikely the two incorrect interpretations are.

4. Urgency of baptism
    - Acts 16:3—the middle of the night!
    - Acts 22:16—*"what are you waiting for?"*
    - Acts 8:38—"Stop the chariot!"

So why do so many denominations today leave baptism to a convenient time (once a month, annually at Easter, etc.)? Because it isn't seen as essential to salvation.

5. Joy

Study the following verses: Acts 2:46, 8:39, 16:34. Joy follows after baptism. Why? Because that's when people were forgiven of their sins.

6. "Get up!"
    - Acts 22:16—Paul had been fasting/thinking/praying for several days, but now he was asked to do something. The blessing depends on action!
    - 2 Kings 5:1–14—Parallel: Naaman had been to see the prophet, but wasn't cleansed from leprosy until he did as Elisha instructed.

7. Is the power "in the water"?

No, but it is God's power (Colossians 2:12), and that power becomes available—when? Only when we obey. (The term "baptismal regeneration" is the belief that the faith of the one being baptized is irrelevant, that the true power is "in the water." This, of course, is a false teaching! So if someone asks you, "Do you believe in baptismal regeneration," the correct answer is "No.")

8. Repentance first!

It is best not to study baptism with someone who hasn't yet repented (i.e., coming to the services, convinced the Bible is God's word, beginning to share his or her faith, reading the Scriptures on their own without prodding). There are a few exceptions:
    - Someone who is *not religious*, who has no religious preconceptions and no religious friends who might "poison" them (Acts 14:2). In Northern Europe, for example, where faith in God is rare and even going to church is seen as a bit unusual, studying baptism earlier on is fairly innocuous. In the United States, on the other hand, where "churchianity" is rampant, the premature study of baptism only leads to strife, as baptism becomes "the issue"—when it is not!
    - *Religious people* who are highly committed, reasonably knowledgeable, and evangelistic. (We are *not* talking about someone only familiar with the Bible, sharing their faith now and again, even if they attend church regularly.) The Apollos type (Acts 18:24ff) is a rare exception among religious people.

9. "But aren't we saved by faith?"

Yes, we are, but *when* are we saved by our faith? Before that faith manifests itself into action, or after? Excellent example: Hebrews 11:30. The walls of Jericho fell "by faith," but the writer is showing us that *action* was involved. This was a matter of obedience. So it is with baptism.

10. "Isn't baptism a work?"
    - Well, it is something you *do* (so is repenting, believing [John 6:29], etc.), but not in the sense of a work by which you obligate God to save you (as spoken of in Romans 4:4).
    - Some say we cannot be saved by a *physical* act. Yet even the sacrifice of Jesus on the cross was a physical act.
    - Baptism is simply redeeming a coupon, collecting that which God has freely promised anyway. The fact that salvation is conditional on our response in no sense detracts from God's generosity, or from his grace.
    - Baptism is a passive event (it is done to us), whereas the ubiquitous "sinner's prayer" is a work—an active event (something we do).

11. But don't we *believe* into Christ?

No! In fact, the "into" Christ terminology is only in connection with baptism (Romans 6:3; 1 Corinthians 12:13; Galatians 3:26). Non-Christians are outside of Christ. Christians are in Christ. To get *into* a right relationship with God, you must be baptized.

12. "But I was born again before I was baptized!"

Romans 6:4—the new life begins in baptism. To claim that new life begins *before* baptism (i.e., that we are born again first) is to say that the new creation is put to death! Many groups implicitly teach that we put to death the born-again self, since baptism is a death as well as a birth.

13. Use "baptism verses"

Many, alarmed when studying out what the Bible says about baptism, prefer to turn to verses on *other* topics (faith, God's love, etc.) anything rather than baptism! We must help people to be logical. When we study sin, we do not turn to the genealogies of Chronicles to find out what is right and wrong. We turn to passages about sin! When we study baptism, let's look at the verses on baptism. So often people try to sidestep the issue by getting off on a tangent.

14. Difficult verse: Luke 23:43

Three points are to be made concerning the thief on the cross:
    - Mark 2:10—Jesus had the authority during his earthly ministry to forgive sins.
    - Romans 6:3–4—baptism is a participation in Jesus' death, burial, and resurrection. The penitent thief could not have been baptized into Jesus' death, since Jesus had not yet died.
    - Hebrews 9:17—the New Covenant (New Testament) was not yet in force, as Jesus had not yet died. The thief died under the Old Covenant.

15. Difficult verse: Romans 10:9–10, 13

This passage is a favorite out-of-context proof of salvation by faith alone. Several things should be noted:
    - The Romans do not need to be told how to be saved. They are

already saved. Romans 6 specifies the time of their rebirth, in baptism.
- *Everyone* who calls on the name of the Lord will be saved. In context (Romans 10), "everyone" means Jew and Gentile alike.
- Calling on the name of the Lord is done in baptism (see Acts 22: 16). The passage does not mention baptism, but that does not mean that baptism is somehow optional.
- Paul's argument is that faith/confession, which makes baptism powerful (Colossians 2:12; Galatians 3:26–27) is something anyone can do, whether or not he is circumcised. We are not saved by works under the new covenant nor were the people saved by works (law) under the old (Deuteronomy 30).
- Paul is discouraging Judaizing tendencies. We must examine Romans 10 in context! This is not written to non-Christians, telling them how to be saved, but to Jewish and Gentile Christians, urging them to accept one another in Christ.

16. Difficult verse: Mark 16:16

Belief plus baptism equals salvation. But why does it not also say "nonbelief plus nonbaptism equals nonsalvation"? Illustration: *The one who eats their food and digests it will live, but whoever does not eat will die.* Similarly, baptism follows logically from belief. Furthermore, John 3:18 says that whoever does not believe is condemned *already*! Thus there was no need for Jesus to say, "...but whoever does not believe and is not baptized..."

17. Difficult verse: John 3:16

It is incredible to think that this verse is often cited as proof that one does not need to be baptized in order to be saved! True, it does not mention baptism. Nor does Mark 16:16 mention repentance. Nor does Acts 2:38 mention faith. Obviously, we have to put all the pieces together, not playing games, picking and choosing the passages that best suit our purposes! A response to the John 3:16 line of reasoning has been suggested:

Christian: "Do you think you have to repent to be saved?"

Non-Christian: "Sure."

Christian: "I disagree. I don't think you do have to repent."

Non-Christian: "Of course you do. What makes you say that?"

Christian: "Well, John 3:16 doesn't say anything about repentance."

Non-Christian: "Yes, but there are lots of *other* passages that make it perfectly clear that you have to repent to be saved."

Christian: "My point exactly!"

18. Linguistic arguments

- **Insights from the Greek**
    a. *Cheo = pour.* Never used in the New Testament in connection with baptism.
    b. *Hrantidzo = sprinkle.* Never used in the New Testament for

water baptism. Old Testament sprinkling with blood = background (sanctification).

c. *Hygraino* = *apply water*. Never used in the New Testament in connection with water baptism—although it would be the ideal word, since it doesn't specify "mode."

d. *Baptidzo* = *immerse*. This word is the one *always* used for New Testament baptism.

- **Insights from the Syriac**
  Syriac is one of the languages into which the original Greek New Testament was translated. In the Syriac translation, which probably dates from the second century, *hamad* = baptize. (Its derivative, *mamaditho*, appears in John 5:4 and 9:7, and means *pool*.) In secular Syrian authors, *mamaditho* means a *bath* or *baptistery*. *Immersion* is the action of the verb *hamad*, and not sprinkling or affusion.
- **Insights from the Latin**
  Although not the original language of the New Testament Latin is another of the early versions. Often it is said that the King James translators (1605–1611) chose to *transliterate* the word *baptidzo* instead of to *translate* it, in order to avoid embarrassing the king. In fact, transliteration of the word dates back at least as early as the fifth century. The Latin Vulgate translation (completed in 405 AD) of Acts 2:38 reads:

  > *Petrus vero ad illos: Paenitentiam, inquit, agite, et baptizetur unusquisque vestrum in nomine Iesu Christi...* (Peter replied to them, "Do penance, and let every one of you be baptized in the name of Jesus Christ...")

  The Catholic Church adopted *baptidzo* into their language (Latin) as *baptizo*. Why? Infant baptism appears to have been first practiced in the late second century (in emergency situations where the baby was going to die, and the parents mistakenly believed it might die in a graceless state unless it was immersed), although it was rare until the fifth century. By then it was widespread, special thanks to Augustine. In light of this, it is hardly surprising that the Latin church chose to create a new word, *baptizo*, instead of using the normal Latin verb *immergere* (to immerse).

19. Light from the Patristic Literature

References to baptism in the patristic literature (early church "fathers") abound! It is clear from a survey of the early writings that for the first few centuries everyone was in agreement that baptism was *for the forgiveness of sins*, meant *immersion*, and was the only way to become a Christian. Consider the following examples (emphasis ours):

- Justin, *Apology, 1, 61,* c.150–165 AD: "As many as are *persuaded* and *believe* that the things are true which are taught by us...and decide to live *accordingly*, are instructed to pray and to entreat God with fasting, for the *remission of their past sins*, and we pray and fast with them. Then they are brought by us where there is

*water*, and are *born again...*"
- Hermas, *Shepherd, IV. iii.*, c.140–150 AD: "...when we went *down into the water* and received remission of our former *sins*."
- Irenaeus, *Dem. 3.41f, haer. 5.11.2*, c. 180–200 AD: "We have received *baptism for the remission of sins...* And this baptism is the seal of eternal life and the *new birth* unto God..."
- Creed of the Council of Nicaea, fourth century: "...I acknowledge one baptism for the remission of sins..."

Naturally, such evidences from early church history do not stand on an equal level of authority with the Bible, but they do shed light on the understanding of early Christians of what was involved in becoming a Christian. It is undisputable, baptism in New Testament times was *immersion for salvation*—which was understood for the first few centuries!

20. Other assorted proofs
    - Combination proofs:
      a. Acts 2:41 + 2:47
      b. Galatians 3:26–27 + 4:6
      c. Ephesians 4:5 + 5:26
      d. 1 Peter 1:3, 23 + 3:21
      e. Ephesians 5:26 + 1 Peter 1:23 (James 1:18)
    - Passages showing death and resurrection in Baptism:
      Romans 6:2–7 | 1 Corinthians 1:13–17
      Gal 2:20, 5:24, 6:14 | Colossians 1:13, 22, 2:20, 3:1, 3, 5
    - Other verses:
      1 Cor 6:11, 12:13 | Titus 3:5 (John 3:5)
      Hebrews 6:2, 10:22

---

# 10
# The Holy Spirit I

Since the Spirit is received at baptism, at least a few verses on the Spirit ought to be covered next, or in connection with, the Baptism unit.

- Acts 5:32
- Acts 8:18
- Romans 1:11
- Romans 8:9
- 2 Corinthians 12:12
- 2 Timothy 1:7

### Points

1. Indwelling
   - Received at baptism (Acts 2:38, 5:32; Galatians 3:26–27, 4:6).
     a. Hence necessary for salvation (Romans 8:9; John 3:5; Titus 3:5).

b. Also described as baptism in the Spirit (1 Corinthians 12:13).[6]
- Helps us be transformed.
  a. The Spirit changes us to become more and more like Jesus (2 Corinthians 3:18).
  b. The Spirit makes us fishers of people (2 Timothy 1:7).
- Helps us to overcome our timidity.
- Gives us power to live a dynamic life.
- Helps us to focus on others more than on ourselves, and so become more loving people.
- Increases our self-discipline—every area of our lives comes under the Lordship of Jesus.

2. Miraculous gifts of the Holy Spirit
   - Could be passed on through apostolic laying on of hands (Acts 6:6, 6:8, 8:6, 8:18; Romans 1:11; 2 Timothy 1:6, etc.).
   - When the generation after the apostles died, the supernatural gifts of the Holy Spirit became more and more rare.
     a. There were no apostles around to transmit them.
     b. The supernatural gifts were a confirmation of the message (Acts 14:3; Hebrews 2:3–4; Mark 16:20), but miracles only confirmed the *spoken* word of God, never the *written* word. Once the New Testament was completed, therefore, there wasn't the same need for them any longer.
     c. Signs, wonders and miracles were marks of the apostles (2 Corinthians 12:12). Once the apostles completed their work and laid the foundation for the church (Ephesians 2:19–20), the supernatural apostolic ministry was no longer needed.
     d. Conclusion: there are no supernatural gifts of the Holy Spirit today.

3. Are miracles impossible today?
   - God still answers prayer (e.g. James 5:16), so you can't say that God never does anything fantastic anymore.
   - But many "miracles" are of the devil (2 Thessalonians 2:9; Deuteronomy 13:1; Matthew 24:24, 7:22), or psychosomatic. The latter is particularly true of neopentecostalism.
   - Remember, apparently miraculous activity doesn't prove one's salvation (Matthew 7:22; 1 Samuel 19:18, etc.).

*Conclusion*

The Holy Spirit study in the next chapter (Series C) covers ten difficult questions about the Holy Spirit.

**Conclusion to Series B**

Well, that's it for Series B. In the next chapter we find yet another round of useful studies. Reminder: This material is meant to be used, not only read. Do something with it! Get out there, let your light shine, and teach anyone who will listen.

## Notes

[1] The regular cigarette smoker runs a risk of death from lung cancer ten times greater than the nonsmoker does. Smoking more than a pack a day increases the risk of death from lung cancer twenty times greater than nonsmokers' risk level. Only one out of twenty cases of lung cancer is cured. The death rate from all causes is about 60% higher among smokers as compared to nonsmokers. A pack of cigarettes takes six hours off your life. Nonsmokers may live 10 to 15 years longer than smokers. The death rate from heart attacks is three times greater with smokers than nonsmokers. Cigarette smokers between the ages of 45 and 64 miss 40% more workdays than nonsmokers.

[2] Although something you ship is a shipment, there is actually no such word as "disfellowship*ment.*" The opposite of fellowship is disfellowship; the opposite of disfellowship is fellowship, not "fellowshipment." (E.g., "Unfortunately there was a disfellowship at midweek service last week.")

[3] A divisive person is by definition one who is dividing the body of Christ by beginning his or her own group, apart from the body. N.b.: Merely disagreeing with a leader does not constitute "divisiveness." Nor does 1 Corinthians 1:10 forbid differences of opinion. See also Romans 14:1, 1 Corinthians 16:12, Acts 15:39.

[4] There have been many books written on the resurrection, such as Gary Habermas and Michael Licona's *The Case for the Resurrection of Jesus* (Grand Rapids: Kregel, 2004).

If you would like more material but do not have time to read an entire book, you may appreciate chapters 9 (That's Impossible! The Miracles of Jesus) and 10 (Many Convincing Proofs: The Resurrection) of my book *Compelling Evidence for God and the Bible: Finding Truth in an Age of Doubt* (Eugene, Oregon: Harvest House, 2010).

[5] This is better news than you may realize. When Jesus returns, we will be resurrected. Without our "resurrection body" (see 1 Corinthians 15) we cannot be taken up to heaven! See how vital the resurrection is? By the way, the order of events biblically, beginning with our own exit from the world of the living, is: death—paradise—resurrection—judgment—heaven. Simply put: No resurrection, no heaven!

[6] For more on this, see *The Spirit* (Spring, Texas: Illumination Publishers, 2017), which deals with this intriguing subject. Simply stated, my view is that, just as the new birth involves water and Spirit (John 3:5; Titus 3:5), so baptism is immersion in water (Acts 8:36) and Spirit (1 Corinthians 12:13).

# 13
# Guard the Gospel
## *Series C*

Whereas the Series A and B *Guard the Gospel* studies are intended to teach you how to bring non-Christians to a positive decision for Christ, Series C goes far beyond the elementary teachings. Its purpose is to meet specialized needs. All the studies are usable by those without formal training, but several of the topics in this chapter are more challenging to master.

**The Word II**
**Jesus III**
**Repentance III**
**Calvinism / Once Saved, Always Saved**
**Hot-Cold-Lukewarm**
**Old Covenant, New Covenant**
**Messianic Prophecy**
**Premillennialism / The Coming of the Kingdom**
**The Holy Spirit II / Feelings**
**The Judgment / Is Sincerity Enough?**

Notice that several of the units incorporate a second study—for example, the unit on Calvinism includes Once Saved, Always Saved.

---

### 1
### The Word II

The Series C Word Study (The Word II) will equip you to answer a number of questions commonly arising about the trustworthiness of the Bible. Accordingly, a question-and-answer format has been followed for this chapter.

- Proverbs 30:6
- Hosea 4:6
- Matthew 22:29
- John 7:17
- Colossians 2:8
- Psalm 119
- Dead Sea Scrolls

1. Do we know anything about Christ or Christianity apart from what the Bible tells us?
   - Sources: Tacitus, Suetonius, Thallus, Pliny (Roman sources), Josephus, Rabbinic literature (Jewish sources), New Testament Apocrypha, Patristics (more than 30,000 citations before 325 AD) (early Christian sources), Koran (Muslim source, seventh century AD). Conclusion: the Bible is only one of many sources for early Christianity. Many of these sources will be found in *Evidence That Demands a Verdict*, McDowell, and *Jesus and Christian Origins outside the New Testament*, Bruce.

2. How did the Bible come together?
   - "Canonization" was a lengthy and intricate process, governed by God's providence. (*Kanon*—Greek for "reed, measuring rod, cane," canon is the norm by which the inspiration and or authority of a book is measured.) The earliest written canon we have is probably the "Muratorian Canon," dating from around 180 AD. The majority, if not all, of the books of the New Testament were in circulation earlier than that date. The earliest canon that corresponds exactly to our present NT canon dates from the early fourth century. The OT canon seems to have been settled around the end of the first century AD. See *The Books and the Parchments,* Bruce; *The New Testament Documents: Are They Reliable?,* Bruce.

3. Is the Bible accurate?
   - The Dead Sea Scrolls (DSS) show the excellent textual transmission of the Old Testament. They date from around 200 BC to 68 AD. See *Second Thoughts on the Dead Sea Scrolls,* Bruce. They were discovered in 1947 in the vicinity of the Dead Sea by a shepherd boy (named Muhammad). *Before* the discovery of these MSS (manuscripts), which include all OT books except Esther, as well as other materials, the earliest surviving OT MSS dated from around the tenth century AD. The most celebrated find is probably the complete Isaiah scroll (two complete and seventeen partial copies were discovered) that proves the excellent textual transmission of Isaiah 53, a key messianic prophecy.[1]

4. Is the King James version the only "authorized" version?
   - It was a good translation for its day (completed 1611) but is now out of date.[2] Never officially "authorized," the KJV did not have access to DSS for the Old Testament, or the Greek papyrus finds (nineteenth century) for the New Testament. There were 500 errors in the first edition, and until the eighteenth century, the KJV still included the Apocrypha. Furthermore, the English language has undergone many significant changes since Elizabethan times.

5. What about other English versions?
   - Be wary of *paraphrases* (The Living Bible, New Living

Translation), exercise caution with *free translations* (New English Bible, Jerusalem Bible, Today's English Version), teach from *dynamic equivalence versions* (New International Version, Holman Christian Standard Bible, English Standard Version), rely on *stricter translations* for study and lesson preparation (New Revised Standard Version, New American Standard Bible). In the English speaking world, the New International Version (dynamic equivalence translation) is now the most popular, and is reasonably accurate.[3]

6. Do we have everything the apostles wrote?
   - By no means! See Colossians 4:16; 1 Corinthians 5:9; 2 Thessalonians 3:17, etc. The New Testament furnishes us with part of what the apostles wrote, but not all. It is sufficient, but not exhaustive—otherwise our Bibles would be very fat indeed! See John 20:30 and 21:25. (There also exist the NT Apocrypha and NT Pseudepigrapha, not to be confused with these. NT Apocryphal writings for the most part date between the second and fourth centuries AD, and contain speculations about the childhood of Jesus, the travels of the apostles, the end of the world, etc. Pseudepigrapha are writings that claim [falsely] to be written by someone other than the true author. For example, men in the fourth century may have written a book and ascribed it to a first-century person, such as the Apostle Thaddaeus. Such fraudulent works are not difficult to detect.)

7. Are Paul's writings really inspired? Do they have equal authority with the words of Jesus?
   - See 2 Peter 3:15–16 ("wisdom that God gave him," "other Scriptures"). Peter certainly seems to have thought so! Furthermore, Paul's writings were recognized by the early church.
   - For another line of reasoning, see 1 Timothy 5:18, quoting Luke 10:7.
   - In 1 Corinthians 7, Paul is *not* saying his views are mere opinion, as compared to the teachings of Jesus. In 1 Corinthians 7:12 he is legislating on a subject the Lord had not addressed (mixed marriages), whereas in 7:10 he refers to the words of Jesus on a subject Paul also refers to (on marriages between Jews), and on which there was no need for him to offer further instruction.

8. Are there other inspired writings in addition to the Bible?
   - Galatians 1:6–9, 12. E.g., Mormons: *Book of Mormon* (1827), *Pearl of Great Price, Doctrine and Covenants;* Unification Church: *The Divine Principle;* Christian Scientists: *Science and Health with Key to the Scriptures.* The gospel is nonadjustable and must not be tampered with or added to (1 Corinthians 4:6; Deuteronomy 4:2, 12:32). There is no "latter-day revelation" (Jude 3; 2 Peter 1:3; Ephesians 4:13; 1 Corinthians 13:10–11). The canon of inspired writings was apparently fixed by the late first century.

9. What about the Apocrypha?
   - Written in the period 200 BC–100 AD, and brought into the Latin Christian Bible c. 400 AD, these writings have not been considered inspired by many Protestants since the later sixteenth century (during the later Reformation). The Apocrypha had been widely used by the Catholic Church since inception. I would encourage you to study these writings and make your own decision as to their usefulness. They fill in the gap between the end of the Old Testament (late fifth century BC) and the beginning of the New (early first century AD). For example, 1 Maccabees (second century BC) is of considerable historical value. There are a number of allusions to the Apocrypha in the New Testament.

10. What if people do not believe in the Bible? What should we do then?
   - Get them to read it! (Romans 10:17; John 20:30–31).
   - They must be willing to put it into practice (John 7:17). Following God's word is fundamentally a *moral*, not an *intellectual*, issue.

---

## 2
## Jesus III: The Great "I Am"

This study follows the "I am" statements of Jesus in John, and is excellent for beginners, adherents of other world religions, and "enlightened" or liberal thinkers offended by the idea that one single religion might have the truth.

Jesus is "the great 'I Am'" (John 8:58). This epithet refers to God himself. In Hebrew, YHWH (the Lord's name) is related to the word for "I am." The gospel of John is filled with allusions to a well-known OT text—Exodus 3:14, with its overtones of deliverance and redemption.

- "I Am" (Exodus 3:14)
- John 6:35
- John 8:12
- John 10:14
- John 11:25
- John 14:6

John 6:35—Jesus is the bread of life.
- He keeps us going when we are spiritually hungry.
- God has set eternity in our hearts (Ecclesiastes 3:11). But until a relationship with God fills the empty place in our heart, we will never be truly satisfied.
- OT connection: Exodus 16 (Manna).

John 8:12—Jesus is the light of the world.
- "Darkness" involves being unsure where you are going in life, confused, fearful...
- This is a bold claim! Jesus does not say, "*There* is the light of the

world," but *I am* the light...
- OT connection: Isaiah 9:1–2 (messianic prophecy).

John 10:14—Jesus is the Good Shepherd.
- Sheep (biblically and pastorally) tend to wander.
- We need a shepherd.
- He cares for us sheep.
- OT connection: Ezekiel 34 (the Messiah as a new "David").

John 11:25—Jesus is the resurrection.
- It's not reincarnation that Jesus is offering (Hebrews 9:27).
- Nor is it "afterlife" that Jesus promises (everyone will have that), but eternal life with God!
- Because of Jesus (and his resurrection), we too will be resurrected.
- OT connection: Psalm 16 (prediction of resurrection of Messiah).

John 14:6—Jesus is the only way.
- An incredibly exclusive claim!
- People don't "accidentally" believe in Jesus (without knowing it)! It's a conscious decision (John 3:18). In the same way, you don't get married by accident. It's by mutual agreement and happens at a specific point in time. If Jesus is right, no other position or religion is valid.
- No wonder Jesus received such opposition!
- OT connection: Deuteronomy 18 (the prophet like Moses who must be heeded).

*Conclusion*

There are many other "I am" verses we could have looked at (John 8:58, 10:7, 15:1, etc.). But this assortment of just five of the amazing statements of Jesus is enough to give us a good picture of how radical a character he was!

---

## 3
## Repentance III: The Rich Young Ruler & Zacchaeus

This study is a comparison of two men with two different responses to Jesus. The episode of the Rich Young Ruler is found in Matthew 19, Mark 10, and Luke 18. Zacchaeus is found, however, only in Luke 19. What do we see when we compare and contrast these two would-be disciples of Jesus Christ? The difference between the two may be just the thing to help your religious friend see where he or she really stands with God.

In addition to Luke 19, for Zacchaeus, choose one of the three parallel passages on the Rich Young Ruler. Begin with the rich man (the negative example) end with Zacchaeus (the positive example).

- Matthew 19, Mark 10, Luke 18 (Rich Young Ruler)
- Luke 19 (Zacchaeus)

Characteristics:

- Both appear to be well-known individuals.
- Both have money.
- Both took the initiative to find Jesus.
- Both "humble themselves" to approach Jesus—the rich man *down* on his knees, the tax collector Zacchaeus *up* in a tree.
- The rich man looks better on the outside. He speaks the religious lingo and is impressive to others. Zacchaeus is not; his profession is despised, he is corrupt, and even his physical appearance does not command respect.
- Both need to repent! Each has a major shortcoming, involving wealth.

Differences:

- Only Zacchaeus repents.
- The rich man is unwilling to let go of his "god," his money.
- Zacchaeus responds quickly to Jesus.
- Zacchaeus *volunteers* to make restitution for his sins (2 Corinthians 7:10).
- Paradoxically, the "less likely" disciple finds salvation, whereas the "shoe-in" fails the crucial test.

*Conclusion:*

The disciples are shocked when they realize the kind of repentance Jesus is looking for. (See the section following the failure of the rich man to put Jesus first.) And yet God's plan is to bless us a hundredfold! Remember, end positively.

---

## 4
## Calvinism

- T.U.L.I.P. (acronym)
- Romans 5:7
- Acts 13:46
- 1 Timothy 2:4
- Hebrews 10:29–30
- 2 Peter 2:20

*Introduction*

John Calvin (1508–1564) was one of the leading thinkers in the Protestant Reformation. He retaught many of the ideas of Augustine, bishop of Hippo (in North Africa), who lived 354–430 AD. Denominations that follow his thinking are numerous: Baptists, Presbyterians, Reformed, many Anglicans, even the original "Churches of Christ" (1667–1830).

Calvinism is a unified and internally consistent system. The basic teachings are described by the convenient acronym T.U.L.I.P.:

Total Depravity
Unconditional Election
Limited Atonement
Irresistible Grace
Perseverance of the Saints

This is one of the most academic of our studies, and is intended to show the consistent error of Calvinism. (This is also called "Reformed Theology.")

1. Total Depravity
    - *Doctrine:* There is absolutely no good in fallen humankind. Before a person is converted, all their actions and thoughts are sinful and selfish. Therefore there is absolutely nothing they can do to save themself; salvation is completely from God, and the person plays no part in it. Only when God's Spirit quickens a person and enables them to believe can they be saved.
    - *Supporting passages:* Calvinists appeal to Ephesians 2:1, Romans 3:12 and many other passages to prove that we are no more able to save ourselves than a corpse can rise up and walk.
    - *Biblical emphasis:* Calvinism stresses the sinfulness and lostness of humankind. This is an emphasis sadly lacking in the religious world, which prides itself on its good deeds and empty rituals. It also emphasizes the majestic sovereignty of God.
    - *Error:* The Bible does indeed paint a dark picture of human selfishness, but to say that there is no good at all in an unsaved person is going too far. Romans 5:7 and many other passages assume or imply that there is some good in the world at large. Cornelius was a good man (Acts 10:2, 35). As far as salvation goes, Calvinism grossly undervalues the part we play in accepting the salvation that God offers. To illustrate, we'd all agree that there is nothing a drowning man can do to save himself. But when he is thrown a life preserver, he must *decide* to accept it and then *do something* about it (grab on). Calvinism errs because it denies that people have *free will.*
    - *Logical link* (to next section): Total Depravity logically leads to the next of the five basic Calvinistic doctrines, Unconditional Election. Since there is nothing a person can do to save themself, God and God alone decides who will be saved.

2. Unconditional Election
    - *The doctrine:* Unconditional Election, or Predestination, teaches that the decision about who will be saved is 100% God's. He has decided in advance exactly who will be saved. Not only is there no way for us to save ourselves, but *even if we wanted* to be saved, unless God had already chosen us, we would have no chance of going to heaven.

- *Supporting passages:* God's *grace* saves us, and faith is a gift from God (Ephesians 2:8–9). Acts 13:48 speaks of "those who were appointed for eternal life." Revelation 20:5 mentions the "book of life," in which the names of the saved have been written. Romans 8:29 mentions predestination, so obviously who will be saved has already been determined
- *Biblical emphasis:* This doctrine emphasizes *God's sovereignty*, another truth missing in our selfish world, where everyone wants to determine the course of their own life. Furthermore, it is true that God is willing to save men and women of *any* race, nation, social class, income bracket or religious background; salvation is unconditional in that sense.
- *Error:*
  a. To begin with, Ephesians 2:8–9 doesn't teach that faith is a gift from God (though ultimately God does help us to believe, through his Word, Christians, circumstances, etc.). Ephesians 2:8–9 says that *salvation* is a gift from God!
  b. Acts 13:48 discusses God's involvement in our salvation, but Acts 13:46 shows that we are justly responsible for accepting or rejecting the gospel. Again, free will has been overlooked!
  c. Revelation 20:5 mentions the Lamb's book of life, but Revelation 3:5 implies that it is possible for our names to be erased from it. Psalm 69:27–28 is yet another passage shattering the notion that God's book contains only the names of the saved, and that the list is unchangeable.
  d. Romans 8:29 says that Christians are predestined to become like Christ (not the same as being predestined to salvation), but in Ephesians and other books there is a sort of predestination that *is* mentioned. Two analogies may be helpful:
    (1) Train destination: You board a London train, and the destination is clearly marked "Heathrow Airport." This destination has been decided in advance. Heathrow Airport is its "pre-destination." As long as you stay on the train, you are fine. If, however, you choose to leave the train, you forfeit your "predestination." The train still goes to the airport, but you will miss your flight—unless of course you manage to get back on the train. This analogy assumes, unlike Calvinism, that we have free will.
    (2) Aerial view: From the top of a tall building you are able to view two intersecting streets. Down the first street a speeding sports car approaches the deadly intersection, down the other street zooms a motorcycle. From your vantage point, you can "see" the accident even *before* it happens. But are you responsible for the collision? Foreknowledge does not imply predestination.
  e. 2 Thessalonians 2:14 clearly teaches that God *does* call us, but the call is not arbitrary, or through strange sensations, but through the gospel. There is an inseparable link between the gospel and the "sanctifying work of the Spirit." No one is saved in a vacuum! See also Romans 10:13–17.

f. Finally, Unconditional Election is unfair! Imagine the scenario: you are standing before God's throne, hoping to be saved, and hear the sentence pronounced on you: damned! Moreover, God informs you that the deck was stacked against you from the beginning; there never was any hope of your being saved. Would you or would you not be justified in accusing God of unfairness? Calvinism promotes a distorted, negative concept of God. It's not going too far to say that in Calvinism, conversion is a mere formality, since people are saved or damned even before they are born.

- *Logical link:* Since God does nothing in vain, and since only the few "elect" will be saved, Christ must have died only for those who would be saved. Thus the doctrine of Limited Atonement flows logically from Unconditional Election, or Predestination.

3. Limited Atonement
   - *Doctrine:* Christ's sacrifice on the cross was limited to those who would be saved. In other words, he did not bear the sins of all humankind, only those of the elect.
   - *Supporting passages:* In Matthew 26:28, the blood is said to provide forgiveness of sins for "many," and in Ephesians 5:25 Christ is said to have given himself up for the church. Acts 20:28 teaches that God bought the church with his blood (not the world at large).
   - *Biblical emphasis:* This doctrine enhances the "success" of the crucifixion, and affirms that God does nothing in vain. So many in our world today have no appreciation of the cross, and like to think that, if there is a God, everybody will be saved anyway.
   - *Error:*

     a. The Bible teaches that all people are potentially saved through the cross (Romans 5:18). In fact, 1 Timothy 2:4 says that God wants all people to be saved. If this is God's sovereign will, why did Christ die only for the elect? Thus Calvinism contradicts 1 Timothy 2:4.

     b. Matthew 26:28: Either the word "many" refers to all humankind, or we can say that while the blood was shed for humankind, the "blood of the (new) covenant" mentioned here implies that salvation is only for those in the covenant, not that the blood was shed for a set number of persons.

     c. Ephesians 5:25 and Acts 20:28: The idea that God bought the redeemed with his blood is certainly biblical, but that in no way necessitates that he only shed enough blood to redeem those who would be saved. A good illustration is found in 1 Timothy 4:10: "God... is the Savior of all people, and especially of those who believe." The Bible teaches that *anyone* willing to believe and repent can be saved.
   - *Logical link:* Since Christ died only for the elect, no grace is "wasted" on nonelect unbelievers. So when God's grace, through his Spirit, starts to work in an unbeliever's heart, it cannot be resisted.

4. Irresistible Grace
    - *Doctrine:* The Spirit of God draws people to Christ, and it is utterly impossible to resist God's grace once this has begun to happen.
    - *Supporting passages:* John 6:44 says that God the Father draws people to Christ. Acts 16:14 discusses Lydia's conversion, and says that the Lord opened her heart to believe.
    - *Biblical emphasis:* This doctrine certainly emphasizes the Spirit's power.
    - *Error:*
        a. John 6:44 only says God draws all people to himself, not how or on what basis he draws them. Other passages in John make it clear that the people God chooses to draw are those who will accept God on his own terms (1:12, 8:31, etc.).
        b. It is not denied that the Lord opened Lydia's heart, but *how* did he open her heart? *Through the message* (Acts 16:13). As always, faith comes through hearing the Word! (Romans 10:17).
        c. Acts 7:51, Galatians 5:4, Hebrews 10:29–30, Hebrews 12:15, and many other passages teach it is possible for people to resist God's grace. How can grace be "irresistible" if so many people *do* in fact resist it?
        d. Calvinism, through teachings such as Irresistible Grace, makes humans into robots. Once again, there is no free will.
    - *Logical link:* Since grace is irresistible, it follows that once saved, you're always saved. In other words, falling away is impossible.

5. Perseverance of the Saints
    - *Doctrine:* Once a person is saved, it is impossible for that person to become "unsaved." And if someone seems to be saved, but later leaves God, that is proof that they were never saved to begin with. Only the saints persevere to the end.
    - *Supporting passages:* John 10:29 says that no one can snatch the sheep (Christians) out of the hand of the Shepherd (Christ). And Romans 8:38–39 teaches that nothing can separate us from the love of God.
    - *Biblical emphasis:* We need to feel secure in our salvation. So many religions and denominations do not offer their members the security of knowing that they are saved. It will be difficult for us to live effectively as disciples if we are always doubting our salvation.
    - *Error:*
        a. John 10:29 says that no one can snatch a Christian away from their secure position, but it never says that a Christian cannot *choose* to walk away from the flock (and the Shepherd). Isaiah 53:6 says that all of us like lost sheep had gone astray. Even the chosen people, the Jews, were able to go astray, and Jesus told his disciples to go first to "the lost sheep of Israel."
        b. Romans 8:38–39 is certainly a great comfort to real disciples, but Jude 21 shows that we need to do our part to stay in God's love.

c. Ironically, far from providing any real security, Calvinistic teaching destroys it; you can never really know you're saved, since if you give up, that means you never were in the elect to begin with! The Bible, on the other hand, says that you absolutely *can* know that you are saved (1 John 5:13—see 1 John 2:3–6).
d. James 5:19–20 (see 1:15) shows that a Christian can wander from the truth.
e. The Bible repeatedly says that we will be saved "if" we obey God or persevere: John 15:6; Hebrews 12:25; 1 Corinthians 15:2; 2 Peter 1:10. Salvation is unconditional in the sense that there is nothing we can do to *earn* it, but it is *not* unconditional in the sense that we can't lose it.
f. It is often (correctly) said that we are saved by faith. If this is true, what happens when we give up our faith? Will God force us to be saved? Again, where is free will?
g. 2 Peter 2:20 makes it abundantly clear that a Christian can fall away, as do many other passages. (See discussion in Supplementary Study, below.)
h. Moreover, Perseverance of the Saints is contrary to experience! There are many men and women who became Christians, were doing well spiritually, bearing fruit, and growing in the Lord, but who allowed their hearts to stray and harden. They are not with us today—but that does not mean that they were never saved initially! They most certainly *were* saved, but they have wandered away!
i. Perhaps the gravest error of this doctrine is that Perseverance of the Saints, or Once Saved, Always Saved, is a great disincentive to evangelism and commitment in general:
   (1) Although a noble heart should be eager to do good, discipleship is in fact secondary, or irrelevant, since our salvation was decided in heaven long before we were born. Not surprisingly, most Calvinists are lukewarm in their commitment.
   (2) Why evangelize the "lost" when there's nothing you can do to save them? If they're damned (not of the elect), no amount of evangelism can help them. And if they are in the elect, sooner or later God will make that plain to them, but in the meantime your evangelizing them really doesn't matter, since they will be saved anyway! Sadly, but consistently with their system, historically most Calvinists have not actively sought to reach out to the lost and lead them to salvation.

- *Logical link:* By now you can see that Calvinism, although it contradicts the Bible over and over, is internally a highly consistent system.

*Concluding Thoughts and Strategy*

We have studied the five petals of the Calvinistic tulip, and have seen that they do not fit with what the Bible teaches. This is obviously a complex subject, and many non-Christians would be unable to grasp the study as it stands. A helpful alternative is to go through the supplementary study below, which focuses on the fifth petal of the tulip, Perseverance of the Saints. Then, refer to the main study as necessary. This is probably the best strategy for helping someone to see the error of Calvinism.

On the positive side, we have seen that Calvinism is correct to emphasize the:

Sinfulness of humankind
Sovereignty of God
Success of the crucifixion
Spirit's power
Security of grace

However, on the negative side, we saw that there were many faults with Calvinism:

Too negative a view of humankind
The denial of free will
No salvation by faith
Little incentive for evangelism
Creation of an unjust God
Contrary to experience
Can breed lukewarm commitment
Refuted by hundreds of verses

---

## Supplementary Study: **Once Saved, Always Saved**

There are literally hundreds of scriptures that demolish the position of those who claim it is impossible, once one has come to know Jesus Christ, to lose salvation.

- Hebrews 10:26–31
- Hebrews 6:4–8
- John 10:28
- Romans 8:39
- 2 Peter 2:20–22

**Hebrews 10:26–31**—Deliberate sin can cause us to lose our salvation. This is clear, yet some insist this passage applies only to non-Christians, or unsaved churchgoers. But verses 29 ("the blood of the covenant that sanctified them") and 30 ("The Lord will judge his people") show that the writer has in mind the covenant people—who are already saved.

**Hebrews 6:4–8**—It is impossible to bring certain people back to repentance. Where the "point of no return" is God only knows.[4]

"Crucifying the Son of God all over again" implies they have already shared in Jesus' death and resurrection. (Hebrews 6:7–8 continues the thought.) This is the strongest passage in Hebrews refuting Once Saved, Always Saved (see also 3:12–14, 4:1, 4:11, 6:11–12, 10:36, 12:14–15, 13:4). And yet there are hundreds of other verses in the New Testament that disprove this false doctrine—not even to consider the Old Testament.

**John 10:28**—This verse is often cited as proof of the impossibility of apostasy. However, it does not state that it is impossible for someone to turn their back on God (Luke 9:62) and walk away, only that it is impossible for external powers to drag away a disciple against their will.

**Romans 8:39**—Nothing can separate us from the love of God, but it's our responsibility to "keep ourselves in God's love" (Jude 21). Again, there is free will. Most advocates of Once Saved, Always Saved (Perseverance of the Saints, Eternal Security), at some point, deny free will.

**2 Peter 2:20–22**—This verse clinches the argument. These people have "escaped the corruption of the world," which is possible only through participating in the divine nature (see 1:4). The corruption of the world is vividly symbolized by vomit and mud. It is tortuous to argue that the "washing" applies to a non-Christian. Finally, if they give up on God, they are worse off at the end than they were if they had never become Christians. Clearly it is possible for a Christian to lose their salvation!

*Conclusion*

Although at first Once Saved, Always Saved appears to take on an academic point, in fact it strikes directly at the heart of the issue: one's willingness to follow Christ. Properly done, it's quite a challenging study.

---

## 5
## Hot, Cold, Lukewarm

- Revelation 3:14–22
- Revelation 2:4–5

Revelation 3:14–16 is the text for this basic study.[5] Here are the main points to cover:

- Jesus knows our hearts and deeds. Deeds do matter!
- There are three degrees of commitment: hot, cold, and lukewarm.
  *Note: In the context of Revelation 3 and the water systems of Laodicea, either hot or cold water would be acceptable. It was only the lukewarm that was repulsive. Thus this study is a creative expansion of the original meaning.*
  a. As in any area of life, for example, sports, a "hot" person is

characterized by fervent commitment. A hot person will be characterized by such things as Bible study, prayer, evangelistic zeal, devotion to the church, desire to repent of sin, etc.

b. Cold people are either uninterested or negative. They have no desire to perform the deeds the hot person performs, and probably have no interest in church, reading the Bible, etc.

c. Ask your friend whether they think they are hot. If they are honest, they will probably say no. Then ask them whether they are cold. Again, a yes answer is unlikely, so tell them there is only one other category: lukewarm. Don't allow your friend to plead that they are "lukewarm-hot" or "sometimes hot, sometimes lukewarm." Jesus spoke of only three degrees; there are no half–categories. Make sure they agree they are lukewarm.

- Ask them which temperature is most pleasing to God. The answer, of course, is "hot." Then ask them which temperature comes next. The answer, for most people surprisingly, is "cold." And, yes, "lukewarm" is the worst temperature possible.
- Revelation 2:4–5 shows us that all Christians begin "hot"—at a certain "height," and may need, from time to time, to be called back to their original standard.
- Since they have already agreed that they are lukewarm, drive the implications home: their salvation is in jeopardy, if they ever were truly saved. Jesus prefers that we be either hot or cold, but not lukewarm. That makes Jesus sick to his stomach. In the passage, Jesus is about to spit his lukewarm followers out of his mouth. (Do not try to drive home the implications too early, or you will find your friend doing exegetical gymnastics, redefining "hot," telling you, "That's just your interpretation," etc.)
- Now that your friend knows where they stand, ask them what they are going to do about it. Set up a study. Get a commitment to come to church, or to accept the "three-week challenge" to attend all the meetings for three weeks. Encourage them to start evangelizing. Also commend them for their honesty in admitting where they stand.

---

## 6
## Old Covenant, New Covenant

*Introduction: the Sabbath*

Many in the religious world today insist that Christians must observe the Sabbath. Most interpret this to mean that on Sundays Christians should have a day of rest. But what does the Bible say? For one, the Sabbath is the seventh day of the week, not the first. But Saturdays aren't the only Sabbath days, according to the Old Testament. Sabbatical and Jubilee years (Leviticus 25) count too, and thus in a fifty-year span a typical Jew would have observed over 5,000 Sabbath days, as compared to only 2,600 for the modern "Sabbath keeper." Moreover, on the Sabbath the people of God had to stay at home (Exodus 16:29). No sports, no visiting friends, and (strictly speaking) no attending church services! Nor may any cooking be done—all food must be prepared in advance (Exodus 16:23–29). All work is prohibited. Finally, the Old Testament teaches that failure to observe the Sabbath is punishable by *death*! (Numbers 15:35). Who really observes the Sabbath today? No one!

Obviously, there are parts of the Old Testament that have not carried over into the New Testament (e.g. sacrificing lambs and pigeons). Are we bound by the Sabbath? Or other holy days ("holi-days")? Is there a priesthood today, a clergy-laity system? Is the church building the "house of God"? In short, exactly what *is* the relationship between the Old and New Covenant?

The following study may be done as a group Bible discussion or as a personal study. It is invaluable for those from a ritualistic and traditional background, and even for those from other world religions. Old Covenant, New Covenant highlights the uniqueness of New Testament Christianity and explains much of the confusion in Christendom today.

- Colossians 2:16
- John 4:24
- Ephesians 1:1
- 1 Timothy 2:5
- Colossians 2:17

Two Covenants

- Hebrews 9:15–17 shows that the new covenant (will, testament) superseded the old covenant. Just as two wills cannot be in effect at the same time, neither can two testaments.
- Although the heart of the law carries over into the New Testament (see Galatians 5:14; Matthew 22:37–40), the law and its specific commandments were nailed to the cross, invalidated (Colossians 2:13–14).
- Thus Christians are not bound to observe the regulations of the Old Testament.

Double Standards

- If some days are *holy*, the others must be *unholy*.
- In practice this means that people try harder to please God on the special, or holy, days than at other times. *Two* standards of commitment have thus emerged.
- But Christianity is meant to be a daily lifestyle (Luke 9:23; Romans 12:1), not a weekly observance. *All* time is holy!
- These double standards are seen in a variety of areas:
  a. holy time
  b. holy space
  c. holy people
  d. holy things

- Since the Old Testament distinction between holy and unholy has been invalidated, or transformed, now *all* days are holy, *all* space is holy, *all* people are holy.

Holy Time

- Christians are not bound by Sabbath observance (as in the fourth commandment, Exodus 20). This is made explicit in Colossians 2:16.
- Attempts to be justified by observing special days, seasons, etc. will lead to condemnation (Galatians 4:8–11).
- It is true that the early church often met on Sundays (Acts 20:7; Revelation 1:10), partly in commemoration of Christ's resurrection (Matthew 28:1), which took place on a Sunday, but Sunday is nowhere called a "Sabbath."
- The lesson for us: we should be on our best behavior, striving to be disciples, *all the time.* It is not a *sin* to observe a special day (Romans 14:6), but it is a sin to try to make others do so.

Holy Space

- God cannot be confined to "holy" space (Acts 7:48-49; John 4:24).
- The Old Testament subdivided space, physically restricting access to God (Hebrews 9:1–8—see Matthew 27:51), but the New Testament does not limit access to God in this way (Ephesians 2:18).
- We worship God wherever we are; our whole lives are our worship (Romans 12:1).
- Although the church is called the "household of God" (Ephesians 2:19), the *church building* is no more a "holy place" than any other building.
- The lesson for us: we should strive to do our best for God *wherever we are.*

Holy People

- There are no "saints," in the traditional sense of the word. All Christians are holy, or "saints" (Ephesians 1:1).
- There is no priesthood today except that of Jesus himself (Hebrews 7:23–28). It is true that all disciples form a "royal priesthood" (1 Peter 2:9), yet no one needs to go through another person in order to reach God, and there is no need for the presentation of sacrifice, as Christ has been sacrificed once for all.
- There is only one mediator between God and humankind, and that is Jesus Christ (1 Timothy 2:5). Thus, praying to the saints and Mary is wrong.
- There is no "clergy" (Matthew 23:9). All Christians are to be equally committed. Christians have different gifts and functions, but *all* disciples are expected to obey *all* the commands *all* the time. All disciples are called into the full-time ministry.
- The lesson for us: nothing could be further from the spirit of Jesus Christ than the clergy-laity system, which upholds a double standard of commitment.

Holy Cow!

- Miscellaneous
  - a. Holy foods (1 Timothy 4:3; Hebrews 13:9; Mark 7:19)
  - b. Holy altars (Hebrews 7:27, 13:10)
  - c. Images and icons (Exodus 20:4; 1 John 5:21)
  - d. Vestments, water, censers, medals, relics, languages, formulae, crosses...
  - e. The importing of OT categories into the New Testament simply will not do!

*Conclusion: from Shadows to Light*

Colossians 2:17 teaches that the Law was only a shadow of the reality—or that which creates the shadow—which is found in Christ. Yes, there are many parallels between OT "shadows" and NT realities, but the two covenants are distinct. Today the Old Testament is obsolete (Hebrews 8:13), and yet most of modern Christianity resembles OT Judaism more than the original NT faith! Let's leave the shadows of the Old Covenant and come into the light! That's where real freedom is.[6]

---

## 7
## Messianic Prophecy

This is an Evidences study. Evidences is the area of religion concerned with showing the reasonableness of the Christian faith. (Other areas of evidences, or apologetics, include biblical archaeology, the existence of God, the reliability of the Bible, comparative religion, philosophical proofs, etc.) Messianic prophecy was a crucial study in the early church (Acts 2:25–28, 2:34–35, 4:11, 4:25–26, 8:32–33, 13:33–35).

- Micah 5:2
- Isaiah 7:14
- Psalm 110:1
- Isaiah 9:1–2, 6
- Isaiah 52:13–53:12 (location only)

Prophecies of Jesus' birth

- To be born at Bethlehem (Micah 5:2).
- To be born of a virgin (Isaiah 7:14).
- God to become man (Psalm 110:1; Isaiah 9:6).

Prophecies concerning his ministry

- To be heralded by John the Baptist (Isaiah 40:3–5; Malachi 3:1; 4:5–6).
- To minister in Galilee (Isaiah 9:1–2).
- To be a wise counselor (Isaiah 9:6) and champion of the needy (Isaiah 11:1ff).

- To be the shepherd in the spirit of David (Ezekiel 34).
- To heal the sick (Isaiah 53:4).

Prophecies concerning his death

- To come into Jerusalem on a donkey (Zechariah 9:9).
- To be betrayed (Psalm 41:9).
- To be abandoned by his disciples (Zechariah 13:7).
- Lots to be cast for his clothes (Psalm 22:18).
- To be crucified (Psalm 22).
- To be pierced (Zechariah 12:10).
- To bear our sins on the cross (Isaiah 53).

Prophecies concerning his resurrection and ascension

- Divine rescue (see foreshadowing in Genesis 22).
- Physical resurrection (Psalm 16:10).
- To ascend to God and receive everlasting dominion (Daniel 7: 13–14).

A note on different levels of prophecy

- Foreshadowing: Genesis 22:1–18 (nine parallel details between sacrifice of Isaac and sacrifice of Jesus).
- Prophecy: Psalm 22 (finds deeper fulfillment in events surrounding Jesus, but also makes sense in its original context).
- Strict prophecy: Isaiah 52:13–53:12.
- Be careful! Interpretation of prophecy is tricky.

*Conclusion*

The prophecies are clear and the implications inescapable. Jesus was the Messiah predicted in the Old Testament centuries in advance. There are dozens of other important prophecies about the Christ. This study (intended to be manageable) is, however, a good representation of these remarkable passages. For more on messianic prophecy, please study the material at www.douglasjacoby.com.

---

## 8
## Premillennialism

"Premillennialism" is hard enough to pronounce, let alone to understand. It is a system of doctrines taught by many denominations today, including most evangelical groups.[7] The first major millenarian group, condemned by the church for taking Revelation literally, dates to about 130 AD. Since premillennial teaching is so prevalent in religious circles, the fully equipped Christian worker must grasp the teachings and gain competence in refuting them.

Whereas the doctrines of Calvinism appeal to the mind, the teachings of premillennialism appeal more to the emotions. The basic notion is that we are living in the "last days," under the haunting specter of the second coming of Christ; doomsday is on the way! But for the faithful, it is claimed, great blessings and riches are in store. Since the kingdom of God has not yet arrived (we are said to be living in the "church age"), when Jesus returns he will establish a physical, political, earthly kingdom on this earth. This will come to pass after the "rapture" snatches the saved up to heaven, sparing them the agonies of the painful "tribulation" period, which will punish the unbelievers of the earth. Support for these speculations comes from an assortment of Old Testament passages (out of context), Matthew 24 and its parallel passages, and especially Revelation (the favorite book of premillennialists).

Below is the basic Premillennialism study. We will examine five tenets of premillennialism. Afterward follows a study you can teach on The Coming of the Kingdom.

- "Premillennialism"
- Matthew 24:34/Revelation 1:3
- Acts 2:16
- Revelation 13:17
- Luke 17:20/1 Thessalonians 5:1
- Colossians 1:13/John 18:36

The prophesied end of the world

- The Old Testament is said to prophesy modern political events (Amos 3:7, etc.).
- To support this view, many passages (especially prophecies) are claimed to have "double meanings."
- Matthew 24 (paralleled by Mark 13 and Luke 21) is said to apply to our time, despite the fact that it describes first-century Jewish history and Jesus said that all of it would be fulfilled in his generation (Matthew 24:34).
- Revelation is said to describe the awesome events immediately preceding and following the Second Coming, despite the fact that Revelation claims immediate fulfillment (Revelation 1:3).
  a. Daniel had a vision around 550 BC (Daniel 8:1) that was to be fulfilled around 165 BC, nearly 400 years later. The vision was to be fulfilled "in the distant future."
  b. Surely Revelation 1:3, which states that the prophecy of Revelation will be fulfilled in the "near" future, cannot be any farther away in fulfillment than Daniel's vision! How then can premillennialists claim it applies (mainly) to events around the year 2000?

The last days

- Although a look at the Scriptures clearly shows that the "last days" began with Christ's first coming (see Acts 2:16; Hebrews 1:2; James 5:3; 2 Peter 3:3), premillennialists believe that the last days began quite recently.[8]
- Premillennialists historically have proposed various dates for the start of the last days. In the twentieth century, some popular guesses were 1901, 1914, 1967, 1987 and 2000.
- Although God's word commands every generation to live in

anticipation of the end of the world—be ready!—it simply isn't possible to pinpoint the "end times" of earth's history.

Literalistic interpretation

- When premillennialists say that they take the Bible "literally," they mean that they try to take literally the book of Revelation and other similar parts of the Bible.
- Definition of terms:
  - a. *literal:* straightforward, not symbolic at all: Luke 8:26: "They sailed to the region of the Gerasenes:" The word "sailed" means they traveled by boat, a sail being filled and pushed by the wind. It does not mean (figuratively) that they sailed across the sky, sailed in their minds, or that their friends hallucinated their transit.
  - b. *figurative:* symbolic, metaphorical, not literal: Psalm 91:4: "He (God) will cover you with his feathers, and under his wings you will find refuge." Here God's "wings" symbolize his concern, care, and shelter for his people. God doesn't *literally* have wings (or an arm, ear, mouth, etc.), but that doesn't mean the passage is "incorrect." Figurative passages are normal in biblical poetry and prophecy.
  - c. *literalistic:* taking figurative passages literally. In the previous passage, God would have real feathers: either physical, birdlike feathers or spiritual feathers. This is clearly nonsense!
  - d. *face value:* the natural sense of a passage. We are to take literal passages literally and figurative passages figuratively. Taking the Bible "at face value" avoids the confusion of the literalistic approach.
- Thus, believing that the Bible is *literally* the word of God doesn't mean that every passage must be taken *literally*.
- The literalistic approach leads to many abuses, particularly with the book of Revelation:
  - a. The plagues against the ungodly (which symbolize God's judgment against the sinful world, and particularly against the Roman Empire, who are persecuting the Christians) are taken literally. (Hal Lindsay writes that the torturing locusts of Revelation 9:7–10 are actually Cobra helicopters!)
  - b. The pictures of the victorious church (and the glimpse of heaven) at the end of Revelation are literalized (streets of gold, pearly gates, wealthy Christians!).
  - c. Premillennialists expect a literal battle of "Armageddon" (Revelation 16:16).
  - d. Endless speculations on the meaning of "666" in Revelation 13:18. (Premillennialists love to play with numbers.)
  - e. A typical example is Revelation 13:17, which is construed to mean that every man and woman who does not follow God will have a mark (silicone implant) under the skin of the hand (or forehead) with the number 666, without which they will have no credit. It is a sort of international credit card.

Timetable predictions

- The basic premillennial view of the flow of time divides history into seven 1000-year periods:
  a. about 4,000 years before the coming of Christ
  b. about 2,000 years from then until about now
  c. and a final 1000 years (Latin *millennium*), predicted in Revelation 20, of the triumphant rule of Christ on earth.
- Yet it is clear from Scripture that 1000 is often a symbolic number (Psalm 50:10; Deuteronomy 7:9; Psalm 90:4; 2 Peter 3:8), and it's certainly a symbolic number in Revelation.
- Premillennialists find in the Bible "predictions" of persons, dates, times, events. They try to use prophecy as a sort of timetable. But 1 Thessalonians 5:1 clearly discourages any predictions of the times and dates surrounding the final years of earth's history.
- There is a common pattern to premillennial predictions:
  a. *prediction*: A scripture is taken out of context to "predict" a historical event—usually the end of the world.
  b. *postponement:* The predicted event fails to happen. At first this is rationalized, but soon it becomes an embarrassment.
  c. *depression:* Disappointment sets in, morale drops, confidence in the current leadership is lost.
  d. *recalculation:* The date is refigured. The prediction is seldom dropped; after the initial depression has lifted, followers are willing to assume that the predictors made a mistake in calculation, or made wrong initial assumptions. One premillennial group, the Jehovah's Witnesses, has calculated the end of the world over and over and over: 1874, 1914, 1918, 1925, 1941, 1954, 1975...

Physical, political, earthly kingdom

- Premillennialists wait for the second coming of Christ to usher in a physical, political, earthly kingdom. It is to be based in Jerusalem, and Christians will become "top nation," so to speak. The faithful expect all kinds of thrills and rewards, and it is obvious that wrong motivations abound where the nature of the kingdom is misunderstood. In the first century, Jews took the prophecies literally and expected an earthly kingdom ruled by a conquering warrior Messiah. But Jesus discouraged these would-be "premillennialists" (John 6:15); they completely misunderstood the nature of his messiahship and mission.
- Jesus stated emphatically that his kingdom is "not of this world" (John 18:36).
- Premillennialists take several different approaches:
  a. Jesus meant to establish the kingdom, but had to delay it due to opposition.
  b. The kingdom is only partially here. The Bible does speak of heaven as the "heavenly kingdom" (2 Timothy 4:18), but premillennialists are looking for an intermediate state between the church and heaven: the millennial reign of Christ.

c. Some think that the church will convert the entire world, and thus the kingdom will be ushered in through evangelism (total saturation) and (Christian) political legislation. This position is really "millennialism."

- All these approaches fail to deal with the fact that the kingdom of God expressed itself on earth in a unique way through the church (Colossians 1:13).

Major weaknesses of the premillennial approach

- Passages are taken out of context; Bible study tends to become one-track and superficial.
- Disproportionate emphasis is placed on biblical prophecy.
- Evangelism suffers, as many believers are made to feel that the end of the world is the most important thing.
- The Christian message loses credibility in the eyes of non-believers as predictions are shown to be wrong.

Recommended reading:

- Robert G. Clouse, Robert N. Hosack and Richard V. Pierard, *The New Millennium Manual: A Once and Future Guide* (Grand Rapids: Baker, 1999).
- Gordon Ferguson, *Revelation Revealed* (Spring, Texas: Illumination Publishers, 2012).
- Jim McGuiggan, *Revelation* (Fort Worth: Star Bible Publications, 1976). (800) 433-7507.
- N.T. Wright, *The Millennium Myth: Hope for a Postmodern World* (Louisville: Westminster John Knox Press, 1999).

---

## Supplementary Study: **The Coming of the Kingdom**

This study is a good companion to—and is somewhat less complicated than—the Premillennialism study. In some cases you may wish to use this study as an alternate to the basic Church study.

Many OT passages discuss the kingdom, which is described as present but also as future.[9] See Daniel 2:31–45 (c. 600 BC).

| *Kingdom* | *Substance* | *Dates* |
|---|---|---|
| Babylonian | gold | 605–539 BC |
| Medo-Persian | silver | 539–333 BC |
| Greek | bronze | 333–63 BC |
| Roman | iron + clay | 63 BC |
| Kingdom of God | mountain of stone which fills the earth | 30 AD |

Approach of the kingdom in the first century AD

- John the Baptist's message—Matthew 3:2; see Malachi 3:1, 4:5 (Matthew 11:11–14).

- Jesus' teaching—Matthew 4:17
- Jesus' disciples' teaching—Matthew 10:7
- Luke 24:49; Acts 1:3–8
- Peter to hold keys to the kingdom—Matthew 16:19

Nature of the kingdom

- Not political—John 6:15, 18:36
- Not visible—Luke 17:20–21
- Entered spiritually—John 3:3, 5, 7
- Grows!—Matthew 13:31–33

Day of Pentecost (Acts 2)—Coming of the kingdom: all the loose ends are tied up on that day. (All the prophecies are fulfilled.)

Perspective of the New Testament: The kingdom is especially manifest on earth in the church (Acts 2:30; Colossians 1:12–13; Revelation 1:5–6, 5:10). Yet we may pray for it to continue to "come" (Matthew 6:9), and we eagerly anticipate the kingdom in heaven, as our citizenship is already there (Philippians 3:20).

Seek first the kingdom! Put God first, and seek to do his will (Matthew 6:33, 7:21).

---

## 9
## The Holy Spirit II

The format of this unit is, as with The Word II, a question-and-answer format.

- Matthew 7:22
- Luke 16:31
- John 7:39
- 2 Timothy 1:6

1. Can God heal today?
   - Few have actually seen "healings." Beware of secondhand information.
   - Most "healings" are frivolous (e.g. colds, short legs).
   - Many "healings" are psychosomatic. Positive attitudes or "vibrations" speed up the healing process.
   - Nevertheless, God does heal through *prayer*, even though there is no supernatural *gift* of healing today.

2. Don't miracles prove one's salvation?
   - Deuteronomy 13:1–5. Even if someone performs a miracle, if they aren't preaching the Word, they aren't right with God. Do not go after them; God may be testing you.
   - 1 Samuel 19:18–21. God enables Saul and others to prophesy. Doesn't prove they were saved. (They were opposing God, and by this point Saul has fallen away from God.)

- Revelation 13:13; 2 Thessalonians 2:9. Some "miracles" are of the devil.
- Acts 19:13. *Jews* are casting out demons.
- Mark 13:22. False Messiahs.
- Matthew 7:22. Perhaps the most useful passage. Doing the will of God, not miracles, leads to salvation.

3. Doesn't the Spirit lead us today?
   - Yes, but what does that mean?
   - It is not "reading your feelings": Proverbs 14:12; Jeremiah 17:9.
   - Galatians 5:16–26; Romans 8:1–16. Putting the flesh to death; becoming more like Jesus.
   - Psalm 143:10. Being taught by God to do his will—through the precepts of the Word. Ezekiel 36:27. This is a learning process, a matter of discipline. No shortcuts!

4. Didn't people have the Holy Spirit in the Old Testament?
   - No, not in the *indwelling* sense. John 7:39; Romans 8:9. Strictly speaking, there were no Christians before Pentecost, neither in the Old Testament nor in the gospels. And yet many in the Old Testament are spoken of as having the Spirit, or having the Spirit fall on them: Balaam (Numbers 24:2), Othniel (Judges 3:10), Jephthah (Judges 11:29), Saul (1 Samuel 19:18), David (1 Samuel 16:13), Amasai (1 Chronicles 12:18).

5. Can we nail down the idea that miraculous gifts were passed on only by the apostles?
   - Basic verses: Acts 6:6, 8; 8:6, 17–18.
   - Also 2 Timothy 1:6; Romans 1:11; 1 Corinthians 1:4–7.
   - Paul was in Corinth 18 months, in Ephesus 3 years—a considerable time. They had miraculous gifts because Paul had been there.

6. What about Holy Spirit baptism?
   - There is only one baptism (Ephesians 4:5), and the "rules" are unchanging (Acts 2:39).
   - John the Baptist said that Jesus would baptize us with the Spirit (Mark 1:8).
   - This baptism is the alternative to damnation ("baptism" with fire).
   - Christian baptism involves two elements: water and Spirit (John 3:5; 1 Corinthians 12:12–13). Both are crucial, and we were all baptized with/in/by the one Spirit.
   - No supernatural abilities are conferred through this baptism.
   - In other words, baptism in the Spirit is simply another way of describing Christian conversion.
   - *For more on this subject, see chapter 24 of my book* The Spirit.

7. Don't we need to be filled with the Spirit?
   - Absolutely, but what does it mean?
   - Acts 6: The apostles laid hands on men already filled with the

Spirit (v. 3). "Spirit-filled" has no connection with ability to perform miracles.
- John the Baptist was Spirit-filled from birth (Luke 1:15), but he never performed miracles (John 10:41).
- Ephesians 5:17–20; Colossians 3:16. Counseling one another, singing to one another, putting the Word into our lives. It's a progressive thing, not just one time. We should strive to be filled with the Spirit every moment of the day.
- Being "filled with the spirit" means being spiritual.

8. Does the Spirit do things for us beyond what the Word enables us to do?
   - The Spirit convicts of sin, for example (John 16:8), but *not* apart from the Word (Romans 10:17).
   - The Spirit operates through the Word. For example, it
     a. Quickens us (Psalm 119:50)
     b. Strengthens us (Psalm 119:28)
     c. Sanctifies us (John 17:17)
     d. Gives us wisdom (2 Timothy 3:14–15)
     e. Enlightens us (Psalm 119:130)
     f. Allows us to participate in the divine nature... (2 Peter 1:4)
   - All these things are normally attributed to the power of the Spirit, and rightly so. But notice that in these passages it is the word of God that provides all these blessings.

9. Are there any miracles outside Christianity?
   - Montanism (second-century AD heretical charismatic sect).
   - Sufis (charismatic Islamic sect).
   - God may answer the prayer of a non-Christian and heal them, for example, just to draw them onward in their search for God.
   - But 99.99% of "miracles" are fraudulent, psychosomatic, or exaggerated.

10. Don't we still need miracles today?
   - The historical purpose of the miracles was to confirm the spoken word (Exodus 4:5; 1 Kings 17:24; Mark 16:20; Acts 14:3; Hebrews 2:4). There is no record of confirmation given for the written word (Scripture).
   - Luke 16:19–31. If they don't listen to the Word, they won't believe even if someone rises from the dead. The Word is sufficient for anyone with a pure heart (John 20:30).

*Further Reading*

Please see *The Spirit* (Spring, Texas: Illumination Publishers, 2017). This book contains an extensive bibliography for further reading.

## Supplementary Study: **Feelings**

For neopentecostals, this study is a good prelude to the study of The Word of God, although in some cases it may be wise to study The Word first. The Feelings study presents material you will want to cover with almost all who have neopentecostal leanings.

**Proverbs 3:5**—Trust in God, not your own feelings.

**Proverbs 14:12**—We'll pay the penalty if we follow our own feelings.

**Proverbs 28:26**—It is foolish to follow perceptions, hunches, feelings, intuitions...

**Jeremiah 17:9**—The human heart is deceitful.

**1 Kings 13:1–26**—The story of the young prophet and the old prophet. Particularly useful because it deals with the issue of ultimate authority.

**Galatians 1:6–9**—Even if you were convinced that you had received an angelic visitation, or a revelation from an Apostle, no one has the right to change the gospel message.

**Jeremiah 23:16, 21–22, 25–32, 35–36**—False prophets of OT times:

- Claim to speak from God (verse 16).
- Their messages are purely psychological, not from God (verse 16).
- They water down the word of God (verse 22).
- Their dreams (see Numbers 12:6) are delusions, merely psychological (verses 25–26), and lessen the commitment of the people by imparting false hope (verse 27).
- Although they fancy God to be speaking his word through them, he is not; their messages have absolutely nothing to do with the word of God (verses 28–29).
- They borrow "messages" from one another; they exchange "oracles" (verse 30).
- They do not benefit the people (verses 31–32).
- They do sincerely expect the Lord to speak to them (verse 35).
- They suffer terrible theological confusion as God's word and their word are completely confused (verse 36).
- The end result: they distort God's word (verse 36).

**Jude 19**—These people confuse natural instincts with the Spirit.

**Luke 9:23**—Discipleship means denying your selfish feelings, not following them.

- Deny feelings, follow Christ.
- Follow feelings, deny Christ.

**Matthew 7:21–23**—"Charismatics" and Judgment Day

- Many will be surprised on Judgment Day.
- God expects obedience.
- True spirituality is obeying God, not just feeling him.
- Are you sure you know the Lord? (1 Corinthians 8:3).

# 10
# The Judgment

This study is intended to convict, to awaken, to bring a man or woman more quickly to a decision for God and Jesus Christ. The points are straightforward, and the thrust of the message is clear. Preaching about "the judgment to come" is both powerful and biblical (Acts 24:25; Matthew 3:10, 10:28).

- Revelation 20:15
- Hebrews 10:27
- Luke 12:47
- Luke 16:26
- 2 Thessalonians 1:8

Judgment is universal.
- There are three inescapable facts for all humankind: life, death, and judgment.
- Regardless of position, knowledge, race or nation, all humankind will stand before the throne of God. Anyone who has not lived according to God's word will be condemned (Revelation 20:15).

Hell is dreadful.
- It is terrible and to be feared (Hebrews 10:27).
- It's foolish to laugh at fear as an illegitimate motive; it's healthy to have a fear of dark alleys, high voltage, too close to the edge of a tall building, etc. How much more should we fear hell!

Punishment is proportional to knowledge.
- God is not an ogre or a sadist: he wants everyone to be saved (Romans 2:4; 2 Peter 3:9).
- Nevertheless, there will be punishment for everyone who sins (Romans 3:9–20).[10]
- The severity of punishment after death will vary individual to individual, depending on knowledge (Luke 12:47).
- (This is not to say that anyone who has never understood the gospel can be saved—John 3:18.)
- One thing is sure: if we reject the gospel (understanding it), our judgment will be the most severe!

Hell is irreversible.
- In life, some choices have irreversible consequences: suicide, arson, murder, etc. Hell, too, is a choice (we choose to go there by persisting in living by our own standards instead of God's) that cannot be reversed.
- Once we have died, there is no purgatory, no "upgrading," no second chance (Luke 16:26).
- Since the decision to obey God is so crucial, and the consequences are irreversible, we must choose to put God first as soon as possible—before it's too late.[11]

The only hope is the gospel.

- There is hope, but only those who obey the gospel will be saved (2 Thessalonians 1:8).
- Jesus died in our place; he bore our sins (1 Peter 2:24). Sin must be judged and punished, but Jesus has already borne the penalty.
- Paradoxically (since no self-righteous person can go to heaven—Luke 18:14), in order to go to heaven we must believe that we deserve to go to hell.
- Worried that God will let someone slip through the cracks? Anyone who seeks God's kingdom with all their heart can be saved (Matthew 6:33). But we must take the good news to them! If they listen and obey—even though they don't deserve it—they will be saved. (But if they do not obey the gospel, whether or not they have heard the Word, they will be forever lost—also what they "deserve.")
- Sin is that serious! Sin is so horrible, and God is so loving, that he gave his Son to die for our sins.

---

## Supplementary Study: **Is Sincerity Enough?**

This little study (fifteen to twenty minutes long) is helpful for disciples and future disciples alike. It addresses the question, "What about the sincere religious person?" It also applies, on another level, to those who have never heard the Word in any form.

There are only three passages, though feel free to "flesh it out" according to the needs of your friend.

- 1 Corinthians 4:4
- Romans 10:1–2
- Romans 9:1–3

**1 Corinthians 4:4**—Sincerity is not enough. A clear conscience does not mean you are in the clear. Analogy: *fuel gauge.* You may not be aware that your gasoline/petrol gauge indicates you are on empty, but that does not change the fact of the matter. Someone who has not heard the gospel, or someone who has been mistaught, is not saved if sincere. Ignorance is not bliss.

**Romans 10:1–2**—Sincerity and commitment in religious people are not sufficient for salvation. Paul's fellow Jews were "zealous." Yet, as Paul says, they are lost ("that they may be saved").

**Romans 9:1–3**—Paul was deeply disturbed by the lostness of the religious person. Yet for him this wasn't just an academic question, or a matter of doctrinal irritation. He was willing to contemplate trading places with these people, for, like Moses (Exodus 32:32), he loved them.

Ask, "If you became convinced that your religious friends/those who have never heard/all the people in the world were lost, would you be *willing* to go and take them the message?" If the answer is no, your friend's objections are not entirely sincere. If yes, then challenge them to embrace the teaching of the Bible, regardless of how painful personally it may be.

For sincerity is not enough.

*Conclusion to Series C*

The word of God is powerful! (Jeremiah 23:29). If we learn to communicate it effectively, there is tremendous potential for good! But if we are lazy, we'll wield it wildly and unwisely. God is calling each of us to a deeper knowledge of his word in order that we may equip ourselves to take the Word to an unbelieving and skeptical world. It is to this end that all the *Guard the Gospel* series was designed.

Conclusion to the *Guard the Gospel* Series

Let's never grow content with our level of Bible knowledge, whether we've been in the Lord's church for a long time, are just starting out on our Christian walk, or (especially) if we are serving as Christian leaders. For, as the Hebrew writer says, many of us "by this time...ought to be teachers."

## Notes

[1] For more on this, see *How We Got the Bible* (Spring, Texas: Illumination Publishers, 2005). This is a four-part MP3 audio set with notes.

[2] The KJV was completed in 1611 and revised in 1629, 1638, 1762 and 1769. See Jack P. Lewis, *The English Bible from KJV to NIV: A History and Evaluation, 2nd ed.* (Grand Rapids: Baker Books, 1991) and Adam Nicolson's *God's Secretaries: The Making of the King James Bible* (San Francisco: Harper Collins, 2003). Listen to "Is the King James Version the True Bible?" at https://www.douglasjacoby.com/kjv-king-james-version-true-bible/.

[3] In the United States, the NIV has, since the early 1990s, outsold the veteran KJV more than two to one. (The NT translation was completed in 1973, the OT in 1978.)

[4] The Bible distinguishes between those who have "wandered away" (James 5:19) and those who have "fallen away" (Hebrews 6:4). For those in the first category there is hope; for those in the second, none. Incidentally, when Jesus predicts that his apostles will, on the night of his arrest "all fall away" (NIV mistranslation), this is a different verb to that normally used for "falling" or "falling away." (To illustrate, the verb in connection with these predictions is consistently translated "be offended" in the KJV.) Hence, we must distinguish between stumbling and falling.

[5] Note: the root cause of the Laodiceans' lukewarmness, in the context of the passage (Revelation 3:14–22), is *materialism*. Lukewarmness is a symptom of misplaced priorities, not a root sin in itself. The same holds with the lives of true disciples. Urging them to "get fired up" when there are significant root problems (relationship strains, major disappointments, unconfessed sins, unanswered [serious] doctrinal questions, marriage problems, and so forth), is bound to backfire, even to encourage the habit of feigning zeal. Deal with the heart (the internals), not just the externals.

[6] The abolition of the various OT categories does not mean that we should downplay our "priestly" responsibility to bring others to God, or behave irreverently when gathered for worship. Sometimes in the name of "freedom" we can lose our sense of "reverence and awe" (Hebrews 10:28)—which was *not* nullified at Calvary!

[7] Strictly speaking, the term applies to an interpretation of Revelation which holds that Christ's second coming will come before the establishment of his thousand-year reign on earth. Postmillennialists assert the second coming follows the millennial reign. Millennialists believe that through our words and actions the people of God will bring about the "kingdom" on earth. Amillennialists deny that there is any such "millennium."

[8] A worthy consideration is that the Last Days are the last days of Judaism, particularly the forty-year period between 30 AD (Pentecost, as Peter declares in Acts 2) and 70 (the Destruction of Jerusalem).

[9] For more material on the kingdom, see Jim McGuiggan's *The Reign of God: A Study of the Kingdom of God* (Fort Worth: Star Bible Publications, 1992) and *The Kingdom of God and the Planet Earth* (Ft Worth: Star Bible Publications, 1978).

[10] The Bible teaches that punishment for the lost commences after death. However, this is not the same as hell (the lake of fire), which follows the Last Judgment. The two possible sequences of events after death, then, are:

- For the lost: Sin—Death—Hades—2nd coming—Resurrection—Judgment—Hell
- For the saved: Salvation—Death—Paradise—2nd coming—Resurrection—Judgment—Heaven.

[11] For an intriguing exploration of the nature of hell, please see the article on "Terminal Punishment" at www.DouglasJacoby.com.

# 14

# Old Testament "Guard the Gospel"

## *Sharing Your Faith from the Old Testament*

**How well do you know your OT?**

"OT" does not mean occupational therapist, overtime, or on time, but it's—*about time* we raised our standards when it comes to knowledge of the OT, or Old Testament.

Most of us who have been around church for a while are familiar with the New Testament. We may describe ourselves as a "New Testament" church. We hear many lessons from the New Testament (henceforth NT), do much of our personal Bible study in the NT and have done most of our Scripture memory from the NT. But what about the OT? Although we may have read the NT through five, ten, or more times, few of us have completed the OT even once! Considering that the OT is the basis for the NT (and is about four times the length of the NT), shouldn't we make a serious effort to master the Old Testament? Are you convicted about your Bible knowledge?

**The Bible of the Early Christians**

For the early church, the Old Testament was their Bible! Probably the earliest NT writings date from around the mid-40s AD, and the NT was certainly not completed until the latter part of the first century. And even this does not guarantee that everyone had the same gospels and letters—that did not occur until around the latter part of the second century!

When Jesus rebuked the Sadducees for their defective Bible knowledge (Matthew 22:29), he was referring to the OT (certainly not 2 Peter or Philippians!). When Paul urged Timothy to devote himself to Scripture reading (1 Timothy 4:13), he was referring primarily to the OT (see 1 Timothy 5:18 for a possible exception). Even the much beloved 2 Timothy 3:15–17 refers to the Old Testament (though by extension the principle applies to the new as well).

**Recreating the Scene**

Imagine that you are living in the middle of the first century! Few NT books have been written or become available, although from time to time your leaders may read aloud a letter from Paul—before it is sent by special courier to sister congregations (see Colossians 4:16). How would you study with those interested in the new faith?

The fact is that virtually everything we teach our non-Christian friends could be taught from the OT. We surely get a clearer picture of Jesus in the NT (1 Peter 1:10–12) than in the OT, but most of the great NT doctrines are first found in the OT.

**First Principles Class?**

How do you think the first-century church patterned their instruction for prospective members? Topics were evidently arranged and studied out (Hebrews 6:1–2; Ephesians 4:21–24; Romans 6:17). Scripture memory may have played a part (Proverbs 22:18). But all of the material in the beginning, at least, must have come from the Old Testament.

Do you know your OT well enough to come up with five or ten passages for every great theme of the faith? Whatever evangelistic approach you are most familiar with, hopefully you are competent to share them with your non-Christian friends.

**A Fresh Approach**

The following course series comes completely from the Old Testament. Each study is arranged in one of many possible arrangements of the verses. For example, in our New Testament series, the Word class uses such scriptures as Hebrews 4:12–13, 2 Timothy 3:16, and Matthew 22:29. Instead of Hebrews 4:12, which compares the Word to a sword, try using Jeremiah 23:29, which compares it to a hammer. A possible illustration: "Have you ever been hammering in a nail and the hammer slipped? God's Word is powerful, and although we may feel pain (challenge) at times, we must press on." Instead of 2 Timothy 3:16, which discusses the inspiration of all Scripture, how about Psalm 12:6? Good alternates to Matthew 22:29, which explains that ignorance of God's word is a major reason why the religious world is in such a muddle, might be Hosea 4:6 or Jeremiah 8:7.

To get the most out of the material, I encourage you to take out your Old Testament (right now!) and study each topic in your own Bible. What are the major points you would come up with? How about your illustrations?

**Seeking God**
Isaiah 1:2
Jeremiah 29:11–14
Proverbs 4:7
Psalm 10:4
Psalm 42:1–2
Psalm 63:1
Psalm 62:1
Psalm 61:2

**Sin**
Ecclesiastes 7:20
Leviticus 18
Leviticus 19:1–18
Ecclesiastes 4:4
Genesis 4:7
Proverbs 6:16–19
Isaiah 59:1–3
Psalm 26:1–2

**The Kingdom**
Daniel 2:31–45
Isaiah 2:2
Isaiah 4:2
Genesis 49:10
Isaiah 40:3
Malachi 3:1
Malachi 4:1–6

**Messianic Prophecy**
Isaiah 52:13–53:12
Genesis 22:1–18
Psalm 16:8–10
Psalm 2:7
Genesis 3:15
Genesis 12:3
Deuteronomy 18:15
Micah 5:2
Isaiah 7:14
Isaiah 9:1–2
Isaiah 9:6

**The Cross**
Isaiah 53
Psalm 22
Zechariah 9:9
Zechariah 11:12–13
Zechariah 13:7
Zechariah 12:10
Deuteronomy 21:23

**Evangelism**
Exodus 19:6
Isaiah 49:6
Zechariah 8:23
Proverbs 11:30
2 Kings 7:3–9
Esther 4:14

**Repentance**
Ezekiel 18:30–32
Lamentations 2:14
Psalm 139:23–24
Job 42:5-6
2 Samuel 11:1–12:13
Psalm 34:18

**Commitment**
Deuteronomy 6:5
Leviticus 19:18
Malachi 1:10
Isaiah 6:1–8
Jeremiah 48:10

**Baptism**
Proverbs 30:12
2 Kings 5:1–15
Leviticus 14:1–7
Isaiah 1:18-20

**Decision**
Deuteronomy 30:11–20
Joshua 24:14–15
Ezra 10
Psalm 84
Daniel 3

**The Word**
Jeremiah 23:29
Hosea 4:6
Jeremiah 8:7
Psalm 12:6
Proverbs 30:5–6
Deuteronomy 4:2
Psalm 119

**Grace**
2 Sam 11–12
Psalm 102
Psalm 103
Isaiah 30:18–19
Jonah 2:8

### Concluding Challenge

The challenge is clear: to do our best to become familiar with the whole word of God (2 Timothy 2:15). For most of us, that means a renewed determination to learn how to teach the OT (Ezra 7:10). That is the only way we will be like Philip (Acts 8), who "began with that very passage of Scripture and told him the good news about Jesus." Some of you may even take up the challenge to study with a man or woman exclusively from the Old Testament!

Just as Jesus did his best to master God's word, let us all determine to do our best to master the Old Testament.[1]

## Notes

[1] Recommended: *Foundations for Faith: Old Testament Survey* (Spring, Texas: Illumination Publishers, 2004), and *A Quick Overview of the Bible* (Eugene, Oregon: Harvest House, 2012).

# 15

# A Medical Account of the Crucifixion

## *Simplified and Amended*[1]

Hanging, electrocution, knee-capping, gas chamber: these punishments are feared. They all happen today, and we shudder as we think of the horror and pain. But as we shall see, these ordeals pale into insignificance compared with the bitter fate of Jesus Christ: crucifixion.[2]

Few persons are crucified today (except by ISIS and various other terrorists). For us the cross remains confined to ornaments and jewelry, stained-glass windows, romanticized pictures, and statues portraying a serene death. Crucifixion was a form of execution refined by the Romans to a precise art. It was carefully conceived to produce a slow death with maximum pain. It was a public spectacle intended to deter other would-be criminals. It was a death to be feared.

*Sweat like blood*

Luke 22:24 says of Jesus, "and being in anguish, he prayed more earnestly, and his sweat was like drops of blood falling to the ground."[3] His sweat was unusually intense because his emotional state was unusually intense. Dehydration coupled with exhaustion further weakened him.

*Beating*

It was in this condition that Jesus faced the first physical abuse: punches and slaps to the face and head while blindfolded. Unable to anticipate the blows, Jesus was badly bruised, his mouth and eyes possibly injured. The psychological effects of the false trials should not be underestimated. Consider that Jesus faced them bruised, dehydrated, exhausted, possibly in shock.

*Flogging*

In the previous twelve hours Jesus had suffered emotional trauma, rejection by his closest friends, a cruel beating, and a sleepless night during which he had to walk miles between unjust hearings. Despite the fitness he must certainly have gained during his travels in Palestine, he was in no way prepared for the punishment of flogging. The effects would be worse as a result.

A man to be flogged was stripped of his clothes and his hands tied to a post above his head. He was then whipped across the shoulders, back, buttocks, thighs and legs, the soldier standing behind and to one side of the victim. The whip used—the flagellum—was designed to make this a devastating punishment, bringing the victim close to death: several short heavy leather thongs, with two small balls of lead or iron attached near the end of each. Pieces of sheep's bone were sometimes included.

As the scourging proceeds, the heavy leather thongs produce first superficial cuts, then deeper damage to underlying tissues. Bleeding becomes severe when not only capillaries and veins are cut, but also arteries in the underlying muscles. The small metal balls first produce large, deep bruises which are broken open by further blows. The fragments of sheep's bone rip the flesh as the whip is drawn back. When the beating is finished, the skin of the back is in ribbons, and the entire area torn and bleeding.

The words chosen by the gospel writers suggest that the scourging of Jesus was particularly severe: he was certainly at the point of collapse when he was cut down from the flogging-post.

*The mocking*

Jesus was allowed no time to recover before facing his next ordeal. Made to stand, he was dressed in a robe by jeering soldiers, crowned with a twisted band of thorny twigs, and to complete the parody, given a wooden staff as a king's scepter. "Next, they spat on Jesus and struck him on the head with the wooden staff." The long thorns were driven into the sensitive scalp tissue producing profuse bleeding, but even more terrible was the reopening of the wounds on Jesus' back when the robe was torn off again.

Further weakened physically and emotionally, Jesus was led away to be executed.

*The crucifixion*

The wooden cross used by the Romans was too heavy to be carried by one man. Instead, the victim to be crucified was made to bear the detached crossbar across his shoulders, carrying it outside the city walls to the place of execution. (The heavy upright portion of the cross was permanently in position there.) Jesus was unable to carry his load—a beam weighing around 75 to 125 pounds (approximately 35–55 kg). He collapsed under the burden, and an onlooker was ordered to take it for him.

Jesus refused to drink the wine and myrrh offered him before the nails were driven in. (It would have dulled the pain.) Thrown down on his back with arms outstretched along the crossbar, nails were driven through Jesus' wrists into the wood. These iron spikes, about 6 inches long and 3/8 inch thick, severed the large sensorimotor median nerve, causing excruciating pain in both arms. Carefully placed between bones and ligaments, they were able to bear the full weight of the crucified man.

In preparation for the nailing of the feet, Jesus was lifted up and the crossbar fixed to the upright post. Then with legs bent at the knee, two nails were used to pierce the ankles, so that his legs were astride the base of the upright part of the cross. Again there was severe nerve damage, and the pain caused was intense. It is important to note, however, that neither the wounds to the wrists or feet caused substantial bleeding, since no major arteries were ruptured. The executioner took care to ensure this, so that death would be slower and the suffering longer.

Now nailed to his cross, the real horror of crucifixion began. When the wrists were nailed to the crossbar, the elbows were intentionally left in a bent position so that the crucified man would hang with his arms above his head, the weight being taken on the nails in the wrists. Obviously, this was unbearably painful, but it had another effect: It is difficult to exhale in this position. In order to breathe out, and then take in fresh air, it was necessary to push the body up on the nailed feet. When the pain from the feet became unbearable, the victim would again slump down to hang by the arms. A terrible cycle of pain began: hanging by the arms, unable to breathe, pushing up on the feet to inhale quickly before again slumping down, and on and on.

This tortured activity became more and more difficult as Jesus' back was scraped against the upright post,[4] as muscle cramps set in because of the inadequate respiration, and as exhaustion grew more severe. Jesus suffered in this manner for several hours before, with a final cry, he died.

*Cause of death*

Many factors contributed to Jesus' death. A combination of shock and suffocation killed most victims of crucifixion, but in Jesus' case acute heart failure may have been the final trauma. This is suggested by his sudden death following a loud cry, after only a few hours: a quick death, it seems (Pilate was surprised to find Jesus already dead). A fatal cardiac arrhythmia, or perhaps cardiac rupture, are likely candidates.

*The spear wound*

Jesus was already dead as the executioners broke the legs of the criminals crucified alongside (in order to speed their deaths). Instead, we read that a soldier pierced Jesus' side with a spear. Where on his side? The word chosen by John suggests the ribs, and if the soldier intended to make Jesus' death certain, a wound to the heart was the obvious choice.

From the wound came a flow of "blood and water." This is consistent with the spear blow to the heart (especially from the right side, the traditional site of the wound). Rupturing the pericardium (the sac surrounding the heart) released a flow of watery serum, followed by blood as the heart was pierced.

*Conclusion*

The detailed accounts given in the gospels combined with the historical evidence on crucifixion bring us to a firm conclusion: modern medical knowledge supports the claim of the Scriptures that Jesus died on the cross.

## Notes

[1] This is a simplified medical account of Jesus' crucifixion (an adaptation of the well-known Truman Davis version). Other medical reports have been written—all useful but usually rather technical. This account aims to be readable to the average reader. I made this adaptation, with the assistance of Alex Mnatzaganian, in December 1989.

[2] Highly recommended: Martin Hengel, *The Cross of the Son of God* (London: SCM Press, Ltd: 1981).

[3] The original of our version of the Medical Account of the Crucifixion included these sentences: "*Haematidrosis*—bloody sweat—is rare, but well documented. Under great emotional stress, capillaries in the sweat glands can break, mixing blood in with the sweat. Luke's account is consistent with modern medical knowledge: Jesus was in emotional torment so intense that his body could not bear it." However, Luke only says that Jesus' sweat was *like* blood as it fell to the ground, not that it *was* mixed with blood. As disciples, we must be careful not to overstate the case. There is no evidence that the early Christians preached the gore of the cross in an effort to sicken or shame those they were trying to convert.

[4] In some locations, trees were plentiful, while in others upright posts needed to be fixed into the ground. It is quite possible that in the place where Jesus was crucified there was an abundance of trees, in which case the patibulum he and Simon of Cyrene carried was simply attached to a tree. Of course, whether Jesus was killed on a tree literally, or on a tree by metonymy (on the wood of a tree) is incidental to the point of the crucifixion.

# 16

# Grounding New Christians in the Word

## *Thirteen Follow-Up Studies*

Entering the kingdom of God is amazing, yet there is so much more still to come! After our friends have become Christians, they need to be grounded in the faith (Colossians 2:6–7) and continue the learning process begun before conversion (Ephesians 4:20–24).

We understand the imperative, methods, and urgency of evangelism. We teach it, preach it, and know what it means to be a "minister of reconciliation." And yet we have a chronic weakness. Too often we see conversion as the end of the process of evangelization, rather than as the middle. What, the *middle?* Yes, the middle! Our work is certainly not even *half* finished when we have influenced someone to obey the gospel (Romans 1:5, 16:26; 2 Thessalonians 1:8). Obedience to the gospel is an *ongoing* process. Spiritual maturity (Ephesians 4:16) cannot be achieved in just a few Bible study sessions. In fact, to lead someone to the point of faith, repentance and baptism without ongoing study and discipleship is terribly careless! (2 Peter 2:20–22). The result of this weakness: a poor retention rate, as people come into the church through the front door and just as rapidly exit out the back door. Certainly we will want to do all that we can to keep faithful those who have confessed Jesus as Lord.

These studies have been designed to do something about that, to be used *after* baptism. The order in which you make use of them will vary from person to person. Perhaps you will want to come up with your own studies. In the meantime, take these as a suggestion, as a model. To aid you in bringing the principles to life, several practical suggestions have been added to most of the studies.

**I. THE BASIS: Relationship with God**

1. Prayer: speaking to God
2. Bible study: listening to God
3. Faith, works and grace: the balance

**II. THE CHURCH: The Body of Christ**

4. Relationships in the body
5. The New Testament church
6. One-another relationships: God's plan

**III. THE WORK: Becoming like Christ**

7. Hindrance: the heart
8. Laziness, idleness, discipline
9. Evangelism, boldness, tact
10. Service with a smile

**IV. OTHER NEEDS: Following God's Way**

11. Academics: obstacle or opportunity?
12. Christian marriage: cord of three strands
13. The Christian family: parents & children

---

## I. THE BASIS: Relationship with God

### 1—Prayer: Speaking to God

What could be more natural between two people who love each other than to communicate? Surely one would expect to see an enormous amount of communication between someone and the God they love with all their heart, soul, mind, and strength. And yet this is far from what we observe! Communication of this sort is not natural; it must be learned. There are many hindrances, all of which Satan will gladly use in his campaign to keep us off our knees. Yet they can all be overcome if we are willing to rely on God and give prayer the priority it deserves.

Priority

- Mark 1:35—Jesus, a *busy* man, finds time to pray.
- He finds a *place* free from distraction.
- He finds a *time* free from distraction.
- Suggested: Psalm 42:1, 63:1; Luke 6:12; Hebrews 5:7.

Learning process

- Luke 11:1–13—It's *not* natural (even Jesus' apostles had to be taught).
- Develop *structure* in your prayer life.

Hindrances

- 1 Peter 4:7—Lack of concentration. May wish to pray aloud.
- Psalm 66:18—Lack of personal righteousness.
- Luke 18:1–8—Lack of persistence.
- 1 John 5:14—Prayer contrary to God's will.
- Mark 11:24—Lack of faith.
- Suggested: Matthew 6:5; John 9:31, 14:13–14; Ephesians 6:18; Colossians 4:2–4; James 5:16–17.

*Conclusion*

- Philippians 4:6–7—Cast your worries upon God.
- Jeremiah 20:21b—God is looking for people who will devote themselves to be close to him. Take up the challenge!

- Psalm 5:3—Have a *daily* prayer time.
- Suggested—1 Thessalonians 5:17; 1 Peter 5:7; 1 John 5:14.

*Practicals*
- Set a time and length to pray every day.
- Write out a prayer list.

Fasting
- Often associated with prayer in the Bible.
- Matthew 6:17–18—shows that this is expected of Christians.
- Suggested: Nehemiah 1:4; Isaiah 58; Joel 2:12; Acts 14:23.

**2—Bible Study: Listening to God**

Assisting young Christians to become rooted in consistent and productive personal Bible study is one of the top priorities of those helping them to mature in Christ. This is an excellent way to take our stand against Satan and his schemes, wielding "the sword of the Spirit" (Ephesians 6:18). Let us listen to God's voice.

*Introduction*
- Matthew 4:4—"Every word." Comparable to physical bread, therefore essential. If you don't stay in the Word, you won't stay in the faith.

Work at your Bible study
- 2 Peter 3:15–16—Possible to distort Scriptures to own destruction. Tremendous responsibility on us personally to stick with the truth.
- Yes, some passages are difficult to understand—but not impossible! (2 Corinthians 1:13). Strive to comprehend them yourself first, before asking others what they mean.
- 2 Timothy 2:15—Becoming a well-equipped workman (3:17), not being ashamed, developing competence in teaching God's word to others.
- 1 Peter 3:15—Equipped for evangelism: not just Bible knowledge, but being able to answer questions, helping others, gently and respectfully.
- James 1:22–25—It is useless to study the Bible without making the applications to our lives.
- Suggested: Psalm 1:2–3, 119 (entire); Ezra 7:10; Isaiah 66:2b; Matthew 24:35; Romans 15:4; 1 Corinthians 10:11; Colossians 3:16; 2 Timothy 2:7.

*Practicals*
- Have a set time to study your Bible daily. Spend daily time in the word (Joshua 1:8; Acts 17:11; Deuteronomy 17:18–20).
- Write down the convicting points and pray about them.
- Do well in church classes; make the most of any available local teaching programs.
- If you're reading the Bible for the first time, don't try to read straight through. Focus on the New Testament until you are quite familiar with it, then venture out into the Old Testament.

### 3—Faith, Works, and Grace: The Balance

One of the greatest travesties in the church today is that new Christians are taught to depend on self, to struggle up the road of salvation by works. This attitude may be created before he/she comes to Christ, in the Bible study setting. But more often this is an acquired deficiency, learned through observation of "older" Christians. Such an orientation undoes the work of the cross. Equally sad, however, is the school of thought that prides itself on having arrived at a true understanding of grace, only to condone and even encourage lukewarm commitment to our Lord Jesus Christ. Clearly we must strike the balance—hence this study.

Faith

- Hebrews 11:6—We need faith to please God, but what is faith?
- James 2:14–16—Faith is more than intellectual belief—it results in action. Compare verses 20–24 with Genesis 22. Note the interrelationship between faith and obedience.

Works

- Ephesians 2:8–10—The Bible clearly teaches that we are not saved by our own effort, but this doesn't mean that God doesn't expect anything from us. It is an unearned gift, but it is conditional on obedience (2 Kings 5:1–15).

Grace

- Titus 3:5—We're saved not because of our righteous deeds, but by his mercy.
- Grace is unmerited favor or mercy. But the fact that we do not earn or deserve it does not mean that we can do as we like (Jude 4).
- 1 Corinthians 15:10—Grace will have its effect.
- Titus 2:11–14—It is because of grace that we strive to live self-controlled, upright, and godly lives.

---

## II. THE CHURCH: The Body of Christ

### 4—Relationships in the Body

When one enters the community of the redeemed, relationships are radically transformed! Instead of having ourselves as the center of our focus, we are to "consider others better than ourselves" (Philippians 2:3). However, implementation of these biblical principles will never occur as long as we retain a defective concept of fellowship and the body. Church is not something we attend; it is an opportunity to tend to needs. And there are many needs to be tended to! If young Christians are not grafted into the body in a functional way, they may well be reclaimed by the world. And if that is what happens, we are failing (1 Corinthians 2:12–15). The most crucial time for integrating the young convert into the local congregation is the first few weeks—and even days.

Why different from the world's relationships?

- John 13:34–35—Jesus commands us to love each other as he has loved us. This quality of love is what makes us distinct as Christians.
- Mark 3:35—We are Jesus' brothers and sisters if we do God's will. Because of this common purpose, Christian relationships transcend even blood relations.

How are they different?

- 1 Peter 1:22—Our love for each other must be sincere and from the heart.
- 1 John 3:16—Jesus is our example. Our love for others can be measured by how much we are willing to sacrifice for them.

What does this mean in practice?

- 1 Thessalonians 5:12—Different people have different needs.
- 1 John 3:17—Look after each other's material needs.
- Colossians 1:28—Let's be concerned about each other's spiritual well-being.

*Conclusion*

- Ephesians 4:29—Be edifying.
- Ephesians 5:21—Be submissive not only to leaders (Hebrews 13:17), but also to each other (Ephesians 5:21).
- Suggested: Acts 2:42–47, 4:32–35; Romans 12:5; 1 Corinthians 12:12–27; Hebrews 10:24–25, 13:1–2; James 1:19; 3 John 5.

*Practicals*

- Make it a point to phone and email other Christians.
- Spend time with other believers in order to build relationships (Hebrews 3:12–14).
- Pray for each other daily.
- Introduce yourself to at least one new person in each service for the next month.
- Write notes and cards to your brothers and sisters.

**5—The New Testament Church: Three Aspects**

We demand book, chapter, and verse for all our doctrines and practices, and rightly so. Hearing our restoration pleas, how does a young Christian respond when they see practices they may never before have seen in their life? They are not used to *weekly* communion, and certainly not to *sacrificial* contributing. And what about the strange custom of "going forward"? This study provides scriptural explanation for these three practices in the New Testament church.

*Communion (Lord's Supper, Eucharist)*

- Matthew 26:26–29—Passover supper (Jewish background).

Bread is the body of Christ, wine is blood.
- 1 Corinthians 11:23ff—Jesus instituted the Lord's Supper. It is a proclamation of the Lord's death until he comes. Examine yourself before eating.
- Acts 20:7—Christians came together in order to break bread.
- It appears from the evidence of the New Testament and that of early church history that the Christians broke bread together at least once a week in an actual meal.[1]
- Suggested: Exodus 12 (historical background); Mark 12:12–26; Luke 22:7–20; John 6:48–58; Acts 2:42.

*Contribution (for needs of the church)*
- Matthew 6:21—Your treasure is where your heart is.
- Matthew 6:24—Cannot serve both God and money, so make sure that God is first.
- Proverbs 3:9–10—Are you honoring God with your money? Give him the "firstfruits" of your income. Be responsible when you are away; leave your contribution behind (the church needs it).
- 1 Corinthians 16:1–2—Taking up a collection to meet the needs of the poor is biblical.
- 2 Corinthians 8:1–15—Advance planning.
- 2 Corinthians 9:6ff—Good material on sacrificial giving.
- Suggested: Exodus 36:6–7; Mark 12:41–44; Luke 6:38; 1 Timothy 6:5–10, 17.

*Confession of sin (e.g. coming forward in response to the preached message)*
- James 5:16—Public confession. No private "confessional" in the Bible. Ask spiritual people to pray for you. Their prayers will be effective.
- Proverbs 28:13—You will not prosper if you keep sins inside.

**6—One-Another Relationships: God's Plan**

Although you will not find a doctrine of "discipling partners" explicitly spelled out in the New Testament, it is indisputable that the Scriptures teach the necessity of one-another relationships. The importance of ongoing discipleship should be clear to someone before he makes Jesus Lord. This study aims to cultivate an attitude of openness to input on the part of the young Christian, as well as to remind them that, in the final analysis, it is the responsibility of the one who has confessed Jesus as Lord to persevere in their Christian growth.

Discipleship is not a human expedient; it is a clear command of God (Matthew 28:19).

*Levels of discipling*
- Hebrews 3:12—Others disciple us. This can take place in several ways: one-one discipling; groups of three; group discipling

- Hebrews 4:12—The Word disciples us.
- Hebrews 5:12—We disciple ourselves.
- Hebrews 6:12—We are discipled by the faithful examples of biblical figures.
- Hebrews 12:12—The Lord (through circumstances requiring patience) disciples us, too.

*Being discipled*

- 2 Timothy 2:2—The teaching process: a chain reaction.
- Colossians 1:28-2:1—The goal is maturity/completeness/ perfection. There will be difficulties in any one-another relationship, but try to realize that the challenges you receive are made in love. This is hard work.
- Proverbs 10:17—Attitude of openness to correction. If you have the wrong attitude, you will lead others astray.
- Proverbs 11:14—Ask for advice.
- Proverbs 12:15 and 15:12—Cherish challenge and initiate with the one helping you.

*Discipling yourself*

- Hebrews 5:11–14—Don't be slow to learn. By constant use (habit), train yourself. Ultimately, you are the one responsible for how you do spiritually. You cannot blame your failings on others.

*Practicals*

- Arrange a regular time to meet together each week with an older, more mature Christian.
- Strive for daily contact.

---

## III. THE WORK: Becoming Like Christ

### 7—Hindrance: The Heart

The Bible speaks of the heart as the governing center of the whole person—intellectual, physical, and psychological, and thus a person's heart makes them what they are and gives rise to all their thoughts and actions. It is imperative that a young disciple be taught to guard their heart, to keep it sensitive and open to God's word.

*Introduction*

- 1 Samuel 16:7—God looks at the heart.

*Problems of the heart*

- Jeremiah 17:9—Deceitfulness: in the sense of feelings and impulses. Deceitful with regard to discerning the truth, or what is best.
- Mark 7:21—Sinfulness: the heart is the source of sin, as well as evil desires.
- Hebrews 3:12—Hardening: hearts can become hard, become unbelieving (doubt) and turn away from God.

*The remedy*

- Jeremiah 29:13—*Seek* God with all our heart. This verse is not just for non-Christians!
- Psalm 51:17—Cultivate a penitent, *contrite heart,* which responds quickly to God's word.
- Psalm 119:11—Hide *God's word* in our hearts.
- Proverbs 3:5–6—*Trust* in the Lord with all our hearts.
- Ezekiel 11:19–20—The Lord has placed his Spirit in our hearts to lead us in the right way.

*Conclusion*

- Proverbs 4:23—Above all else, guard your heart! It is the source of our spiritual life.
- Suggested: Genesis 6:5; 2 Chronicles 16:9; Psalm 51:10; Proverbs 14:12, 28:26; Ezekiel 18:31; 1 John 3:20.

*Practicals*

- Pray for a pure heart.
- Confess sin; be humble.
- Write out Bible verses that pertain to your heart.

**8—Laziness, Idleness, Discipline**

How many of us have had great dreams for how God was going to use us—how he would mold us into what he wanted us to be—and just when the going got rough, and the process became painful, we resisted, and perhaps even took a couple of steps backwards! Few of us are naturally disciplined; discipline must be learned. And yet without it, how do we suppose we will really grow? Surely that is fantasy! Discipline, therefore, must be built into our Christian lives from the earliest moment.

*Introduction*

- 1 Timothy 4:7—Train yourself to be godly. Physical training (sports) is of limited value, but spiritual training is immeasurably valuable. The Christian life is a process of training in righteousness.

*Laziness*

- Hebrews 6:12—Don't become lazy. Laziness is a constant threat to the life of every Christian, young or old. Imitate those who are patient, faithful and disciplined. Look for good examples; learn from them. Realize laziness is a sin!
- Suggested: Proverbs 12:1, 24:30–34, 26:13–16.

*Idleness*

- 1 Thessalonians 4:11ff—Be constructive members of society and of the church. Hardworking people win the respect of others. Try not to be dependent on anybody (do not go into/remain in debt).

Both unemployment and underemployment can be detrimental to spiritual growth.

- 2 Thessalonians 3:3ff—Follow the example of disciplined people. Don't be a busybody—appearing busy but not really achieving anything.

*Discipline*

- Hebrews 12:11–12—No discipline is pleasant, but it yields a more satisfying life. Make your life count!
- Suggested: 1 Corinthians 9:24–27; 2 Timothy 2:4–6; Hebrews 5:14.

*Practicals*

- Make a timetable of how you use your time. Get some suggestions.
- Set some goals.
- Spend time with a disciplined person and learn from him or her.
- If you are not a punctual person, try to always be early.
- If you are given to gluttony, take this seriously. Get some accountability in your life for this sin.
- Don't spend too much time online, watching TV, or gaming. These activities can involve many sins: materialism (online shopping), online gambling, sexual lust, and more. Get help and get accountable.
- Suggested: *The Disciplined Life* by Richard Taylor and *The Seven Habits of Highly Effective People* by Stephen Covey.

**9—Evangelism, Boldness, Tact**

When it comes to evangelism, few young Christians possess both boldness and tact. We are tempted toward one extreme or the other: so tactful we say little, if anything, or so bold that tact is thrown to the wind. Boldness comes via prayer, and tact is developed through observation of those who are diplomatic. In view of the crippling effect of fear on new Christians—and old—and considering the number of tactical errors that are made by all, we need a separate lesson on this important subject.

*Evangelism*

- 2 Corinthians 5:10–21—Because we know and fear God, we try to persuade others. We are Christ's ambassadors, and God has given to us the ministry of reconciliation. It is not an option.
- Acts 8:1, 4—The early Christians were evangelistic—not just the leaders!
- 1 Peter 2:9–10—We are *all* a royal priesthood. There is no "clergy" today!

*Boldness*

- Romans 1:16–17—The gospel is nothing to be ashamed of, because it has the power to save.

- Luke 9:23–26—If we are ashamed of Jesus and his words, he will be ashamed of us.
- Acts 4:29–31—Pray for boldness! God will answer your prayer.

*Tact*

- Matthew 10:16—Need to be wise/shrewd in our evangelism.
- *Negatives:*
  Proverbs 12:18—Beware reckless words.
  Proverbs 25:17—Avoid *too* frequent contact.
  Proverbs 27:14—Don't come on too strong.

- *Positives:*
  1 Corinthians 9:20–23—Accommodate yourself to your hearer.
  Titus 2:10—Make the gospel attractive.
  1 Peter 3:15–16—Show gentleness and respect.
- Suggested: Matthew 7:6; 2 Timothy 2:23-26.

*Practicals*

- Push yourself to be friendly and start conversations wherever you go. The Lord will use this.
- Invite people to come to church with you.
- Work on improving one area of your life in order to make the gospel more attractive.

**10—Service with a Smile**

When Jesus came to the earth, he came as a suffering servant (Mark 10:45). And he is still a servant, since he always lives to intercede for us (Hebrews 7:25). In following the Master, this is one area that we dare not play down, no matter how unglamorous it may seem. For, as Jesus taught us, the road up is the road down.

- Matthew 20:26–28—The way up is the way of service, opposite to the way of the world. Jesus came to serve, not to be served.
- Philippians 2:3–8—Do nothing out of selfish ambition or vain conceit. Consider others better than yourselves—then you'll look to see others' needs met. For Jesus to come to earth was the supreme act of self-humiliation. We need to imitate this selfless example in our everyday lives.
- Luke 17:7–10—When we have served, our attitude should be that we have only done our duty. No complaining (Philippians 2:14); no expectation of reward.
- Colossians 3:23–24—Serve with all your heart! Realize that you are serving the Lord Christ, not human beings.
- Suggested: Psalm 100:2; Proverbs 3:27–28; John 13:1–17; Galatians 6:2, 10; Ephesians 6:7–8; Philippians 4:4–5.

*Practicals*

- Learn to serve without being asked. Look for needs.
- When asked to help in a particular way, *be responsible!* for example, duties such as children's ministry, ushering, communion, teaching, cleanup, office duty, and food preparation.

---

## IV. OTHER NEEDS: Following God's Way

### 11—Academics: Obstacle or Opportunity?

God certainly expects excellence of Christian students: if not excellent results, at least excellent effort. Too often (undisciplined) students become Christians and then use evangelism or "church" as an excuse for mediocre performance. We must help students to see academics as a God-given responsibility. There is nothing "unspiritual" about studies. The unspiritual course to take is to neglect academics. Without perseverance, the student suffers loss in character, discipline, confidence, and credibility—not to mention future prospects.

*Clear commission*

- 1 Corinthians 7:25—God called us to be Christians as students for a reason! We have a responsibility to glorify God in academics and evangelism.
- Colossians 3:22–23—*Attitude* is more important than *aptitude.* Academics are a vital part of your "spiritual" life. To have consistent motivation, work for God, not for self.

*Evangelistic example*

- 1 Thessalonians 4:11—A consistent example has an impact! Classmates will be drawn to those who can help others.
- Mark 7:37—People were amazed by Jesus' all-around excellence. You will amaze family and friends if you excel in all areas. "Ministry *through* academics, not *in spite of* academics."

*Powerful preparation*

- James 1:2–4—Persevering with academics leads to spiritual maturity: discipline, focus, faith.
- Suggested: Proverbs 6:6, 18:9; Philippians 2:14–16; 1 Timothy 3:7, 4:15–16.

*Practicals*

- Seek input in the area of academics.
- Get input from professors, lecturers, classmates.
- Attend every lecture. This is important for your example.
- Take good notes, and catch up on missed lectures.
- Go through homework within a day of receiving it and plan how you will get it done.
- Keep current at all times! For conscience's sake, as well as for practical reasons.

- Aim to sleep reasonably, especially during exams.
- Read "Effective Study Habits for University Students" at www. DouglasJacoby.com.
- Get a copy of Jacoby, *Campus Core: How to Have an Impact on Campus, Get Good Grades, and Figure Out Your Future* (Spring, Texas: Illumination Publishers, 2016).

**12—Christian Marriage: A Cord of Three Strands**

God's word and power provide us with everything we need for happy, godly, fulfilling lives in every area (2 Timothy 3:17; 2 Peter 1:3; John 10:10). The area of marriage is crucial, and if marriage is not going well, serious spiritual problems will also be present. Indeed, Christian marriage is one arena in which disciples of Christ will dramatically outshine the many worldly examples surrounding them. A great marriage draws others to Jesus!

*God's plan*

- Marriage meets many of our deepest needs (Genesis 2:24; Proverbs 18:22). Your husband or wife should be your closest friend!
- Marry a Christian! (1 Corinthians 7:39).
- Marriage is for life (Matthew 19:9).
- Take advice! (Proverbs 15:22).

  *Note, however, that marriage is not God's plan for all singles. Both Jesus and Paul taught that the preferred path for singles is celibacy (if they have the gift). See Matthew 19:10-12 and 1 Corinthians 7:6–7.*

*Worldly vs. spiritual marriages*

- Communication
  1. Time together (meals, spiritual talks, unscheduled time)
  2. Listening (especially needful for husbands)
  3. Express, don't suppress feelings
  4. No festering resentments (Colossians 3:13)
  5. Coordinate schedules; don't leave each other in the dark about the other's plans!
  6. Communication may increase conflict; expect it, don't avoid it!
- Selfishness
  1. Harsh husbands? (Colossians 3:19). Husbands must serve their wives, being considerate (1 Peter 3:7). Husbands should do their share of the housework, cleaning, taking care of children...
  2. Bossy/nagging wives? (Proverbs 21:19, 25:24, 27:15). Wives must learn submission (Colossians 3:18; 1 Peter 3:5–6).
  3. Weak husbands (henpecked)? The man; must be the spiritual leader in the relationship (Ephesians 5:22–33).
- Hospitality
  1. Is home life centered only around each other, life in a cozy, selfish, private world?

2. Hospitality is God's will! (1 Peter 4:9). Open your home.
3. Use hospitality in evangelism.
4. This is the husband's responsibility even more than the wife's! (1 Timothy 3:4).
5. An untidy home isn't inviting! (Proverbs 24:30–34).

- Spirituality
  1. Talk about spiritual things when together.
  2. Pray with your spouse daily.
  3. Don't "protect" each other when there is sin or compromise (Acts 5:1–11); speak the truth in love! (Ephesians 4:15).
- Romance
  1. Don't deprive one another (1 Corinthians 7:5).
  2. Remember the special touches! (cards, flowers, presents, surprises...)
- Input
  1. Are you (two) closed to input? Are there festering problems?
  2. Every marriage needs counseling! No one is above it!

*Practicals*

- Pray together every day!
- Share your faith together.
- Share quiet times from time to time.
- Work on the church classes together. Expect the best of each other!
- Spend an evening a week alone together, showing your love for each other and really communicating.
- Read and discuss 1 Corinthians 13.
- Read Song of Songs to one another! (*Lover* and *Beloved* parts).
- Pray daily that you will be able to study with one couple together.
- "Double dates."
- Discuss your schedules together.
- Plan an overnight trip together (without the children).
- Read a great book on marriage and discuss it.[2]

**13—The Christian Family: Parents and Children**

The family is the basic social unit, and to understand the desperate plight our society is in, you need only to look at the desperate straits the average family is in! In stark contrast to families in the world, with their narrow outlook, poor communication, brewing resentments, undisciplined children and decaying marriages, the Christ-centered family is a breath of fresh air and a ray of hope.

The family following God's word is a happy, communicative, warm, loving, committed and fruitful family. Just as Christian marriage is God's wise plan for men and women to love and live together, so the Christian family is both God's answer to the ungodliness and selfishness of society and his plan for character development in his most precious gift to parents: their children.

*Spiritual focus*

- Chain of command (Christ—husband—wife—children)
- If you want a great family life, you need input!
- Aim to have an evangelistically fruitful family!

*Bringing up children*

- Basic need for security and happiness:
  1. Time—you'll need to reorder your priorities!
  2. Affection—without it, they will become insecure, cold, introverted, awkward around strangers.
  3. Spiritual examples (parents)—Ephesians 6:4; Deuteronomy 6:7.
- Discipline—it's unloving not to give it (Proverbs 23:13–14). Discipline is training.
  1. Encouragement is necessary (Colossians 3:21)
  2. Discipline is essential.
     a. God commands it (Proverbs 22:15, 29:15, 17, 19, 21).
     b. The husband is the chief "discipler."
     c. Wife and husband should agree on the "rules," lest the children pick and choose whom to obey!
     d. Areas of training (Proverbs 22:6)
        - Respect toward authority
        - Speech and openness
        - Affection
        - Manners
        - Tidiness
        - Moodiness
     e. Regular spiritual times with each child!

*Other Important Matters*

- Regular, consistent family devotionals.
- Be on time to church. Allow extra time, particularly considering the children. Plan to come early!
- Pray with the children before they go to bed.
- Have a weekly family time.
- If you have Christian children, work with the preteen or teen ministry. Embrace feedback. Don't be defensive.

*Practicals*

- Create a simple system of allowances and incentives for the children.
- Take the whole family out evangelizing. Reach out to other families as a family.
- Ask Christians you respect to recommend helpful books.[3]

*Follow-Up Studies: Closing Considerations*

Follow-up studies can be covered at the rate of about one to two per week over the period of a few months. Depending on the needs, they may be used in any order. In addition to the studies presented in this chapter, it may be helpful to use some of the *Guard the Gospel* studies not covered in your personal study with the young Christian. And, by all means, do not consider that your work with a young Christian ends after the follow-up studies have been completed! No, for you are still only in the *middle.*

## Notes

[1] See my article "The Lord's Supper" at https://www.douglasjacoby.com /the-lord-s-supper/.

[2] For example, Sam and Geri Laing's *Friends and Lovers: Marriage as God Designed It* (Spring, Texas: Illumination Publishers, 2017).

[3] For example, Sam and Geri Laing, *Raising Awesome Kids in Troubled Times* (Spring, Texas: Illumination Publishers, 2017) and Douglas and Victoria Jacoby, *Principle-Centered Parenting* (Spring, Texas: Illumination Publishers, 2017).

# 17
# In the Hall of Tyrannus
## *Effective Group Bible Discussions*

An invaluable part of shining ever brighter is learning to share the faith not just with individuals, but also with groups. If you are like me, you will benefit greatly from the practicals offered in this chapter.

Luke records, "But some of them became obstinate; they refused to believe and publicly maligned the Way. So Paul left them. He took the disciples with him and had discussions daily in the lecture hall of Tyrannus" (Acts 19:9). Two thousand years ago, Paul saw how informal discussions were a great way to get the word out. His flexibility and creativity allowed him to try new things and go with what worked. And so preaching in the synagogue gave way to the discussion group in the rented facility.

Discussion is fundamentally different from preaching. Preaching confronts forcefully; discussion confronts gently. Preaching is primarily one man interacting with the group, while discussion is every member in the group interacting. Many people not so eager to come to a "big" church service are actually enthusiastic when invited to a discussion. Another positive aspect is that the discussions give women opportunities to teach and to lead other women.

And so "the hall of Tyrannus" becomes a forum more attractive for many than the "synagogues." Ten suggestions on how to lead effective group discussions follow.[1]

### 1. Preparation

The first principle of effective discussions is preparation! Put in as much time as you need to produce an excellent study. (You want people to come back!) I can never forget my first study—though I would like to! My friend Gary asked me several times if I had practiced it, if I had thought it through. Even though my thinking was muddled, I did not realize how ill prepared I really was. When my embarrassing, rambling stab at a unified discussion was finally over, one of my visitors patted me on the back, and said, "Nice try." More comments like that eventually sold me on the importance of preparation.

From that initial attempt as a bumbling teenager, within a few short years I would be leading effective group discussions brimming with visitors and interactive dialog—keeping the guests in my dormitory room long after the study had officially concluded. A few years later and I was leading two studies that saw twenty people become Christians in the span of six weeks.

Preparation does take time, though. Don't shortchange the "workers" who are inviting their friends to your study. Be prepared; your people will appreciate it!

**2. Atmosphere**

The physical atmosphere of the room is important. Is the room a bit warm? We don't want our guests getting *too* "comfortable"! Are there enough chairs? Are there refreshments—especially things to drink? (Refreshments also discourage people from running off as soon as the Bible is closed—singles especially!) Good lighting is helpful. I also suggest music as a cue for discussion. The music plays as people are coming in and socializing. You turn it off when it's time to start—and back on again once the study is over. This creates a relaxing "wind-down" effect, as well as making it easy to control the overtalkative guest! Be alert and consider how you can improve the physical atmosphere of the discussion setting.

**3. Opening question**

An opening question breaks the ice for visitors who may be wondering, "Why am I here?" Just getting people talking builds their confidence and imparts strength to the group. Obviously, when you are choosing an opening question, strike a balance between the overwhelming "Can you explain the meaning of the universe?" and the less taxing "What part of town do you live in?" Ideally, pose a question related to the topic of the discussion. (Do be wise who you start with —it may be best to begin with a friend you can rely on to share smoothly and relatably.)

Ask questions throughout the discussion. Draw people out and prompt them to agree, disagree, or simply add a different thought. Well-presented and well-thought-out questions mean the difference between a dull, dry study and a stimulating, interesting discussion.

**4. Illustrations, analogies, and humor**

Without these elements, though you may preach the truth well enough, it is unlikely your audience will really grasp what you are trying to get across.

As for illustrations, never "preach" them. Always let your illustrations illuminate your scriptures. If you are telling a story, never drag the story out. Once you say "to make a long story short," it's already too late. And don't try to construct discussions around a single illustration. Analogies should be simple enough to require no further explanation. (Woe to the analogy that requires a second analogy to illumine it!)

As for humor, the best kind is that which arises spontaneously from your situation, whether originating in comments of the group or in creative lateral thinking. If you are planning humor into your "script," be careful that you do not belittle others, laugh at another's pain, or joke about sensitive areas—mental health, death, surgery, etc. Also, in these days of easily available and often recycled internet humor, watch out for the "new" joke that others may have already read six months ago!

**5. Personal sharing**

It's worth noting that humor is best used and easiest done through personal sharing. People enjoy laughing with people at their foibles, and humor used in this way will draw the people to the speaker. And remember, the main reason for being humorous in group Bible discussions is to make people relax, so that their hearts will open more easily to the Word.

Personal sharing should not shift the focus from Christ to you. Paul said, "We do not preach ourselves, but Christ Jesus as Lord, and ourselves as your servants for Jesus' sake" (2 Corinthians 4:5). Sharing is not entertainment, though it may be entertaining. It is to illumine the Scriptures and to give people hope that they will be able to obey them.

**6. Use of Scripture**

A Bible discussion is focused above all on *the Bible*. It is not an encounter group, therapy session or ventilation forum. A few tips for bringing the word of God to life:

- Use a contemporary version. In English there are over a hundred versions, of which the NIV (New International Version) is currently the most popular. Compare, for instance, the NIV rendering of 1 Peter 3:21 against the traditional KJV. ("The like figure whereunto even baptism doth now save ye also..."!)
- Don't use too many passages in the study. Sometimes it is best to stick with just one passage. For example, you could base a whole study around Philippians 1:21 ("For to me to live is Christ, and to die is gain").
- Passages should be presented in context. It is poor training for the group, even if your point is correct, if the passages on which you are basing it do not support the point.
- Make it clear at the outset that the assumption of the study group is that the Bible is God's word—that it will serve as the standard and authority for the discussion.

**7. Overall length**

My personal policy is to start the discussion a little "late" and finish a little early. Thirty to forty-five minutes is normally plenty of time! For example, with a 7:30–8:30 slot, guests begin arriving around 7:15 or 7:20 for an informal time of getting to know each other. Begin the discussion proper (turn off the music) at 7:40 and aim to finish around 8:20. With the music, refreshments, and more individual discussion following, most people will probably not begin leaving until after 8:45 or 9:00. As one sage said, "The mind can only take in as much as the seat can endure." (And remember, you said "discussion," not sermon!)

**7. Rapport and captivation**

It is interesting how some Bible discussion leaders just seem to "have a way" with visitors, and how others often seem to have conflicts. This comes down to rapport. Rapport with visitors starts before the discussion begins. Befriending potential troublemakers at this point can eliminate unnecessary embarrassment later. As the visitors are giving their names during the opening question, make a mental note of them—it will make a tremendous impression on them when they are called by name later. Ask visitors to read a chosen scripture. It is an easy task, and yet it helps them to feel involved and part of the discussion. Always thank whoever reads, whether a Christian or a non-Christian, but don't flatter. ("Wow, thanks, that was really great! I've never heard anyone read so eloquently before!") It's also vital not to belittle visitors' comments, no matter how much they disagree with you or how odd or silly they may sound. Try to correct them respectfully, but don't make fun of anybody. After the study, personally thank the visitors for coming and also thank them for their comments and/or questions and feedback. Make sure the evening ends on a positive note, so that the visitors are encouraged and want to come back again.

Contrary to how the word sounds, "captivation" is the ability to make the discussion and the evening so gripping that no one wants to leave. (Not making them feel captive against their will!) There will be the unspoken feeling, "What—the study is already over? I was enjoying myself so much I lost track of the time." Captivation requires that you as leader speak with dynamism, animation, depth, conviction, and personal warmth. Your enemies: monotone presentation, lack of gestures, shallowness, absence of heartfelt sharing and challenge, and clinical presentation of truth. Overall captivation will be a result of all ten points in this lesson. Like rapport, captivation for most of us is more of an art than a given. You can tell in your heart (after the study and even during it) whether the group was captivated.

**9. Concluding the discussion**

Imagine you are on an airplane. The flight (running on time) is nearly over, and the captain announces that you are beginning the descent. The landing gear is down. You've put your seat into the upright position, stowed your tray table, and are enjoying the view out the window as the plane approaches the runway. Suddenly, about to land, it touches down—only to lift off awkwardly back into the air!

So it is with some Bible discussions. They should have ended seven minutes earlier. The "captain" falsely led the group to prepare for "landing," yet he hadn't adequately prepared for the conclusion. The troops are getting restless and the returns diminishing.

To avoid this situation, plan your wrap-up. Ensure that, when it is time end, there is no false sense of conclusion. Recap the major points—not reteaching, just summarizing them. This ensures that visitors will leave with a clear idea of what they have just learned. Plan a firm and definite conclusion. Do not assume you will "just know" when to stop!

**10. Bringing visitors**

What can be said after point 9, "Concluding the discussion"? Only one thing. It goes without saying that a discussion without guests is a superfluous evangelistic event. The best way to guard against this is for you, as the leader, to set the pace in bringing non-Christians to the meeting. Leaders, you need to bring your own visitors!

How about you? Are you working that hard to spread the Word? I learned to lead discussions in my university years. Throughout most of this period (it was not short!), I averaged three or four guests a week to my group Bible study. (There were a good few times when ten or fifteen men and women I invited showed up!) Yet in the years following, I did not bring visitors as frequently.

I was an evangelist, and I remember clearly a challenge in 1990 from a fellow evangelist. He said, "It seems to me that *evangelists* should *evangelize*. What do you think about that, Doug? I don't see you bringing many guests." Instead of acknowledging my sin, I was defensive. "That isn't really my role. Others can bring them, I can give direction." (The problem was, I *was* "giving direction"—wrong direction!) Several years later (yes, years!) I repented of this lazy attitude. The visitors came, my personal ministry flourished, God gave (and still gives) the increase.

At this very moment, are you (evangelist or not) deftly deflecting challenges to share your faith? Are you "hard to pin down"? Don't be like I was. Isn't this why you bought this book, anyway? I guarantee you that if you as leader set the pace, you will rarely have to "challenge" the group to follow. They will appreciate your genuineness, imitate your faith, and arrive at the discussion with a sense of anticipation and enthusiasm.

**Conclusion**

Brothers and sisters, that's how to lead stellar discussions! Nothing further needs to be said, does it?

## Notes

[1] If you want even more ideas, consider the following *dos* and *don'ts*, which are good suggestions for everyone taking part in the discussion.

- Do share from your life—people are always interested in personal stories, provided they are of reasonable length. It makes them see you as a normal person with a normal life and helps them relate to you. Involve names of other people in the group Bible study in stories, as well as other comments.
- Do introduce your guests to others and vice versa—it makes them feel special and part of the group. They become more comfortable once they know people's names. Also, the more relationships that they develop in the church, the easier it is for them to make the transition to being Christians.
- Do share Bibles—make sure every visitor is looking at a Bible. Have Christians near all the visitors, to help them find the passages. Be relaxed and natural when helping them find a book in the Bible, lest they feel stupid. Be patient.
- Do be positive about your friends—avoid sarcasm and try to be as encouraging as possible without being false. It is unusual in the world for people to express appreciation for qualities in anybody else's life. We should take the time to say things like, "Joy is an important quality in anyone's life, and that's why I like spending time with Linda—she's a lot of fun."
- Don't use religious jargon—"quiet time," "prayer partner," and "when I was a [name of denomination], before I was a Christian" will be confusing at best and offensive at worst. People do not understand, and the jargon is perceived as bizarre. It makes it difficult for them to relate to you, and they may view you as part of a strange religious group.
- Don't come in late—lateness is selfishness! Group Bible discussions are designed to meet the needs of non-Christians. As a Christian, you are there to serve and help to fulfill those needs. By coming in late you can easily destroy the atmosphere that has developed.
- Don't answer every question—wait a few seconds. Give the more timid people a chance. However, don't let silence go too long. Visitors can answer some of the questions, and it makes them feel more at ease and part of the group when they get a chance to contribute.
- Don't be silent or appear bored—the visitors will reproduce your behavior. You are there to set an example, and if you look interested and excited, they are more likely to feel that way themselves. Avoid thumbing through the Bible or fiddling with your nails, glasses, shoelaces, etc.
- Don't strongly disagree with (undermine) the leader in public—if you have a crucial question to raise, do it later, after the study. You do not want to get the study off track. It distracts everyone and reduces the impact. If you are seen as conflicting with the leader, it can undermine the people's confidence that a right answer can be found. They may well reason, "If these two Christians can't even agree, you must not be able to know what is right—so why bother trying?" Of course, this does not mean the leader is always right, or that it is always wrong to take a stand (Galatians 2:11). But the group discussion is probably not the best setting for this.
- Don't be too intense after the study—the group discussion was probably intense enough for them, so make them feel relaxed and at ease in the fellowship time afterward. People can take challenge for only so long, and then the law of diminishing returns takes over. Allow people to "digest" their spiritual food—don't force-feed another meal.

If each member will follow these simple *dos* and *don'ts*, the study will go smoothly. In short, each member must do their part—no more, no less.

# 18

# A Fountain of Life

## *Fourteen Studies and How to Lead Them*

Proverbs 13:14 states, "The teaching of the wise is a fountain of life, turning a person from the snares of death." To enable you to become the "wise teacher" whose evangelistic discussion group leads many to Christ, this chapter contains fourteen group Bible studies.

Each discussion is thoroughly presented, including passages, questions, and points. For group Bible discussion leaders, it's always a joy to come across new material. Hopefully these studies will whet the reader's appetite to design other new studies. The standard format studies in this chapter are:

| | |
|---|---|
| **I.** | **Jonah** |
| **II.** | **The Demon-Possessed Man** |
| **III.** | **Matthew 7** |
| **IV.** | **Naaman** |
| **V.** | **The Blind Man** |
| **VI.** | **Jesus, a Man of Power!** |
| **VII.** | **The Woman at the Well** |
| **VIII.** | **The Great "I Am"** |

Variety is the spice of life, and innovation is the spice of group Bible studies. There are many times, in fact most times, when a "standard" study is the best choice. But if you are like most discussion leaders, you can slide into the rut of using those old, familiar studies time and time again. Non-Christian visitors—and especially the regulars!—will appreciate a change of pace or a variation in format. The following are six such studies.

| | |
|---|---|
| **IX.** | **Jehoiakim** |
| **X.** | **The Seven Churches** |
| **XI.** | **Herod's Dilemma** |
| **XII.** | **Convert the Heathen** |
| **XIII.** | **The Book of James** |
| **XIV.** | **The Man at the Pool** |

These last six studies "break the monotony" of the "one-more-night-on-the-Parable-of-the-Sower" syndrome. Relief is on the way!

Since one of the easiest ways to "break the ice" is to ask a good (interesting or thought-provoking) opening question, most studies begin with a question ("Q") to get things rolling.

---

## I. Jonah (8th century BC)

This study moves through the four sections of the book of Jonah, allowing each person in the discussion group to identify which phase of Jonah's life best relates to his or her life.

*Opening*

- Q: If you had $50,000 to spend on a trip, what part of the world would you visit? Another good opening question is, What is the farthest away from (your current) home you have ever been?

1. Running away from God
   - Reading: Take turns reading the first eleven verses. Assign different parts: Jonah, God, narrator, captain, sailors (in unison).
   - Q: What is Jonah doing and why?
   - A: We don't run from God—but from his will. (May read Psalm 139:7–9.)
   - Q: How do we do the same?
   - A: For non-Christians—avoiding becoming Christians... For Christians—not living Christian life—being caught up in materialism, sin, etc.
   - Personal illustration
   - Jonah slept—slept during storm, like Jesus (Mark 4:38), but Jesus slept because he knew he was in the hand of God. Do we have the humility to admit we're running from God, or do we blame God? Jonah had the humility to admit that he was the problem.
   - Q: What does Jonah do in verse 12?

2. Turning back toward God (repentance)
   - Reading: 1:12–2:1.
   - Jonah's prayer—turning to God (repentance). God wanted Nineveh saved whether Jonah saved it or not. They too had to make a firm decision—repent.
   - Illustration: Share about one or two people you have studied the Bible with who illustrate the point.
   - Q: How do you define repentance?
   - A: Repentance means more than just saying "sorry." (May read 2 Corinthians 7:10–11—actions must back up our sorrow.)

3. Walking with God (obedience)
   - Reading: 3:1–5, 10.
   - Jonah could have made excuses: the city was too large, people too hard-hearted...
   - Q: What kinds of excuses do you make for not obeying God?

- Jonah obeyed—and the city repented in one day. This made Jonah so mad that he wanted to die—but he still obeyed God. (Jonah, representing the Jews of his day, was prejudiced against the Gentiles.)
- With us—obedience means going against our feelings and doing things not convenient at the time—resisting temptations to sin, giving up immoral relationships, evangelizing even when not inspired to do so, going to church even when tired.
- Q: Have you denied yourself—are you going against feelings in your obedience to God or does your obedience entail only going with your feelings?

4. Running ahead of God (If time is running short, omit this point.)
    - Leader summarizes Jonah 4.
    - Jonah doesn't have a good ending—Jonah wasn't happy that everyone repented. This is like us today—prejudice against _____ (ethnic or national group). We think ____ are hard-hearted and have no chance of being right with God. Other prejudices—poor against rich, rich against poor, etc.
    - Q: Jonah "obeyed God"—but why was he still wrong?
    - A: The problem was that Jonah did not deal with his heart. We can sometimes obey God on the outside but our hearts may not be right.
    - Q: In what areas might we obey outwardly but not with our hearts?
    - A: Going to church, reading Bible, praying without one's heart being in it.

*Conclusion*

- Get the visitors to summarize the points of this study.
- Challenge: Make sure you're running with—not from—God, and when you do, run with God from the heart.

---

## II. The Demon-Possessed Man

*Opening*

- Q: What is one of the most frightening things you've ever seen?
- Reading: Mark 5:1–20 (assign to a series of volunteers, or go around the room).
- Note: The study is not centered on demon-possession or exorcism, but on how life is changed after an encounter with Christ.
- We will take a look at three aspects of his conversion: his (1) condition, (2) change and (3) commission.

1. His condition
    - Paint the picture of this strange man. Believe it or not, you can learn from how this insane man, who lived naked in a graveyard and cut himself with stones, changed when he met Jesus.

- Q: As for us today—what are we living for? What is our purpose?
- Q: What difference does our life make?
- Q: Are we restless—always looking for more?
- Q: "Cut with stones"—How do we hurt ourselves today?
- A: Self-destructive habits
- Q: He was controlled by an evil spirit—what are some things we are controlled by?
- Personal illustration of a controlling sin.
- Q: He was scared of Jesus. Why do you think people today are scared of facing the truth?
- We must admit the condition we are in. Don't be proud. Face up to Jesus and find the truth in the Scriptures.

2. His change
    - Reading: Mark 5:6–7
    - Q: What does this tell us about him?
    - A: He has a desire to change, yet there is resistance. If you are undecided, come to church, come to a group Bible discussion, study privately...
    - If you are afraid of this challenge—you are more like this man than you thought. When you come to Jesus, there will be change.
    - Note: the pig farmers were doing nothing illegal. They were Gentiles raising pigs in Gentile territory (on the east side of the Sea of Galilee) for Gentile consumption.
    - Reading: Mark 5:16
    - Q: If you were one of the crowd, what changes would you notice?
    - A: The man is sitting there—at Jesus' feet! Fully clothed, in right mind, no longer the wild look—but peace, no longer hatred in heart—instead love, no longer confinement and frustration—now, right mind, purpose, etc. He met Jesus, and was changed drastically.
    - Reading: 2 Corinthians 5:17
    - Q: What does it mean to be a new creation?
    - A: Not just read Bible, not just go to church, not just have Christian friends. Concerns thoughts, motives, desires, purpose.
    - Q: Have there been such changes in your life?
    - Excellent time for leaders to share personally.
    - Q: Why did they plead for Jesus to leave?
    - A: He challenged them (verses 14–17)—he highlighted their own need.
    - Q: What are some things you need to give up to become a Christian?

3. His commission
    - Q: What motivated him to spread the good news?
    - A: The mercy of the Lord (verse 19).
    - Note: the Decapolis, where "Legion" shared his faith, is the name of the Gentile *region* in which the demoniac had been living. (Speaking in the Decapolis does *not* mean that Legion

evangelized ten cities.)
- Q: Did he have to be coerced into sharing his faith?
- Q: Is being evangelistic an option?
- Q: Why do people/Christians today not share their faith?

*Conclusion*
- We must realize our condition—lost. We must find truth in Scriptures.
- We need to make a firm decision to change.
- As Christians, we have been commissioned to share our faith. It is our mission in life.

---

## III. Matthew 7

Often an entire chapter of the Bible can be made into a study. The advantage of such an approach is that it keeps the study in one place, avoiding too much flipping from page to page. It is easier for the regulars to anticipate where the leader is going. Moreover, passages can be explored with much greater depth than in a study that relies on three or four separated sections of Scripture. Finally, if time is getting short or if one passage has received a disproportionate amount of attention, the leader can skip over one or two of their points without losing the effect of covering the chapter thoroughly.

Reading tip: Have only the section you are about to discuss be read. (Read a section, discuss it, read the next, and so on...)

*Opening*
- Explain that we are going to study just one chapter of Matthew, the third and final chapter of the "Sermon on the Mount."

1. Judging others
   - Reading: Matthew 7:1–5
   - Q: Is it wrong to judge others?
   - Describe dramatically what verse 4 is saying.
   - Jesus is condemning hypocritical judging. All judging is not wrong. In the New Testament are many types of rightful as well as wrongful judging: hypocritical (Matthew 7:1), slandering or grumbling against a brother (James 4:11), superficial judging, before getting all the facts (John 7:24), disciplinary "judging" for members of the church (1 Cor 5:12), and final judgment, reserved for God alone (Hebrews 10:30), to name just a few.
   - Q: Why do people so often accuse well-meaning Christians of "judging" them?
   - A: They are defensive because of their own sin. (Concede that sometimes Christians are less tactful than they ought to be.)

2. Pearls to swine
   - Reading: Matthew 7:6
   - Q: What does Jesus mean? Is he saying that some people are swine?

- Explain that Jesus taught we are to love all people, but because of the need to get the message out we need to focus on those who are willing, or open. Refer to Matthew 10:14 if necessary. By the way, here is a perfect example of the need for using one's judgment, proving that the judging condemned in verse 1 is not referring to all judging.

3. Seek and you will find
   - Reading: Matthew 7:7–11
   - This is a positive promise! There are many things you could seek in life and yet never find (riches, UFOs, promotions, good grades, etc.).
   - Q: Why does God promise this?
   - A: God wants people to seek him. Express appreciation for everyone showing up for the Bible discussion.
   - Humor: Illustrate verses 9–10 graphically, describing a restaurant that serves stones and snakes.
   - Q: Why is it that many seem to be seeking but few are finding?
   - A: Looking in wrong place, not seeking the kingdom of God first (Matthew 6:33), seeking with wrong motives, etc.

4. The Golden Rule
   - Reading: Matthew 7:12
   - Point out that in most religions it is the "negative" golden rule that appears. Christianity turns it all around.
   - Q: Which is more challenging, the negative or the positive version?
   - Challenge: Live just *one* day putting others first in everything. Many claim to be living by the Golden Rule, but what they usually mean is that they try not to hurt other people—the *negative* golden rule.

5. The narrow road
   - Reading: Matthew 7:13–14
   - There are only two roads—no comfortable third option.
   - Comment: If you are comparing yourself to everyone else, and think you're as good as the next person, realize that being in the majority is not necessarily a good thing. It means you're lost!
   - Q: Why is it that only a few are finding? Is it that God does not want a lot of people in heaven?
   - A: No—few finding means few are seeking.

6. False prophets
   - Reading: Matthew 7:15–20
   - Q: How can we tell the false from the true prophets?
   - A: Look at their fruit.
   - Q: What sorts of people do you think could be false prophets?
   - A: Fakes and frauds, people who deny Jesus—even nice people and clergymen.
   - Q: How do false prophets gain a following?

- Q: What is it that makes them *false* prophets?
- A: They don't follow God's word.

7. "Lord, Lord"
   - Reading: Matthew 7:21–23
   - Q: Are these religious people?
   - A: Definitely.
   - Q: Are they committed?
   - A: It would seem so—verse 22.
   - Q: Are they sincere?
   - A: There is no indication to the contrary.
   - Q: Are they saved?
   - A: No.
   - Q: Why not?
   - A: They haven't done the will of God (verse 21).
   - They were relying on their own experiences, and they made a dangerous assumption: that they were saved, when in fact they were not following God's word.

8. Wise and foolish builders
   - Reading: Matthew 7:24–27
   - Q: What is the solid foundation we should build on?
   - Q: How do we fail to build on the solid foundation?
   - A: We neglect to put Jesus' words into practice.
   - Q: What does the "great crash" refer to?
   - A: Judgment Day, the storms of life, or both.

*Conclusion*

- Reading: Matthew 7:28–29
- Q: What kind of teacher was Jesus?
- A: Authoritative.
- Q: Why are so few people (including preachers) these days confident and authoritative?
- A: They lack conviction, don't know the Bible, are living double lives, etc.
- Let's be confident as we live out the words of Jesus and share them with others.

---

## IV. Naaman

2 Kings 5:1

- Q; Who was Naaman? What kind of person was he?
- A: Great man, popular, well respected, valiant, good leader, etc. Name a few modern military chiefs.
- Q: What was his problem?
- A: Leprosy (or some similar skin condition).

- Q: Can anyone describe what leprosy is?
- Leader—look up the disease and be prepared to describe it.
- Although Naaman's disease was probably in its early stages, a horrible future was awaiting him if he did not get help.
- Q: Has anyone ever seen the Michael Jackson "Thriller" video?

2 Kings 5:2–6

- Q: What advice is Naaman given?
- Q: What does Naaman do?
- Q: What is the king's response?
- Q: Look at the things Naaman takes with him. Why does he take so much with him?
- A: In order to pay for a cure.
- Q: Is Naaman's health important to him?
- Q: What are the things that we, today, may consider important to us?
- A: Health, money, family, career, academics, food, sports, relationships, etc.
- Q: In eternity, though, what's the only thing that will matter?
- Our relationship with God. Many of the things mentioned are important. We do need to do well academically, take care of our families, health, etc. But ultimately the thing that is most important is not our physical health but our spiritual health!

2 Kings 5:7–10

- Q: What happens when the King of Israel receives the letter?
- A: He gets visibly upset, begins to despair. He thinks that the King of Aram is trying to pick a quarrel with him and in his sorrow, he tears his clothes.
- Q: Who is Elisha?
- A: He was a prophet, the man of God.
- Q: What does he do when he hears of the king's predicament?
- A: He says to send Naaman to him.
- Q: Why does Elisha say, "He will know that there is a prophet in Israel?"
- A: He is expecting God to work through him to cure Naaman. He knows God's power.
- Q: So what does Naaman do?
- A: He goes to Elisha.
- Q: Then what happens?
- A: Elisha sends out his messenger with specific instructions.
- Q: If today we want to find out God's instructions in order to be cured spiritually, where do we go?
- A: The Bible.

2 Kings 5:11–12

- Q: The instructions that Elisha gave, are they difficult to understand?

- Q: What is Naaman's response?
- Q: Why? How do we do this today?
- A: People today may allow pride to prevent them from being cured spiritually—for example, not willing to give up control of their lives to God.
- Preconceived notions—"I thought..." many have preconceived ideas of how to obtain God's spiritual cure, forgiveness of sins (infant baptism, pray Jesus into your heart, born a Christian) rather than obeying God's word.
- Rationalization—these instructions, when considered, do sound too ridiculous to be true. Some today rationalize God's plan of salvation. For example, "How can just being dipped in water cause your sins to be forgiven?"
- Embarrassment—being a respected commander, he might have felt silly obeying these instructions. Some today are embarrassed to be known as Christians and to live the Christian life.

2 Kings 5:13–14

- Q: Would Naaman have been prepared to do "some great thing," like climb Mount Everest to be cured?
- A: Yes (verse 13).
- Too often people are prepared to go out and do great things for God, like raising money for charities, helping the poor, sick, etc., but they are not prepared to follow the simple steps necessary to be spiritually cured—repent and be baptized.
- Q: What does Naaman do?
- A: He obeys—he dips seven times, and he is cured.
- Q: Would he have been cured if he had only dipped five times or six times?
- A: No!
- Q: What if he had been sprinkled as opposed to dipped?
- A: No!
- There was nothing in the water that cured him; it was God's power; but only after he had obeyed completely. Example: when you are prescribed a medicine for an illness, the medicine cures you, but it will do no good if you just sit and look at the bottle. You must obey the instructions and drink the medicine.

2 Kings 5:15–16

- Q: Why does Naaman offer Elisha a gift?
- A: He is grateful and acknowledges God's power working through Elisha.
- Q: Why doesn't he take the credit for himself?—after all, he's the one who dipped himself seven times.
- A: He was cured, but not by his own actions. It was by God's power. Similarly, our salvation is not earned, but comes from God through faith shown by obeying his commands.
- Q: Naaman ended up by saying, "Now I know that there is no God in all the world except in Israel." How did he come to this conclusion?

- A: By obedience. If we are prepared to put God's commands into practice, we can be certain whether or not he exists. Spiritual health is so important, there is so much at stake, that it is illogical not to "test" God's instructions (the Bible) and see if it is true.

---

## V. The Blind Man (John 9)

The entire study comes from this single chapter. As things turn out, all the people in the story are blind, except for Jesus. The incredible irony of the situation (spiritual blindness) is heightened as the story progresses and we see that all of them have this spiritual disease in common, though in different ways.

*Opening*

- Q: "What's one sickness (disease or medical condition) you would dread getting, and why?" Possible answers: cancer, diabetes, leprosy, brain tumor, deafness, amputation... As the leader, you go last, and mention blindness.

Blind Physically

- Explain that the first character on the stage is a man who's been blind from birth. Bring it to life: imagine never having seen nature, buildings, TV, the faces of friends and family... Intense!

Blind Disciples

- Reading: John 9:1–7
- Q: Who's really blind here?
- A: The disciples! They are "blind" because they can't see the man for what he really is: a human being in need. They see him rather as a *theoretical problem*. Discuss their preconception: in this case specifically, that disease is the result of sin—bad karma! It's amazing how religious people throw around terms like "the love of God" and "heaven and hell," and yet are so hardened to the world around them! This discussion is about spiritual, not physical, blindness (verse 5).

Blind Neighbors

- Reading: John 9:8–12
- His neighbors and those who frequently saw him also are "blind."
- Q: Is it surprising they didn't recognize him? How were these neighbors blind? How can we be around the same people day after day without ever really "seeing" them? What are relationships in the world like? Do people care about their neighbors? How should Christians be different? (These are just a few of the questions you could throw out to stimulate discussion.)

Blind Pharisees

- Reading: John 9:13–17
- The Pharisees are "blinded" by their traditions. (Be sure to explain that Jesus did not violate the Old Testament, only the Pharisaic interpretation.)
- Q: What sorts of traditions obscure the truth for us?

Blind Families

- Reading: John 9:18–23
- Peer pressure and fear of rejection are powerful forces in blinding people to the truth. Share about a time *you* gave in to peer pressure.
- Q: Would traditional religion really reject someone today just because he/she was trying to follow Jesus? Why?

The Blindness Continues

- Reading: John 9:24–34 (The leader should read this section. Read dynamically and dramatically! Be animated during this transition section, though spending no more than about three minutes in reading and explanation.)

Spiritual Sight

- Reading: John 9:35–39
- Q: What's 20/20 vision spiritually? What do you notice about the man?
- A: Willing to take a stand on truth, not popular consensus; open to Jesus, despite limited knowledge; respects (worships) God. How can we open ourselves to the truth about Jesus?

Paradox of Blindness

- Reading: John 9:40–41
- The Pharisees are offended by Jesus' comment.
- Q: What did he really mean?
- A: People who claim already to see (who aren't really open) are blind, while those who recognize their blindness (or ignorance) can see.
- Are you an open person? Can you really see? Or are you controlled by your preconceptions, traditions or what others think?

*Conclusion*

- Q: Which is worse, *physical* or *spiritual* blindness?
- A: Spiritual blindness is much worse—you never learn the truth about life, God or even about yourself. Many think they see, but they're blind.
- Q: If the story continued and *you* were included, what would be said about you?

## VI. Jesus, a Man of Power

This study has many possible verses, so choose the ones you can best teach with conviction. As we will see, Jesus was a man of power! For first-timers, this will be a study full of surprises!

*Opening*

- Q: What pictures of Jesus are common in our society? Or what concept were you taught growing up?
- Emphasize what Jesus is *not*: (1) effeminate—he was not "a woman with a beard" who uttered nice things, (2) a weakling—he was a strong ex-carpenter, no fixed address, direct and to the point, (3) insecure or indecisive—he had a clear life objective and a calm demeanor, not from meditation, but from knowing he was doing the right thing. This strength and confidence can be traced back to his childhood.
- Reading: Luke 24:19—After his death, people remembered Jesus Christ as a powerful man, not a sissy.

Pictures of Jesus:

- Luke 4:1–4—Power to resist temptation! Discuss several activities associated with "being a man." Real men don't follow the crowd at parties to show they can "hold their liquor"; real men go against the stream when it's flowing in the wrong direction.
- Luke 4:28–30—Authority! Taking a stand against prejudice, first message to hometown! They try to throw him off a cliff. If twenty or thirty men tried to throw you out the window, could you stop them? Clearly Jesus was no pushover! His authority was felt.
- Luke 4:33–37—Speaks sternly to demon. I would have fled in terror!
- Luke 4:42—Up early after busy night. *Packed*, not *wimpy* schedule!
- Luke 7:14—Against social convention when necessary. Imagine the guts needed to stop a funeral procession!
- Luke 11:37–39, 44–46—Strong talk to religious leaders—as guest at a dinner party! Have you ever talked to anyone that way?
- Luke 12:49–51—What drive he had! What a radical message!
- Luke 13:24—"Make every effort": Greek *agonidzesthai*, contend for the prize = agonize. To follow Jesus you have to really "go for it"!
- Luke 23:34—It takes strength to forgive. Any fool can harbor a grudge or take revenge, but it takes a real man to love and to forgive!

*Conclusion*

- Reading: Luke 2:34–35
- People reacted strongly to Jesus, because he was such a strong character. Is this the Jesus you want to follow? If so, you are destined to become more and more like him. Watch out!

## VII. The Woman at the Well (John 4)

Have you ever had a study with only a few visitors? Don't get frustrated—get creative! This study meets needs of both Christians (we need to share our faith) and non-Christians. It's rewarding to study an entire chapter of the Bible, and avoids unnecessary turning of pages in an extended trek across the testaments.

*Opening*

- This simple story has two main figures: a woman of Samaria and Jesus. The Samaritans were half-caste racially and half-Jewish in their religion, hated by the Jews as compromisers. But Jesus never gave in to prejudice. In fact, he makes Samaritans the heroes of his stories (remember the Parable of the Good Samaritan [Luke 10]?) and appreciates their hearts (the healing of the ten lepers, Luke 17). Background: the Samaritans, who came into existence in the eighth century BC (2 Kings 17), eventually built their own temple atop Mt. Gerizim. It was destroyed in 129 BC, but the Samaritans still claimed that this was the place where people were to worship the Lord, not Mt. Zion (in Jerusalem).

Jesus at the well

- Reading: John 4:4–6.
- Q: How many of you have had a long day?
- Q: What are you like when you're tired?
- Describe what you are like when you first wake up, or how you feel when you come home from work.
- Jesus is taking a break. He didn't just cruise through life without any effort. He was human. He felt fatigue, understood all the pain, sweat, hunger and thirst that we experience.
- Q: What do you like to drink when you're really thirsty? Jesus offers something far better.

Jesus initiates a conversation

- Reading: John 4:7–9.
- Jesus goes against social conventions. In his day, it was not the custom for Jews to talk to Samaritans.
- Q: What is your experience of prejudice? (Good opportunity for personal sharing.)
- Also, this is a *man* starting a conversation with a *woman*.
- Q: What do you think she might have been thinking when he first started speaking to her? What would you feel if you were the woman?
- Following Jesus means we need to see social conventions in perspective. It *can* be okay to talk to strangers. And men can talk to women out of pure motives.

Jesus shares his faith

- Reading: John 4:10–26.

- He is willing to speak personally to her, even though she's a stranger (verse 18).
- Q: How readily do you talk to strangers?
- He turns the conversation in a spiritual direction, and arouses her curiosity (verse 10). Jesus knows he has something to offer! People pay money for books and courses on becoming confident people. When we know the truth and what life is all about, we don't have to psyche ourselves up to feel important or act big. It's natural.
- Q: What is "living water"?
- What a contrast to her daily routine: making the journey on foot to the well and back a couple of times a day, carrying the heavy water jar, running out of water and having to return again. Outside of Christ our limited resources are fast depleted. In Christ, they need never run dry.
- The woman at the well progresses in her realization of who Jesus is: from Jewish man (verse 9) to "sir" (verses 11, 15) to "prophet" (verse 19), and finally Messiah (verse 25). Your appreciation of Jesus will deepen the longer you know him.
- If you're meeting him for the first time, you'll soon realize he's far more than a wise teacher, or even a prophet. You're meeting God!

Disciples challenged by Jesus' example

- Reading: John 4:27–35.
- Q: What does he mean by the fields being "ripe"? What happens when a crop is left too long in the field?
- A: People are ready and waiting; we must act fast!
- Q: How do you refresh yourself when you are tired?
- Jesus' food is evangelism (verse 34)—it keeps us going when we're tired, too. Some say, "I feel too tired to give." Give, and your energy will come back!

The result of one conversation

- Reading: John 4:39–42.
- The Samaritan woman affects her whole community.
- Q: Are you having any noticeable impact on your community? What difference does your life make in the world?
- Anyone can share their faith! This woman was a "beginner." Share about yourself as a young Christian—how little you knew but how a simple faith moved you to action.

*Concluding challenges*

- "Now, having studied John 4, we all know as much about Jesus as she did—even more! Doesn't God expect us to respond in the same way?"
- Take time after the study to read the rest of the gospel of John.
- Disciples—share your faith and have the perspective of Jesus.
- Others—begin a relationship with Jesus as soon as possible. Jesus offers all of us "living water." Why wait? Go for it today.

## VIII. "I Am" Statements of Jesus

This study follows the "I am" statements of Jesus, and is excellent for beginners, members of other world religions, and "enlightened" or liberal thinkers who are offended by the idea that one single religion might have the truth. Expect lots of discussion—the points are simple.

*Opening*

- Q: If you were *extremely* hungry, where would you go to eat?

Jesus the bread of life

- Reading: John 6:35
- Q: What keeps you going when you are tired or inwardly hungry (lack of motivation, focus, perspective, joy, good relationships...)?
- Q: What does it mean to be *spiritually* hungry or tired?
- The Old Testament says (Ecclesiastes 3:11) God has set eternity in our hearts. We are *all* religious, or spiritual, whether we realize it or not. But until a relationship with God fills the empty place in our lives, we will never be truly satisfied.
- This statement is either true or false. If it's false, don't worry; but if it's true, the implications are incredible!

Jesus the light of the world

- Reading: John 8:12
- Q: As a child, were you afraid of the dark? Why were we afraid? What's the darkest place you've ever been in? What does it mean to be in "darkness"?
- A: Not sure where you are going in your life, confused, fearful, accidentally injuring yourself...
- Q: Do you know where you're going in your life? (Or are you always guessing, hoping...?)
- What a bold claim: "I am *the* light of the world"! Jesus does not point to the light and say, "*There* is the light of the world," but "*I am* the light..."
- There's no in-between! Darkness *or* light, no "gray area." Again, this statement cannot be true *and* false; it's *either* true *or* false!

Jesus the Good Shepherd

- Reading: John 10:14
- Q: What's the difference between a good boss and a bad boss?
- A: Honesty, personal concern, being a good listener...
- In the same way, Jesus is a *good* shepherd. We are the sheep.
- Q: Why do you think the Bible describes us all as "sheep"?
- God cares about our happiness, about our feelings. He wants us to have the best life possible (John 10:10). But it's not just a good feeling God is offering us; God desires a personal relationship with us. He's even willing to go after us when we stray away. Maybe he's going after you now!

- Jesus is the bread of life and the light of the world, yet the concept of the shepherd is more personal.

Jesus the resurrection

- Reading: John 11:25
- Q: Do you believe in eternal life? What does that mean?
- It's not reincarnation Jesus is offering (Hebrews 9:27), nor is it an "afterlife" Jesus promises (everyone will have that), but eternal life with God! We all will die one day. For worldly people, that is the end. It's awful, irreversible. But for people who know Jesus, it's just the beginning. It's terrific, and no one would want to reverse it!

Jesus the only way

- Reading: John 14:6
- This is an incredibly exclusive claim! People don't "accidentally" believe in Jesus (without knowing it)! It's a conscious decision. (Possibly refer to John 3:18.) In the same way, you don't get married by accident. It's by mutual agreement and happens at a specific point in time. Thus, if Jesus is right, no other religion is valid. (We can see why Jesus received such opposition!)
- Like all the other claims of Jesus, it's either true or false; don't monkey around with Jesus' claim! Accept it or reject it.
- Q: How would someone's life change if they really believed this?
- A: In his or her attitude to the Bible, praying to God, eagerness to be at church, evangelism...

*Conclusion*

- There are other possible "I am" verses we could have looked at (8:58, 10:7, 15:1, etc.). But this assortment of just five of the amazing statements of Jesus is enough to give us a good picture of how radical a character he was.
- Q: Is this the Jesus you were shown before? Or is a lot of this brand new?
- Q: Why do you think people misunderstand Jesus today? Why do they fail to realize the seriousness and uniqueness of his claims?
- A: People are unwilling to face opposition, make the time for study and activities, come clean... We need to think through the implications of what Jesus said about himself and make changes accordingly.
- Read one of the gospels and get an accurate picture of Jesus.
- Begin studying the Bible with someone who has a relationship with Jesus already.
- Start taking a stand on the teachings of Jesus. You will notice how well they work, how few practice them, and how your own life is changing for the good.

## IX. Jehoiakim

This study is a highly creative way to approach the subject of the word of God. It falls into two parts. The beauty of the discussion is that the participants create the study.

*Opening*

- Begin by turning to Jeremiah 36. Assign readings: verses 1–3, 4–6; then the leader summarizes verses 7–19; then have verses 20-26 read.
- Explain that everyone present in the room will be creating the study. The object is to play "Jehoiakim"—to identify undesirable elements in the Bible and then "cut them out." The leader explains the aspects of the Bible to be deleted may be things which people have a hard time accepting, or which the individual offering the suggestion has a hard time obeying. Each alteration must be identified by an "undesirable" scripture.

Break

- It is during the break that the difficult parts and accompanying scriptures are to be located. Make sure that all the non-Christians come up with something—after all, the study is for them! Christians need to be alert and help them voice what they are thinking during the intermission.
- Let the break run for ten minutes (serve refreshments).

Second part

- The group reassembles.
- The leader has each participant read the passage he has chosen for deletion. (No need for everyone to turn there.) The reason for deleting the passage from the Bible is explained.
- This is not a time for discussion; the leader just takes down the verses and objections on paper. (Common deletions include verses against lust, church attendance, the existence of hell, etc. It is fun to see what the group comes up with!)
- Next the leader brings to life the new "version" of Christianity. Going through the list of corrections he got from the group, he paints an enticing picture of the "easy" version of Christianity now that the Bible has been edited. "Wouldn't that be great?" the leader says.
- You may also suggest a name for this new, improved Bible.

Then return to Jeremiah 36:27–28, 31–32. Ask the group what the lessons to be learned are.

*Conclusion*

- Ignoring the Bible, or parts of it, no more changes the truth than ignoring a problem or a disease makes it go away (Jeremiah 6:13–14). Something must be done. We have no right to play games with God's word.
- Telling the truth may make you unpopular, but God is the only one whose opinion really counts.

## X. The Seven Churches

Revelation 2 and 3 provide a clear outline for a seven-part study that can be delegated to various members of the discussion group. The leader introduces the topic, and then assigns each church to one or more individuals to study and briefly summarize. After allowing ten to fifteen minutes for preparation, people report on the messages to each of the churches.

The leader follows each report by making practical applications.

### Tips

- This is an especially good study for larger groups, especially where there are at least seven guests and seven believers.
- Be sure to place at least one fairly knowledgeable person in each group.
- The leader usually takes the seventh church because it is the most challenging.

---

## XI. Herod's Dilemma

Get ready for a lively time! (Not a study for leaders afraid of the theatric!)

*Opening*

- Q: What is one difficult decision you have had to make?
- Reading: Mark 6:14–25
- Q: Why did Herodias have a grudge against John?
- A: Because he said it was morally wrong for Herod to marry her.
- Q: What decision must Herod now make?
- A: To kill or not to kill John.
- At this point, split the group into two teams. Assign a leader to each team. Be sure you split the teams in a balanced way, with a dynamic leader for each team.
- You take the role of King Herod. One of the teams is to advise you to kill John the Baptist. The other is to advise against it. Give the teams ten minutes while you go out and make the coffee.

Argumentation

- When the ten minutes are up, have the teams take turns advising you for and against killing John.
- (Be sure to speak to the more mature Christians in the discussion beforehand to ensure a great spirit of involvement and enthusiasm.)
- Following are some possible arguments that may be made. This is not the structure of the discussion, just a peek at how it might go. (As "Herod," your job is not to advise them how to advise you, though your helpers may influence the groups through some of these suggestions.)

| *Arguments for Killing John* | *Arguments against Killing John* |
|---|---|
| 1) "Think of your guests!" | 1) "Think of John's supporters; there are many." |
| 2) "He is causing trouble all over the place, telling us to repent, sell our possessions, etc. He's upsetting the system." | 2) "It would be murder." |
| 3) "You swore it to your wife's daughter!" | 3) "You know he's righteous!" (See verse 20.) |
| 4) "It'll please Herodias." | 4) "Your conscience will always bother you." |
| 5) "He'll stop bothering you about Herodias." | 5) "If you give in to Herodias, she'll always be one up on you!" |
| 6) "You'll make an example of him for other people who make trouble. People will fear and respect you." | 6) "The Bible says it is okay to free yourself from an unwise commitment" (Proverbs 6:1–5). |

*Closing*

- When the teams have exhausted their arguments, call the debate to a close, and say, "Let's find out what Herod in fact does."
- Reading: Mark 6:26–29
- Q: Why did Herod kill John the Baptist?
- A: Herod gave in to peer pressure (verse 26). Today, we must not give in to the world's view of Christianity, even if our friends and family oppose us.
- Q: By killing John, what did Herod do to his chances of getting right with God?
- A: He may have "killed" his last chance. This can happen to us today when we refuse to change things in our lives and become Christians.
- Q: By killing John, Herod silenced the voice that was convicting him (verse 17). How can we do that today?
- A: Don't study the Bible, don't come to church, don't have Christian friends...
- Challenge: Don't be like Herod. Make the right decision about Christianity.

## XII. Convert the Heathen

In this study the leader plays the role of a heathen—usually a drunk who has come into the study after being told that he has one week to live (cirrhosis of the liver, or something to that effect). The alcoholic appeals to the group to teach them—using the Bible—step by step what they must do to be saved.

**Tips**

- Plan ahead for the kinds of issues you want to focus on. It may be the definition of faith, the need for total repentance, or the terms of discipleship. The discussion of baptism can be extended and explicit or fairly superficial.
- As the leader, you will need to explain the ground rules *before* you start your role playing. Do not break out of character until the end of the session.
- In your acting, invent excuses, throw questions back to the group, ask whether a particularly good point might not just be someone's own "interpretation."
- Be animated!

The study works best when the visitors are either irreligious or already aware of the plan of salvation.

---

### XIII. The Book of James

Like the study on the Seven Churches in this chapter, this is a particularly ripe portion of Scripture to allow members of the discussion to study and present. (It may also be presented by the leader in a more conventional way.)

James divides neatly into five chapters, and the abundance of sharp, penetrating statements gives even the novice confidence in understanding the book. (In fact, there are so many good points that it is possible to extend the discussion into a two- or three-part series.)

For a period of ten minutes or so, five small groups discuss their chapter and the points they would like to share when the whole group reassembles. Proceed chapter by chapter.

**Tips**

- The leader should do his or her best to ensure there is at least one Christian in each group.
- The leader should also know the book (and its background) thoroughly and to have a list of points from each chapter.

Here is an outline of some of the points that may emerge from each chapter.

Chapter 1

- 2–4: Joyful in trials because trials bring maturity (also 1:12).
- 13–15: Truth about temptation and sin. We do not "fall" into sin; we walk into it. Eventually the feeling of guilt subsides, leaving us spiritually dead.

- 19: "Quick to listen..."—a lesson in itself.
- 22–25: Listening is deceiving if not accompanied by action. (I.e. those who attend church or Bible discussion without really changing.)
- 26: "Worthless religion"—convicting for many foul-mouthed nominal Christians.
- 27: "Pure religion" means social concern.

Chapter 2
- 1–12: Condemnation of prejudice.
- 14–19: Faith plus good deeds: good illustration is husband who says "I love you" to his wife but never shows it.
- 24, 26: Faith without deeds is dead.

Chapter 3
- 1: Strict judgment for teachers—discuss why.
- 3–12: Hazards of the tongue. It is useful to discuss various verbal sins.
- 13–17: Wisdom of the world versus wisdom of God.

Chapter 4
- 4: You can't love both God and sin; love of the world equals hatred toward God. E.g., "It's not that I don't love God, it's just that I like getting drunk," etc. Parallel: your wife and another man: "It's not that I don't love you, John. It's just that I love Peter, too." (Create hypothetical examples using people in the discussion for husband, wife, lover.) God is saying you cannot have it both ways; when you choose the world, you sever your relationship with him.
- 13–16: Put God in your plans: decisions about course, career, where to live, etc.
- 17: One of the most convicting verses in the Bible. Sins of *omission* as well as sins of commission.

Chapter 5
- 12: Let your "yes" be yes. Practical areas: punctuality, reliability, openness.
- 16: Confess sins to one another. Why? An opportunity to receive advice on how to overcome sin, grow in your humility, show your seriousness about change.
- 19–20: Bring the wanderers back home (the lost and those who have strayed).

Conclude by summarizing the major points, thanking all present for their participation, and urging them always to read the Bible with a view to letting their hearts be challenged by the Word.

## XIV. The Man at the Pool (John 5)

This may be the liveliest discussion you'll ever lead! It's a debate on whether the man at the pool had a good heart or a bad heart.

*Opening*

- Begin by reading John 5:1–16. Different people take turns reading the story.
- Describe the scene: All those sick people, moaning and complaining!
- Q: How long had he been disabled?
- A: Thirty-eight years! That's longer than many of us have lived! Draw attention to Jesus' question, "Do you want to get well?" (But don't offer any interpretation.)
- Explain that we are going to discuss whether this man had a pure, sincere heart or whether his heart was bad and his motives wrong.
- Make sure you don't "prejudice" the group by sharing your own view.
- Now divide the group in two. The left side argues that the man's heart was good, the right that his heart was bad. It's important that you, as the leader, choose the sides; the participants have no say.

Debate

- Allow each group three to four minutes to confer before beginning the debate.
- The debate begins (twenty to thirty minutes). You're merely the moderator, ensuring the discussion flows. Don't let the crowd address you; rather make sure they debate each other. Many points will come out. (Remember, it's not your job to suggest the points, though the occasional provocative comment can help keep things rolling.)

Possible points—Good heart

- He obeyed Jesus (picked up his mat).
- He shared his faith with the Jewish leaders, telling them it was Jesus who healed him.
- Weak character doesn't mean impure motives.
- Nothing in the passage says he had a bad heart.
- He'd made efforts to get into the water, but was unable.

Possible points—Bad heart

- He made excuses when asked if he wanted to get well.
- He was wavering on whether to give up his soft lifestyle.
- He got Jesus into trouble.
- Jesus told him to "Stop sinning."

A good case can be made on both sides!

Midpoint

- Halfway through, stand up and stop the discussion. Inform the group that anyone persuaded by the opposite view may switch positions. They should actually *change seats*, so that each (reorganized) group still sits together. Then the debate continues. (Don't let it go too long.)

*Close*

- End the debate. (There is no "winner.") They'll want to know which side you hold with, but if you're wise, you *won't* share your opinion. (I won't tell you mine, either!) *Do* make the following points:
- Jesus changes us. We all need healing.
- Q: How long have *you* been spiritually sick?
- You must make your own decision and be personally motivated (verse 6). God doesn't force anyone to follow Jesus.
- Whatever his real motives, God knows. And God knows your heart, too. Is it good? Why are you interested in Jesus Christ? For friendship? Attention? Because you want to get something out of it, or because it is right and you want to give your life for others?

**Conclusion**

Scores of further discussions are "out there"[1]—we suggest you "scrounge" and "scavenge" till your personal repertoire is ample. We hope you enjoyed this "fountain" of fourteen user-friendly discussions. And may God bless your ministry!

## Notes

[1] Just a few other possibilities include "Being exposed," on the character of Peter—Luke 5:1–11, John 3:19, Hebrews 4:12–13; "Whose Fool Are You?"—Intellectual fool, Nearsighted fool, Mocking fool, Self-sufficient fool, God's fool; "Running to win"—1 Corinthians 9:24, 2 Timothy 4:7–8, Hebrews 12:1; "Vision problems"—Farsighted, Nearsighted, Astigmatic, Cross-eyed; and "Aladdin's Lamp"—1 Kings 3, Ecclesiastes 2. To amply expand your horizons, see David J. Schmeling's *52 Bible Talks for Fun and Fruitfulness* (Spring, Texas: Illumination Publishers, 1999).

PART IV

# DON'T STOP NOW!

"I will keep on... and... I will reach my goal. In any case, I must press on today and tomorrow and the next day—for surely no prophet can die outside Jerusalem!" (Luke 13:32-33).

I am confident of this, that the one who began a good work among you will bring it to completion by the day of Jesus Christ (Philippians 1:6 NRSV)..

There are many obstacles and discouragements that can derail us from our mission. Jesus faced opposition on all sides, but resolved to continue to make it to his goal. On his mind was the weighty matter of the salvation of the world.

Have we made a good beginning in our evangelism, only to slowly lose momentum and conviction? Or are we just beginning? The Master bids us continue to fish—till the nets are full (Luke 5:6-7; John 21:6, 8).

Now it is time to put the challenge into action. The concluding chapter calls us to a common decision of faith and commitment.

The appendices that follow provide guidance first for bringing back wanderers, then for navigating and wisely utilizing technology as we fish for people.

# 19
# Translating the Challenge into Action

So far the book has been fairly challenging. Yet the greatest challenge of all is the subject of this final chapter: putting into practice the principles from God's word brought to light in these pages. This is the acid test.

For most of you reading this book, your hearts are pure and you genuinely want to change. You are keen to develop a powerful evangelistic lifestyle or, if you already have one, to increase your effectiveness. But how easy it is to be caught in the trap into which Ezekiel's hearers fell: approving of the truth without acting on it personally!

> "As for you, son of man, your countrymen are talking together about you by the walls and at the doors of the houses, saying to each other, 'Come and hear the message that has come from the LORD.' My people come to you, as they usually do, and sit before you to listen to your words, but they do not put them into practice. With their mouths they express devotion, but their hearts are greedy for unjust gain. Indeed, to them you are nothing more than one who sings love songs with a beautiful voice and plays an instrument well, for they hear your words but do not put them into practice" (Ezekiel 33:30–32).

These people were not overtly negative. In fact, they were enthusiastic about the things God was trying to show them. (Perhaps some of the most obstinate of them shouted the loudest amens.) No, God does not fault them for a lack of zeal. They lacked obedience; that was their downfall. Yes, with their mouths they expressed devotion, talked about total commitment, fancied themselves to be growing spiritually—but their hearts were greedy for unjust gain.

Could it be that, just like the people of God 2,600 years ago, churches have grown "greedy for unjust gain"? Brothers and sisters, the world is lost. Therefore any lifestyle which does not seek at all costs to improve the situation is fundamentally "unjust." Any congregation of the Lord's people which has forgotten the mission—love for the lost and concern for the needy—is *de facto* unjust. We have no right to focus inward, to surrender our distinctiveness and blend into the world around us, to hoard our salvation, while the vast majority of humankind has never heard the truth about Jesus.

Many of us, instead of of pushing forward in our mission, have grown silent. We know the truth, but have found obedience—or church, or leadership, or life—disagreeable. That is unjust! (What are we waiting for?)

Every Christian, every congregation, must continue in the teaching of Christ—the one who told us to go into all natio ns. We have the truth. And yet it is possible to *applaud* the Great Commission without truly *applying* it. If this is the case, we are being *entertained* by the truth, but not *entering into it* and incorporating it into our deepest being.

In my ministry I have struggled to understand these principles, and realize that my understanding of evangelism is at this point "under construction." I, for one, have far to go in the area of relational evangelism, and far to go in the fight against "the pattern of this world" (Romans 12:2), which vies for our very souls. Certainly there is much the Lord will continue to teach us, and much ground to cover before we will have evangelized this planet.

Hopefully you have been not only stimulated by these exciting principles, but also sensitized to the will of God. As God promised Israel in Ezekiel 36:26–27,

> "I will give you a new heart and put a new spirit in you; I will remove from you your heart of stone and give you a heart of flesh. And I will put my Spirit in you and move you to follow my decrees and be careful to keep my laws."

Has your heart been changing? It is sad that the people of Israel frequently lost their capacity to respond to the voice of the Lord; their hearts were like stone. All of us know what it is to lose our spiritual edge, to be dull to the living and active word of God. Yet God yearns for all his children to have "hearts of flesh." That is why it is so important not to forget what you have heard.

The key is obedience. In the words of James (1:22), "Do not merely listen to the word, and so deceive yourselves. Do what it says!"

An action plan is needed. I would urge you to (1) pray through the ideas that struck you, (2) talk about them with a Christian brother or sister, seeking advice, and (3) set some goals. The conviction you feel at this very moment—capture it, fan it into flame. Let that burning heart never be extinguished!

Don't be afraid. Go fishing! Put out into deep water. And don't ever stop. Not until the nets are full.

# Appendix A

## *Bringing Back the Stray*

> "My brothers and sisters, if one of you should wander from the truth and someone should bring them back, remember this: Whoever turns a sinner from the error of their way will save them from death and cover over a multitude of sins" (James 5:19–20).
>
> "Brothers and sisters, if someone is caught in a sin, you who are spiritual should restore them gently. But watch yourself, or you also may be tempted. Carry each other's burdens, and in this way you will fulfill the law of Christ" (Galatians 6:1–2).

Whereas the Lord *restores* our souls (Psalm 23), and those who are spiritual ought to restore the one caught in sin (Galatians 6:2), this appendix is talking about *bringing back the stray*. Properly speaking, this is not "restoration," since restoration, though in some ways a similar process, is not limited to those who have wandered away from the flock. In many cases they have wandered far from the Lord. What exactly is bringing back the stray?

- It is a process of freeing a drifting brother or sister (Hebrews 2:1) from the allure of the world and bringing him or her back to the fold. This process takes time. It is much more than simply adding someone's name back to the membership list.[1]
- It is carried out gently (Galatians 6:2). This means caring for the individual, hearing him or her out, not rushing but carefully retracing steps back to the place he or she got off the narrow road. More often than not, those wishing to return to the fold already have plenty of guilt and shame. They need assurance, not just an "I-told-you-so" telling off (2 Corinthians 2:6–8).
- Not all Christians are able to bring back the stray. Maturity, experience, and spirituality are essential. This is a pastoral duty, though not necessarily limited to church leaders. All Christians are "shepherds" of the flock in some sense. Many congregations contain plenty of mature Christians,

and these are the ones who will be most qualified to bring the wanderers home.
- The process itself is somewhat precarious by its very nature. The temptation to overidentify with the lapsed disciple, taking on their attitudes or championing their grievances, is more than some disciples can handle. In some cases, the sin which the person to be restored must relinquish is still ongoing.
- To bring back the stray is Christlike. At times all of us need help in carrying our burdens, don't we?

*Practicals*

Here is some distilled wisdom concerning working with those who drifted back into the world.[2]

- Always ask, What are the causes of the person's leaving the church? We must make sure that we are dealing with true causes, not *symptoms*. Otherwise, after being welcomed back, they may slip back into the same well-worn ruts.
- Remember that God holds the individual responsible for quitting—no matter what (Romans 2:5ff).
- Sometimes it is largely a leader's fault. Shepherds, through harsh leadership, can scatter the sheep (Ezekiel 34). In addition, sometimes people stumble through the sin or lack of forgiveness of another (Luke 17).
- False teaching also has a role in dragging many back to the world (2 Peter 2:1–3).
- Spiritual "starvation" (1 Corinthians 3:2) may also be an issue. Lack of proper appetite may be a factor, but so may lack of proper diet. Milk and meat are both needed. Shallow preaching and or humanistic leadership inhibit our potential to grow. (Still, the onus is on the individual.)
- Always speak to those who were involved in the person's life before they lapsed. Realize, in addition, that in some cases there are "two sides" to the story (Proverbs 18:17). Make sure you are properly informed.
- Call for additional help as required.
- If someone is not open to returning at the moment, "leave the light on and the door open"! (The Parable of the Lost Son shows the example.) Don't be resentful or take sinful decisions personally. This only causes us to turn a cold shoulder to them, and it prohibits them from coming back.
- Be urgent to see the person progress, but don't rush them. Beware of flash-in-the-pan decisions. Give them time to once again implement spiritual disciplines (personal devotional times, to begin with) and to reintegrate the church schedule into their own routine.

- Study the Bible together. Pray together.
- Expect them to do the same on their own.
- When they have true conviction, they will probably start sharing their faith with their friends again.
- If the lapsed Christian is married, ask the spouse what he or she thinks about the change. The spouse probably has a better vantage point from which to evaluate what is going on than anyone else.
- While not withholding gentle assistance, expect the individual to exhibit initiative. Ultimately, it is not hand-holding that will set them back on the path to the Lord's heavenly kingdom (2 Timothy 4:18).

Probably the best wisdom is to "shepherd" others as Christ would (John 10). The biblical formula for salvation is *not* faith—repentance—baptism. It is faith—repentance—baptism—perseverance (Hebrews 11:6; Acts 2:38; Hebrews 3:14). We all need ongoing input, mentoring, discipling, guidance—call it what you will! Far too many are baptized and then quit. When we love people more—concretely, spiritually, sincerely—they will not want to leave the Lord or their brothers and sisters. An ounce of prevention is worth a pound of cure.

**Conclusion**

In most cities around the world there are not only active Christians, but also a number of men and women who have turned back from following the Lord. We must reach these individuals to "save their souls from death and cover over a multitude of sins."[3]

Be proactive and preemptive in your ministry. Build solidly and carefully. There will always be some who are lured back to the world (Luke 8:13–14; John 6:60–67), but the number will be reduced when we shepherd the right way. "Restore" *before* they wander off, not just when things have reached a critical point.

## Notes

[1] I am avoiding the term "fallaway" for a lapsed disciple, since the term does not appear in the Bible, and implies, in its simplest understanding (Hebrews 6:4–6), that there is no chance the individual will return to the Lord. The New Testament speaks of those who "wander away" (James 5:19–20) as those we need to seek and bring back into the fold. It is beyond the scope of this appendix to explore the theological implications of the terminology.

[2] For much of this appendix I owe thanks to Wyndham Shaw, a wise elder whom I admire deeply. He has helped to turn many back to the Lord. Adapted from his contribution in the DPI *Leader's Resource Handbook* (Woburn, Mass.: Discipleship Publications International, 1997).

[3] Theirs, not ours.

# Appendix B

## *Harnessing Technology for Effective Outreach*

God's people have always had an ambivalent relationship with technology. Technology is used to build a monument to human ego in Genesis 11, the story of the Tower of Babel. There are also negative overtones in Genesis 4, where the metalworkers are not part of the godly lineage of Abel or Seth (chapter 5), but of the wicked Cain. This might lead some to feel justified in rejecting technology.

Yet building a house can be good (Psalm 127). Paul took advantage of ships to spread the gospel (Acts 13). Some of the clothing Jesus wore was probably spun from wool or other material (Matthew 27). Spinning, sailing, building—these are examples of technology in action. Technology itself should not be considered inherently good or evil (beneficial or detrimental); it is how we use it and what we do with it that matters.

For those leery of technology, or who feel hopelessly behind the learning curve, consider this: Postal letters use technology. So does a phone call. So do driving, cycling, or taking the bus to your friend's home. Everyone uses technology. Moreover, it's normal when new technologies come out for people to feel a little weird. ("What—a horseless carriage?") My grandmother told me about how excited she was when the "talkies" first came out. (When she was a little girl, the black-and-white movies were soundless—unless you count the pianist playing along with the film.)

I remember when I first attended a class on the future of the internet, around 1997. (You may recall that it was only invented in the early 1990s.) The teacher said we would need to create "websites." If we didn't "get with it," the world would pass us by—and our ministries would be ineffective. I was terrified. As a church leader, was I really going to have to become tech savvy? At that time, I'd been using a (clunky) mobile phone for three years. We sent messages by Lotus Notes. No texting. No Outlook.

I desperately hoped what the teacher was saying wasn't true, but I had a sinking feeling in my heart because I knew the technological wave was unavoidable (and crashing over my head). My computer-whiz friend at the time assured me this was indeed the way of the future.

I'm happy to say that now I use technology all the time. I'm a devout computer user. You're not impressed? Hey—when I went to college, everyone used typewriters.1 I remember my first computer with PowerPoint. I ignored the program for ten years, instead going to a photographic company when I needed slides. But once a friend showed me the ropes (and I had finished kicking myself), I embraced the technology. This not only saved a lot of money, it made me more effective in my public presentations.

I record fifty podcasts a year. I've been on Facebook for years. Earlier this year I started tweeting. And a few months ago, a close family friend (she's about one-third my age) set up an Instagram account for me.

When it comes to evangelism, technology should be our friend. You're never too old to get started. So let's consider some real-life examples:

- Every week we have visitors at church who found us through our website. (A common search term, besides our city, is the word "diversity.") This has led to people being baptized.
- On one of my trips to the Middle East, I met an Arab woman, recently converted to Christ. She told me that the sister who shared with her lived four hours away. They communicated through Skype, going through Bible studies long distance. When she was ready, they met, and she was baptized.
- A brother in Christ placed an ad at Craigslist. It read, "Who wants to study the Bible?" Not only did this generate interest, but the brother set up a Bible study and the person became a Christian.
- Some Christians I know text prayers for their friends to those friends. Although these are just texts, the prayers are personalized. Many non-Christians are pleased when they know people are remembering them in prayer, even when they are at only a basic level of faith.
- I like computer games. And—okay, I'll admit it—games

on my phone. Many are played with random, anonymous people. This often gives me a chance to share my faith, and I have had guests come to church as a result.

- BibleGateway.com is a terrific website—though one among many—for finding Bible translations in various languages. I also take advantage of all the translations in my Bible computer software Logos, as well as in BibleWorks for Windows. This is helpful when you're reaching out to someone who's native language isn't English.
- Ed Stetzer persuasively reminds us that while "there are unintended side effects of technology that are both de-personalizing and dehumanizing... there are some wonderful benefits of technology that enable the mission of the church." If we're smart we can "use technology in [our] church to enable communication, community, and discipleship."[2]
- Toni Birdsong makes a number of valuable suggestions on sharing Christ through mobile technology, like sending someone an interesting or humorous video from GodTube.[3] This could be a great way to break the ice with someone you're reaching out to.
- A helpful book, especially if you're trying to figure out how much technology is too much, is Andy Crouch's *The Tech-Wise Family: Everyday Steps for Putting Technology in Its Proper Place.*[4]
- These days there are hundreds of faith-based websites and apps out there. Look around!

## Notes

[1] Invented in 1829, "a typewriter is a mechanical... machine for writing characters similar to those produced by printer's movable type," according to the fount of all knowledge, Wikipedia (at https://en.wikipedia.org/wiki/Typewriter).

[2] "3 Ways Technology Enables the Mission of the Church," article in Christianity Today, 27 October 2014. Access at http://www.christianitytoday.com/edstetzer/2014/october/3-ways-technology-enables-mission-of-church.html.

[3] "7 Ways to Share Christ Using Mobile Technology," at http://stickyjesus.com/2011/03/7-ways-to-share-christ-using-mobile-technology/.

[4] Andy Crouch, *The Tech-Wise Family: Everyday Steps for Putting Technology in Its Proper Place* (Grand Rapids: Baker, 2017). Also check out the excellent article by Daniel Berk at http://www.disciplestoday.org/campus/content/read/item-6900-alias-christians#%2EVNp5m0KpefQ.

# Index

## *The Study Materials*

This index includes thirty-four personal Bible studies and thirteen follow-up studies. (It does not include the fourteen group Bible discussions of chapter 18.)


*Series A (11 units)*

Jesus I: Jesus the Only Way 102
Seeking God 103
The Word of God I 104
Discipleship I 106
Serving the Poor 108
Sin I 111
The Cross of Christ 113
Repentance I 115
Baptism I 117
False Doctrines about Conversion 118
The Church 120

*Series B (10 units)*

Jesus II: Jesus in Action 125
Sin II 127
Repentance II: Self-Righteousness 130
Obedience 131
The Resurrection 132
Grace 136
Faith 137
Discipleship II: Excuses and Fear 138
Baptism II 140
The Holy Spirit I 146

*Series C (14 units)*

The Word II 149
Jesus III: The Great "I Am" 152
Repentance III: The Rich Young Ruler & Zacchaeus 153
Calvinism 154
Once Saved, Always Saved 160
Hot, Cold, Lukewarm 161
Old Covenant, New Covenant 162
Messianic Prophecy 165
Premillennialism 166
The Coming of the Kingdom 170
The Holy Spirit II 171
Feelings 174
The Judgment 175
Is Sincerity Enough? 176

*Follow-Up Studies (13 units7*

| | |
|---|---|
| Prayer: Speaking to God | 187 |
| Bible Study: Listening to God | 188 |
| Faith, Works, and Grace: The Balance | 189 |
| Relationships in the Body | 189 |
| The New Testament Church: Three Aspects | 190 |
| One-Another Relationships: God's Plan | 191 |
| Hindrance: The Heart | 192 |
| Laziness, Idleness, Discipline | 193 |
| Evangelism, Boldness, Tact | 194 |
| Service with a Smile | 195 |
| Academics: Obstacle or Opportunity? | 196 |
| Christian Marriage: A Cord of Three Strands | 197 |
| The Christian Family: Parents and Children | 198 |

**Alphabetical Listing** (with series indicated: A = Guard the Gospel A, B = Guard the Gospel B, C = Guard the Gospel C, F = Follow-Up Studies)

| | | |
|---|---|---|
| Academics: Obstacle or Opportunity? | F | 196 |
| Baptism I | A | 117 |
| Baptism II | B | 140 |
| Bible Study: Listening to God | F | 188 |
| Calvinism (including Once Saved, Always Saved) | C | 154 |
| Christian Family: Parents and Children | F | 198 |
| Christian Marriage: A Cord of Three Strands | F | 197 |
| Church | A | 120 |
| Coming of the Kingdom | C | 170 |
| Cross of Christ | A | 113 |
| Discipleship I | A | 106 |
| Discipleship II: Excuses and Fear | B | 138 |
| Evangelism, Boldness, Tact | F | 194 |
| Faith | B | 137 |
| Faith, Works, and Grace: The Balance | F | 189 |
| False Doctrines about Conversion | A | 118 |
| Feelings | C | 174 |
| Grace | B | 136 |
| Hindrance: The Heart | F | 192 |
| Holy Spirit I | B | 146 |
| Holy Spirit II (including Feelings) | C | 171 |
| Hot, Cold, Lukewarm | C | 161 |
| Is Sincerity Enough? | C | 176 |
| Jesus I: Jesus the Only Way | A | 102 |
| Jesus II: Jesus in Action | B | 125 |
| Jesus III: The Great "I Am" | C | 152 |
| Judgment (including Is Sincerity Enough?) | C | 175 |
| Laziness, Idleness, Discipline | F | 193 |
| Messianic Prophecy | C | 165 |
| New Testament Church: Three Aspects | F | 190 |
| Obedience | B | 131 |
| Old Covenant, New Covenant | C | 162 |
| Once Saved, Always Saved | C | 160 |
| One-Another Relationships: God's Plan | F | 191 |

| | | |
|---|---|---|
| Prayer: Speaking to God | F | 187 |
| Premillennialism (including The Coming of the Kingdom) | C | 166 |
| Relationships in the body | F | 189 |
| Repentance I | A | 115 |
| Repentance II: Self-righteousness | B | 130 |
| Repentance III: (The Rich Young Ruler & Zacchaeus) | C | 153 |
| Resurrection | B | 132 |
| Seeking God | A | 103 |
| Service with a Smile | F | 195 |
| Serving the Poor | A | 108 |
| Sin I | A | 111 |
| Sin II | B | 127 |
| Word of God I | A | 104 |
| Word of God II | C | 149 |

# Bibliography

Barna, George, *Evangelism that Works: How to Reach Changing Generations with the Unchanging Gospel.* Ventura, Cal.: Regal Books, 1995.

Cahill, Mark, *One Thing You Can't Do In Heaven.* Bartlesville, Okla.: BDP, 2005.

Chan, Francis, *Crazy Love: Overwhelmed by a Relentless God.* Colorado Springs: David C. Cook, 2008.

Claiborne, Shane. *Irresistible Revolution: Living as an Ordinary Radical.* Grand Rapids: Zondervan, 2006.

Ferguson, Gordon, *The Power of Discipling.* Spring, Texas: Illumination Publishers, 2010.

_____, *Dynamic Leadership. Principles, Roles and Relationships for a Life-Changing Church.* Spring, Texas: Illumination Publishers, 2012.

Green, Michael, *Evangelism in the Early Church.* Grand Rapids: Eerdmans, 1970.

Hedman, Tom, *A Life of Impact: Leadership Principles of Jesus.* Toronto: New Life Publications, 1992.

Jacoby, Douglas, *Campus Core: How to Have an Impact on Campus, Get Good Grades, and Figure Out Your Future.* Spring, Texas: Illumination Publishers 2016.

_____, *Compelling Evidence for God and the Bible: Finding Truth in an Age of Doubt.* Eugene, Oregon: Harvest House, 2010).

_____, *A Quick Overview of the Bible: Understanding How All the Pieces Fit Together.* Eugene. Oregon: Harvest House, 2012.

_____, *The Spirit: Presence & Power, Sense & Nonsense.* Spring, Texas: Illumination Publishers, 2017.

Jennings, Alvin, *How Christianity Grows in the City.* Fort Worth: Star Bible Publications, 1985.

Kim, Frank and Erica, *How to Share Your Faith.* Woburn, Mass.: Discipleship Publications International, 1998.

Little, Paul, *How to Give Away Your Faith.* Downers Grove: Intervarsity Press, 1988.

Pippert, Rebecca Manley, *Out of the Saltshaker: Evangelism as a Way of Life.* Downers Grove: Intervarsity Press, 1979.

Schmeling, David J., *52 Bible Talks for Fun and Fruitfulness.* Spring Texas: Illumination Publishers, 2007.

More books by Douglas Jacoby

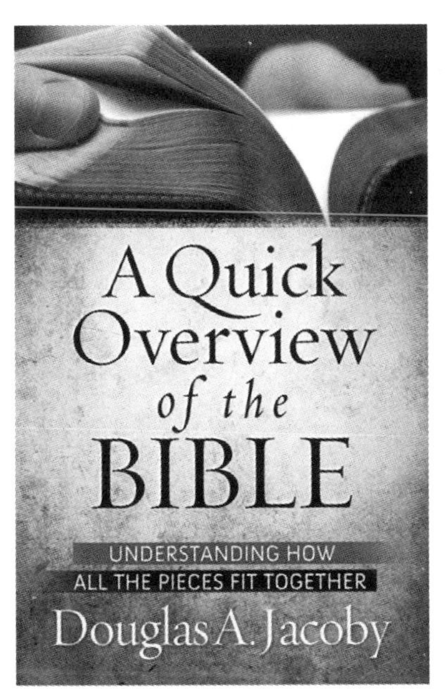

**More books by Douglas Jacoby**

For the latest news, teaching archives, and teaching schedule, see www.DouglasJacoby.com

All of Douglas Jacoby's books and teaching series are available at www.ipibooks.com